Future flooding and coastal erosion risks

Edited by
Colin R. Thorne, Edward P. Evans
and Edmund C. Penning-Rowsell

Published by Thomas Telford Publishing, Thomas Telford Ltd, 1 Heron Quay, London E14 4JD.
www.thomastelford.com

Distributors for Thomas Telford books are
USA: ASCE Press, 1801 Alexander Bell Drive, Reston, VA 20191-4400
Japan: Maruzen Co. Ltd, Book Department, 3–10 Nihonbashi 2-chome, Chuo-ku, Tokyo 103
Australia: DA Books and Journals, 648 Whitehorse Road, Mitcham 3132, Victoria

First published 2007

Also available from Thomas Telford Books
Flood Risk Management. Edited by G. Fleming. ISBN 0 7277 3112 3
Coastal Defence – ICE Design and Practice Guide. Institution of Civil Engineers. ISBN 0 7277 3005 3

A catalogue record for this book is available from the British Library

ISBN: 978-0-7277-3449-5

Typeset by Academic + Technical, Bristol
Printed and bound in Great Britain by MPG Books, Bodmin, Cornwall

Contents

Contents

Contents

Contents

Dedicated to

Elieen, Pia and Jacky

Preface

I am delighted to provide a preface to this publication on the research that lay behind the important and highly influential Foresight Future Flooding Report, published in two volumes in 2004.

Flooding is an issue that affects us all. Over £200 billion worth of assets are at risk around British rivers and coasts and those risks are likely to increase over the next 100 years due to changes in climate and society. In 2002 I therefore commissioned the Foresight Project on Flood and Coastal Defence to address a number of issues surrounding how the flood risk might change and how government and the private sector might best respond to the future challenges. The report that emerged had several key messages for government – flood risk would continue to rise to unacceptable levels; those risks had to be tackled on a broad front and hard choices would have to be made regarding where to direct investment. This work established a new paradigm for futures work and, with the issues of flooding and flood prevention continuing to be in the headlines worldwide, it rightly continues to command widespread interest.

This book is edited by three of the team who undertook the original Foresight study and elaborates on the work undertaken by approximately 60 leading experts in the field, over 20 months between 2002 to 2004. A great deal of work was necessary to produce the evidence base that underpins the Future Flooding Report. However, the published documents contain only brief summaries of the deep descriptions, quantitative analyses and risk models developed and applied in the study. It is therefore most welcome that Thomas Telford have published this monograph as a detailed record of the science and engineering research performed during the Foresight Project on Flood and Coastal Defence.

The UK government fully appreciates the threats posed by flooding and is already supporting cutting-edge techniques and policies for managing flood risk. It is investing heavily in research to develop new and innovative approaches to flood risk management, based on applying holistic principles and achieving sustainable outcomes. However, the government is not complacent and recognises that more needs to be done. At the conclusion of the Foresight Project in 2004, the Minister with responsibility for flood management acknowledged the important role that the results of that research would play in preparing a government-wide strategy for managing the risks of flooding and coastal erosion. In order to capitalise on the knowledge gained during the study, he therefore established a Flood Action Plan, which is on-going. It involves all the relevant branches of government – a fine example of how scientific evidence can be used to inform better policy decisions.

Of course, the benefits of taking a long-term and far-sighted approach to flood risk management in a changing world are not unique to the UK. There has been a great deal of international interest in the Foresight model – the Foresight team have had some very useful discussions with interested parties from the Netherlands, Japan, the USA and India, and there have also been Foresight Future Flooding missions to China and Russia.

Clearly, the work begun with the Foresight Flooding Project has not ended but will continue in the coming years and decades, both in the UK and overseas. The issues covered by the Foresight study are likely to assume increasing importance as we enter an era of climate change, economic growth and societal evolution. This volume will therefore be a valuable resource to scientists, engineers and a wide range of stakeholders who share a common concern for flood risk management and an interest in evidence-based policy making.

Sir David King
Government Chief Scientific Adviser
June 2006

List of contributors

Nigel W. Arnell — Tyndall Centre for Climate Change Research, School of Geography, University of Southampton, Southampton, Hampshire SO17 1BJ

Richard M. Ashley — Pennine Water Group, Department of Civil and Structural Engineering, University of Sheffield, Sheffield S1 3JD

David Ball — Centre for Decision Analysis and Risk Management, Middlesex University, Enfield, London EN3 4SA

Kevin Burgess — Halcrow, Burderop Park, Swindon, Wiltshire SN4 0QD

John Chatterton — John Chatterton Associates, 32 Windermere Road, Moseley, Birmingham B13 9JP

Nick J. Cooper — ABP Marine Environmental Research Ltd, Suite B, Waterside House, Southampton, Hampshire SO14 2AQ Now, Royal Haskoning, Marlborough Crescent, Newcastle upon Tyne NE1 4EE

Sarah E. Cornell — Tyndall Centre for Climate Change Research, Department of Earth Sciences, University of Bristol, Bristol BS8 1RJ

Rob Deakin — Halcrow, Burderop Park, Swindon, Wiltshire SN4 0QD

Edward P. Evans — 'Bevis', Great Somerford, Chippenham, Wiltshire SN15 5JA

Colin H. Green — Flood Hazard Research Centre, Middlesex University, Enfield, London EN3 4SA

Jim W. Hall — School of Civil Engineering and Geosciences, University of Newcastle upon Tyne, Newcastle upon Tyne NE1 7RU

Claire Hinton — ABP Marine Environmental Research Ltd, Suite B, Waterside House, Southampton, Hampshire SO14 2AQ

Helen Jay — Halcrow, Burderop Park, Swindon, Wiltshire SN4 0QD

Andrew Jordan — School of Environmental Sciences, University of East Anglia, Norwich, Norfolk NR4 7TJ

Stuart N. Lane — Department of Geography, University of Durham, Durham DH1 3LE

Peter H. von Lany — Halcrow, Burderop Park, Swindon, Wiltshire SN4 0QD

Laure Ledoux — Environmental Futures, 54 Rue Jean Baptiste Esch L1473, Luxembourg

Joe Morris	Institute of Water and Environment, Cranfield University, Silsoe, Bedfordshire MK45 4DT
Robert J. Nicholls	Tyndall Centre for Climate Change Research, School of Civil Engineering and the Environment, University of Southampton, Southampton, Hampshire SO17 1BJ
P. Enda O'Connell	School of Civil Engineering and Geosciences, University of Newcastle upon Tyne, Newcastle upon Tyne NE1 7RU
John Palmer	Halcrow, Burderop Park, Swindon, Wiltshire SN4 OQD
Mike Panzeri	HR Wallingford, Howbery Park, Wallingford, Oxfordshire OX10 8BA
Edmund C. Penning-Rowsell	Flood Hazard Research Centre, Middlesex University, Enfield, London EN3 4SA
Paul F. Quinn	School of Civil Engineering and Geosciences, University of Newcastle upon Tyne, Newcastle upon Tyne NE1 7RU
Nick S. Reynard	Centre for Ecology and Hydrology, Wallingford, Oxfordshire OX10 8BB
Adrian J. Saul	Pennine Water Group, Department of Civil and Structural Engineering, University of Sheffield, Sheffield S1 3JD
Paul B. Sayers	HR Wallingford, Howbery Park, Wallingford, Oxfordshire OX10 8BA
David A. Sear	School of Geography, University of Southampton, Southampton, Hampshire SO17 1BJ
Jonathan D. Simm	HR Wallingford, Howbery Park, Wallingford, Oxfordshire OX10 8BA
Stuart Suter	Halcrow, Burderop Park, Swindon, Wiltshire SN4 0QD
Sue Tapsell	Flood Hazard Research Centre, Middlesex University, Enfield, London EN3 4SA
Colin R. Thorne	School of Geography, University of Nottingham, University Park, Nottingham NG7 2RD
Robert Tinch	Tyndall Centre for Climate Change Research, Schools of Biological and Environmental Sciences, University of East Anglia, Norwich, Norfolk NR4 7TJ
Ian H. Townend	ABP Marine Environmental Research Ltd, Suite B, Waterside House, Southampton, Hampshire SO14 2AQ Now, Hydraulics Research Wallingford Ltd, Howbery Park, Wallingford, Oxfordshire OX10 8BA
Andrew R. Watkinson	Tyndall Centre for Climate Change Research, Schools of Biological and Environmental Sciences, University of East Anglia, Norwich, Norfolk NR4 7TJ
Alan Werritty	Department of Geography, University of Dundee, Dundee DD1 4HN
Howard Wheater	Imperial College London, South Kensington, London SW7 2AZ

Part I
Introduction

1 Overview

Edward P. Evans, Jim W. Hall, Edmund C. Penning-Rowsell
and Colin R. Thorne

The task we have undertaken

This volume presents the research base that supports a major and innovative initiative in thinking about long-term flood risk management in the UK. For the first time a multi-disciplinary group of scientists has conducted a comprehensive study of the factors that affect flood risk at the national scale in an economically developed country and sought to look up to a 100 years ahead at the possible flooding futures that might be realised in the UK. We have published the main outcomes of our work in a two volume, peer-reviewed document that summarises the findings of the Foresight Project on Flood and Coastal Management, and which considers the implications for the future of UK flood risk management and governance (Evans *et al.*, 2004a, 2000b).

This volume delves more deeply into the science behind the *Future Flooding Report*. It presents, for each of the substantive elements of the report, the intellectual and empirical base underpinning the research outcomes and advice that was given to government. This base is built on the synthesised wisdom of decades of practical experience in the field of flood risk management, supported through team research by academics from leading universities and national centres, complemented by expert inputs from internationally recognised professional specialists employed in civil and environmental engineering consultancies and reviewed by independent experts at home and abroad.

The main characteristics of this work, which define it as unique in the study of flood risk, may be summarised as:

- Its national in scope, which directly addresses the role of national government and its agencies in managing flooding, its consequences and its risks.
- Its far horizon vision, which, in looking up to a 100 years ahead, extends well beyond the scope of practically all current, conventional assessments of flood risk and its management.
- Its radical stance in seeking new responses to the substantial increases in risk that projected futures for climate and socio-economic change may otherwise bring.

In this chapter we attempt to position the work in the context of modern thinking on flooding, and the application of risk-based approaches to the analysis and management of pluvial, river and coastal floods. Consequently, we do not seek to summarise what the authors contribute in the chapters that follow, but rather to produce an overview of those efforts, that provides a wider perspective than can be gained from the detailed treatment of the flooding system that is the main topic of this book.

The evolving policy context

Until recently, the management of flooding in the UK, as worldwide, was performed within static or slowly evolving policy and technical environments, characterised by incremental change rather than revolution, but punctuated by some radical developments stimulated by the catalytic effects of major floods (Johnson *et al.*, 2005). Government policy throughout the 1970s and 1980s was dominated by reliance on the construction of hard flood defences as the primary means of reducing flooding. However, by the early 1990s, increasing credence was being given to the concept that mitigating or avoiding flood *losses* also have a role to play. For example, the 1993 strategy document for flood and coastal defence in England and Wales (MAFF/Welsh Office, 1993) described its aim as:

> Reducing the risks to people and the developed and natural environment from flooding and coastal erosion by encouraging the provision of technically, environmentally and economically sound and sustainable defence measures.

This aim was to be achieved by:

- encouraging the provision of adequate and cost-effective flood warning systems;
- encouraging the provision of adequate, technically, environmentally and economically sound and sustainable flood and coastal defence measures;
- discouraging inappropriate development in areas at risk from flooding or coastal erosion.

Clearly, although hard flood defences remained the primary 'weapon of choice' in fighting against floods, the contributions that could be made by effective flood warning systems and taking account of flood risk, when planning development in areas at risk, were increasingly being recognised.

The 1993 document called for a strategic view to be taken through the development of flood management plans that should be integrated with the work of local planning authorities, so that statutory development plans could take account of shoreline management issues and river catchment plans. These plans did not, however, strongly influence the flood defence investment process, which continued to be dominated by engineering-led approaches, aimed at flood prevention.

In the latter part of the twentieth century, the policy context in the UK changed gradually in other ways too, with the Ministry of Agriculture, Fisheries and Food (MAFF) increasingly expected to make the potential impact of flood defence works on wildlife habitats and the environment more generally a key consideration in flood management planning. By the end of the century, the presumption was that natural river and coastal processes should not be disrupted at all except in situations where life, national assets or valuable habitats/ecosystems were at risk. The requirement to consider the environment through, for example, environmental impact assessments of all flood defence and coastal protection schemes had already been extant for some time, due to UK government legislation when the law concerning environmental protection was progressively strengthened by successive European Union (EU) directives that were subsequently incorporated into UK law. These developments were being mirrored internationally, as exemplified by the World Bank's decision in the early 1990s to require environmental analysis of all the investments it funded (World Bank, 1991).

However, one thing that did not change was that, within the realm of flood management economics, the guiding principle remained that schemes should have a benefit to cost ratio of at least unity to be considered for a grant from central government, with the apportioning of grant aid being the main mechanism by which central government sought to influence its regional operating agencies, including the National Rivers Authority. In this respect, the economic policy, set out in the 1993 strategy document, was little different from the general practice that had developed in the UK during the 1970s and 1980s.

The science and technology backdrop

The 'technical basis for flood defence', as the 1993 document termed it, was, in many ways, stable and conservative up until the end of the twentieth century. Estimates of catchment runoff and flood flows, the source terms for inland flooding, were determined in the UK from the *Flood Estimation Handbook* (CEH, 1999), which was itself derived from the earlier *Flood Studies Report* (CEH, 1993).

Crucially, the methods in the *Flood Studies Report* were based on statistical analyses of historical records of rainfall and runoff that depended on the assumption of stationarity in the data. Consequently, the approach was fundamentally rooted in an unchanging world. While the *Flood Estimation Handbook* represented a considerable technical advance, representation of climate as variable but unchanging was still implicit.

Statistical analyses of coastal flooding due to extreme water levels associated with waves, tides and surges were also based on an assumption of stationarity. While it is true that the Thames Barrier study (Gilbert and Horner, 1984) took account of historical rates of relative sea level rise, at that time the possibility that the effects of accelerated, anthropogenically driven climate change should be accounted for was being debated mostly in academic and scientific circles, and was some way away from being considered as part of either engineering best practice or government policy.

While methods used to estimate flood risk source terms remained essentially the same, there were very significant technical advances that paved the way for future step changes in policy. One of the key advances was the development of computational hydraulic modelling which, during the period between the 1970s and the 1990s, emerged from the research domain with its room-sized computers, very long run times and demand for highly specialised, academic expertise to become available for routine use on desk-top computers in the planning and design of flood alleviation schemes (Abbott, 1991).

Other important technical advances that began during the 1980s were the adoption of Geographical Information Systems (GIS) as the platform for flood mapping and the uptake of remotely sensed information from aeroplane- and satellite-based imagery of landforms, terrain, land-use and vegetation cover. The combined use of GIS and remote-sensing technologies was highly significant in two ways. First, it provided a much more complete and spatially referenced representation of the physical flooding system, including the assets at risk. Second, it supplied, for the first time, the capability for physical data to be combined and analysed in conjunction with economic and social data from sources such as the postcode and census databases (Tomlinson, 1970).

These technical developments were significant not only for their practical utility in flood management, but also because they enabled major shifts in the breadth and scope of flood studies and schemes. First, the capability to undertake spatial analysis of multiple databases over large geographical areas opened the way for flood management and planning on a regional basis and at the catchment scale. Second, by allowing assessment of the socio-economic consequences of flooding in conjunction with the physical and hydrological attributes of the catchment and the disposition of flood and coastal defences, GIS and remote sensing opened new and broader horizons in long-term, integrated planning of flood and coastal management.

Internationally, advances in the application of new technologies were led by the World Bank and its sister international finance institutions that, during the 1980s and 1990s, specified spatial studies and catchment-wide master planning as necessary precursors to the funding of investment in water resource development schemes (World Bank, 1996). Consequently, integrated analysis and planning in the water sector became a very active field, both academically and practically. This was not only in those more economically developed countries (MEDCs), from whence the technologies derived, but also in the planning of water resource investment in those less economically developed countries (LEDCs) that benefited from overseas aid and investment. Integrated river basin management in the UK took somewhat longer to emerge, with a string of European directives on habitats, biodiversity and ecology acting as a major stimulus.

In parallel to these technology based advances, considerable progress was also made in the cognitive and practical basis for estimating the damage, caused by flooding, to people, their property and their health, largely through a sustained research programme at the Flood Hazard Research Centre at Middlesex University (Penning-Rowsell and Chatterton, 1977; Penning-Rowsell et al., 1992, 2005; Parker et al., 1987). However, government policy, as expressed through the Planning Advisory Guidance (PAG) series of detailed project appraisal guidance manuals (MAFF, 1999) continued to stipulate that the benefits of flood alleviation schemes should be based solely on people and property in the flood risk zone at the time of analysis. There was no requirement of, and indeed a presumption against, looking into the economic and societal future when planning and implementing flood alleviation schemes. Hence, to complement the hydrological stationarity, there existed socio-economic stationarity as the basis for forward planning.

It is only when viewed in this context of the flood management approaches and policies in place during the late twentieth century that the revolutionary nature of the Foresight 'future flooding' work, summarised by Evans et al. (2004a, 2004b) and reported here in depth, may be properly appreciated.

Flood impacts and policy change

While the planning of flood management in the UK remained quite conservative at the beginning of the twenty-first century, the use of so-called 'baskets' of structural and non-structural measures, together with appraisal of their social, environmental and economic consequences based on modelling and GIS technologies, was common-place in internationally financed studies. In this context, structural measures include physical interventions in the flooding system, such as flood embankments or coastal shoreline protection, while non-structural measures encompass a wide range of instruments, ranging from flood forecasting and warning systems to encouraging individuals to take steps to reduce the vulnerability of their homes to flood damage. A number of catalysing events were, however, about to prompt scientists, engineers and policy makers involved in UK flood defence to make a paradigm shift away from flood prevention to flood risk management.

Severe and damaging floods in England and Wales in the spring of 1998 and the autumn and winter of 2000 resulted in heightened public and parliamentary scrutiny of arrangements for flood management (House of Commons, 1998; Bye and Horner, 1998; National Audit Office, 2001; Institution of Civil Engineers, 2001) as well as in-depth review on that part of the Environment Agency with operational responsibility for flood risk management along the coastline and main rivers of England and Wales (Environment Agency, 2001).

Of the lessons learned from these events and the reviews they stimulated, the following stand out (Hall *et al.*, 2003):

- Management of flood risk had tended to be institutionally fragmented. For example, urban flooding from sewers and minor water courses has historically been dealt with separately from flooding by main rivers, yet the level of damage is comparable and the flooding processes may interact. A 'whole systems' approach is therefore required if flood risk is to be managed in an efficient and sustainable way (National Audit Office, 2001; Institution of Civil Engineers, 2001).
- The flood threat is greater than has been generally recognised. At the turn of the century it was estimated that approximately 10% of the population of England and property worth over £200 billion were located in areas potentially at risk from flooding or coastal erosion. Improving flood risk management may therefore merit more government investment than is currently provided in the UK and the limited evidence available suggests that this investment is economically justifiable in relation to the risks that the nation faces (Institution of Civil Engineers, 2001).
- Urbanisation of floodplains and the increasing economic value of buildings and their contents have significantly increased flood risk over the past 50 years. During that time flood risk has not always been a primary consideration in the statutory planning process, despite a continuous stream of government guidance, and some planning authorities have chosen to ignore the advice received from the Environment Agency and its predecessors (House of Commons, 1998).
- Between the 1970s and the 1998 floods there was a very low level of public awareness of flooding in England and Wales. The 1998 and millennium floods, as well as other more recent events and flood awareness campaigns, have raised the public profile of flooding, but there is still relatively little precautionary investment by households in improving the flood resistance of their properties and little coordinated, collective, preventative action during floods at the community level (Institution of Civil Engineers, 2001).

The millennium floods and intense media coverage of the government's interpretation of their causes, led to rising public consciousness of, initially, the possibility and, later, the probability that climate change was increasing the likelihood of flooding. While this is not the place to review the history of changing perceptions of climate change, it should be noted that the work of the International Panel on Climate Change (IPCC) and, in the UK, the setting up of the United Kingdom Climate Impact Programme (UKCIP) and its issue of standard guidance on precipitation and relative sea-level change were crucial to the establishment of broad agreement on the implications of climate change for long-term flood management planning.

All these factors led to recognition that the very long life of many flood management measures meant that it was essential to look ahead to the same degree when planning flood risk management policies and schemes.

The need to take a longer view and integrate structural and non-structural measures rapidly gained momentum in the UK during the first years of the twenty-first century (Defra/Environment Agency, 2002). One immediate outcome was to heighten awareness of the need to reject the twentieth-century policy that was primarily centred on flood prevention through the provision of hard defences and accept the new paradigm of managing the risk rather than the probability of flooding. The practical outcome of this paradigm shift was first manifest in the emergence of Catchment Flood Management Plans as the key tool in catchment flood risk management following the 1998 and 2000 floods in the UK (MAFF/Environment Agency, 2001).

The Environment Agency confirmed the intention to adopt flood risk management in England and Wales in 2003 (Environment Agency, 2003). In doing so, they identified six priorities for change:

1. A strategic approach to flood risk management that will target and prioritise investment and resources at those areas where flood risk can most effectively be reduced, which will mean moving from flood 'defence' to flood 'risk reduction' and accounting for future changes in flood risk, whether from development or climate change.
2. Control of any development that could increase flood risk and the prevention of inappropriate development by working to influence spatial planning policy and decision making.
3. Managing flood risk management assets through the whole life cycle of the flood defence system 'from cradle to grave'.
4. Closer integration and streamlining of activities in managing floods, including flood planning, flood forecasting and warning, event management, response, flood event recording and reporting, after-care and recovery.
5. Effective communications to support the development and delivery of flood risk management policies and services.
6. Improvement of business efficiency and effectiveness.

In parallel, acceptance of the concept and need for sustainability in government policies and practices (WCED, 1987; UN, 1992) gained wide recognition during the 1990s. The principles of sustainability emerged in UK government policy at the end of the twentieth century (DETR, 1999) and were another important motivating factor in the revolution in flood management thinking that occurred in the first years of the twenty-first century.

New directions in risk analysis

In fact, it had long been recognised that consideration of 'risk' is essential to providing appropriate flood management measures. Following the devastating East Coast floods of 1953, the Waverley Report recommended that flood defence standards should reflect land use in the protected area, noting that urban areas could expect higher levels of protection than less densely populated rural areas. Despite this, application of quantified risk analysis did not feature in flood analysis and the design of flood alleviation schemes until the 1990s, and then only within the context of better quantifying the economic benefits of conventional flood defences (Sayers *et al.*, 2002).

The traditional engineering paradigm design, that held sway for decades during the second half of the twentieth century, proceeded by:

- Establishing the appropriate standard of service for the defence (e.g. the '100-year return period' river discharge), based on land use in the area protected, consistency of provision and tradition.
- Estimating the design load, such as the water level or wave height associated with the specified return period event.

- Designing (i.e. determining the primary physical characteristics, such as crest level or revetment thickness) of the structures necessary to withstand the design load.
- Incorporating safety factors, such as a freeboard allowance, based on rules of thumb, best practice and local circumstances.

The limitations of this traditional approach in delivering the kinds of environmentally aligned, cost-efficient and socially equitable solutions demanded in the twenty-first century soon emerged and it became clear that over-reliance on flood prevention would constitute a barrier to adoption of catchment-scale, long-term planning in flood management. Once this is recognised and understood, the rapidity with which the risk-based approach replaced the traditional one is no longer surprising.

The risk analysis employed in the Foresight work reported in the *Future Flooding* documents (Evans *et al.*, 2004a, 2004b) and described further in Chapter 13 of this volume, defines risk as the product of the chance of a particular event occurring and the impacts that the event would cause if it did occur. Risk therefore has two components – the probability of an event occurring and the consequences should it do so.

Based on this definition, it could be concluded that events with the same numerical level of risk should have equal 'significance', but it is not always as simple as this. While it is true that, for a 'normal' extreme event, the significance of a given event can indeed be assessed multiplying its probability by its consequences, it is also important to understand the nature of the risk, and in this respect it is necessary to distinguish between the risks associated with very unlikely but truly catastrophic events and those associated with events that are relatively more frequent, but much less severe. In the *Future Flooding* documents, this issue is handled by developing a list of truly calamitous events (such as excessive sea-level rise due to the break-up of the West Antarctic ice sheet or climate regime shift due to the eruption of a mega-volcano) and treating these outside the framework provided by risk-analysis of 'normal' extreme events.

Another factor that influences risk, that is unaccounted for in the simple definition of risk that is usually adopted in flood analysis, is how society or individuals perceive a risk. This is influenced by many factors including, for example, the availability and affordability of insurance, and the degree of uncertainty associated with science underpinning the risk assessment.

Despite its limitations, this simple, risk-based approach remains attractive because it enables direct comparison of the impacts generated by management options that affect either the frequency or the outcomes of flooding in a specified area. A risk-based approach therefore enables informed choices to be made, based on comparison of the expected benefits and costs of very different, alternative courses of action.

Scenario analysis

The risk-based approach outlined above, and discussed in more detail later in this volume, deals with uncertainty in the natural and human phenomena that influence flooding and its outcomes (for example, the possibility that a rain storm might stall over a given catchment or that a flood gate might be left open accidentally) using a probabilistic approach. However, the uncertainties surrounding predictions of long-term socio-economic and climate changes in the UK are very large and are difficult to deal with in probabilistic terms. Recognising this, a scenario-based approach to dealing with future flood risks was adopted throughout the Foresight

Flood and Coastal Defence Project. In this approach, scenarios are used to explore a plausible range of alternative and contrasting futures. In the project, scenarios were applied for both future climates (which are themselves dependent on world-wide scenarios for global greenhouse gas emissions) and for socio-economic change in the UK.

Combined use of climate and socio-economic scenarios allowed exploration of different ways in which the UK might change during the remainder of this century, not only in terms of climate and national economy but also in terms of demography, land use, societal preferences and stakeholder behaviour with respect to flood risk.

In developing the scenarios, it was fortunately possible to draw heavily upon recent cutting-edge research performed in developing climate change models (Hulme *et al.*, 2002) and socio-economic scenarios (SPRU *et al.*, 1999) for the UK. While the existing future scenarios required some refinement to address the particular requirements of flood risk analysis, the availability of authoritative and scholarly future scenarios for the remainder of the twenty-first century was hugely helpful.

In interpreting the results of the scenario-based approach adopted in the Foresight Flood and Coastal Defence Project, it is important to note that no statement is made at any point concerning the relative likelihood of any one of the alternative scenarios of climate and socio-economic change actually coming to pass. On the contrary, in applying a scenario-based approach the intention was to explore contrasting futures in order to challenge the assumption that the future will be either similar to the present or an extrapolation of currently observed trends.

Each scenario is, however, expected to be internally consistent, which is an important feature as flood risk is influenced by a large number of variables, many of which can be expected to change in the future. The scenario approach further seeks to ensure that the postulated changes are consistent with one another. To achieve this, each scenario is developed around a 'storyline' about how the future might evolve given different assumptions, concerning, for example, changes in climate that we might face and societal changes that might develop during the next 80 to 100 years. Subsequent analysis of 'portfolios' of options for future flood risk management (including continuation of current practice under the 'baseline assumption') within these contrasting scenarios provides evidence about their potential effectiveness and, perhaps more importantly, reveals how sensitive they are to the assumptions that we make about how the future may unfold.

Post-project perspective

The research described in this volume was undertaken as a result of a decision by the government to commission a thorough and wide-ranging examination of the long-term future of flood and coastal erosion risks in the UK. This decision can be seen as the culmination of the trends and developments described in this chapter.

Two years after its completion, the Foresight 'Future Flooding' Project appears to have been remarkably successful in progressing the revolution in the way that flood and coastal erosion hazards are regarded and managed; it started in the 1990s and was accelerated by the millennium floods. Evidence for this comes not only from the frequency with which the *Future Flooding* reports are referred to by stakeholders, but also by the substantive progress that has been made towards achieving the goals of the project's Action Plan. To cite just one example, within months of accepting the findings in the *Future Flooding* reports, the Department for Environment, Food and Rural Affairs disseminated a new and radical flood risk management strategy discussion document, *Making Space for Water* (Defra, 2004, 2005) that embraces many of the concepts developed in the Foresight project and promotes a policy of flood and coastal risk management through integrated, sustainable portfolios of responses, covering a wide range of non-structural as well as engineering responses.

Interest in the Foresight approach to exploring future flood risks and their management has not been restricted to the UK. In 2004, the main findings of the Foresight Flood and Coastal Defence (FCD) Project were presented to the European Commission (EC) in Brussels, while in 2005 two DTI-OSI supported scientific cooperation missions related to flood and coastal defence were made to China (Shanghai) and Russia (St Petersburg). In 2006 a high-level delegation from the US House of Representatives visited London and took part in a seminar on Flood Foresight in relation to long-term flood risk management along the Gulf of Mexico. Common areas of interest that were identified during these missions and seminars include:

- The broad implications of moving from flood defence to flood risk management and the precise definitions of these terms.
- The use of scenario analyses to develop alternative visions of the future.
- The capability of the Foresight FCD methodology to provide a mechanism to bring together physical and social scientists and engineers within a common framework, in the examination of both drivers and responses of future flood risk.
- The potential for evidence-based science to inform and underpin improved government policy making on flood risk management.

Experience since the completion of the Foresight Flood and Coastal Defence Project, dissemination of the project's *Future Flooding* reports and reactions from stakeholders in the UK and abroad all suggest that interest in long-term flood risk management is ongoing and likely to remain strong. This volume, therefore, makes accessible the research behind the results presented in the *Future Flooding* documents, and reveals how the project progressed from analysis of the drivers of flood risk to examination of broad portfolios of responses.

In compiling chapters in the volume we have encouraged authors to reflect upon their approaches, methodologies and conclusions and to include as many insights as possible on how the work was performed and what they feel its implications are for future research and flood management practice. In this respect it is, therefore, important to state clearly that the content of the book reflects the views of its authors and not those of HM Government.

References

Abbott, M.B. 1991. *Hydroinformatics: information technology and the aquatic environment*, Avebury Technical, Aldershot and Brookfield, WI.

Bye, P. and Horner, M., 1998. *Easter 1998 Floods: Report by the Independent Review Team to the Board of the Environment Agency*. Bristol, Environment Agency, Vol. 1: 121pp., Vol. 2: 341pp.

Centre for Ecology and Hydrology, 1993. *Flood Studies Report*, the original report and 18 supplementary reports, reprinted CEH Wallingford, Wallingford.

Centre for Ecology and Hydrology, 1999. *Flood Estimation Handbook*, 5 volumes, CEH Wallingford, Wallingford.

Defra/Environment Agency, 2002. *Risk, Performance and Uncertainty in Flood and Coastal Defence – A review*, R&D report FD2032/TR1. Defra/EA, Bristol.

DETR, May 1999. *A Better Quality of Life: a strategy for sustainable development for the United Kingdom*, SO, London.

Environment Agency, March 2001. *Lessons Learned: autumn 2000 floods*, Bristol, Environment Agency, Defra/EA, Bristol.

Evans, E., Ashley, R., Hall, J., Penning-Rowsell, E., Saul, A., Sayers, P., Thorne, C. and Watkinson, A., 2004a. *Foresight. Future Flooding. Scientific Summary: Volume I – Future risks and their drivers*, Office of Science and Technology, 1 Victoria Street, London, 366p.

Evans, E., Ashley, R., Hall, J., Penning-Rowsell, E., Saul, A., Sayers, P., Thorne, C. and Watkinson, A., 2004b. *Foresight. Future Flooding. Scientific Summary: Volume II – Managing future risks*, Office of Science and Technology, 1 Victoria Street, London, 416p.

Gilbert, S. and Horner, R., 1984, *The Thames Barrier*, Thomas Telford, London.

Hall, J.W., Meadowcroft, I.C., Sayers, P.B. and Bramley, M.E., 2003. 'Integrated flood risk management in England and Wales', *Natural Hazards Review*, ASCE, 4(3), 126–135.

House of Commons, 1998. *Agriculture Committee, Sixth Report: Flood and coastal defence, Vol. I, Report and Proceedings of the Committee*, The Stationery Office, London.

Hulme, M., Jenkins, G.J., Lu, X., Turnpenny, J.R., Mitchell, T.D., Jones, R.G., Lowe, J., Murphy, J.M., Hassell, D., Boorman, P., McDonald, R. and Hill, S., 2002. *Climate Change Scenarios for the United Kingdom: The UKCIP02 Scientific Report*, Tyndall Centre for Climate Change Research, School of Environmental Sciences, University of East Anglia, Norwich.

Institution of Civil Engineers, 2001. *Learning to Live with Rivers: Final report of the Institution of Civil Engineers' presidential commission to review the technical aspects of flood risk management in England and Wales*, Institution of Civil Engineers, London.

Johnson, C.L., Tunstall, S.M. and Penning-Rowsell, E.C., 2005. 'Floods as catalysts for policy change: historical lessons from England and Wales', *International Journal of Water Resources Development*, 21, 561–575.

MAFF (Ministry of Agriculture, Fisheries and Food), 1999. *Flood and Coastal Defence Project Appraisal Guidance (3): Economic appraisal*, Ministry of Agriculture, Fisheries and Food, London.

MAFF/Environment Agency, 2001. *Catchment Flood Management Plans: Interim guidelines for consultation and pilot catchment studies*, Environment Agency, Bristol.

National Audit Office, 2001. *Inland Flood Defence*, Report by the Comptroller and Auditor General HC299, The Stationery Office, London.

Parker, D.J., Green, C.H. and Thompson, P.M., 1987. *Urban Flood Protection Benefits: a project appraisal guide* (the 'Red Manual'), Gower Technical Press, Aldershot.

Penning-Rowsell, E.C. and Chatterton, J.B., 1977. *The Benefits of Flood Alleviation: A manual of assessment techniques* (the 'Blue Manual'), Gower Publishing, Aldershot.

Penning-Rowsell, E.C., Green, C.H., Thompson, P.M., Coker, A.C., Tunstall, S.M., Richards, C. and Parker, D.J., 1992. *The Economics of Coastal Management: a manual of benefit assessment techniques* (the 'Yellow Manual'), Belhaven/Wileys, London.

Penning-Rowsell, E.C., Johnson, C., Tunstall, S.M., Tapsell, S., Morris, J., Chatterton, J. and Green, C., 2005. *The Benefits of Flood and Coastal Risk Management: A manual of assessment techniques* (the 'Multi-coloured Manual'), Middlesex University Press, London.

SPRU, CSERGE, CRU, PSI, 1999. *Socio-economic Futures for Climate Impacts Assessment*, Final Report. Science and Technology Research, University of Sussex, Brighton.

Tomlinson, R.F. (Ed.), 1970. *Environment Information Systems*, International Geographical Union, Ottawa, Canada.

UN, 1992. *Rio Declaration and Agenda 21*, United Nations, New York.

WCED, 1987. *Our Common Future*, Oxford University Press, Oxford.

World Bank, 1991. *Operational Directive on EIA* (OD 4.01 Annex A).

World Bank, 1996. *The World Bank and the Environment*, World Bank Publications, Washington, DC.

2 Introduction to the Foresight 'Future Flooding' methodology

Jim W. Hall, Jonathan D. Simm and Edward P. Evans

Overview

The Foresight Project proceeded in three phases:

- Phase 1 established the conceptual framework and scenarios upon which analysis in the subsequent phases were based.
- Phase 2 analysed drivers and potential impacts of future flood risk under a simple baseline assumption that existing flood management policies continued unchanged in the future. This assumption enabled existing policies to be assessed against future risks.
- Phase 3 analysed how flood management in the UK might be changed in future in order to respond to future increases in flood risk.

The analysis had two strands (as shown in Fig. 2.1):

1. a quantified analysis of future flood risks under different socio-economic, climate and flood management scenarios; and
2. a qualitative strand of expert analysis of drivers of and responses to future flood risk, ranking of their importance and analysis of interactions and uncertainties.

The synthesis of quantitative and qualitative research involved an analysis of sustainability. A review of governance issues was also conducted to assess the institutional constraints and requirements for future flood risk management. Finally, the project addressed the identification of strategic choices for present-day policy makers in the context of wider government policies – for example, in transport and housing. These tasks were conducted by a multi-disciplinary team of experts, overseen by a panel of stakeholders and subject to peer review. In addition to the high-level stakeholder panel, stakeholder input was obtained in workshop sessions, reviews and consultations at decisive points in the project.

This chapter describes the main conceptual and methodological approaches upon which the analysis was based. Further details are provided in following chapters, while the aim here is to provide an overview and, in the discussion at the end of this chapter, to reflect upon the methodological advances, their strengths and weaknesses.

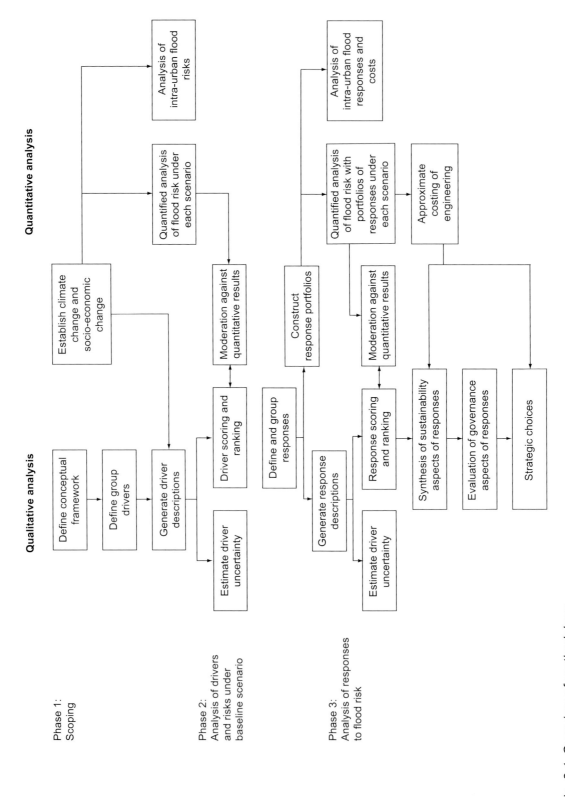

Fig. 2.1 Overview of methodology

Conceptual framework

Integrated assessment of flood risk involves a broad definition of the flooding system. For the purposes of this study, the flooding system was viewed as encompassing all of those physical and organisational systems that influence or are influenced by flooding (Hall *et al.*, 2003a), as follows:

- The physical attributes of the Earth's surface involved in the water cycle, i.e. the processes of rainfall, snow melt and marine storms that lead to fluvial and coastal flooding, runoff from the land, groundwater flows, and flood inundation in fluvial floodplains and coastal lowlands.
- The artificially created systems of drainage, storage and flood defence that are intended to convey flood discharges and resist or control inundation of floodplains.
- The economic, social and environmental assets that are located in floodplains, and are impacted upon by flooding and/or have an impact on the flooding process.
- The organisations with a statutory responsibility for managing flood risk. These may be government or other organisations with duties or powers to manage flood risk.
- Insurers who provide cover for flood risks.
- Broader stakeholder groups that have an interest or role in the impacts (both positive and negative) of flooding and the actions that they may take to manage flooding.

The processes in the flooding system operate at different scales. At the highest level, fluvial and coastal flooding is caused by weather events at the scale of catchments and their estuarial and coastal equivalents. In urban areas, flooding usually results from intense localised rainfall that overwhelms the urban drainage system. While often localised, these intra-urban floods can be very damaging in economic, social and environmental terms. Dispersed episodes of flooding detached from the floodplain, such as groundwater flooding, can also be harmful in particular localities.

Change in the flooding system can be conceptualised using the pressure-state-impact-response (PSIR) model (Turner *et al.*, 1998), based on Rapport and Friend's (1979) pressure-state-response model. In the PSIR model:

1. Socio-economic drivers lead to environmental pressures.
2. Environmental pressures lead to changes in environmental state.
3. Changes in environmental state are reflected in environmental and socio-economic impacts.
4. Stakeholder gains/losses from impacts lead to policy responses.

While the PSIR framework deals with the changes in system state, further conceptual structure is required to evaluate instantaneous system state in terms of risk. A well-established framework in environmental risk assessment is the source-pathway-receptor (SPR) model (DETR *et al.*, 2000), which is based upon the causal linkage between the source of environmental hazard (e.g. a pollutant), the mechanism by which it is transmitted (e.g. in the groundwater) and the receptor, which suffers some harmful (in the case of pollution) impact. The same framework is useful in the context of flooding, as it reflects the physical processes by which flooding occurs. In the case of flooding:

- *Sources* are the weather events or sequences of events that may result in flooding (e.g. heavy or sustained rainfall, marine storms).
- *Pathways* are the mechanisms that convey floodwaters that originate as extreme weather events to places where they may impact upon receptors.

Pathways therefore include fluvial flows in or out of river channels, overland urban flows, coastal processes, and failure of fluvial and sea defence structures or urban drainage systems.

- *Receptors* are the people, industries and built or natural environments that may be impacted upon by flooding.

The division between sources, pathways and receptors is not crisp, and depends upon the context of the analysis, though this indeterminacy should not, in principle, be problematic.

The instantaneous flooding system state can be captured in terms of a set of state variables that characterise flooding sources, pathways, receptors, or a combination thereof. Typical state variables might be flood defence levels, numbers of properties in the floodplain, etc. Some state variables may be naturally fluctuating, for example rainfall intensity or tide level in an estuary, so will be characterised by probability distributions representing (stationary) time-averaged behaviour.

The changes in the flooding system captured in the PSIR model are reflected in changes in the state variables over a range of timescales. Any phenomenon that may change the time-averaged state of the flooding system is referred to as a *driver*. Some of these drivers will be under the control of flood risk managers, e.g. construction and operation of flood defence systems, or use of flood warning systems to reduce the consequences of flooding (i.e. reduce the number of human receptors). Many other drivers, e.g. rainfall severity or increasing values of house contents, are outside the control of flood risk managers and even government in general. The distinction between these two types of drivers is not crisp and in terms of policy relates to the extent to which government has power to influence change and the level of government at which power is exercised (see Fig. 2.2). For example, decisions regarding local flood defence improvements are devolved to

---

Definitions

Drivers: Phenomena that may *change the state* of the flooding system, such as climate change, urbanisation or changing agricultural practices. A driver may change *sources, pathways, receptors* or a combination of them.

Flooding system: All physical and human systems that cause, influence, or are influenced by flooding.

Flood risk: A combination of the probability and consequences of flooding. To estimate flood risk requires a system model that may be conceptual or quantified, which includes sources, pathways and receptors.

Pathways: Mechanisms by which water travels from its source to places where it may affect receptors (e.g. runoff, fluvial flows, sea defence overtopping, floodplain inundation).

Receptors: People, industries and built or natural environments that flooding can affect.

Responses: Changes to the flooding system that are implemented to reduce flood risk.

Scenario: A consistent storyline embracing a set of changes to the flooding system.

Sources: Weather-related phenomena (rainfall, marine storms, snow melt, etc.) which generate water that could cause flooding.

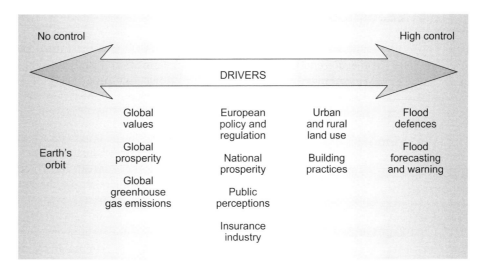

Fig. 2.2 Example drivers classified according to degree of control

local decision makers, whereas decisions to limit emissions of greenhouse gasses are taken at a national and international level.

The conceptual framework introduced above is summarised in Fig. 2.3. The flooding system is described in terms of a set of state variables that characterise flooding sources, pathways, receptors, or a combination thereof. A multi-attribute risk measure is used to characterise flood system behaviour with respect to stakeholder values. Future changes in risk (due to the influence of drivers) are estimated by making appropriate changes to state variables and estimating the consequential change in risk.

There may be feedback in the flooding system, particularly as the consequences of an impact on the environment may result in an alteration of the flooding pathways (and potentially sources) that then influence future SPR relationships. This is particularly important for climate change where long-term impacts are likely to result from interaction of earth surface and socio-economic processes perhaps leading to wholesale changes in land-use, aquatic character, etc. It is conceivable that these interactions may represent some of the greatest threats and opportunities for flood management in the long term. It is argued that these complex interactions over timescales of decades do not succumb to conventional quantified risk analysis (IPCC, 2000) so a scenarios-based approach has been adopted.

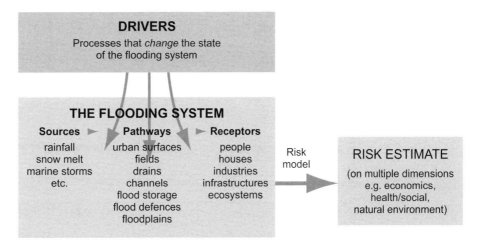

Fig. 2.3 Summary of conceptual framework

Scenarios analysis

The use of scenarios for policy analysis far into the future has been stimulated by the long-term nature of climate change and the socio-economic uncertainties surrounding greenhouse gas emissions and projections of societal vulnerability. Flood risk management is an interesting application of the scenarios-based approach because it involves integrated use of two different types of scenarios:

- Climate change projections are based on *emissions scenarios*. Climate change is the key driver relating to the flooding 'source' variables in the SPR model.
- *Socio-economic scenarios* provide the context in which flood management policy and practice will be enacted and relate to the extent to which society may be impacted upon by flooding.

Climate change scenarios

The UKCIP02 climate scenarios for the UK (Hulme *et al.*, 2002) have been used. These scenarios are based on four emissions scenarios: low emissions; medium-low emissions; medium-high emissions; and high emissions, corresponding to the IPCC's SRES (IPCC, 2000) scenarios B1, B2, A2 and A1F1 respectively. The scenarios encompass a range of global greenhouse gas emissions and changes in global mean temperature (Figs 2.4 and 2.5). To separate climate change from natural climate variability, it is customary to average results from climate models over many years. The UKCIP published climate scenarios for three time slices: 2020s, 2050s and 2080s. To be consistent with the UKCIP approach, and to make use of the widely accepted UKCIP scenarios, the Foresight project focused on the 2050s and 2080s.

The UKCIP02 scenarios are based upon runs of the Hadley Centre's HadCM3 model. HadCM3 was used to simulate global climate from 1860 to 2100 for the four selected emissions scenarios. For the period from 1860 to 1990, the model was driven by observed, or deduced, human-induced changes in greenhouse gases and sulphate aerosols, plus natural changes in volcanoes and solar output. From 1990 to 2100, the model was driven by changes in individual greenhouse gas and sulphate aerosol concentrations, based on the selected A1FI, A2, B1 and B2 emissions. The effects of unpredictable volcanoes or uncertain solar changes in the future were not considered. The model does simulate, however, natural variability generated internally within the climate system and to quantify this effect the model was run three times using the A2 emissions, each time using a different and randomly selected initial condition.

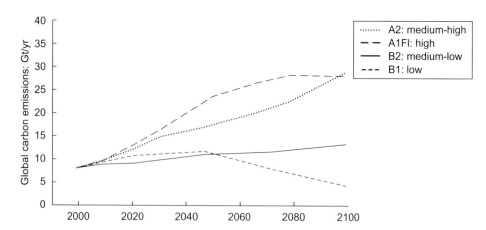

Fig. 2.4 Global greenhouse gas emissions associated with the UKCIP02 scenarios (Hulme et al., *2002)*

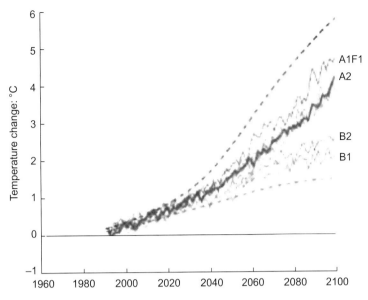

Fig. 2.5. Scenarios of annual global-average surface air temperature relative to 1961–1990 average. The dotted curves represent the full IPCC range of global temperature change when both emissions uncertainties and model uncertainties are considered. Labels A1F1, A2, B1, B2 relate to IPCC SRES.

The UKCIP02 scenarios predict that annual average precipitation across the UK may decrease slightly, by between 0 and 15% by the 2080s depending on scenario. The seasonal distribution of precipitation will change, with winters becoming wetter and summers becoming drier, the biggest relative changes being in the south and east. Under the high emissions scenario, winter precipitation in the south and east may increase by up to 30% by the 2080s. By the 2080s the daily precipitation intensities that are experienced once every two years on average may become up to 20% heavier. By the 2080s, and depending on scenario, relative sea level may be between 2 cm below and 58 cm above the current level in western Scotland and between 26 and 86 cm above the current level in south-east England. For some coastal locations, a water level that at present has a 2% annual probability of occurrence may have an annual occurrence probability of 33% by the 2080s for medium-high emissions. The climate change scenarios included within UKCIP02 do not include allowance for model error and do not therefore represent the maximum potential range of climate change effects.

The choice of these four emissions scenarios provides a reasonable spread of possible future climate change against which to assess future flood risk. However, the scenarios do not necessarily include the most extreme possibilities. Uncertainties in emissions scenarios, global climate modelling and downscaling to the sub-UK scale could mean that the future climate may vary more than the four scenarios used here (Jenkins and Lowe, 2003). Until the 2050s, uncertainties in climate models, reflected in the differences between models, exceed the uncertainties due to alternative emissions scenarios, even for the most 'stable' climate indicators, such as global mean temperature.

There is considerable variation in the degree of confidence with which one can predict different climate variables. UKCIP02 attaches 'high confidence' to predicted temperature increases, winter precipitation increases, snowfall decreases, summer soil-moisture decreases and sea-level rise. Predicted changes in storminess have lower confidence associated with them. It is possible to predict mean values of variables with much more confidence than extremes. For example, one can be more

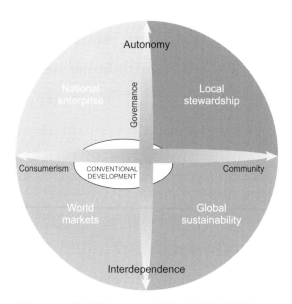

Fig. 2.6 Foresight Futures (SPRU et al., 1999; OST, 2002)

confident about changes in mean sea level than about events with a return period of decades or more, yet it is extreme events that are of most interest in flood risk analysis. Moreover, averaging a variable over a longer period gives higher confidence in the predictions. Thus one can predict monthly average rainfall with more confidence than one can forecast hourly average rainfall. Some systems, notably urban drainage systems, respond very rapidly to changes in rainfall, so we need to predict rainfall over durations as short as 10 or 15 minutes. Predictions of the impact of climate change on such short-duration rainfall are very uncertain.

Socio-economic scenarios

The Foresight Futures socio-economic scenarios (SPRU *et al.*, 1999; OST, 2002) are intended to suggest possible long-term futures, exploring alternative directions in which social, economic and technological changes may evolve over coming decades. The scenarios are represented on a two-dimensional grid (see Fig. 2.6). On the vertical dimension is the system of governance, ranging from autonomy, where power remains at the national level, to interdependence where power increasingly moves to other institutions, e.g. the EU or regional government. On the horizontal dimension are social values, ranging from individualistic values to community oriented values. The four Foresight Futures that occupy this grid are summarised in Tables 2.1 and 2.2.

There is no direct correspondence between the UKCIP02 scenarios and the Foresight Futures, not least because the Foresight Futures are specifically aimed at the UK whereas the emissions scenarios used in UKCIP02 are *global* emissions scenarios. However, an approximate correspondence can be expected, as shown in Table 2.3. This is not the only conceivable correspondence and several alternatives are explored by the UK Climate Impacts Programme (2000).

Future flood risk is greatly influenced by flood management policy and practice, perhaps more so than it is by changes outside the control of the flood risk manager, such as climate change or economic growth. In order to evaluate flood risk for the different future scenarios, assumptions must first be made about future flood management. First, in order to test the effectiveness and weaknesses of the current approach to flood management in Phase 2 a simple 'baseline assumption' was used in which the current pattern of expenditure and technical approach were assumed. Then in Phase 3 of the project a range of different approaches to flood

Table 2.1 Summary of Foresight Futures (OST, 2002)

	World markets	National enterprise	Local stewardship	Global sustainability
Social values	Internationalist, libertarian	Nationalist, individualist	Localist, cooperative	Internationalist, communitarian
Governance structures	Weak, dispersed, consultative	Weak, national, closed	Strong, local, participative	Strong, coordinated, consultative
Role of policy	Minimal, enabling markets	State-centred, market regulation to protect key sectors	Interventionist, social and environmental	Corporatist, political, social and environmental goals
Economic development	High growth, high innovation, capital productivity	Medium-low growth, low maintenance innovation, economy	Low growth, low innovation, modular and sustainable	Medium-high growth, high innovation, resource productivity
Structural change	Rapid, towards services	More stable economic structure	Moderate, towards regional systems	Fast, towards services
Fast-growing sectors	Health and leisure, media and information, financial services, biotechnology, nanotechnology	Private health and education, domestic and personal services, tourism, retailing, defence	Small-scale manufacturing, food and organic farming, local services	Education and training, large systems engineering, new and renewable energy, information services
Declining sectors	Manufacturing, agriculture	Public services, civil engineering	Retailing, tourism, financial services	Fossil-fuel energy, traditional manufacturing
Unemployment	Medium-low	Medium-high	Medium-low (large voluntary sector)	Low
Income	High	Medium-low	Low	Medium-high
Equity	Strong decline	Decline	Strong improvement	Improvement

Table 2.2 Snapshot statistics for 2050s for Foresight Futures (UK Climate Impacts Programme, 2002)

	Today	World markets	National enterprise	Local stewardship	Global sustainability
GDP growth per year: %	2.5	3.5	2	1.25	2.75
Total investment: % of GDP	19	22	18	16	20
Agricultural activity: % of total activity	2	1	2	3	1.5
Newly developed land: hectares per year	6500	6000	4500	1000	3000
Primary energy consumption: million tonnes of oil equivalent	230	280	270	230	230
Primary energy consumption: % average change per year		+1.7	+1.5	+0.1	+0.1

risk management, broadly consistent with the socio-economic and climate scenarios, was tested. The following assumptions were made in Phase 2:

1. Flood defence structures were kept in the same alignment and the distribution of condition grades was kept constant.
2. Practices of channel/beach management were continued as at present, modified as necessary by the regulatory arrangements associated with each scenario.

Table 2.3 Correspondence between UKCIP02 scenarios and Foresight Futures

IPCC-SRES	UKCIP02	Foresight Futures	Commentary
A1F1	High emissions	World markets	Highest national and global growth. No action to limit emissions. Price of fossil fuels may drive development of alternatives in the long term.
A2	Medium-high emissions	National enterprise	Medium-high growth, but with no action to limit emissions. Increasing and unregulated emissions from newly industrialised countries.
B2	Medium-low emissions	Local stewardship	Low growth. Low consumption. However, less effective international action. Low innovation.
B1	Low emissions	Global sustainability	Medium-high growth, but low primary energy consumption. High emphasis on international action for environmental goals (e.g. greenhouse gas emissions control). Innovation of new and renewable energy sources.

3. The rate of floodplain urbanisation depended upon the average rates of urbanisation for the scenario modified by current practices of development control.

Clearly, flood defence policy will change in the future and will tend to reflect the nature and public expectations of future society, i.e. flood risk management is scenario-dependent. However, the aim of Phase 2 was to subject present-day flood risk management policy to particular scrutiny by analysing its effectiveness in a range of scenarios. Changing scenarios were superimposed on this fixed flood policy (including the current pattern of expenditure and technical approach), in order to assess the capacity of the current policy to cope with long-term changes.

Quantified flood risk assessment

In recent years, it has become possible to do approximate national-scale analysis of the risks from river and coastal flooding in England and Wales. The same is true of the risks of urban flooding (due to sewer flooding and insufficient capacity in the urban drainage system), where urban drainage models can be up-scaled to generate national estimates of the risks of urban flooding. Inevitably, these approximate models contain a great deal of uncertainty and are not appropriate for detailed local analysis. However, they do provide a broad impression of the scale and distribution of flood risk, and so provide a powerful tool for policy analysis.

Hall *et al.* (2003b) developed a quantified model for assessment of flood risk from rivers and the sea that takes explicit account of the reliability of flood defences and their modifying effect on flood risk. Further details are provided in Chapter 11. The methodology was developed to make use of GIS databases for all of England and Wales and no other site-specific data. The flood risk assessment method operates on a GIS, first identifying interconnected floodplain areas and the system of defences protecting them from flooding. Information on the flood defence design standard, type, and condition is used in an approximate reliability analysis of each system of flood defences. A parametric flood spreading routine is used to estimate flood depths in a large number of combinations of flood defence failure in flood events of different severity, and hence estimate a probability distribution of flood depth in each area, no greater than 1 km × 1 km, in the floodplain. These depth-probability relationships are combined with census data and commercial databases of property and population location, together with relationships between flood depth and economic damage that have been developed from empirical analysis of past flooding events (Penning-Rowsell *et al.*, 2003). No discounting or inflation is applied to economic risks. Risk is estimated at time points in the future using today's prices. The results have been aggregated and are reported nationally, regionally and on a 10 km × 10 km grid. An estimate of the risk to lives, health, and communities was obtained by analysing population density and census data indicating the potential vulnerability of difference sectors of the community to flooding (Tapsell *et al.*, 2002).

In addition to the national-scale risk modelling of flooding from rivers and the sea, quantified analysis was made of the effects of long-term change on the frequency of urban flooding. The approach adopted was based on analysis of three typical cities: a market town in northern England, an inland city with major water-courses in Scotland and a coastal city in Wales. Results from these locations were then up-scaled based on asset data from water service providers. This present-day analysis was combined with scenarios of rainfall depth, duration and frequency, asset deterioration, urbanisation and changing vulnerability.

The models outlined above were used to analyse long-term change by making appropriate changes to the model parameters to reflect the time and scenario under consideration. The four scenarios listed in Table 2.1 were analysed for the 2080s and chosen to coincide with the years for which climate scenarios were available (Hulme *et al.*, 2002). The input data required by the risk assessment models did not correspond exactly to the information provided in either climate change or socio-economic scenarios. It was therefore necessary to construct approximate relationships between the variables for which scenarios information was available and the variables required for flood risk analysis. The cumulative effect of each of the changes in the given scenario was then calculated. Where feasible, regional variation was applied to these adjustments in order to take account of, for example, regional differences in climate or demographic projections. There is no unique mapping between a scenario, which is an inherently vague entity, and a realisation of the risk model. In other words, there is not a unique representation of the scenario in the risk model. The quantified analysis was one of many equally plausible representations of the same four scenarios. While no claim is made to the uniqueness of the results, they do illustrate some striking contrasts between different scenarios of change and provide the basis for exploring responses to flood risk that are robust across plausible futures. The approach is summarised in Fig. 2.7. The final step in Fig. 2.7 represents a cross-check with the expert analysis of drivers described next.

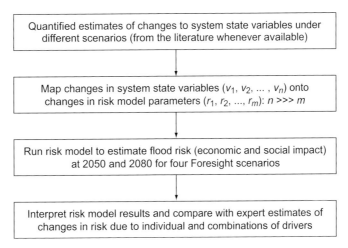

Quantified estimates of changes to system state variables under different scenarios (from the literature whenever available)

Map changes in system state variables (v_1, v_2, ... , v_n) onto changes in risk model parameters (r_1, r_2, ..., r_m): $n >>> m$

Run risk model to estimate flood risk (economic and social impact) at 2050 and 2080 for four Foresight scenarios

Interpret risk model results and compare with expert estimates of changes in risk due to individual and combinations of drivers

Fig. 2.7 Overview of methodology for implementation and interpretation of national-scale flood risk analysis

Quantified analysis of responses

The quantified analysis of flood risks under the base-line scenario was followed in Phase 3 of the Foresight Project by analysis, using the same quantified risk models, of the effectiveness of a range of flood management measures, implemented across the UK in strategic portfolios. A portfolio is a set of hard and soft flood risk management measures implemented across the UK. It was not feasible to test each individual flood management response in the national-scale flood risk analysis. Nor would it be realistic to do so, as flood management, whether it is implemented in a strategic fashion or in a more *ad hoc* manner, tends to be composed of a range of measures tailored to particular localities and socio-economic contexts.

The construction of flood risk management portfolios is discussed in more detail in Chapter 22. As with the scenarios analysis introduced above, portfolios of responses should be regarded as examples of possible futures, rather than predictions or recommendations. The four different portfolios of responses (one for each scenario) were drawn from a pool of possible responses identified in the qualitative strand of the analysis. The choice for each was influenced by the characteristics, values and wealth of the scenarios in which they were to operate. For example, a very costly response might not be selected for a scenario that embodied relatively low national wealth, whereas a response that required a high degree of regulation might not be selected in a scenario that embodied laissez-faire governance. The portfolios were designed to be reasonably distinct from each other. Together they covered a wide spectrum of possible types of response and spatial implementations. They were set against four climate-change and socio-economic scenarios, including different trajectories of national wealth and governance.

Approximate analysis of some of the costs of implementing the flood management portfolios was conducted by costing the engineering component of each set of responses. It is recognised that the engineering component does not represent the full cost to society, especially in scenarios with a relatively small engineering component.

Estimates of flood risk were produced for each portfolio of responses in their respective scenario. Two types of model were used, as mentioned above:

- For catchment and coastal scale risks, the national-scale flood risk assessment model described here was applied to all of England and Wales. This model is well suited to analysis of the effectiveness of structural responses and measures to reduce vulnerability as it includes an explicit representation of flood defence infrastructure as well as the location and socio-economic vulnerability of floodplain occupants.
- For intra-urban risks, urban drainage models of sample cities were used and the results scaled up to cover all of the UK.

Expert analysis of drivers

The quantified analysis of future flood risk, described above, provided an impression of how, in future, risk may change under a range of different climate change and socio-economic scenarios. However, it did not provide specific insights into the contribution that different drivers of change make to the total risk. To do so would require a large number of sensitivity runs, which were not feasible given the considerable computational expense of each national-scale flood risk assessment model run. Moreover, the approximate risk analysis tools described above could not resolve the effects of all of the potential drivers of change.

In order to provide an insight into the importance of individual drivers to the overall flood risk, a ranking methodology, based on expert judgement, was employed. First, the drivers of changing flood risk were identified in a brainstorming session and clustered into a manageable number of driver sets. The future change in each driver was described (and each is discussed in subsequent chapters of this volume) and, where possible, quantified using evidence from the literature. As in the quantified flood risk analysis described above, flood risk management activities were assumed to remain constant and were excluded from the analysis.

Drivers were ranked according to an expert assessment of their impact on total flood risk in England and Wales at two specified times in the future (2050s and 2080s) under four scenarios, relative to present-day flood risk. For the purposes of this analysis, flood risk was defined as the product of the likelihood and consequences of flooding, and an aggregate measure of economic and health/social consequences was adopted. Drivers that influence the sources or pathways in the flooding system change the likelihood of flooding. Drivers that influence the receptors in the flooding system change the consequences of flooding. The effect of the driver was expressed as a multiple of present-day risk. Thus, climate change that increased the frequency of flooding by a factor of 1.9 on average nationally would be scored as having an impact of 1.9 on the likelihood of flooding. A driver that increased the quantity of assets at risk in the floodplain by a factor of 1.6 on average nationally would be scored as having an impact of 1.6 on the consequence of flooding. In addition, an assessment was made of the range of uncertainty on each of the driver scores. Some drivers are spatially distributed in their impact. For example, sea-level rise only impacts upon coastal floodplains. In order to compare drivers, the impact score was factored according to the spatial extent of the driver's influence.

Elicitation of ranking values began with circulation of a protocol explaining the ranking methodology to each of the 15 experts. Their expertise overlapped so each driver was the subject of the judgement of multiple experts. First, each driver was evaluated independently. These scores were then presented, discussed and, if necessary, amended in a group moderating session. Finally, the scores were further reviewed when compared with the results of the quantified risk analysis introduced above and then subjected to wider peer review by way of two workshops with 21 and 34 attendees, one open meeting attended by 131 people, and the electronic publication of draft results.

Expert analysis of responses to flood risk

A similar process to the one described above for expert evaluation and ranking of drivers was also applied to the potential responses to flood risk (see Fig. 2.1). First, a wide variety of potential responses was identified in a brainstorming session and supplemented by way of literature review. The responses were then clustered into groups and each response was described in detail, including:

- the mechanism by which they reduce flood risk and interact; and
- the constraints and limitations to implementation under the different scenarios.

The responses were then scored against a range of economic and sustainability metrics, which are discussed in detail in Chapter 24. The potential for risk reduction of any given response will depend strongly on the scenario under which it is implemented, e.g. due to regulatory or funding constraints implicit in the scenario. The responses were therefore scored in the context of each of the four scenarios. The scoring and ranking of responses was based on today's values and preferences. No attempt was made to interpret future preferences implicit in each socio-economic scenario.

The purpose of the scoring process was to provide a consistent and concise means of reporting expert judgements of the potential effectiveness and impacts of responses to flood risk. An assessment of uncertainty was also made in the expert scoring. The multi-attribute scoring of responses was used as a basis of comparison, but it was not, however, possible to generate a precise ranking because of the uncertainties involved in scoring responses, and because the extent to which people value different criteria such as the environment, economics and equity, varies. Nevertheless, it was possible broadly to compare the responses and identify those that are more desirable than others.

Discussion

Long-term policy analysis has a chequered history (Lempert *et al.*, 2004), the limits to growth analysis (Meadows *et al.*, 1972) being among the most notorious projections that proved, with the benefit of hindsight, to be misconceived. The Foresight Flood and Coastal Defence Project is vulnerable to the same fallibility and only time will tell whether it has succumbed.

There are, however, a number of features of the methodological approach introduced in this chapter that are intended to guard against the fallibility of foresight. While many aspects of the distant future are quite uncertain, others can be known with some confidence in all but the most surprising of scenarios. For example, because of the thermal inertia in the oceans, sea-level rise can be predicted with some confidence, regardless of greenhouse gas emissions scenarios, at least for the first half of the twenty-first century. Aspects of socio-economic change, e.g. the rate of turnover of the building stock in the UK, are slow. The rate of long-term economic growth in the UK tends to vary within a fairly narrow range. Maximising use of relatively stable predictions can help to build confidence in long-term projections. The socio-economic figures in Table 2.2 were derived for UKCIP (2000) based upon this approach, although there are aspects of the future where projections are quite divergent.

In the Foresight study, contrasting alternative futures were examined through the use of scenarios. Versions of the scenarios framework that was adopted have been used in the IPCC's *Special Report on Emissions Scenarios* (IPCC, 2000) and in previous UK Foresight studies. However, the approach is not without its limitations. The number of scenarios considered is small (only four) and they have been designed to be contrasting, when it might be argued that the future for the UK is most likely to be a hybrid of world markets and global sustainability. This, perhaps more likely, hybrid has not been assessed. The scenarios approach is, by exploring contrasting futures, intended to dispel the notion that the future is determined along a 'business as usual' trajectory. However, while contrasting, the scenarios do not explore extreme possibilities – indeed distressing extremes scenarios were excluded from the SRES process (IPCC, 2000).

The scenarios approach, as implemented in the Foresight study, does not explicitly examine transitions and the path-dependence of institutions (Putnam, 1993). In other words, it did not examine whether there are feasible mechanisms by which future scenarios are reachable from the present. However, the inertia in the built environment and institutions is implicit in the interpretation of the scenarios in the context of flood risk management.

The project's focus upon flooding and flood risk management did mean that other processes going on at the same time, e.g. changes in water resources or transportation infrastructure, did not attract the same level of attention. We return below to the problem of isolating changes and their causes from a future of multiple inter-related processes.

The methodological approach involved a combination of quantitative and qualitative analysis, with the two approaches being used to compensate for the defects of quantitative or qualitative analysis alone. The quantified analysis relied upon models developed specifically for the analysis of flood defence and urban drainage systems. These had to be adapted to represent the effects of changes elsewhere in the flooding system, e.g. due to changes in rainfall or runoff. The use of multiple experts and peer review helped to identify anomalies in model behaviour and key uncertainties in the quantitative analysis. At the same time, the quantitative analysis generated a benchmark risk estimate that could be used to calibrate and moderate expert judgements of future risk. The biases in individual expert judgements were addressed by use of group sessions and peer review. Given more time it would have been desirable to undertake more formal elicitation studies and cross-calibration of experts.

The design of the Foresight methodology was a compromise between, on the one hand, thorough representation of all of the complex processes of change in the flooding system, and more broadly, that may occur over the next century, and, on the other hand, preserving simplicity so that the method and results are intelligible and useful to stakeholders and policy makers, whose emphasis was naturally upon decisions that will be made in the coming years. Analysis in Phase 2 of the study of a scenario in which current flood management practices were projected, unrealistically, into the future, was used to provide evidence about the robustness and weaknesses of current policy. Analysis of future policies inevitably introduced circularities in the setting of standards of flood risk reduction in the context of particular scenarios: societies will tend to reduce risks to a level that is consistent with expectations, preferences and competing opportunities and risks (Adams, 1995). In the context of this changing landscape of society, the economy and the environment it is indeed hard to isolate flood risk management and generate valid, policy-relevant conclusions. The methodology presented here has been an attempt to do that. Its strengths, and weaknesses, should serve as a lesson to future researchers embarking upon a similar challenge.

References

Adams, J., 1995. *Risk*, Routledge, London.

DETR, 2000. Environment Agency, Institute for Environment and Health, *Guidelines for Environmental Risk Assessment and Management*, The Stationery Office, London.

Hall, J.W., Meadowcroft, I.C., Sayers, P.B. and Bramley, M.E., 2003a. 'Integrated flood risk management in England and Wales', *Natural Hazards Review*, 4(3), 126–135.

Hall, J.W., Dawson, R.J., Sayers, P.B., Rosu, C., Chatterton, J.B. and Deakin, R., 2003b. 'A methodology for national-scale flood risk assessment', *Water and Maritime Engineering*, 156, 235–247.

Hulme, M., Jenkins, G.J., Lu, X., Turnpenny, J.R., Mitchell, T.D., Jones, R.G., Lowe, J., Murphy, J.M., Hassell, D., Boorman, P., McDonald, R. and Hill, S., 2002. *Climate Change Scenarios for the United Kingdom: The UKCIP02 scientific report*, Tyndall Centre for Climate Change Research, School of Environmental Sciences, University of East Anglia, Norwich.

IPCC, 2000. *Special Report on Emissions Scenarios (SRES): A special report of Working Group III of the Intergovernmental Panel on Climate Change*, Cambridge University Press, Cambridge.

Jenkins, G. and Lowe, J., 2003. *Handling uncertainties in the UKCIP02 scenarios of climate change*. Technical Note 44, Hadley Centre, Exeter.

Lempert, R.J., Popper, S.W. and Bankes S.C., 2004. *Shaping the Next One Hundred Years: New methods for quantitative, long-term policy analysis*, RAND, Santa Monica, CA.

Meadows, D.L., Meadows, D.I., Randers, J. and Behrens, W.W., 1972. *The Limits to Growth*, A Report to The Club of Rome.

OST, 2002. *Foresight Futures 2020: Revised scenarios and guidance*, Office of Science and Technology, Department of Trade and Industry, London.

Putnam, R.D., 1993. *Making Democracy Work: Civic traditions in modern Italy*, Princeton University Press, Princeton, NJ.

Rapport, D. and Friend, A., 1979. 'Towards a comprehensive framework for environmental statistics: a stress-response approach', *Statistics*, Ottawa.

SPRU, CSERGE, CRU, PSI, 1999. *Socio-economic Futures for Climate Impacts Assessment*, Final Report, Science and Technology Research, University of Sussex, Brighton.

Tapsell, S.M., Penning-Rowsell, E.C., Tunstall, S.M. and Wilson, T.L., 2002. 'Vulnerability to flooding: health and social dimensions, *Philosophical Transactions of the Royal Society, London – Series A, Mathematical, Physical and Engineering Sciences*, 360(1796), 1511–1525.

Turner, R.K., Lorenzoni, I., Beaumont, N., Bateman, I.J., Langford, I.H. and McDonald, A.L., 1998. 'Coastal management for sustainable development: analysing environmental and socio-economic changes on the UK coast', *Geographical Journal*, 164(3), 269–281.

UK Climate Impacts Programme, 2000. *Socio-economic Scenarios for Climate Change Assessment: A guide to their use in the UK Climate Impacts Programme*, Oxford, UKCIP.

3 Environmental impacts of future flood risk

Andrew R. Watkinson, Robert J. Nicholls, David A. Sear and Laure Ledoux

Introduction

Many drivers of flood risk are affected by the environment. For example: agricultural land management affects catchment runoff (Chapter 5); river vegetation affects conveyance (Chapter 6); and relative sea level affects the frequency with which land adjacent to coasts and estuaries is flooded (Chapter 10). In this chapter we consider the other side of the coin – the environmental impacts of flooding and the environment as a receptor. In particular we:

1. analyse the environmental impacts of flooding and flood risk management in fluvial and coastal zones;
2. consider the environmental implications of current trends of change in flood risk management policies;
3. examine how the environmental impacts of flooding might differ under the four Foresight Socio-Economic Futures; and
4. provide an environmental economic assessment of the impacts of flooding.

In so doing our aim is to provide the environmental context for the assessment of the impacts of future flood risk. This is because coastal and fluvial flooding affect the physical characteristics of the environment, the coastal, riverine and floodplain ecosystems, and the species those ecosystems contain. Moreover, regular flooding is essential for the health and survival of many of these ecosystems. The size of natural alluvial river channels, for example, generally depends on the magnitude of the flood that occurs once every one to two years. Biodiversity within river channels depends on the frequency of flooding and associated movement of sediment. Floodplain wetlands are often maintained by inundation, and coastal saltmarshes require regular tidal flooding.

Infrequent 'large' floods can disturb landforms and ecosystems, which may take significant periods to recover. While these floods can be seen as 'natural' parts of the environmental system, a *changing* frequency of flooding can disturb the equilibrium of a landform or ecosystem. The result may be seen as adverse environmental consequences: the area of saltmarsh may decline, or a river channel may be destabilised.

Whether a changed frequency of flooding has an impact depends not only on the extent of the change but also on how close the system is to a *threshold* of change. A relatively large flood may have little effect in one location, and a relatively smaller flood a larger effect in another. However, the assessment of adverse environmental impact depends on the timescale over which we view the change. Longer timescales may see morphological change as part of a process of natural adjustment, driven by large-scale influences on flooding, such as climate change.

For centuries people have set out to reduce the effects of flooding, through the construction of embankments to separate a river or coastline from its floodplain, or through the realignment or reconstruction of river channels. These measures to control flooding also affect physical landforms and ecosystems (Nordstrom 2000; Sear *et al.*, 2000).

In the twenty-first century, the changes in the drivers of flood risk can be expected to result in continued changes to the magnitude and frequency of flooding, with a range of environmental implications. Some factors, such as climate change, may also directly influence floodplain ecosystems, including the species they contain (Harrison *et al.*, 2001).

Environmental impacts of flood risk management

Although flooding in most fluvial, estuarial and coastal systems in the UK has been managed for many decades or centuries, it is only with the recent advent of catchment flood management plans and shoreline management plans that there has been significant interest in the ecological implications of fluvial and coastal flood management. Data are therefore limited, with none in the consolidated form required to allow the full range of potential ecological effects of the wide range of flood management practices to be established.

In the most general terms (Burton *et al.*, 1993), measures to reduce the flood risk to a community can seek to reduce the physical hazard, reduce the exposure to the hazard, or reduce the vulnerability to loss and increase ability to recover (Table 3.1).

'Flood defence' is traditionally concerned with reducing the physical hazard, although current flood risk management practice seeks to consider and include all three groups of measures in Table 3.1. In themselves, measures to reduce exposure and vulnerability usually have no negative environmental impact. In some cases, as in the case of land-use planning, they in fact may bring considerable environmental benefits when implemented in the place of measures to reduce the physical hazard. In this section we concentrate on the environmental impact of measures to reduce the physical hazard.

Table 3.1. Examples of measures to reduce flood risk

Measures to reduce the flood risk	Example measures
Reduce the physical hazard	Flood embankments/sea defences River channelisation Washland storage Reservoir impoundment Catchment management
Reduce exposure to the hazard	Land-use planning Property-scale flood proofing
Reduce vulnerability to the hazard	Warning and preparedness Insurance

Fluvial systems

Flood management has traditionally included modification of the morphology of channels and floodplains to increase conveyance, to reduce flood levels or to contain higher flood elevations. Many approaches have been used, including channel maintenance to reduce sediment accumulation or vegetation growth, channel realignment, the construction of artificial channels, and the construction of embankments to separate the river from its floodplain (Sear *et al.*, 2000). As a consequence many rivers have highly simplified and modified channels, steep banks and little connectivity with their floodplains (Harrison *et al.*, 2004).

The effects of flood management on the ecosystems of rivers, their surroundings and downstream are well-documented (Sear *et al.*, 2002b). In the most general terms, increasing water conveyance or reducing the storage capacity at a site increases flood peaks downstream. Habitat diversity (the result of flood-driven physical processes) at the site tends to decline, and elimination of the natural connection between channel and floodplain has substantial impacts on riparian and floodplain wildlife. Downstream, changes in water flow and sediment also impact on ecosystem structure and function, while secondary ecological impacts are associated with changes in land-use and water quality.

River flow in many UK rivers has been modulated by the construction of dams. While any reservoir can alter flood flows and the discharge of sediment, few reservoirs in the UK exist solely to reduce downstream flood risk. Lower flood peaks reduce the channel size downstream of reservoirs: the effects depend not only on the extent of the reduction but also on changes in sediment load and the characteristics of the bed and banks (Petts, 1984). Vegetation can stabilise bed and banks but may also reduce water conveyance.

Over the past few years, flood defence practice in the UK has shifted towards 'softer' management approaches. These include such techniques as the restoration of channels and floodplains and the provision of washland storage (Mance *et al.*, 2002). A washland is an area of the floodplain that is allowed to flood or is deliberately flooded by a river or stream for flood management purposes, with the potential to form a wetland habitat. The provision of temporary washland storage is increasingly being considered as a flood management action (e.g. on the River Cherwell upstream of Banbury). Such schemes are essentially seeking to maintain and enhance 'natural' processes of flood-water storage, and appear to have no major adverse environmental implications on site and often have considerable environmental benefits. However, by allowing storage areas to fill early in the development of a flood they may exacerbate flooding downstream (ICE, 2001) – modelling of the Cherwell restoration scenario demonstrated a significant effect on flood timing and hence flood level downstream.

Channel and floodplain restoration schemes have, in contrast, been primarily intended to improve aquatic environments rather than as flood management measures. The schemes completed so far produce relatively little benefit in terms of flood protection. Two schemes – for the River Cole and River Cherwell – have demonstrated the restoration of floodplain connectivity through manipulation of the channel morphology and roughness (Sear *et al.*, 2000). There is, however, considerable uncertainty associated with the longer term morphological and ecological performance of restored rivers (Wissmar and Bisson, 2003) A recent assessment of local rehabilitation structures in lowland UK rivers indicated that they have relatively minor biological effects (Harrison *et al.*, 2001; Pretty *et al.*, 2003).

Coastal and estuarine

Management of flood and coastal defences has been important in the evolution of the British coast for at least the past 600 years. Some influences date back to Roman times. Over that time, land reclamation and flood defence has greatly reduced the intertidal area around estuaries, creating new land uses at the expense of mudflats, saltmarshes and other intertidal habitats. This change in land use includes extensive low-lying areas claimed for grazing – usually termed coastal grazing marshes – and for arable farming. In the UK, coastal grazing marshes are virtually always constrained in their capacity for landward migration by a break of slope or changes in land use, such as arable farmland or urban development. Hence they require active flood management to maintain the species assemblages that they support.

More recently, and especially since the 1950s, protection of the open coast against erosion has directly degraded many cliff, shingle and dune environments. It has also greatly reduced the input of both beach and fine sediment to the coastal system (Hanson et al., 2002). This has certainly degraded beach environments in areas such as north-east Norfolk (Dickson et al., 2005). The implementation of shoreline management planning (Defra, 2001) is, in part, a response to this problem of sediment starvation. Under a scenario of rising sea level, maintaining both human safety and sustaining coastal ecosystems is a major challenge both in the UK and across Europe (Nicholls and Klein, 2005)

Shoreline management

The rising costs of shoreline management, more rigorous appraisal of flood management projects and continued degradation of coastal habitats, have triggered an important shift in thinking towards softer, more strategic flood and coastal defence. Just as flood management in fluvial regions has moved towards less aggressive techniques, similar notions influence thinking on shoreline management. Instead of an assumption of protection and 'holding the line', managed realignment of flood defences is now being actively considered in many locations.

There have already been some trial schemes (Ledoux et al., 2005), especially along the south and east coasts of the UK, where degradation of intertidal habitats has been most marked. The re-establishment of intertidal habitats through managed realignment involves the landward relocation of flood defences and the breaching or removal of former outer defences. To date it has produced mixed results (Atkinson et al., 2001). Creating mudflats has generally been more successful than saltmarsh where functional equivalence, in terms of bird usage, may or may not occur, while sites in high-energy environments tend to reach equilibrium quicker than low-energy environments.

Intertidal habitat gain is, however, often coastal grazing marsh loss (Nicholls and Wilson, 2001). This habitat is important in its own right and is recognised as a priority for conservation because of its widespread decline (for example, 82% loss of coastal grazing marsh in Essex between 1938 and 1981 (Williams and Hall, 1987)) and the nationally and internationally important plant and animal populations it supports. Of particular importance are the breeding populations of waders and wildfowl, wintering populations of wildfowl and the plant and invertebrate fauna of the grassland and associated ditches. Given that the opportunities for creating new areas of coastal grazing marsh are limited, one option to help conserve these species would be to rehabilitate existing areas of inland grassland or recreate areas of grassland from arable fields (arable reversion) in riverine floodplains. This would result in compensatory habitat creation rather than a direct replacement for the loss of intertidal and coastal habitats. The advantages of this option are that space for habitat creation inland is less limiting than in the coastal zone. However, the disadvantages are that proximity to intertidal resources may be an important factor in the habitat selection criteria of species which use coastal grassland more extensively than inland grassland. A recent study (Smart et al., 2006), however, has highlighted the scope for improving the management of inland marshes for redshank *Tringa tetanus* by deliberately establishing wet features.

Mudflats and sandflats in estuaries could also suffer from coastal squeeze (the process whereby an area of intertidal habitat is prevented from migrating landwards in the face of rising sea levels, owing to the presence of a hard boundary such as a sea defence), with concomitant impacts on highly productive populations of invertebrates and birds (Austin *et al.*, 2001). The UK's estuaries support millions of waterfowl during the winter months, principally because the mild winter climate allows invertebrates to flourish. Reductions in the area of intertidal mudflats may, therefore, significantly alter the capacity for estuaries to support these internationally important populations.

Sand and shingle habitats are already declining (Pye and French, 1993). We can expect erosion to accelerate in response to sea-level rise under all the futures, although the details are uncertain (see Chapters 16 and 25). These systems are intrinsically dynamic and often depend upon continued supplies of new sediment. These are priority habitats in the UK's biodiversity action plan and play important roles in both coastal protection and conservation of biodiversity.

Shingle habitats support a distinctive flora and nesting birds of conservation concern, such as terns. Populations of Little Tern, for example, inhabit a diminishing number of nesting locations. Sea-level rise can therefore be both a threat and an opportunity for such species, if managed realignment can create new habitat. In addition, shoreline management and engineering works to manage and reduce erosion, especially beach nourishment, can also maintain sand and shingle habitats, with potential benefits for both coastal protection and biodiversity Hanson *et al.*, 2002). Efforts to link these processes through the appropriate design of such technologies can thus provide a dual benefit. However, we need to consider the wider consequences, especially at the sites from where sand and gravel have been extracted and on beaches that are downdrift.

Environmental impacts of changes in flooding

Fluvial systems

Extreme flood events are part of the 'natural' environment, creating diverse habitats through processes of erosion and deposition. They may, nevertheless, have large and long-lived environmental impacts (Whol, 2003) that river managers or others believe to be adverse. Factors that influence the impact of large floods include the characteristics of the flood regime, channel gradient, bedload characteristics (the larger or heavier particles such as gravel and pebbles that are moved along the bottom of a channel by moving water), the strength of the river bank and the shape of the channel (Hey, 1997).

The floods of 2000/2001 allow us to assess the impacts of a series of large flood events on river channels in England and Wales (Sear *et al.*, 2002a). In general, there was little morphological change in lowland river channels with their low gradients and cohesive banks. In contrast, morphological change was more widespread in upland channels. Deposition of fine sediment was a characteristic process in lowland river channels, a consequence of the erosion of the land surface during these storms.

The summary description for drivers in the catchment runoff and fluvial processes driver sets (Chapters 5 and 6) show that both the magnitudes and directions of *change* in flood magnitudes and sediment loads are very difficult to assess. Table 3.2 summarises how the various drivers might change river flows and sediment loads, and the effects of these changes on river channels that are sensitive to change. Most of the drivers lead to an increase in flood flows and sediment discharge. Historical analysis has demonstrated catchment-scale changes in channel form in response to increased flood frequencies during the Little Ice Age (Rumsby

Table 3.2. Changes in flood flows and sediment discharge under different drivers, and potential impacts on the form of natural river channels

Driver	Change in flood flows	Change in sediment loads	Impact on natural river channel form
Climate change	↑	↑	Channel widening, deepening and deposition
Rural land cover			
Field drainage (on impermeable soil)	↓	↓	Deposition and narrowing
Field drainage (on permeable soil)	↑	↑	Channel widening, deepening and deposition
Afforestation (short term)	↑	↑	Channel widening, deepening and deposition
Afforestation (long term)	↓	↓	Deposition and narrowing
Intensive grazing	↑	↑	Channel widening, deepening and deposition
Arable farming	↑	↑	Channel widening, deepening and deposition
Urbanisation	↑	↓	Channel deepening and widening
Upstream river channel change	↑	↑	Channel widening, deepening and deposition
Impoundment	↓	↓	Deposition and narrowing

and Macklin, 1994) and it can be supposed that increased future flooding will produce changes in channel form and physical habitat. In practice many channels in Britain are heavily managed. Some will be less sensitive to changing river flows, but some may actually be made more sensitive, e.g. channelised upland rivers. The floods of 2000/2001 affected engineered channels as much as natural channels (Sear *et al.*, 2002a), although the types of change were often different. Extreme floods may also lead to contamination through the flooding of sewage treatment works and the subsequent dispersion of low-level household wastes, flooding of sites storing hazardous materials, or the remobilisation of contaminated sediments on floodplains (such as mine wastes (Macklin, 1996)).

Fluvial ecosystems

Extensive land drainage and river channelisation have resulted in the loss of vast areas of wetland in the UK (HMSO, 1995). Consequently, many important habitats and species are now restricted to a small number of sites that are highly vulnerable to alteration in flooding regimes. Careful management of such sites is often required if the water requirements of specific animal and plant species are to be maintained (English Nature, 1999).

Changes in the frequency, duration and lateral and vertical extent of flooding can have significant implications for wetland and aquatic habitats (Robinson *et al.*, 2002). Flooding may also influence communities and species directly by washing individuals out of their preferred habitat into sub-optimal downstream locations. For fish species, however, sediment movement is a major issue, with sedimentation of spawning habitats being implicated in the declines of populations of many species of freshwater fishes in Europe (Lelek, 1980).

Along rivers, some habitats may be very stable and unchanging, as is often the case in low-energy lowland rivers, or highly unstable and dynamic, a state that is usually associated with higher energy, upland streams. In dynamic systems, where conditions change constantly, the ecosystem is likely to be relatively robust, adapting within a relatively short timescale. However, if the frequency and magnitude of flooding change significantly, the geomorphology of the system, and hence the habitats, will also change. We can see an example of this in upland rivers across the UK, where changes in flood frequency and duration may have significantly affected the availability of good spawning areas for salmon. Salmon productivity has suffered badly in many rivers as a result of scouring of gravel from spawning beds – and in some cases a subsequent lack of gravel recharge – and smothering of spawning grounds with fine sediments. This has affected the recruitment of young fish into breeding populations (Greig *et al.*, 2005).

Lowland rivers usually have relatively well modulated and managed flows with ecosystems that reflect the expected range of flows and inundation levels. Where rivers are subject to significant change in substrate or the velocity and level of the water, there can be profound effects on ecosystems (Vervuren *et al.*, 2003). Increasingly, water-level management sets out to encourage the development and integrity of wetland communities, using flooding to recreate habitats and promote the desired species to return. We can see examples of this practice on the Ouse Washes and Somerset Levels. Within floodplain meadows, hydrologically defined niches, defined in terms of soil drying and soil aeration, have recently been identified as being important for the maintenance of species richness in meadow plant communities (Silvertown *et al.*, 1999).

Changes in vegetation affect all the communities and species supported by an ecosystem, although we are only now beginning to investigate these complex interactions. For example, detailed studies of flooded grassland sites across England and Scotland have demonstrated the impact of flooding on soil invertebrates and consequent impacts on breeding birds (Ausden *et al.*, 2001). While increased flooding of grassland can benefit species of conservation concern in many floodplain areas, the timing of flooding, the underlying soil type and the flooding history are all important in determining the impact on the soil's invertebrate community in an area.

We should note here that pollution and other factors affecting fluvial ecosystems may compound the impact of changes in the flooding regime. In many cases, it is difficult to isolate the implications of changes in flooding from the complex of interactions influencing the ecosystem.

Coastal and estuarine systems

Coastal and estuarine areas contain a diverse range of important intertidal habitats. These include vegetated shingle ridges, saltmarsh, saline lagoons, reed beds, mudflats, coastal grazing marsh, sand dunes and various cliff environments. These habitats are sensitive to varying degrees to the drivers affecting flooding and erosion.

Many such habitats are related to coastal landforms that will naturally fluctuate morphologically in response to erosion and accretion. The long-term sedimentary balance is critical to maintaining sand dunes and beaches, shingle habitats, saltmarshes and mudflats. This is especially important as relative sea levels are already rising around most of the UK coast. Without a net input of sediment these landforms must retreat landward on average (see Chapters 15 and 16).

Increased coastal protection can reduce the input of sediment to other regions (Thomalla and Vincent, 2003) where there may consequently be widespread erosion and landward migration of coastal landforms and habitats, for example in Norfolk and Essex. However, some areas, such as Morecambe Bay, are stable in the long term, with erosion and accretion roughly in balance. In a few areas of high sediment availability, accretion is occurring, around the Ribble Estuary for example.

The flora and fauna of coastal habitats are adapted to these dynamic processes. We would expect a healthy coastal ecosystem to include landform dynamics. However, if these changes significantly reduce the area of habitats, they can have important long-term environmental consequences. For example, loss of shingle habitats could threaten the small number of remaining breeding sites for Little Terns, *Sterna albifrons*.

Erosion is required to sustain cliffs and their associated habitats. We can see this in areas where accretion in intertidal areas has removed wave action, preventing further cliff erosion. For example, this has happened in front of Hadleigh Castle, in Essex, where the former active cliff cut in the London Clay has now degraded to a steep vegetated slope.

Saltmarshes and mudflats need regular tidal inundation to sustain the species within them. The dynamic conditions created by frequent tidal inundation result in hugely productive mudflat habitats, which can support high densities of invertebrates and migratory birds. Saltmarshes are inundated less frequently than mudflats but are also highly productive habitats. The frequency with which such land is submerged depends on its relative elevation within the tidal range and is a critical determinant of saltmarsh zonation and species distribution (Bockelmann et al., 2002).

Coastal grazing marsh and reed beds form the limited remains of the once extensive and diverse transition habitats between marine and freshwater ecosystems, although their current location is nearly always artificial, comprising reclaimed areas of mudflat, saltmarsh and other intertidal areas. Marine flooding of these freshwater and brackish habitats can have significant environmental consequences, generally causing a change to more salt-tolerant habitats. Where the coastal grazing marsh derives from land reclamation, there is usually limited space for onshore migration so they are especially vulnerable to such changes. In many areas around the British coast where it was uneconomic to repair defences, there has been unplanned realignment and a transition back to marine intertidal habitats (Atkinson et al., 2001). This reduces the area of coastal freshwater habitats and is likely to continue to do so.

Implications of current trends of change in flood management for the environment

A number of factors are changing the thrust of flood risk management in the UK and their environmental implications cannot be ignored, even given the baseline assumption on flood risk management. We have already described the move towards less aggressive flood defence and coastal protection (Defra, 2004). Another related factor is the change in the pattern of environmental regulation (Jordan, 2002). These changes are occurring at both the national and European level.

Directives and designations promulgated by the EU have become increasingly important (Jordan, 2005). Implementation of the Water Framework Directive has the objective of improving water quality and requires all coastal and inland waters to reach 'good status' by 2015. The EU's Habitats and Species Directive requires member states to designate Special Areas of Conservation (SACs) for particular habitats and species. The Conservation of Birds Directive designates special protection areas (SPAs). Significant parts of the British coast are so designated (English Nature et al., 2000), and consequently the British government is required to take steps to maintain these areas in favourable condition.

A number of national policy and regulatory drivers also influence flood management in the UK. The main drivers include the Strategy for Flood and Coastal Defence in England and Wales (MAFF, 1993) and initiatives to plan more sustainable flood and coastal management. This is recognised through fluvial catchment flood management plans (CFMP) and estuarine and coastal shoreline management plans (SMP). A wide range of other planning processes also interact, most notably the Local Planning Authorities development planning processes (e.g. Planning Policy Guidance 23 and 25).

The main environmental focus of flood risk management policies is enshrined in these objectives:

- The Strategy for Flood and Coastal Defence in England and Wales, published in 1993 and subsequently revised (Defra, 2004), states that there should be 'provision of adequate, technically, environmentally and economically sound and sustainable flood and coastal defence measures'.
- High-level targets for flood and coastal defence, agreed in 1999, set out to: 'avoid damage to environmental interest; to ensure no net loss to habitats and species covered by biodiversity action plans (BAPs); to seek opportunities for environmental enhancement'.

The recent guidelines for the Flood Management Plans have more focused objectives, including:

- Shoreline management plans 'should comply with international and national nature conservation legislation and biodiversity obligations'.
- Catchment flood management plans 'should have no significant detrimental effect on the environment and, where possible, opportunities will be sought for environmental enhancement'. However, ... 'This will not always be possible, but should be a key goal at CFMP level'.

In the future it is expected that there will be a move towards a more sustainable approach to flood and coastal risk management, with flood management and coastal protection contributing to the maintenance and integrity of Natura 2000 (the European Union-wide network of nature conservation sites) and Ramsar sites (wetlands of international importance), the achievement of the PSA target to have 95% of SSSIs in favourable condition by 2010, delivering biodiversity action plans, and the implementation of actions in the England Biodiversity Strategy. As an integral part of the policy assessment process, this may require the development of high-resolution integrated models, involving catchment and coastal zone hydrology, hydrodynamics and geomorphology, to test the policy options against the ecosystem criteria (Martin *et al.*, 2000).

Foresight futures and the environment

Here we examine the relationship between flood management policies and the environment, assuming the four Foresight Socio-Economic Futures (see Chapter 2). Two questions are posed:

- What is the likelihood of active consideration of the environment in flood risk management under these four futures?
- What is the likelihood of environmentally-orientated measures being implemented in each world, and what would be the barriers to their implementation?

The four Foresight Futures have very different implications for the environment (Table 3.3).

Table 3.3 The potential environmental impacts of flood management policies under the four Foresight scenarios

	World markets	National enterprise	Local stewardship	Global sustainability
Summary	A market orientated approach with little incentive to implement environmentally orientated flood risk management measures	A market orientated approach with low regulation and little emphasis on the environment. Actions would focus on meeting immediate local needs for defence against flooding with an emphasis on 'traditional' flood defence	A community orientated approach with flood risk management seen as a component of broader environmental management. A diversity of approaches across UK regions. Measures to reduce exposure and vulnerability to flooding would be favoured over measures to reduce the physical hazard; where these are necessary there would be a preference towards 'soft' engineering approaches	A community orientated approach that would favour environmental protection, with a preference for flood risk management measures that have minimal environmental impact. Flood risk management would be seen as a component of broader environmental management, integrated with policies for land use and water supply
Urban environments	Unregulated land-use and urban development with little demand for reduced development in flood-prone areas	Unregulated land use and urban sprawl with little adaptation of urban form and planning to accommodate changing flood risk	Reconfiguration of urban areas to reduce flooding and accommodate runoff	Efforts at reconfiguration of urban areas to reduce runoff and accommodate flooding. Urban storage, above and below ground. Design of cities for surface flows
Rural environments	Much agricultural land goes out of production and consequently there might be inadvertent benefits to the environment, such as the abandonment of all Grades 4 and 5 agricultural land, possibly allowing more space for natural or semi-natural ecosystems in areas where land pressures are lower, such as uplands	Little change in type and level of agricultural output. Limited concerted action to reduce runoff	Agricultural land remains under production but there is some intensification and shift towards more environmentally sound practices. Flood-prone areas are abandoned. Major retreat from floodplains sees restoration of natural floodplain functions	Land-use planning, for example, would be preferred over physical measures to reduce the flood hazard. Such measures, where implemented, will work with the environment and will include, for example, inland measures to maintain and enhance connections between rivers and floodplains, and to minimise the effect of activities in the catchment on flood runoff. Major strategic storage systems

Fluvial environments	River management to maximise conveyance, protecting environments with high-value amenity	River management to maximise conveyance	Widespread restoration of natural river systems but the downstream implications of actions would not necessarily be considered due to the local focus, and it may be difficult to manage large basins, such as the Thames, covered by several agencies	Multi-use river management for conveyance and environment. The downstream implications of upstream actions would be explicitly considered
Coastal environments	Some coastal grazing marsh areas would be abandoned due to increasing flood risk and insufficient resources for defence upgrade, but again environmental benefits (e.g. saltmarsh gains) are inadvertent and there is a net loss of freshwater coastal habitats	Piecemeal approach to coastal management. Some coastal grazing marsh areas would be abandoned due to increasing flood risk and insufficient resources for defence upgrade	Where coastal defences could not be maintained within the available budget, there would be active managed realignment or planned abandonment. Natural processes reinstated. Habitat creation would compensate for loss of coastal grazing marshes and other freshwater habitat, taking a local perspective. This would be problematic in most areas given the limited areas of suitable coastal sites for such creation	Strategic coastal management, regionally and nationally coordinated. Where the available budget would be too low to maintain coastal defences, there would be active, managed realignment or planned abandonment. Habitat creation would compensate for losses of coastal grazing marshes and other freshwater habitat, but this would tend to be in more inland locations due to the lack of suitable coastal sites. A broad-scale perspective would be taken focusing on sustaining and enhancing stocks of habitats rather then preserving sites. As an example, gains in neighbouring regions, or even neighbouring countries, might replace losses in areas such as East Anglia

39

World markets: a market-orientated approach

This is the wealthiest of the Foresight Futures in terms of gross domestic product (GDP) and, as a wealthy society, can protect against the risks to which it is exposed. There will be a tendency to provide flood risk management and many other services through markets rather than through government. Protection of the environment will also be increasingly privatised, with protection and improvement for environmental assets and services that generate economic rents. An emphasis on economic efficiency and relative neglect of environmental consideration means that in the world markets scenario hard-engineering measures will dominate flood management.

National enterprise: a market-orientated approach

Although less wealthy and more inward looking than the world markets scenario, this is still a consumer-orientated scenario with economic development rated as more important than the environmental quality of rivers and coasts. It will be characterised by piecemeal and reactive engineering measures, with an emphasis on protecting strategic industries such as agriculture.

Local stewardship: a community-orientated approach

This scenario is characterised by approaches to flood risk management that are regionally devolved and environmentally conscious. There will be a variety of approaches across the UK. Growth in wealth is not, however, expected to keep pace with the rate of increase of flood risk. Consequently, some coastal and fluvial floodplains will be abandoned, with communities working to reinstate natural systems. At the same time there is an emphasis on agricultural self-sufficiency, so some key agricultural land in flood plains will be preserved regionally.

Global sustainability: a community-orientated approach

This future world would favour environmental protection, with a preference for flood risk management measures that have minimal environmental impact. Government plays a leading role in providing a range of structural and non-structural measures to reduce flood risk. Flood defence engineering is employed, particularly in dense urban areas, but there is an emphasis on soft engineering, to work with, and possibly restore, natural processes.

Environmental futures

Table 3.3 shows that the environmental impacts of flood management policies will differ between the four Foresight Futures. Under the two more market-orientated futures, environmental change is benign with gains being possible, but a much greater likelihood of losses. While local stewardship will stress the environment, the local focus might raise problems. Global sustainability with its deliberate broad-scale perspective on the environment would appear to offer the best environmental outcomes.

A detailed example of how different scenarios might impact on the environment is provided by the RegIS project (Holman *et al.*, 2005; Nicholls and Klein, 2005), which explored the impact of managed realignment on changes in saltmarsh and coastal grazing marsh habitats in East Anglia and north-west England to the 2050s. Analysis on the basis of two climate change scenarios (low and high) and two socio-economic storylines, Global sustainability and regional enterprise (similar to national enterprise), gives some idea of the potential impact of flood risk management practices on coastal grazing marshes. Under the global sustainability scenario it was assumed that there would be considerable interest and application of managed realignment, whereas under the regional enterprise scenario the opposite would be true. It was found that saltmarsh habitats can be expected

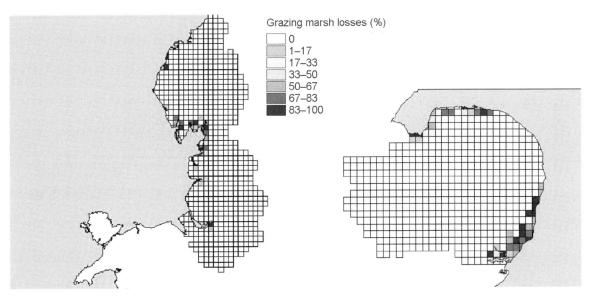

Fig. 3.1. The worst-case scenario for the loss of grazing marshes in the north-west of England and East Anglia under the global sustainability scenario as a result of sea-level rise and flood management practices (Nicolls and Wilson, 2001)

to decline with rising sea level if the existing defence line is maintained, especially in East Anglia. However, there is likely to be a net expansion in the area of salt-marsh, and related intertidal habitats in both the global sustainability and regional enterprise scenarios as a result of planned realignment in the former case and forced realignment in the latter case. Forced coastal abandonment may result from many flood compartments containing coastal grazing marsh seeing a dramatic increase in flood frequency and it being uneconomic to maintain defences. A significant decline in coastal grazing marsh is therefore likely under both socio-economic futures (Fig. 3.1).

Environmental economics

Because it is difficult to quantify environmental goods, our earlier definition of flood risk takes no account of the environmental dimension of flood risk. Changes in climate and flooding regime will, however, lead to different impacts on environments, habitats and ecosystems under the four Foresight scenarios. There will be environmental gains in some types of system, while others might show losses. In this section we consider the current preferences and the values that we place on the environments most likely to be affected and then the specific implications of the future scenarios and how these values might evolve, taking into account the results of our earlier assessment on the evolution of drivers of changes in flood risk.

Current preferences for environmental assets

The main problem with including environmental services in economic choices is that markets attach no economic value to many of the goods and services we derive from our landscapes, habitats and ecosystems. There is a gap between market valuation and the economic value of environmental resources. To fill these gaps, we must first identify, and then where possible monetise, these goods.

Environmental economists use various methods to estimate current preferences for environmental assets. The processes, composition and functions of ecosystems

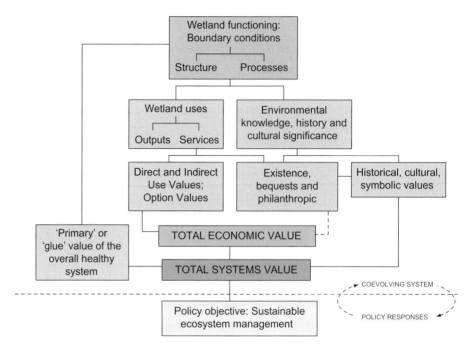

Fig. 3.2. Functional and other dimensions of wetland values (adapted from Turner et al., 2001)

provide 'goods' and services, to which we can try to assign monetary economic values (Turner *et al.*, 2001) (see Fig. 3.2). For wetlands, these include flood mitigation, regulation of water flows, supply of freshwater, nutrient cycling, waste treatment and the maintenance of biodiversity. The overall picture emerging from the literature is that the values involved in coastal and non-coastal wetlands are high (Brander *et al.*, 2003; Schuyt and Brander, 2004). Brander *et al.* (2003) concluded that the average annual wetland value is just over US$2800 per hectare per year, but that the median value is US$150, indicating considerable skew. The median total economic value of salt/brackish marsh and freshwater marsh (Schuyt and Brander, 2004) are relatively similar (US$164 and US$145 per hectare per year, 2000) but the component values differ (Table 3.4). Estimates indicate that we derive the highest values from coastal wetlands through fisheries (commercial or recreational) and coastal defence. For freshwater wetlands, the highest values come from flood control and pollution control, with wetlands as contaminant sinks. Overall, flood control ranks a close second to amenity/recreation in the services provided by wetlands (Schuyt and Brander, 2004).

Future preferences for environmental assets

Economic valuations of the environment depend critically on the preferences that individuals have for environmental goods and services as both consumers and citizens (Sagoff, 1988), and also on the level of provision of goods and services. These are both likely to change in the future with important consequences for any attempt to place an economic value on environmental factors in our futures scenarios.

Projecting environmental values into the future involves assumptions at four different levels: 1) the preferences for environmental goods and services may vary between socio-economic scenarios; 2) incomes and income distribution will influence the expression of these preferences by way of demands; 3) different levels of economic activity will have a direct impact on the level of environmental goods

Table 3.4. Coastal and non-coastal wetland values (for the references cited in this table see Evans et al. (2004))

Type of value	Coastal (Year 2000: GBP/ha/yr)	Freshwater (Year 2000: GBP/ha/yr)
Commercial fishing	7.7–963 (oyster, Batie and Wilson, 1978) 1.5 (blue crab, Lynne *et al.*, 1981) 1.78–3.34 (blue crab, Fischer *et al.*, 1986) 1.8–28.8 (Costanza and Farber, 1987) 77.4–309.7 (Amacher *et al.*, 1989) 20.6 (Costanza *et al.*, 1989) 16 (saltwater fishing, Farber, 1996) 731.7 (fish, Stephenson, 2001)	
Recreational fishing	12.3 (Amacher *et al.*, 1989) 1324.4 (saltmarsh – fish, Bell, 1997)	114.7 (van Vuuren and Roy, 1993) 4.28 (Farber, 1996)
Waterfowl hunting	7 (Farber, 1996)	139.8 (Gupta and Foster, 1975) 26.1–281.8 (van Vuuren and Roy, 1993)
General recreation	3.09 (Costanza *et al.*, 1989) 7.2 (Bergstrom *et al.*, 1990)*	152.9 (Thibodeau and Ostro, 1981)
Coastal defence/flood control	1.7–2.1 (Farber, 1987) 128.9 (Costanza *et al.*, 1989) 7334 (King and Lester, 1995) 74–380.1 (Farber, 1996)	2984.9 (Thibodeau and Ostro, 1981)
Pollution control	1 (Farber, 1996)	2337.8 (Thibodeau and Ostro, 1981) 5051.2–11747.1 (Gren, 1990) 385.7–1146.3 (Dehnhardt, 2002)

* Studies done for general wetlands (no distinction between coastal and non-coastal)

and services; 4) institutional structures will influence levels of provision and the extent to which demand and supply can interact to find equilibrium.

Individual preferences can vary among the Foresight scenarios. For example, the world markets scenario could be characterised by preferences focused on individual, capital-intensive, perhaps conspicuous, consumption. Demand for environmental services for recreation might be correspondingly lower than in other scenarios. This might imply that the marginal value of these services could also be lower, despite the reduced level of provision through rampant growth and weaker environmental protection.

Average incomes and income distribution will be radically different between scenarios. This could be significant for environmental values. Since economic value is expressed through 'willingness to pay', which in turn is predicated on ability to pay, alterations in the income distribution could substantially influence the total willingness to pay for particular environmental provisions.

The costs of supply of environmental goods and services will also be influenced by the level and type of economic activity, and the ways in which economy-environment interactions are managed. These will vary across scenarios. This will create further differences in values for changes in provision, e.g. the value of a hectare of coastal wetland depends partly on the amount of similar wetland existing in neighbouring areas and further afield.

While in theory there will exist for each scenario some balance between demand for and supply of environmental goods and services, we also need to consider the likely roles, and failures, of institutions. For example, the world markets scenario could be characterised by greater conversion of public to private goods, in particular in terms of private landowners being able to exclude others from enjoyment of the landscape. On the other hand, in the Foresight Futures global sustainability and local stewardship we can imagine 'right to roam' legislation. This could make the value gained from a given piece of land substantially higher under global sustainability and local stewardship than the world markets scenario.

Such differences in value have nothing to do with preferences as such, but rather depend on the institutional structures within which individuals can express their preferences. Similarly, the individualist scenarios might be characterised by the wealthy taking measures to protect themselves and their property from the worst effects of environmental degradation, while leaving the poor to fend for themselves. The communal scenarios would be characterised by concerted communal action to defend communities more generally.

Finally, the way in which decisions are made will vary across scenarios. Decision making in the scenarios that place a premium on community values, such as global sustainability and local stewardship, will occur more through democratic processes and social debate. In world markets or national enterprise, decision making would be based more on individual preferences, rather than with community based approaches.

Conclusions

In this chapter we have shown that changes in the drivers of flood risk can be expected to result in continued changes to the magnitude and frequency of flooding, with a range of environmental implications. While there are still considerable gaps in our understanding of how changes in flooding might impact on both the physical and biological environment, the future is likely to see a move towards a more sustainable approach to flood and coastal risk management (Chapters 25 and 26) with greater emphasis being placed on the environmental goods and services that are delivered by both fluvial and coastal ecosystems.

Acknowledgements

We should like to thank Nigel Arnell, Kieran Conlan, Jennifer Gill and Robert Tinch for their valuable inputs into the preparation of this chapter.

References

Atkinson, P.W., Crooks, S., Grant, A. and Rehfisch, M.M., 2001. *The Success of Creation and Restoration Schemes in Producing Intertidal Habitat Suitable for Waterbirds*, English Nature, Peterborough, English Nature Research Report 425.

Ausden, M., Sutherland, W.J. and James, R., 2001. 'The effects of flooding lowland wet grassland on soil macroinvertebrate prey of breeding wading birds', *Journal of Applied Ecology*, 38, 320–338.

Austin, G.E., Rehfisch, M.M., Viles, H.A. and Berry, P.M., 2001. 'Impacts on coastal environments', in *Climate Change and Nature Conservation in Britain and Ireland – Monarch – Modelling Natural Responses to Climate Change*, eds Harrison, P.A., Berry, P.M. and Dawson, T.E., UKCIP, Oxford, 177–228.

Bockelmann, A.C., Bakker, J.P., Neuhaus, R. and Lage, J., 2002. 'The relation between vegetation zonation, elevation and inundation frequency in a Wadden Sea salt marsh', *Aquatic Botany*, 73, 211–221.

Brander, L.M., Florax, R.J.G.M. and Vermaat, J.E., 2003. *The Empirics of Wetland Evaluation: A comprehensive summary and a meta-analysis of the literature*, Institute for Environmental Studies Working Paper W-03/30.

Burton, I., Kates, R.W. and White, G.F., 1993. *The Environment as Hazard*, The Guilford Press, New York.

Defra, 2001. *Shoreline Management Plans: A guide for coastal defence authorities*, Department for Environment, Food and Rural Affairs, London.

Defra, 2004. *Making Space for Water*, Department for Environment, Food and Rural Affairs, London, PB 9792.

Dickson, M.E., Walkden, M.J.A., Hall, J.W., Pearson, S.G. and Rees, J.G., 2005. 'Numerical modelling of potential climate-change impacts on rates of soft-cliff recession, northeast Norfolk, UK', *Proceedings of the 5th International Conference on Coastal Dynamics*, ASCE, New York.

English Nature, 1999. *Water Level Requirements of Selected Plants and Animals*, English Nature, Peterborough, English Nature Science 43.

English Nature, Environment Agency, LIFE and The Centre For Coastal and Marine Sciences, 2000. *Coastal Habitat Management Plans: An interim guide to content and structure*, English Nature, Peterborough, Living with the sea LIFE project, available online www.english-nature.org.uk/livingwiththesea/champs/default.asp

Evans, E., Ashley, R., Hall, J., Penning-Rowsell, E., Saul, A., Sayers, P., Thorne, C. and Watkinson, A., 2004. *Foresight, Future Flooding. Scientific Summary:Vol. I – Future risks and their drivers*. Office of Science and Technology, London.

Greig, S.M., Sear, D.A. and Carling, P.A., 2005. 'The impact of fine sediment accumulation on the survival of incubating salmon progeny: implications for sediment management', *Science of the Total Environment*, 344, 241–258.

Hanson, H., Brampton, A., Capobianco, M., Dette, H.H., Hamm, L., Laustrup, C., Lechuga, A. and Spanhoff, R., 2002. 'Beach nourishment projects, practices, and objectives – a European overview, *Coastal Engineering*, 47, 81–111.

Harrison, P.A., Berry, P.M. and Dawson, T.E., 2001. *Climate Change and Nature Conservation in Britain and Ireland – Monarch – Modelling Natural Responses to Climate Change*, UKCIP, Oxford, available online www.ukcip.org.uk

Harrison, S.S.C., Pretty, J.L., Shepherd, D., Hildrew, A.G., Smith, C. and Hey, R.D., 2004. 'The effect of instream rehabilitation structures on macroinvertebrates in lowland rivers', *Journal of Applied Ecology*, 41, 1140–1154.

Hey, R.D., 1997. 'Stable river morphology', in *Applied Fluvial Geomorphology*, eds Thorne, C.R., Hey, R.D. and Newson, M.D., Wiley, Chichester, 223–226.

HMSO, 1995. *Biodiversity: The UK Steering Group Report – Vol. II: Action Plans*, HMSO, London.

Holman, I.P., Nicholls, R.J., Berry, P.M., Harrison, P.A., Audsley, E., Shackley, S. and Rounsesvell, M.D.A., 2005. 'A regional, multi-sectoral and integrated assessment of the impacts of climate and socio-economic change in the UK', *Climatic Change*, 71, 9–41.

ICE, 2001. *Learning to Live with Rivers*, ICE, London, Final report of the Institution of Civil Engineers' Presidential Commission to review the technical aspects of flood risk management in England and Wales.

Ledoux, L., Cornell, S., O'Riordan, T., Harvey, R. and Baynard, L., 2005. 'Towards sustainable flood and coastal management: identifying drivers of, and obstacles to, managed realignment', *Land Use Policy*, 22, 129–144.

Jordan, A.J., 2002. *The Europeanization of British environmental policy*, Palgrave, Basingstoke.

Jordan, A.J., 2005. *Environmental Policy in the European Union: Actors, institutions and processes*, Earthscan, London and Stirling.

Lelek, A., 1980. *Threatened Fishes of Europe*, Council of Europe, Strasbourg.

Macklin, M.G., 1996. 'Sediment associated heavy-metals in floodplain systems', in *Floodplain Processes*, eds Anderson, M.G., Walling, D.E. and Bates, P.D., Wiley, Chichester, 441–460.

MAFF, 1993. *Strategy for Flood and Coastal Defence in England and Wales*, MAFF, London, PB 1471.

Mance, G., Raven, P.J. and Bramley, M.E, 2002. 'Integrated river basin management in England and Wales: a policy perspective', *Aquatic Conservation*, 12, 339–346.

Martin, J.F., White, M.L., Reyes, E., Kemp, G.P., Mashriqui, H. and Day, J.W., 2000. 'Evaluation of coastal management plans with a spatial model: Mississippi delta, Louisiana, USA', *Environmental Management*, 26, 117–129.

Nicholls, R.J. and Klein, R.J.T., 2005. 'Climate change and coastal management on Europe's coast', in *Managing European Coasts: Past, present and future*, eds Vermaat, J.E., Bouwer, L., Turner, K. and Salomons, W., Springer, Berlin, 199–225.

Nicholls, R.J. and Wilson, T., 2001. 'Integrated impacts on coastal areas and river flooding', *Regional Climate Change Impact and Response Studies in East Anglia and North West England (RegIS). Final Report*, eds Holman, I.P. and Loveland, P.J., UKCIP, Oxford, 54–101.

Nordstrom, K.F., 2000. *Beaches and Dunes of Developed Coasts*, Cambridge University Press, Cambridge.

Petts, G.E., 1984. *Impounded Rivers*, Wiley, Chichester.

Pretty, J.L., Harrison, S.S.C., Shepherd, D.J., Smith, C., Hildrew, A.G. and Hey, R.D., 2003. 'River rehabilitation and fish populations: assessing the benefit of instream structures', *Journal of Applied Ecology*, 40, 251–265.

Pye, K. and French, P., 1993. *Targets for Coastal Habitat Recreation*, English Nature, Peterborough, Research and Survey in Nature Conservation 13.

Robinson, C.T., Tockner, K. and Ward, J.V., 2002. 'The fauna of dynamic riverine landscapes', *Freshwater Biology*, 47, 661–677.

Rumsby, B.T. and Macklin, M.G., 1994. 'Channel and floodplain response to recent abrupt climate-change – the Tyne Basin, northern England', *Earth Surface Processes and Landforms*, 19, 499–515.

Sagoff, M., 1988. *The Economy of the Earth: Philosophy, law, and the environment*, Cambridge University Press, Cambridge.

Schuyt, K. and Brander, L., 2004. *Living Waters Conserving the Source of Life: The economic values of the world's wetlands*, WWF, Gland and Amsterdam, available online: http://assets.panda.org/downloads/wetlandsbrochurefinal.pdf

Sear, D.A., Wilcock, D., Robinson, M.R. and Fisher, K.R., 2000. 'River channel modification in the UK', in *The Hydrology of the UK: A study of change*, ed. Acreman, M.C., Routledge, London, 55–81.

Sear, D.A., Darby, S.E. and Van de Weil, M., 2002a. *The Hydraulic Performance of the River Restoration Demonstration Site, River Cole at Coleshill, UK*, Report submitted to the Thames Region Environment Agency.

Sear, D.A., Geerman, S.E., Hill, C.T. and Branson, J.B., 2002b. *Impact of Recent Floods on Channel Morphology and Physical Habitat Uusing RHS Re-survey*, Environment Agency/Defra, WRc, Swindon.

Silvertown, J., Dodd, M.E., Gowing, D.J.G. and Mountford, J.O., 1999. 'Hydrologically defined niches reveal a basis for species richness in plant communities', *Nature*, 400, 61–63.

Smart, J., Gill, J.A., Sutherland, W.J. and Watkinson, A.R., 2006. 'Grassland-breeding waders: identifying key habitat requirements for management', *Journal of Applied Ecology*, 43, 454–463.

Thomalla, F. and Vincent, C.E., 2003. 'Beach response to shore-parallel breakwaters at Sea Palling, Norfolk, UK', *Estuarine, Coastal and Shelf Science*, 56, 203–212.

Turner, R.K., Bateman, I.J. and Adger, N., 2001. *Economics of Coastal and Water Resources: Valuing environmental functions*, Kluwer Academic Publishers, Dordrecht.

Vervuren, P.J.A., Blom, C.W.P.M. and De Kroon, H., 2003. 'Extreme flooding events on the Rhine and the survival and distribution of riparian plant species', *Journal of Ecology*, 91, 135–146.

Whol, E.E., 2003. 'Geomorphic effects of floods', in *Inland Flood Hazards: Human, riparian, and aquatic communities*, ed. Whol, E.E., Cambridge University Press, Cambridge, 167–193.

Williams, G. and Hall, M., 1987. 'The loss of coastal grazing marshes in south and east England, with special reference to east Essex, England', *Biological Conservation*, 39, 243–253.

Wissmar, R.C. and Bisson, P., 2003. *Strategies for Restoring River Ecosystems*, American Fisheries Society, Bethesda, MD.

Part 2
Drivers of flood risk

4 Climate change

N.S. Reynard

Introduction

The Foresight Flood Risk Project included the two climate drivers of precipitation and temperature. However, in terms of determining river flows (the source drivers for coastal flooding are dealt with elsewhere), whether high or low, the main climate drivers are precipitation and evapotranspiration. In this context, the main influence of temperature is as a driver for the water losses through evapotranspiration.

This chapter briefly outlines the role of these three climate drivers in affecting flood probability, concentrating on the ways in which these climate variables, at various time- and space scales, might change over the next 100 years in the UK, and how these changes might influence future flood risk. In addition there is a discussion of some of the main sources of uncertainty encountered when considering such long-term changes in climate and runoff.

For the sake of determining acceptable climate change scenarios, the four Foresight socio-economic scenarios (described earlier) have been aligned to the four UKCIP02 scenarios (Hulme *et al.*, 2002). The world markets scenario is assumed to produce climate changes equivalent to the high emissions UKCIP02 scenario, the national enterprise scenario produces the UKCIP02 medium-high climate change, the local stewardship scenario produces the medium-low climate change, and the global sustainability scenario produces the low emissions climate change scenario. This assumption allows some quantitative assessment change in the climate drivers over the next 100 years, and the subsequent impact on flood flows. However, it is very important to stress that these scenarios capture only a limited range of the uncertainty in future projections for the UK climate. The issue of uncertainty in climate change projections, and the possible implications for future flood risk, are discussed in the final section of this chapter.

Precipitation

It is a somewhat obvious statement that precipitation is the main driver for inland flooding. However, it is the subsequent distribution of the water, from it falling on hill slopes to, eventually, creating an excess of water in the river channels, that actually causes the flood event. In other words, the hydrological distribution of precipitation in space and time is the means by which this driver contributes to

49

flood risk and nowhere is flooding a simple, linear response to precipitation. All catchments differ in their responses to precipitation events. In general terms, catchments that are smaller, steep-sided or responsive (in terms of their geological or land-cover characteristics) are sensitive to intense, short-duration rainfall events. Larger, rural catchments, particularly those with a large element of groundwater storage, flood in response to the accumulation of precipitation over longer time periods of weeks to months.

As well as the more typical river flooding, there is also non-river, inland flooding. Long-term (seasonal) precipitation defines the groundwater recharge season. An excessive amount of recharge can bring the water table to ground level causing localised saturation and groundwater flooding, which may be very persistent. Direct pluvial flooding also bypasses the river channel as direct, rapid runoff in response to intense rainfall, or rain falling on impermeable, compacted or frozen ground. This can be especially important in the urban context and generally responds to short-duration, extreme rainfall.

The means by which we understand how precipitation is translated into river flow is through the science of hydrological, rainfall–runoff modelling. It is also by way of modelling that we try to understand how changes in all aspects of precipitation (amount, intensity, duration, location and clustering) will impact the flood regime.

Temperature

Temperature influences flood risk in several indirect ways. The first operates during the winter when the temperature determines the partitioning of precipitation into rain or snow. This is critical for the flood regime as it determines the degree to which winter precipitation is stored on the land surface as snow before it melts and eventually reaches the river channel. Less snow, but the same total precipitation, would mean an increase in winter river flows but a decrease in early spring flows. The floods of March 1947 are an example of a major snowmelt (on frozen ground) flood event, and we have seen nothing similar since. It is likely that, in a warming world, this type of flood will become increasingly rare. However, probably the most significant impact of temperature on river flows and flooding is as a driver, through evaporation, of the moisture status of catchments, hence determining antecedent conditions.

Evapotranspiration

While precipitation is the key driver for flooding, it is the effective rainfall, after allowing for evaporation, which actually contributes to runoff. This is obviously a more critical aspect of the water balance during the summer, when potential evapotranspiration rates are at their highest, but even during the autumn and winter the evaporative regime contributes to the antecedent conditions, which is critical in determining how a catchment responds to a rainfall event. The evapotranspiration rates are determined by a number of climate drivers: temperature, solar radiation, wind speed and humidity, and by the terrain in terms of the land cover (vegetation or urban) and soil types.

Changes in precipitation, temperature and evapotranspiration

Climate change brought about by human-induced global warming will alter the climate drivers for flood risk in the UK. Of course the precise detail of how the climate regime will change remains uncertain, particularly with regard to possible changes to the extreme events. In general terms, there is more certainty about changes in temperature than in rainfall. This is particularly true for annual or seasonal changes, or changes at large geographic scales such as the possible change in average annual global temperature. Uncertainty increases for shorter duration and more extreme events, and for more local, site-specific changes. These issues of uncertainty in future climate change projections are discussed in more detail later. The following sections quantify some of the current scenarios of change in rainfall, temperature and evapotranspiration for the UK. These are primarily but not exclusively based on the UKCIP02 scenarios (Hulme *et al.*, 2002) as these were the fundamental sources that were aligned with the Foresight Flood Risk socio-economic scenarios.

The following sections include several examples of work from a range of catchments across the UK. The locations of these catchments are shown in Fig. 4.1 and some of the catchment characteristics are summarised in Table 4.1.

Future changes in precipitation

Future climate change will affect all aspects of the rainfall regime in the UK. The precise nature of these changes is uncertain, particularly for those extreme events, whether of short or long duration, which tend to lead to flooding. This means that it is crucial to understand possible changes to all aspects of the precipitation (rain and snowfall) regime over the next 30–100 years. Increases in rainfall at all scales will increase the risk of flooding to a greater or lesser extent, depending on how these increases manifest themselves in space and time, and of the rainfall–runoff characteristics of the catchment in question. However, decreases in *average* rainfall could also *increase* flood probability, if the mean decrease is coupled with an increase in the intensity or clustering of events. Both these scenarios are suggested within UKCIP02 (Hulme *et al.*, 2002).

Possible future changes in precipitation can be ascribed to broad-scale changes to the annual or seasonal regimes, changes in the nature of both short- and long-duration events, or changes in precipitation variability. Much of the discussion below concentrates on rainfall, with the snowfall element of precipitation being dealt with at the end of this section and in the following section on temperature.

The impact of any given rainfall event on a catchment is a function of the catchment's physical characteristics and the antecedent hydrological conditions. For larger, slow-responding catchments, a sequence of rainfall events is critical to replenishing any soil moisture deficits and establishing conditions so that any subsequent rainfall contributes mainly to runoff. For smaller, urban, or other fast-responding catchments, it is the characteristics of the specific rainfall event that are critical, as these catchments do not have the hydrological 'memory' of larger catchments. Understanding the possible changes to both long- and short-duration rainfall, such as the temporal and spatial structure and sequencing of winter frontal events and summer convective storms, is critical to the understanding of how flood risk might change in the future. Changes in these types of rainfall statistics remain highly uncertain and it should be noted that these changes will take place against a back-drop of (changing) natural variability. For this exercise the definition of long duration is not based on events, but accumulations over periods longer than one week. Short-duration is defined as rainfall accumulations for periods from sub-hourly to seven days.

The UKCIP02 scenarios, based on the output from the UK Hadley Centre's Global and Regional Climate models, suggest that UK annual rainfall will decrease slightly, with a reduction of between 0 and 15% by the end of the century, depending on location and which scenario of future greenhouse gas emission is assumed (Hulme *et al.*, 2002). This annual reduction masks a range of changes to rainfall at different timescales, from seasonal to sub-hourly, and therefore should

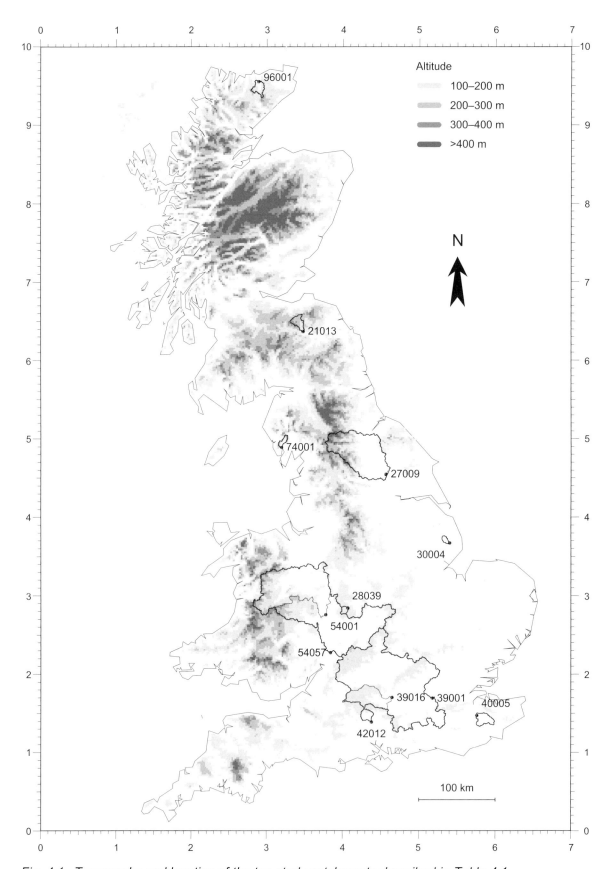

Fig. 4.1. Topography and location of the ten study catchments described in Table 4.1

Table 4.1. Catchment number, name and description

Catchment number	Catchment name	Comments
21013	Gala Water at Galashiels	Fairly natural upland catchment, mainly impervious with grazing and some arable land.
27009	Ouse at Skelton	Predominantly rural catchment with mixed geology, including limestones, grits, sandstones and clay.
28039	Rea at Calthorpe Park	Very responsive, almost totally urbanised catchment.
30004	Lymn at Partney Mill	Entirely rural catchment on sandstone and Boulder clay.
39001	Thames at Kingston	Diverse geology including Oolitic limestone, chalk and Oxford, London and Weald clay. Land-use mainly agricultural but with substantial urban development particularly in the lower catchment.
39016	Kennet at Theale	A mainly pervious catchment (80% chalk) with rural headwaters. Some urban development along the river valley.
40005	Beult at Stile Bridge	Predominantly rural catchment with scattered settlements on Weald clay.
42012	Anton at Fullerton	Unresponsive chalk catchment. Rural land use with some urban centres.
54001	Severn at Bewdley	Mixed geology with land use covering moorland, forestry and agriculture.
54057	Severn at Haw Bridge	As 54001 plus catchment of the Avon, which includes substantial urban areas.
74001	Duddon at Duddon Hall	Steep impervious catchment with agricultural land-use.
96001	Halladale at Halladale	Largely moorland with a peat based cover.

not be misinterpreted as indicating that rainfall changes will not worsen future flood probabilities. Moreover, it should be borne in mind that scenarios derived from other Global Climate models undoubtedly give different results in terms of both the magnitude and direction of changes in rainfall for the UK.

Some recent high-impact flood events, such as the autumn 2000 and winter 2002/03 flooding have occurred because of extreme long-duration rainfall. Such events are characterised by their large spatial extent, reflecting both the driving mechanism of frontal rainfall, often with embedded high-intensity cells, and the large catchment type that is typically vulnerable to such rainfall. The UKCIP02 scenarios indicate that mean winter precipitation might increase for most of the UK, typically by 20–30% by the end of the century, suggesting that extreme, long-duration winter rainfall might also become more frequent. However, these changes are for seasonal (90-day) totals rather than changes in the extreme 30- to 60-day accumulations that gave rise to the autumn 2000 flooding. Work by the Centre for Ecology and Hydrology (CEH) at Wallingford and the Met Office (Defra, 2001; Huntingford *et al.*, 2003) using the Hadley Centre regional climate model (RCM) data (the same model used to derive the UKCIP02 scenarios) found the frequency of such events (30-day accumulations) increases in a warmer world, increasing potential flooding in these larger catchments, given the required antecedent conditions. However, Fig. 4.2 illustrates a possible effect of a change in the seasonal distribution of rainfall (Reynard *et al.*, 2005). It was found for the Thames (39001 in Fig. 4.1), which is a predominantly winter flooding catchment, that despite this increase in winter rainfall there is very little change in peak flows under all but the high-emissions scenario, and that decreases are possible for lower flows. This

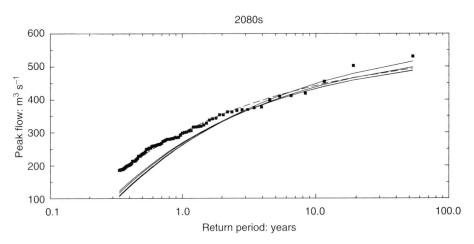

Fig. 4.2. Flood frequency curves for the Thames catchment (39001) for the baseline (dashed line) and the four UKCIP02 emissions scenarios for the 2080s (the solid lines: the uppermost line being the high emissions, and the lowest being the low emissions scenario)

reflects the fact that the increased summer temperatures, and hence higher evaporative losses, produce large and long-lasting soil moisture deficits, reducing the effective flood season. Despite the long-duration nature of rainfall of autumn 2000 and winter 2002/03, it remains the shorter duration, exceptional 1 to 3-day rainfall events that actually trigger flooding. One possible consequence of an increase in winter rainfall, if it manifests itself as more rain days rather than higher intensities, is that the UK will experience more high-flow episodes but fewer extreme events.

Two of the most notable recent flood events in the UK have been caused by short-duration, but intense rainfall events, these being in the Cornish town of Boscastle, where over 150 mm fell on 16 August 2004, and Hawnby in Yorkshire in June 2005, when it is thought that around 70 mm fell in just three hours (Fenn et al., 2005).

Although changes in daily precipitation extremes remain difficult to quantify, it is possible to identify some features based on the Hadley Centre (and other) RCM simulations. For example, while there is a simulated increase in the number (up by a factor of 1.5) and severity (up by 25%) of intense events during the winter by the end of the century, the headline increase in winter rainfall is mainly brought about by an increase in the average number of wet days during the season. For the summer, UKCIP02 generally indicates a decrease in extreme rainfall, along with the average. Some regions do experience an increase, however, and there is evidence (Christensen and Christensen, 2003) that such increases in extreme rainfall, in spite of mean seasonal reductions, could be widespread and significant. For example, Ekström et al. (2005) suggest a 10% increase in short-duration (1 to 2 days) rainfall totals across the UK.

The expected frequency for a rainfall event of a given duration is defined not only by the average climate but also by year-to-year variability in the climate. Care must be taken to incorporate changes in this type of variability in any future scenarios of climate change. Rainfall is currently, and will remain, variable at all time- and space scales. At present it is possible to construct scenarios of change for only some aspects of this variability. The UKCIP02 scenarios indicate some change in the inter-annual variability of annual and seasonal rainfall for the UK, expressed as percentage changes in the standard deviation of rainfall. Most of the country sees an increase during the winter, reaching a possible maximum of 25% on the east coast. The summer experiences a decrease, particularly in the south and east, where reductions might be as much as 20% by the 2080s (Hulme et al., 2002). However, this summer reduction in the standard deviation will still result in a relative increase in the variability of summer rainfall, if the mean reduces by *more* than 20%.

The UKCIP02 scenarios suggest significant reductions in snowfall, of up to 90% by the end of the century. For flooding, the important implication of a warmer world with reduced snowfall is that there will be a change to the partitioning of winter precipitation between rain and snow. Scenarios suggest that there will be fewer winters, anywhere in the UK, where significant snow lies and accumulates over long periods during the winter. This will change the flood regime of those rivers that currently exhibit peak flows during the spring associated with melting of the winter accumulation of snow.

Future changes in temperature

Human-induced climate change is predicted to increase average annual temperatures across the UK by between 2°C and 3.5°C (Hulme *et al.*, 2002). The increases will be generally higher in the south and east of the country, and during the summer and autumn. As with all climate variables there will be changes to the annual, seasonal, daily and sub-daily temperatures and uncertainty increases at higher temporal resolutions. In other words, there is more certainty in changes to annual temperature than in changes to maximum daily summer temperatures, for example. However, there is some indication from the UKCIP02 scenarios that such changes in temperature extremes could lead to intensification of summer convective storms, and the possibility of local flooding. The scenarios suggest that the temperature of an 'extremely warm' day (defined, for southern England, as a day with an average temperature that might be expected on 10% of days – currently about 23°C) will increase by between 4°C and 7°C by the 2080s. Put another way, under the medium-high scenario, an average daily temperature of 30°C or more might be expected once every ten days during the summers of the 2080s. For daily maximum temperatures analyses show that the one in ten year maximum for southern England (currently about 33°C) might increase by about 7°C by the 2080s under the medium-high scenario.

Future changes in potential evapotranspiration

Potential evapotranspiration (PET) data are not produced as standard output from global or regional climate models, meaning that they need to be modelled from the climate drivers: temperature, humidity, wind speed and radiation. All these variables are predicted to change in ways that would contribute to increased evaporative losses. Increasing temperatures, particularly during the summer will, in themselves, drive up potential evaporative losses. It is predicted that, while the absolute amount of water in the air will increase, the relative humidity will decrease during the summer, thus allowing more evaporation to take place. Cloud cover in the summer and autumn may decrease, thereby increasing summer sunshine and solar radiation. Wind speed changes are notoriously difficult to predict, but indications are that they will, on average, change little. The net impact of these changes and the subsequent increase in PET will tend to ameliorate flooding.

The use of time-series climate data produced either by statistical methods, using relationships fitted on present-day observations, or dynamical methods, such as the RCMs, provides alternative techniques for producing evapotranspiration scenarios. Prudhomme *et al.* (2005) produced scenarios generated using these techniques at a daily time step for a range of catchments across Great Britain and considered the output from a number of GCMs, including the UK Hadley Centre model (the use of multiple GCMs in impact studies such as these is discussed in the section on uncertainty, later in this chapter). Figure 4.3 shows some results for the river Kennet (39016) for the 2080s time horizon. All the scenarios indicate increases in PET during the summer months, ranging from 2 to 20 mm (up to a 30% increase).

55

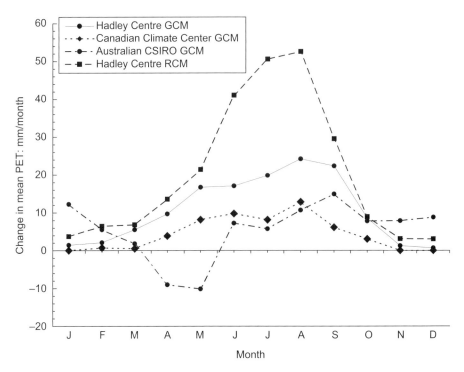

Fig. 4.3. Change in mean PET (mm/month) for the 2080s for each month for the River Kennet. Results from the Hadley Centre GCM and RCM, the Canadian GCM and the Australian GCM

The smallest increases are from the Canadian GCM while the largest and most consistent increases are projected by the Hadley Centre RCM.

It is important to remember, however, that the impacts of changes in the PET, although important, are often less significant than changes in rainfall, particularly when analysing the impacts on high flows. Increases in PET losses reduce the potential soil moisture, for example, by up to 40% by the 2080s under a high-emissions scenario. These changes affect future flood risk in two ways. First, dry and baked soils could present a far more efficient surface for rapid runoff (assuming limited surface cracking) during convective storms in the (on average) warmer and drier summers. Second, an extended dry season will produce increased soil moisture deficits which need to be replenished before effective winter runoff, or groundwater recharge, can begin. This suggests a reduced window for winter flooding, particularly for larger or geologically slow-responding catchments. This is one of the reasons why hydrological modelling results suggest a much reduced impact on flood frequencies under the UKCIP02 scenarios compared with those under the UKCIP98 scenarios (Crooks and Reynard, 2003; Kay *et al.*, 2003; Reynard *et al.*, 2005). The expected increases in modelled PET, however, can only have an effect if there is water available for evaporation. Actual evaporation is likely to decrease during long warm periods, as it did during the droughts of both 1995 and 2003, for example. It is likely, therefore, that the main implication of a 30% increase in PET will be to delay the onset of the flood season.

Estimating the effects of climate change on flooding

Assessing the impact of climate change on flooding presents many challenges (Arnell, 1996). This is due to the uncertainty in current estimates of extreme flood frequencies and magnitudes, as well as the difficulty in generating scenarios of change for the types of extreme events that lead to flooding in the UK.

Traditionally, flood frequency estimation in the UK has been undertaken using statistical approaches, such as those described in the *Flood Estimation Handbook* (Institute of Hydrology, 1999). Because such methods are designed under the assumption that the underlying processes are stationary in time, direct use of such statistical methods to predict future flood frequencies is inappropriate. However, the design flood obtained through such a statistical method may be enlarged by a factor to accommodate a change in the future climate. This method has been adopted for the modelling and decision support framework for catchment flood management plans (Defra, 2002).

An alternative approach is to use a rainfall–runoff model specially designed to provide reliable estimates of high flows. The assumption is that the rainfall–runoff processes described by the models (either through conceptual modelling, or physical approaches) will remain the same in the future. Most modelling studies that investigate potential changes in flooding due to climate change take a physical hydrological modelling approach, and generally use a continuous flow simulation. Climatic input data series (principally precipitation, potential evaporation and temperature) are used to generate hydrological time series (e.g. river flows or groundwater levels) for both the current climate situation (typically represented by 1961–1990) and for selected time periods in the future. The models are run under the current climate (i.e. using observed series, or a series generated to represent the current climate) and under future conditions, i.e. using future scenarios, or future climatic series assumed representative of the future (Reynard *et al.*, 1999; 2001; 2005; Crooks and Reynard, 2002; Prudhomme *et al.*, 2001; Werrity *et al.*, 2002; Kay *et al.*, 2005b). Generally, the climatic time series for the current climate are perturbed so that they represent possible future climate conditions. The degree and complexity of these perturbations depend on the type of analysis being undertaken. For example, studies that seek only to understand the sensitivity of flooding to changes in climate might use simple monthly factors of change in rainfall and PET. More detailed studies of a particular catchment, or those aimed at providing information for the development of a climate change policy, should use a variety of methods for constructing climate change scenarios to capture better the range of possible changes to the flood regime.

Recent development of RCMs (with higher spatial and temporal resolutions) has meant that, for the first time, it is now feasible to use RCM rainfall outputs directly to drive a continuous rainfall–runoff model to estimate flood frequency (Kay *et al.*, 2005a). Some recent work used hourly rainfall data from the Hadley Centre's 25 km European RCM, along with daily PET time-series derived from the RCM outputs, to drive a rainfall–runoff model for five catchments in Great Britain. The results demonstrate that, over the next 100 years, the north and west may experience the largest increases in high flows, with the south-east possibly experiencing decreased flooding (Kay *et al.*, 2005b). Figure 4.4 shows an example of these results, for catchment 21013 in southern Scotland (the Gala Water at Galashiels).

Reynard *et al.* (2005) modelled changes in peak flows for a further ten catchments, finding that changes in flood frequency (magnitude and direction) depend on the catchment type and location. For example, Fig. 4.5 shows the changes in the flood frequency curves for the River Duddon in north-west England (74001) under the four UKCIP02 scenarios. While the changes are small under these scenarios, they all show an increase over the current assessment of peak flows (black dashed line), particularly by the 2080s. The range of changes modelled in this study is illustrated in Table 4.2, which shows the percentage change in the current 20-year return period flow for each of the ten study catchments (location map shown in Fig. 4.1 and catchment summaries given in Table 4.1). Increases in flow are highlighted in bold. The

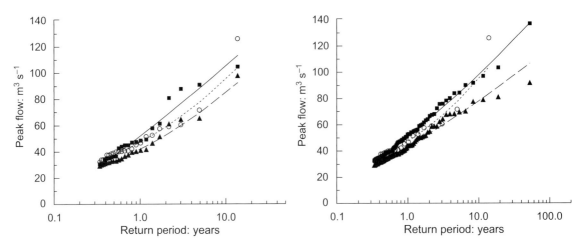

Fig. 4.4. Example flood frequency results for the Gala Water at Galashiels (21013) from Kay et al. (2005a, b). The left-hand graph shows results using RCM data (filled triangles and dashed line), compared to those using observed input data (filled squares and solid line) for the 1961–1990 period. The right-hand graph shows the current (filled triangles and dashed line) and future (squares and solid line) RCM-driven curves. The flood frequencies derived from observed flows, 1985–1993, (open circles and dotted line) are also shown

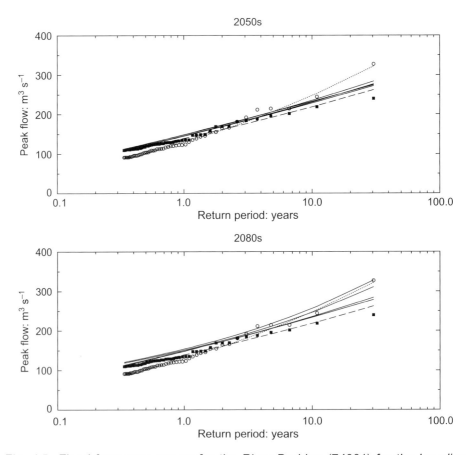

Fig. 4.5. Flood frequency curves for the River Duddon (74001) for the baseline (dashed line) and the four emissions scenarios (the solid lines: the uppermost line being the high emissions, and the lowest being the low-emissions scenario) for the 2050s and the 2080s

Table 4.2. Summary of the percentage changes in the 20-year return period flows for the 2080s. Increases are indicated in bold

Catchment	UKCIP02			
	Low	Medium-low	Medium-high	High
27009	−2.2	−3.6	−3.8	−4.2
28039	**6.4**	−2.5	−2.6	−5.5
30004	−3.5	−5.6	−9.9	−13.1
39001	−1.6	−1.6	0.0	**2.8**
40005	−0.5	−1.5	−3.9	−3.7
42012	**2.5**	**3.2**	**4.6**	**5.0**
54001	−2.1	−2.7	−5.4	−6.7
54057	**1.2**	**1.2**	**3.0**	**4.4**
74001	**6.6**	**8.3**	**16.1**	**21.9**
96001	**0.1**	−0.9	−3.1	−4.6

River Severn at Haw Bridge (54057) shows an increase in flood flows under all UKCIP02 emissions scenarios, whereas Beult at Stile Bridge (40005) shows decreases. This contrast fundamentally reflects the location of the Beult catchment in the south-east, where the scenarios suggest the greatest warming and drying. The Thames (39001) shows decreases under the lower-emissions scenario, but increases under the high-emissions scenario. The largest single modelled increase is for the River Duddon under high emissions (see Fig. 4.5).

Uncertainty

All the potential changes in climate, and subsequent flood flows, described in the previous section are uncertain. Uncertainty in climate change prediction, particularly for addressing changes in extremes such as flooding, is large and comes from many sources. There are several ways of classifying these sources of uncertainty surrounding future changes. The following sections outline some generic sources of uncertainty such as lack of knowledge, statistical variation, measurement error and subjective judgement (IPCC, 2001b). The final section describes an 'uncertainty cascade', which highlights some of the more detailed aspects of uncertainty when considering future changes in rainfall and flooding.

Natural variability

Rainfall and river flows are variable over all spatial and temporal scales. There is uncertainty in the timing, duration and extent of specific events. So, while it is possible to estimate the probability that an extreme event will occur within the next 20 years, it is not possible to say precisely when this will occur. Moreover, the UK experiences relatively flood-rich periods, and those that are more flood poor, a type of 'structured' variability that remains poorly understood. Therefore, natural variability is something we already live with. The important issues are to identify whether, and how, this variability might change in the future and whether, and when, the climate change signal emerges from the noise of current natural variability.

Data uncertainty

There are limitations on the accuracy and precision with which we can measure both rainfall and flood flows. Data uncertainty characterises many of the difficulties encountered when considering extreme events. There is a need, both in the UK and globally, for better quality data on extreme events. This type of data is essential to improve our understanding of the flood-generating processes and, therefore, the development of more effective rainfall–runoff models. For example, much of the information about the flows during the autumn 2000 floods was lost due to the simultaneous failure of so many river channels to contain peak flows at gauging stations; during the Hawnby flood in Yorkshire in June 2005, the flow gauge at Broadway Foot on the River Rye was actually washed away. Therefore, although there is often extensive information on long-term averages, establishing (or predicting) the probability of extreme events (such as the one in 100-year event) remains uncertain.

Model uncertainty

Models are widely used to describe data and processes (e.g. GCMs and RCMs) and to assess impacts of change (e.g. rainfall–runoff models). To understand the impact of climate change on flooding, many types of model can be used, all of which introduce uncertainty through the model structure and parameterisation. Extrapolating model results to, or even directly modelling extreme events, may be particularly prone to model uncertainty.

Knowledge uncertainty

In many cases the current knowledge-base is unlikely to be able to provide complete understanding. We may lack both data and knowledge about the nature of the processes, and interactions between different parts of the system, or the probabilities of possible outcomes. For example, future emissions of greenhouse gases will always remain unknowable, subjecting subsequent modelled future changes in climate to an inherent degree of uncertainty, no matter how much the science of climate modelling develops. On the hydrological side, our knowledge of surface processes is better than our knowledge of the processes operating in the sub-surface or, indeed, the interactions between them.

The uncertainty cascade

As well as the more generic sources of uncertainty described above, there are uncertainties associated with specific aspects of a climate change impact study, particularly when considering changes to extreme events such as flooding. There are many necessary assumptions made during the various stages of an analysis of the impact of changes in the climate drivers for flood risk. The uncertainty associated with these assumptions, or the modelling procedures used, cascades through an impact study to produce an overall uncertainty that is derived from this variety of sources. These sources of uncertainty include:

- Future emissions of greenhouse gases. Scenarios need to be developed concerning future global socio-economic growth, to provide a range of estimates of future emissions, such as the four scenarios used in the Foresight Project. This aspect of uncertainty will always be present and will always be large. The current estimate of the range of possible emissions pathways through this century produce scenarios of emission rates from 5 to 30 GT C/yr (IPCC, 2000).
- Atmospheric concentrations of greenhouse gases. There is a degree of uncertainty associated with how emissions of greenhouse gases translate into actual concentrations of gases in the atmosphere, and are therefore 'available' to affect the Earth's radiative balance.
- Global and large-scale climate response. Scenarios derived from different GCMs produce not only different quantities of change in precipitation, but also changes in different directions (Jenkins and Lowe, 2003; Hulme et al., 2002; IPCC, 2001a). There are also degrees of uncertainty depending on what

aspect of the rainfall regime is being investigated. There is more confidence in changes in average annual rainfall than in changes in the sub-daily patterns and there is more confidence in broad-scale regional change than in changes in the rainfall regime at a local level. Understanding change in rainfall for both of these high-uncertainty areas is important when considering the potential impacts on flooding.

- Local/small-scale climate response. Global models produce climate change scenarios that are generally too coarse in both space and time for application to catchment or site-specific impact models. This means that the additional step of 'downscaling' the scenarios is required, which adds a further modelling procedure and its associated uncertainties. There are broadly two ways of downscaling, either by statistical or dynamical modelling. While the dynamical approach of using RCMs can provide large area projections of future change, at higher resolutions than GCMs, statistical methods can provide scenarios of change for site-specific locations and for short-time durations. Notwithstanding recent projects aimed at providing multiple RCM runs for uncertainty assessments, the relative ease with which statistically downscaled scenarios can be generated makes this method ideal for constructing multi-ensemble scenarios sets, and hence gaining some insight into the scale of this source of uncertainty.

- Natural climate variability. As discussed earlier in this chapter, understanding current natural climate and hydrological variability is vital to be able to place possible changes in rainfall and river flows in context. In many natural systems, variability at all space- and timescales is large and any climate change signal will take many years to emerge from the noise in the natural records. In addition there is considerable uncertainty surrounding how this variability might change in the future.

- Hydrological impact. Understanding how changes in climate will affect hydrological regimes requires a modelling approach, which introduces more uncertainty into the mix. The size of this uncertainty is determined by how well the models represent the physical catchment response to rainfall and PET (model structure), the selection of model parameters (model calibration) or the level of process representation. Moreover, when considering hydrological impacts, it is vital that future changes in land cover and land-use be incorporated within consistent and integrated future scenarios.

Recent research has provided an illustration of the relative contribution to 'overall' uncertainty from a number of these sources. Prudhomme *et al.* (2005) found that the largest single source of uncertainty was that due to the range of outputs from a variety of GCMs, although both hydrological uncertainty and that due to downscaling methods were also significant sources. Uncertainty due to possible future scenarios of greenhouse gas emissions also becomes significant once the time horizons move beyond the 2050s, meaning that for the Foresight time horizon of the 2080s, this too is a significant source of uncertainty in future projections.

Conclusions

This chapter has described the main climate drivers for future flood risk and how they might change in the UK over the next 100 years. These changes have been derived from the UKCIP02 scenarios (Hulme *et al.*, 2002), which have been aligned with the four socio-economic scenarios used within the Foresight Flooding Project, to allow a degree of quantification of these changes. There are many different ways of deriving such changes in climate and their consequent impacts on flows, from simple sensitivity-type analyses, to complex impact analyses incorporating multiple GCMs and RCMs and methods of downscaling.

There is no doubt that the climate drivers, at all time- and space scales, are among the most important drivers of future flood risk. This implies that these drivers will have a profound affect on the future of flooding in the UK. Quantifying these changes in climate and flooding remains a major scientific challenge. Where important decisions or policy options are being examined, impact studies should include at least a discussion of the types of uncertainty listed in the previous section, but preferably present the results as a range of possible changes in flood probability, incorporating a quantitative analysis of these uncertainties.

References

Arnell, N.W., 1996. *Global Warming, River Flows and Water Resources*, Wiley, Chichester.

Christensen, J.H. and Christensen, O.B., 2003. 'Severe summertime flooding in Europe', *Nature*, 421, 805–806.

Crooks, S.M. and Reynard, N.S., 2002. *Initial Assessment of the Impact of UKCIP02 Climate Change Scenarios on Flood Frequency for the Thames*, Report to the Environment Agency. CEH-Wallingford.

Defra, HR Wallingford, 2002. *Catchment Flood Management Plans – Development of a modelling and decision support framework*, Report EX4495 to Defra/Environment Agency, Project number W5F(01)01. HR Wallingford, Wallingford, January.

Department for the Environment, Food and Rural Affairs, 2001. *To What Degree Can the October/November 2000 Flood Events be Attributed to Climate Change?*, CEH-Wallingford/Met. Office report to Defra (FD2304).

Ekström, M., Fowler, H.J., Kilsby, C.G. and Jones, P.D., 2005. 'New estimates of future changes in extreme rainfall across the UK using regional climate model integrations. Part 2: Future estimates and use in impact studies', *Jnl Hydrol*,. 300 (1–4), 234–251.

Fenn, C.R., Bettes, R., Golding, B., Farquharson, F.A.K. and Wood, T., 2005. 'The Boscastle flood of 16 August 2004: characteristics, causes and consequences', in *40th Defra Flood & Coastal Management Conference 2005*, University of York, 5–7 July, 05B.1.1-05B.1.12.

Hulme, M., Jenkins, G.J., Lu, X., Turnpenny, J.R., Mitchell, T.D., Jones, R.G., Lowe, J., Murphy, J.M., Hassell, D., Boorman, P., McDonald, R. and Hill, S., 2002. *Climate Change Scenarios of the United Kingdom: The UKCIP02 scientific report*, Tyndall Centre for Climate Change Research, School of Environmental Sciences, University of East Anglia, Norwich.

Huntingford, C., Jones, R.G., Prudhomme, C., Lamb, R., Gash, J.H.C. and Jones, D.A., 2003. 'Regional climate model predictions of extreme rainfall for a changing climate', *Q. J. R. Meteorol. Soc.* 129, 1607–1621.

Institute of Hydrology, 1999. *Flood Estimation Handbook* (5 volumes), Institute of Hydrology, Wallingford.

Intergovernmental Panel on Climate Change, 2000. *Emissions Scenarios*. Special report of the IPCC: A special report of Working Group III of the Intergovernmental Panel on Climate Change, eds Nakicenovic, N and Swart, R., Cambridge University Press, Cambridge.

Intergovernmental Panel on Climate Change, 2001a. *Climate Change 2001: The science of climate change*, Cambridge University Press, Cambridge.

Intergovernmental Panel on Climate Change, 2001b. *Climate Change 2001: Impacts, adaptation and vulnerability*, Cambridge University Press, Cambridge.

Jenkins, G.J. and Lowe, J., 2003. Handling uncertainties in the UKCIP02 scenarios of climate change, Hadley Centre Technical Note 44.

Kay, A.L., Bell, V.A., Moore, R.J. and Jones, R.G., 2003. *Estimation of UK Flood Frequencies Using RCM Rainfall: An initial investigation*, Met. Office Annex 15a subcontract report to Defra.

Kay, A.L., Jones, R.G. and Reynard, N.S., 2005a. 'RCM rainfall for UK flood frequency estimation, I. Method and validation', *Jnl Hydrol*. In Press.

Kay, A.L., Reynard, N.S. and Jones, R.G., 2005b. 'RCM rainfall for UK flood frequency estimation, II. Climate change results', *Jnl Hydrol*. In Press.

MAFF, 2001. *Flood and Coastal Defence Project Appraisal Guidance – Overview* (FCDPAG1), MAFF Publications, London.

Prudhomme, C., Svensson, C. and Jakob, D., 2001. *Climate Change and Water Management: Managing European water resources in an uncertain future. Vol. 4: Changing streamflow in the UK*, Report to the EU, project ENV4-CT98-0791, November, CEH, Wallingford.

Prudhomme, C., Piper, B., Osborn, T. and Davies, H., 2005. *Climate Change Uncertainty in Water Resource Planning*, Report to UKWIR.

Reynard N.S., Prudhomme C. and Crooks S.M., 1999. *Climate Change Impacts for Fluvial Flood Defence*, Report to MAFF, Project FD-0424-C, March.

Reynard N.S., Prudhomme, C. and Crooks, S.M., 2001. 'The flood characteristics of large UK rivers: potential effects of changing climate and land use', *Climatic Change*, 48, 343–359.

Reynard, N.S., Crooks, S.M. and Kay, A.L., 2005. *Impact of Climate Change on Flood Flows in River Catchments*, Report to Defra/EA.

Werritty, A., Black, A., Duck, R., Finlinson, B., Thurston, N., Shackley, S. and Crichton, D., 2002. *Climate Change: Flooding occurrences review*, Report to the Scottish Executive Central Research Unit, The Stationery Office, Edinburgh.

5 Catchment land-use

Joe Morris and Howard Wheater

Introduction

Catchment land-use describes how the surface of land and its immediate subsurface is utilised by people for specific purposes within an area which shares a common system of drainage. Anthropogenic activities tend to change the characteristics of the land compared to its natural state. Major land-uses are typically classified in broad terms as rural or urban. 'Rural' is characterised by open spaces mainly covered by vegetation, in which agriculture is the main economic activity. 'Urban' is characterised by relatively large concentrations of buildings and infrastructure which make up human settlements. In the context of the UK, given high population pressures on available land, most land is used and managed in some way. Indeed, the retention of land in its natural state, together with the wildlife and landscape features that it carries, is now regarded as a managed land-use.

With respect to flooding, land-use operates as a pathway and a receptor, depending on its location within the catchment. Rural and urban land-use, by changing the bio-physical properties of the land surface and its soils and geographical features, can affect the rate at which precipitation water moves along or through the 'pathway' of land surfaces or soil profiles to join the hydraulic system. Generally, the more impermeable the surface, whether grassland compacted by the feet of animals or car parks covered with asphalt, the greater is the rate of runoff and propensity to contribute to flooding.

Land-use also operates as a 'receptor', defining the anthropogenic assets and activities that are placed at risk in the event of a flood. The more intensive the land-use, the greater is the potential damage when floods occur. Flooding in urban areas is particularly damaging, and this aspect is considered as a separate driver in Chapter 10. Flooding in rural, mainly agricultural and nature conservation areas, is less damaging and in some instances, especially for some forms of extensive farming and nature conservation, is perceived to be beneficial. Furthermore, rural land may offer potential as a 'managed' receptor by providing flood storage facilities in order to alleviate flooding in urban parts of the catchment or coastal area.

This chapter treats rural land-use and urbanisation as pathways and agricultural land-use as a receptor as part of the driver set of flood risk entitled 'catchment land-use'. Urban areas as receptors, including approaches to modifying urban flood impacts, are treated as a separate driver set.

The chapter considers each driver in turn, presenting a definition and explanation of its mode of operation, the parameters used to measure the driver, the significance of the driver, and the major uncertainties associated with its assessment. The linkages within and between other driver sets are considered. The way that these drivers might develop under future scenarios is also explored.

Rural land-use management

Driver definition

Rural land-use management is a broad term representing the use of the land surface for anthropogenic purposes in a rural context as described above. It includes agricultural activities, primary industrial activities such as quarrying that occur in the rural space, and the management of natural and semi-natural environments. The focus here is on:

a. the effects of agricultural management practices, including forestry, on flooding. These are mainly focused on 1) changes to soil structure, vegetation and drainage and, hence, impacts on runoff production, and 2) the management of floodplain land and its impact on flood storage and flood propagation. Secondary issues arise, for example related to agricultural water use for irrigation.

b. 'natural' areas of the rural landscape, which nevertheless commonly have some element of management. These include national parks and sites of special scientific and conservation interest, particularly wetlands. In some environments, specific land-use issues may have particular importance, for example land management for hunting and shooting game.

Driver operation

Catchment runoff is generated from precipitation by a complex set of surface and subsurface flow paths, strongly influenced by topography, which determine the volume and timing of water delivery to stream channels. Flows are subsequently moderated by interactions between the channel and floodplain.

Runoff pathways range from rapid overland flow to highly damped groundwater discharge. Soil structure is a major control on these flow paths; changes to soil structure due to land management (e.g. in the case of agriculture, cropping patterns, tillage practices, grazing management and field drainage) can therefore have a dramatic effect on runoff. The volume of runoff and the pathways are strongly influenced by spatial patterns of soil moisture; soil moisture depends on evaporation, which is also affected by conditions at the land surface. Clearly, land-use is a fundamental control on runoff processes, and land-use management can have a major effect on runoff volume and timing. Land-use and land management can also modify channel–floodplain interactions and the role of floodplains in flood storage. There is thus potential for significant increase in flood generation, and for land management to play a significant role in flood mitigation.

There is also a series of indirect effects of agricultural land and water management. For example, increased demand for irrigation could lead to increased construction of small storage reservoirs or increased groundwater abstraction.

Driver importance and driver uncertainty

There is extensive concern about the possible effects of land management on runoff processes and flooding. Recent reviews and consultation exercises by Defra, the Environmental Agency (EA) and the Engineering and Physical Sciences Research Council (EPSRC) (Calver and Wheater, 2002; Wheater, 2002; EPSRC, 2002;

O'Connell *et al.*, 2004) have highlighted land-use and land management as a high priority for research due to:

a. the perceived importance for flooding;
b. lack of an appropriate science base to quantify local scale effects; and
c. lack of suitable modelling tools to support catchment-scale management.

The effects are therefore highly uncertain. For example, a recent survey of soil degradation commissioned by the EA at the time of the Autumn 2000 floods (Holman *et al.*, 2000) reported extensive soil degradation (e.g. up to 33% of the land in the catchments studied), but was only able to speculate on the catchment-scale effects (an increase of 12% or greater in runoff volume was suggested). There is unknown linkage between local (field) scale effects and catchment-scale impacts. (Analysis of 30 years of land-use change on the Thames catchment, for example, showed no discernable effects at large catchment scale (Crooks *et al.*, 2000). Also, the effects of change are expected to decrease as the magnitude of the flood event increases and so the impacts are likely to be less marked for major floods. Quantification of these issues is needed for the preparation of Catchment Flood Management Plans (Environment Agency *et al.*, 2002).

Case examples and issues

Agricultural policy and economic incentives have led to important changes in land management, with concerns for impacts on the local environment and flooding. An increase in excess overland flow has been noted in the UK and across northern Europe (Boardman, *et al.*, 1994; Evans, 1996; Burt, 2001). There is also anecdotal evidence that the response of rivers to rainfall events is becoming more intense as a result of agricultural soil management practices (O'Connell *et al.*, 2004).

Upland land management and grazing – Pontbren, Wales

Pontbren is a 'grass-roots' initiative involving ten hill farms and over 1000 ha of mainly agriculturally improved pasture along with areas of semi-natural and woodland in the Welsh Borders. The farms are at an intermediate altitude, on hilly terrain with steep slopes intersected by small streams and rivers that flow into the Severn basin upstream of Shrewsbury. Over a period of 30 years, in response to production subsidies and technical assistance, farms became more intensive with increased areas of improved pasture (through drainage, cultivation and re-seeding), removal of hedgerows, and increased stocking densities of sheep. Over-wintering of animals on the land and pressure on available grazing led to increased use of pasture under unsuitable conditions of soil wetness. Anecdotal evidence suggests that the soils are compacted and that surface overland flow is more common and widespread following heavy rainfall. Concerns by farmers themselves about degraded soils and declining profitability led to a reassessment of farming options in the late 1990s. Drawing on support provided for sustainable farming, farmers have recreated forested buffer strips, providing for animal shelter, streamside protection, timber and woodchip (for livestock bedding). Experimental studies (Bird *et al.*, 2003) indicate infiltration rates close to zero for grazed pasture in comparison with 100 cm/hour in wooded areas. This suggests that intensive grazing patterns do seriously affect runoff, and that management interventions can rapidly reduce this impact. This has been of particular concern in the evaluation of the floods in the Severn and elsewhere in winter 2000.

Arable agriculture and soil husbandry

Arable agricultural systems identified as posing a particular problem for soil structure, mainly due to the use of machinery on the land at unsuitable times, include:

a. autumn-sown cereals, oilseed rape and field beans (requiring cultivation and sowing as the land is wetting up, and leaving bare or sparsely vegetated soils over the winter);

b. late-harvested crops such as maize, sugar beet and potatoes (requiring heavy machinery for harvesting during late autumn and early winter); and

c. field vegetables (requiring access to the land over the winter) (Holman *et al.*, 2000).

Anecdotal evidence, largely from England, suggests that arable soils may be becoming less permeable through a combination of surface capping and topsoil compaction. Degraded soil structure reduces the infiltration of rainfall and, if of sufficient extent within a catchment, these effects may alter the catchment hydrology. Adverse effects are compounded by the use of increasingly large machines and a trend to use contractors for land operations, with associated pressures to work land under unsuitable weather conditions. For example, field trials of maize crops show that soil compaction can radically increase runoff, particularly on soils that would normally be free-draining (reported in O'Connell *et al.*, 2004).

Field drainage

The effects of agricultural drainage on flood response have been of concern for several decades, and a good understanding of the qualitative impacts has resulted from a range of experimental studies (Robinson, 1986; Robinson and Rycroft, 1999). For heavy clay soils, agricultural drainage is believed to reduce the occurrence of surface saturation and hence reduce the size of medium to large floods. Conversely, for more permeable soils, the increased efficiency of subsurface flow paths due to drainage can increase flood response. Clearly, impacts depend strongly on the combination of soils, drainage systems and their current efficiency, storm rainfall and antecedent conditions.

Afforestation

The effects of coniferous afforestation in the UK uplands have been extensively studied. From the national and international literature it is clear that afforestation is expected to reduce catchment runoff in the long term, due to increased evapotranspiration, although this effect is strongly dependent on climate (and much greater in the wet uplands of western UK). However, experimental research at Coalburn in northern England has shown that drainage practices formerly used to establish forests in the UK uplands can lead to increased storm runoff in the short and medium term (Robinson, 1986). In contrast, effects of broadleaf afforestation are unclear, yet this is a particular issue for current land-use strategies, including lowland set-aside, upland afforestation under the Habitats Directive, and the planting of buffer strips, coupled with stock exclusion measures, under the Countryside Stewardship (now Environmental Stewardship) Scheme. Current studies from southern England (Black Wood, Hampshire) and the Midlands suggest opposing effects on evapotranspiration, soil moisture and runoff.

Floodplain management

The discussion of land-use management as a pathway for flood generation can obscure the potential of appropriate land-use and management as a means of reducing flooding. An area of current interest to the farming industry, for example, is the role of agriculture in floodplain management. In principle, the reduction of levels of flood protection for floodplain agricultural land can provide additional floodplain storage to reduce flood peak discharges downstream. The Parrett Catchment Project in south-west England, for example, is exploring changes to land-use and land management which include use of temporary flood storage on farmland, detention ponds to retain flood runoff and soil management practices to reduce surface runoff (Thorne, 2003). There is scope in many floodplain areas previously defended against flooding for agricultural purposes, to 'set back' or modify defences to create washlands which provide benefits for flood-water retention and environmental enhancement (Morris *et al.*, 2004a).

Management of riparian and aquatic ecosystems

Increasing concern for preservation of ecological quality has created tensions between water users, and this aspect of water management will become more important under the EU Water Framework Directive (Morris *et al.*, 2004b). One effect in lowland permeable catchments has been the identification by the Environment Agency of 'over-abstracted' catchments and the reduction of licences to abstract groundwater. This restoration of more natural groundwater response could increase the risk of groundwater flooding, particularly under scenarios of strong climate change. More generally, there is pressure to maintain flow regimes which preserve the natural functioning of riparian wetland ecosystems. These rely on regular inundation, and local effects could be variable. For example, maintaining natural wetland dynamics could lead to reduced flood storage during major flood events; conversely, returning floodplains to active connection with the river channel could increase flood storage and attenuation. There is, therefore, current interest in the expansion of wetlands as a flood mitigation measure.

Urbanisation

Driver definition

Urbanisation, here, comprises the process by which the land surface is occupied by buildings and infrastructure for the purpose of human settlement and related economic activities. The focus here is on the effects of urbanisation on flood generation at the catchment scale. The specific issues of urban infrastructure and of urbanisation as a receptor are addressed in Chapter 12.

Driver operation

Urbanisation is probably the most extreme example of land-use change, with relatively well known impacts on hydrological response (e.g. Wheater *et al.*, 1982; Hall, 1984). An increase in impermeable surfaces and provision of storm water drainage systems will normally lead to an increased volume of storm runoff and reduced travel times, thus giving a potentially dramatic increase in flood peaks. However, this effect is known to decrease with increasing severity of event.

Runoff from impermeable areas normally bypasses the soil, leading to reduced groundwater recharge and reduced low flows. Secondary effects can be important, depending on drainage system design, management and performance. Low flows may be increased by water imported into a catchment for water supply and discharged as sewage effluent; leaking services may augment groundwater, as may septic tanks. There is considerable uncertainty about the generation of pluvial flooding in urban areas. Storm sewers are designed for a criterion of pipe-full flow, often only to accommodate a two to three year event. The relationship between this criterion and the frequency of surface flooding is highly variable and poorly understood, and adequate techniques to simulate urban flooding do not exist (Wheater, 2002). However, the capacity of storm drainage systems to accommodate extreme events is very limited.

The potential exists to mitigate the effects on runoff by management of urban drainage systems. Commonly, flood detention reservoirs are used to damp the outflow hydrograph. Active and passive in-sewer management may also be employed to use the storage capacity within the piped network. Other techniques, such as the use of soak-aways and permeable pavements, seek to restore natural infiltration processes and reduce water entry to the piped sewer system.

Under different future scenarios, changes to urban water management can be expected, such as increased use of rainwater harvesting for individual properties, and grey water re-cycling, in addition to the increasing use of more sustainable drainage solutions. There is scope for integrated management of water quantity and quality in urban water systems, including the reduction of uncontrolled storm-water overflows which discharge from sewers to rivers under storm conditions. It is clear that the catchment-scale impacts of development will depend on the detail of urban water, and particularly stormwater, management.

In addition, the location of urban development within a catchment will affect catchment response and should be taken into account in developing mitigation strategies. For example, one solution to suburban development in the upper reaches of a catchment draining through an urban centre might be to improve channel capacity to transmit floods downstream. However, this could aggravate the flood risk downstream; clearly a preferable strategy is to seek to retain flows upstream until the rapid response of the downstream area has been discharged.

A particularly important aspect of urban development is development on the floodplain. This has been widespread in the past, although the situation is changing somewhat with the strengthening of the role of floodplain planning in England and Wales (Office of the Deputy Prime Minister – ODPM, 2005) and similar initiatives in Scotland and Northern Ireland. The primary impacts of floodplain development are: a) to increase runoff generation, as discussed above; and b) to affect floodplain flows in terms of available floodplain storage and flow resistance (hydraulic roughness). Secondary effects may arise due to the impacts at catchment scale of extending or creating local flood defences to protect urban development in floodplain areas.

Driver importance

The potential *local* impact of urban development on flood response is very large. Flood peaks could easily increase by several hundred per cent due to the combination of increased runoff volume and reduced travel time. An average proportion of rainfall running off from urban areas is 70% (Institute of Hydrology, 1999); taking the extreme case of a natural catchment located on permeable chalk geology, this figure might be 2%. Clearly, the contrast between rural and urban response depends on the nature of the urban landscape and the underlying soils and geology. In addition, the effects of urbanisation are believed to decrease with increasing severity of event. Current UK practice assumes that the effect of urbanisation will not be significant for a one in 1000 year event or rarer.

At the *large catchment scale*, the importance of urbanisation on increased runoff is less clear. For example, historical analysis of Thames flows (Crooks *et al.*, 2000) has shown no detectable effects in response to 30 years of urban expansion. This is attributed to the fact that urban development has been accompanied by engineered solutions, such as detention storage ponds, to the relatively small proportion of the catchment which is urban, and to effects of land-use heterogeneity at the large catchment scale.

Driver uncertainty

The effects of urbanisation are well known in principle, and have been characterised, relatively crudely, for the UK, at small catchment scale, by empirical regional analysis (Institute of Hydrology, 1999). However, there are two important methodological gaps in quantifying catchment-scale effects more precisely, and for large catchments (Wheater, 2002). From the above discussion it is evident that these gaps depend on the detail of the design and management of the urban drainage infrastructure. At present, simulation tools are widely used to aid design and management of urban sewer systems. However, the criteria for design relate to the frequency of pipe-full flow. This bears no direct relationship to the frequency of surface flooding. There are no adequate tools to simulate urban flooding at local (street) scale. Second, there are no tools suitable to represent the detailed local response at catchment-scale. These issues have been identified as research priorities by Defra and the Environment Agency (Calver and Wheater, 2002). They are a major source of uncertainty, particularly given the potential for more sophisticated, real-time, control of large urban drainage systems, and the attraction of more integrated solutions to urban drainage (e.g. SUDS – sustainable urban drainage systems).

Case examples

Impacts of urbanisation depend on the natural response of a catchment but can be dramatic. A typical example calculation for a $19 \, \text{km}^2$ catchment in north-west England based on UK practice (Hall *et al.*, 1993) shows that development of 48% of the catchment would lead to an expected doubling of the mean annual flood. However, impacts can, in principle, be much greater, particularly for catchments on permeable geology, although, as noted above, the effects are expected to decrease with increasing severity of event. Flood seasonality may also change (see the analysis of Institute of Hydrology, 1999). Rural catchments typically have major floods associated with wet antecedent conditions in the winter. In contrast summer thunderstorms of high rainfall intensity may represent a more critical case for urban areas.

The River Thames Windsor and Maidenhead flood relief scheme, opened in 2002, is an instructive example of floodplain development and its impacts. Progressive housing development on the floodplain at Maidenhead, against hydrological advice, eventually created a situation where the potential costs of flooding justified flood protection measures. The solution adopted was the construction of the Jubilee River, a parallel channel to the main River Thames, which operated effectively in the floods of winter 2002/3. However, the flood relief channel had to be built through land that had been reserved from development and residents downstream are concerned about the potential for increased flood risk due to the operation of the channel and the loss of floodplain storage.

Agricultural impacts

This section considers agriculture as a receptor of flood impacts (natural habitats as a receptor area are considered in Chapter 3, but some discussion is retained here due to the role of agriculture in maintaining habitats). In the context of overall catchment management, there is considerable interconnectedness of pathway and receptor functions. For example, actions to facilitate flood alleviation and drainage for agriculture and habitats in one location may have major implications for flood risk and standards of land drainage in other parts. Furthermore, washland and wetland creation can contribute to overall catchment flood management, enhance biodiversity and support rural livelihoods through farming, tourism and recreation.

Driver definition

This driver is concerned with the impacts of flooding on agricultural and forestry land and on associated wildlife habitats. Agriculture and forestry involve the use of land for commercial crop, livestock and timber production for food and industrial products, supporting rural livelihoods and communities in the process. Habitats comprise the living environment for naturally occurring plants and animals. In the UK, most habitats are managed in one way or another, either as part of a predominantly farmed countryside, or as designated sites or features which are purposely managed to deliver particular ecological or amenity objectives.

Intensive agriculture is critically dependent on protection against flooding and managed water regimes, typically by means of artificial land drainage. The higher the value of the crop, the greater the degree of flood defence and land drainage that is required and justified.

Habitats are also critically dependent on water regimes, being sensitive to too little or too much water, and to the quality of water. Wetland habitats, and extensively farmed washlands, have potential to regulate hydrological processes which can attenuate peak flows, thereby reducing the risk of flooding and undesirable morphological impacts. Seasonality and duration of flooding are particularly critical factors affecting the impact of flooding (and waterlogging) on agriculture and habitats.

Driver operation

Impact of flooding on agriculture

Agricultural land-use, farming practice and performance are critically dependent on flood defence and land drainage (Smedema and Rycroft, 1983; Castle *et al.*, 1984). Flooding on farmland, whether surface inundation or water-logging of the soil profile, can have a negative effect on the financial performance of farming as a result of crop damage, livestock mortality, reduced crop and livestock yield and quality/condition, increased costs and reduced crop and livestock options.

Commercial crops are sensitive to waterlogged soils and anaerobic soil conditions during critical growth periods, with consequences for crop yield, quality and value. Wet soils have reduced strength and this reduces their bearing capacity which, in turn, restricts field access by machinery or grazing livestock. This leads to delays in critical field operations such as cultivations and fertiliser application, and to restrictions on grazing seasons. In the case of grassland, wet soils inhibit the growth of commercially 'improved' grass species, restrain field access for the early application of fertiliser, and are liable to damage by grazing animals. For these reasons, and other requirements of intensive livestock systems such as quality silage-making, persistently wet field conditions tend to be associated with extensive grassland, whether grazing or hay cutting.

The same type of impacts apply to forestry where flooding can result in direct damage, and waterlogging restricts root development and timber growth. Impacts depend on species type, but even water tolerant plantations, such as willows, may not prosper under permanently water logged soils, and usually require relatively dry field conditions during harvesting periods.

In this context, flood defence for agriculture and forestry involves measures to reduce inundation *and* waterlogging. The impact of flooding and waterlogging on farming varies according to tolerance of the particular crop or land-use activity, and the frequency, duration, depth and seasonality of the event. The latter factor is particularly important: the impact of a flood or waterlogging event varies a lot according to the time of year. Evidence suggests that relatively short duration flooding in winter has limited impact on grassland, but even a brief flood event in summer can completely destroy a standing crop of grass or cereals (Morris *et al.*, 1984; Dunderdale and Morris, 1997).

It is possible to prescribe the water regime standards required to deliver given types of farming activities and practices, from intensive horticulture, through arable systems involving root crops and cereals, to grassland, whether managed for intensive livestock production or extensively grazed or cut for hay. The more intensive the system, the greater is the standard of flood defence required.

Based on observed land-use, Table 5.1 shows the common standards of flood defence associated with, and therefore implicitly required to support, given types of agricultural land-use and productivity. Grassland, as evidence bears out, has a much greater tolerance to flooding than arable crops, especially if confined to winter periods.

Table 5.1. 'Tolerance' of flooding varies according to agricultural land-use

Agricultural land-use type	Common minimum acceptable flood frequency: return period in years	
	Whole year	Summer April–October
Horticulture	20	100
Intensive arable including sugar beet and potatoes	10	25
Extensive arable: cereals, beans, oil seeds	5	10
Intensive, improved grass, usually dairy	2	5
Extensive grass, usually cattle and sheep	<1	3

Sources: Dunderdale and Morris (1996, 1997)

With respect to waterlogging (Table 5.2), experimental and empirical research in Britain and the Netherlands (Morris *et al.*, 1984; Hess and Morris, 1988; Dunderdale and Morris, 1997) has shown that the productivity of agriculture is critically dependent on water-table levels as they determine crop growth conditions and field access, as referred to above. This is especially the case during the spring and early summer periods, and to a lesser extent during the autumn. In the spring, water tables at or below 0.5 m of the surface are indicative of 'good' agricultural drainage

Table 5.2. Drainage conditions for agriculture depend on water levels in fields and watercourses

Agricultural drainage condition	Agricultural productivity class	Depth to water table from surface	Springtime freeboards* in watercourses (natural drainage)	Springtime freeboards in watercourse (field drains)
Good: 'rarely wet'	Normal, no impediment imposed by drainage	0.5 m or more	1 m (sands) 1.3 m (peats) 2.1 m (clays)	1.2 m (clays) to 1.6 m sands (0.2 m below pipe outfall)
Bad: 'occasionally wet'	Low, reduced yields, reduced field access and grazing season	0.3 m to 0.49 m	0.7 m (sands) 1 m (peats) 1.9 m (clays)	Temporarily submerged pipe outfalls
Very bad: 'commonly or permanently wet'	Very low, severe constraints on land use, much reduced yields, field access and grazing season: mainly wet grassland	Less than 0.3 m	0.4 m (sands) 0.6 m (peats) 1 m (clays)	Permanently submerged pipe outfalls

* Freeboard here is the height difference between water in ditch and adjacent field surface level. Required field water tables relate to conditions for crop growth and field access. Very low water tables can result in crop water stress.
Sources: Dunderdale and Morris, 1996, 1997

conditions and will support 'normal' agricultural productivity. Persistently high water-table levels constrain land-use, limit field access, depress yields and result in low financial performance. In many cases such conditions would not support arable cropping and mainly be confined to extensive grassland.

Of course, very low water-table conditions during the summer period can cause water stress in crops (especially if they have poorly developed root systems because of water flooding earlier in the year) and there may be a benefit of raised water tables to provide sub-irrigation. Indeed, traditional meadows draw benefit from high groundwater levels in summer, as indeed can arable crops. But, for the most part, spring/early summer water-table levels are the defining influence on the feasibility of agricultural land-use in Britain.

In summary, an increase in flood frequency, magnitude or duration can have three main types of impact on agricultural land at the farm level:

  a. reduction in the value of crop and livestock outputs due to damage or productivity loss associated with surface flooding and/or waterlogging;
  b. loss of value-added associated with a switch to less intensive, flood tolerant land-uses, e.g. from arable to grassland; and
  c. extra cost associated with defence against or mitigation of flooding and waterlogging.

From a farmer's perspective, increased flood frequency could reduce farm revenues, increase some operating costs and, therefore, reduce profitability. In some cases, there may be savings in farm level costs such as labour and machinery if a farm moves to a less intensive system. Much depends on farm circumstances and especially whether farms have scope to reduce not only direct costs such as fertilisers but also overhead costs such as labour and machinery and other general expenses in the process of adjustment.

From a broader economic perspective, the impact of flooding on the national economy depends whether crops lost in one area can be replaced by production elsewhere in the country. This might not be possible in the short term and imports may be needed. But in the longer term there could be a switch in production to low flood risk areas, displacing less valuable crops (or taking up unused land) in the process. Also from an economic perspective, estimates of agricultural losses must be adjusted to take account of subsidies paid to farmers. Defra provide guidance on this (MAFF, 1999; Penning-Rowsell *et al.*, 2003). This guidance recognises that special consideration is required where increased flood risk could compromise agricultural assets of strategic national or regional importance, or the viability of otherwise vulnerable farming communities.

Impacts of flooding on soils

Flooding may also have implications for the physical, chemical and biological characteristics of soils. Prolonged flooding may affect soil structure through processes such as erosion and compaction. Flooding can cause chemical changes to the soil as a result of the release of unwanted materials due to anaerobic conditions. In low-lying areas, the greatest danger may be associated with iron, although pH is likely to be at or higher than neutrality as the flood waters are predominantly derived from base rich catchments.

Flooding may increase transfer of chemical nutrients which may adversely affect freshwater resources and diverse species rich grassland. There is evidence that there may be an important impact on soil micro and macro fauna, arising from concern that flooding may cause significant loss of fauna due to long duration anaerobic conditions in the soil profile. Recovery of the soils, soil fauna and vegetation post-flooding will depend on the establishment of good water-level management (Morris *et al.*, 2005).

Significance of impacts

The significance of the impact of changes in flood regimes in rural areas, as they affect inundation and waterlogging, will depend on dominant land-use in the flood plain and the balance among the priorities given to commercial farming, nature conservation and other activities. Flood damage costs per event per unit area are much lower on agricultural land than on urban land, and standards of protection are concomitantly lower. As a consequence, lower priority is generally given to protecting all but the most productive agricultural land. There are parts of lowland Britain, in East Anglia, south-west Lancashire and the Trent tidal areas, that are of strategic agricultural importance, comprising large areas of high value, specialist cropping supported by intensively managed flood defence and land drainage schemes. Loss of agricultural output in these areas could be significant at the regional and national scale.

Where flooding is so severe as to preclude agricultural land-use, the impact may be captured in terms of a reduction (or complete loss) of the market value (£/ha) of agricultural land. The costs associated with individual floods depend on land-use as shown in Table 5.3 for infrequent flooding occurring on given agricultural land grades and commonly associated land-uses. Where flood frequency increases beyond the tolerable limits for a given land-use, then land-use will switch accordingly, with consequences for reduced value-added (Penning-Rowsell *et al.*, 2003).

One possible managed use of the floodplain is the purposeful containment and storage of flood waters. If this is the case, the wider impact of floods, when they occur, could be reduced. Furthermore, the use of floodplains for storage, together with extensification of land-use, could result in beneficial impacts for society in terms of wildlife, landscape and amenity.

Case examples

During the period 1950 to 1975, public expenditure on flood defence for agricultural land was an important part of policies for agricultural enhancement. This aimed not only to relieve flood damage, but combined with improvements in land

Table 5.3. The cost of flooding on agricultural land varies by Agricultural Land Class and commonly associated land-use

Agricultural Land Class		Typical land-use by ALC and associated cost of a single annual flood (assuming equal monthly distribution of floods within a year)					Average cost of a single annual flood event
		Horticulture	Intensive arable	Extensive arable	Intensive grass	Extensive grass	£/ha by land class (2001 prices)
1	% of area	5%	85%	10%			
	Flood cost £/ha	4800	1030	450			1160
2	% of area	5%	60%	35%			
	Flood cost £/ha	3080	780	430			770
3a	% of area		30%	70%			
	Flood cost £/ha		530	350			400
3b	% of area			50%	50%		
	Flood cost £/ha			270	50		160
4	% of area				100%		
	Flood cost £/ha				50		50
5	% of area					100%	
	Flood cost £/ha					20	20

Source: Penning-Rowsell *et al.*, 2003

drainage infrastructure, to promote intensive land-use and increased farm output. A review of 22 agricultural flood defence schemes (Morris, 1992) showed benefits of flood alleviation (i.e. avoidance of flood costs) on farm land, adjusted for government subsidies, ranging from £13/ha to over £230/ha in 1982 prices (£32/ha and £558/ha in 2006 prices respectively). These were lowest for flood relief on extensive grassland, and highest where flood alleviation allowed a switch to high-value cropping. The latter often involved much higher capital costs, including investment in pumping schemes. A review of 15 river maintenance programmes involving channel works and vegetation clearance (Dunderdale and Morris, 1996) showed flood alleviation benefits to farm land of between £4/ha and £57/ha/year in 1996 prices (£5/ha and £74/ha in 2006 prices respectively), depending on type of land-use.

These studies confirmed that the cost of flooding on agricultural land varies considerably according to land-use. At a time of agricultural expansion, the biggest 'cost' of flooding was the constraint on the ability to switch to more intensive land-use. However, little if any consideration was given at the time to the environmental costs and benefits of drainage for intensive agriculture. The very different policy context of the early 2000s and the different relative values placed on agricultural and environmental goods and services now mean that flood defence for agriculture, except for the most productive and strategically important areas, is no longer a priority (Penning-Rowsell et al., 2003).

Uncertainties

There is generally a good understanding of the impact of flooding on commercial agriculture based on a mixture of empirical evidence and scientific research. It is possible to prescribe the flooding and waterlogging tolerances of crops and the consequences for physical and financial productivity of increased exposure to flooding and waterlogging. This evidence is mainly based on individual crop- and field-based observations, but it can be extrapolated to catchment scale assessments.

There is an emerging but incomplete understanding of the water regime requirements of natural habitats, both with respect to flooding and soil water tolerances and/or needs as referred to above (Gowing et al., 1994; van Ek et al., 2000), as addressed in Chapter 3 of this volume. There is some uncertainty about whether flood tolerant, wetland compatible forms of agriculture can provide the basis for sustainable livelihoods.

Driver interactions

Within set interactions

There are strong links between the role of agriculture as a pathway and as a receptor. Intensive agriculture in the higher catchment, facilitated by artificial drainage systems to remove excess water, is in most situations likely to increase flooding risk in lowland floodplains, unless the latter are protected. Approaching 50% of Grade 1 and 2 agricultural land in Britain lies in potentially floodable areas, with much of it under intensive and often very high-value cropping, especially in the eastern part of England.

Increased urbanisation of the catchment is likely to increase flood risk to farm land in floodplains because of increased runoff and because flooding to farm land is perceived as a cheaper option than other flood management strategies. Indeed, farm land may be positively managed in order to provide flood storage facilities, especially in areas of low agricultural interest.

Interaction with other driver sets

The interaction among Catchment Land Use and other driver sets is summarised in Fig. 5.1. The driver set has relatively strong interaction with most other driver

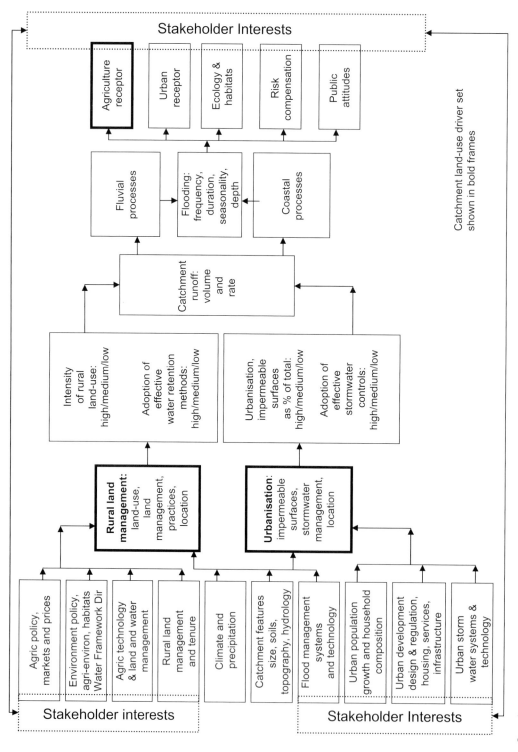

Fig. 5.1. Catchment land-use driver set and linkages

sets and there are many feedback loops, such as between climate change and agricultural impacts.

Urbanisation has strong association with socio-economic drivers as they find expression in stakeholder interests, with consequences for the characteristics and rate of urbanisation. Rural land management is also shaped by societal and stakeholder interest through a mix of agricultural and environment policy, technology change and institutional drivers. Both urbanisation and rural land-use are shaped by climatic and physical factors at the local level, including localised coastal and estuarine processes. Flood management, as this determines hydraulic regulation and catchment management, is also a critical influence on the operation of the catchment land-use driver set.

Agriculture as a receptor is strongly linked to fluvial and coastal processes as they affect flood characteristics. There are important linkages between agriculture and urbanisation as receptors, the former potentially offering sacrificial flood storage to protect the latter. There is potential linkage between agriculture and ecology through integration of flood management and biodiversity on washlands. The relative importance given to receptor impacts reflects societal and stakeholder interests. The whole system is driven by anthropogenic factors which find expression in stakeholder behaviour.

Driver behaviour under possible future scenarios

Native parameters

In order to assess the relationship between the catchment land-use and future flood risk under possible future scenarios, the drivers were described in terms of 'native parameters' and associated units of measurement (Table 5.4).

The Foresight scenarios described in Chapter 2 were interpreted with respect to the driver set with a view to drawing out likely changes in native parameters for the Catchment Land-Use Driver Set. As shown in Table 5.5, differences in economic conditions, social preferences, government policy and technology among scenarios result in differences in the type, extent and intensity of agricultural and urban land-use as well as the degree of control on floodplain development. Furthermore, differences in the type and profitability of agricultural land-use result in differences in the cost of flooding among scenarios.

Table 5.4. Native parameters represent the drivers associated with catchment land-use and flood risk

Driver name	'Native parameter' used to represent the driver for flood risk impact prediction	Units of measurement
Rural land-use management	Soils Land-use Land management practice, location within catchment	ha of soil class ha of land-use type Runoff risk factor (index) Upper, middle, lower
Urbanisation	Urban area as a proportion of total catchment area Stormwater management within urban area	% Retention factor (index)
Agriculture	Agric Land Class Land-use type Flood damage cost, £/ha Decline in land value	ha of Grade, 1 through 4 ha of land-use type, 1 through 5 £/ha damage cost or income loss £/ha reduction in land asset value

Ranking of catchment land-use drivers

Table 5.5 also shows the relative importance of catchment land-use drivers in terms of impacts on flood risk relative to other drivers for each future scenario (see Chapter 12). Flood risk here is a product of the probability and consequences of flooding. The importance (relative to other drivers in the scenario) of rural land-use management as a driver of flood risk is high for world markets and national enterprise due to a tendency towards intensive agriculture. With respect to urbanisation, impacts on flood risk are perceived to be medium relative to other influences, with a

Table 5.5. The influence and relative importance* of native parameters on flood risk vary according to future scenarios**

Driver name	World markets	Global sustainability	National enterprise	Local stewardship
Rural land-use management	Agriculture focused on intensive use of high-quality land, with increased probability of runoff. Marginal areas released for non-agricultural use, reducing runoff and providing scope for flood storage in some areas. HIGH	Sustainable land management practices reduce flood runoff generation. Floodplain management balances production with nature conservation and seeks to enhance flood storage and attenuation. MEDIUM	National self-sufficiency and incentives to farmers promotes intensive agriculture on most land, with limited controls on runoff or use of floodplain storage. HIGH	Self-sufficiency in agricultural products is combined with sustainable farming methods, including land and water conservation. Relatively extensive farming retains a high level of agricultural land-use, with increased pressure on land in some upland areas. MEDIUM
Urbanisation	Increased urban expansion. Flood protection driven by asset values. Limited sustainable urban drainage solutions and floodplain development controls. MEDIUM	Little change to footprint of urban development, adoption of integrated sustainable urban drainage systems and controls on floodplain development. MEDIUM	Increased urban development and floodplain development with limited measures to mitigate flooding impacts. MEDIUM	Urban area constant, but increased urban density. Sustainable storm-water management within urban areas, and controls on floodplain development. MEDIUM
Agriculture	Relative intensification of agriculture on better land, extensification or abandonment of low-grade land. Reduced profitability and lower land values reduces agricultural flood damage cost to about 70% of current levels. MEDIUM	Intensive farming on better land with extensification on other grades, including flood storage and agri-environment options. Lower output prices and extensification result in flood damage costs of about 85% of current levels in flood-prone areas. MEDIUM	Relatively intensive, subsidised agriculture, with high standards of flood defence for farm land. Flood damage costs are about 115% of current levels. MEDIUM	Farming, albeit extensive, is relatively profitable and costs of flooding on high-grade farm land are 150% of current levels. Most floodplain land is confined to uses with low flood damage costs. LOW

* Shown as HIGH, MEDIUM or LOW relative to other drivers in the scenario, see Chapter 12
** Based on Foresight scenarios for year 2050, with further consolidation of trends by 2080

tendency towards high under world markets and national enterprise due to high urban growth and limited regulation. For agriculture as a receptor, risks reflect the product of flood probability and the cost of flooding when it occurs. For example, under world markets, flooding on farm land increases but damage costs per flood event are lower because, in the absence of subsidies farm commodity prices are relatively low and marginal land, including that prone to flooding, is no longer farmed intensively.

Uncertainty analysis

There is, as previously discussed, considerable uncertainty associated with the behaviour of driver sets under alternative possible future scenarios, in some cases because there is limited knowledge of the fundamental relationships among key parameters within a particular driver and of interactions between drivers in possible future situations. Furthermore, there are likely to be factors and relationships that turn out to be significant, which at this point are not known about.

As further discussed in Chapter 12, there is high uncertainty regarding the impact of rural land management and urbanisation on flood risk, both in terms of estimating the magnitude of the impacts and the efficacy of measures to control them. There is a clear need for research to provide a better understanding and a basis for appropriate interventions, especially at the catchment scale. In the agricultural case, the diffuse nature of runoff from farm land presents a particular challenge for governance. There is considerable uncertainty about the willingness of land managers to change behaviour in order to control runoff where there is evidence that to do so will make a difference. Furthermore, there is uncertainty about the best mix of policy instruments to achieve beneficial change, whether regulation, voluntary arrangements or economic incentives (O'Connell *et al.*, 2004).

With respect to agriculture as a receptor, there is good knowledge on water regime management for commercial agriculture, but knowledge gaps on how to integrate farming, flood management and biodiversity options which are important to varying degrees under all future scenarios. There is a clear need for research on this topic.

Conclusions

The way that land is used within a catchment has potential to affect both the probability and consequences of flooding. While the potential of land-use to influence runoff is not questioned, there is uncertainty about the operation of this influence at the catchment scale and how this influence varies according to the magnitude of the precipitation event.

For the most part, modern farming methods are associated with increased runoff from farmed land and, where underdrainage is installed, with rapid evacuation of excess waters from soil profiles. There is considerable evidence that agricultural land-use is a contributor to serious, albeit local, muddy floods. The influence of rural land-use and the detail of land management practices at the catchment scale for infrequent rainfall events is, however, less clear.

A similar story emerges for urbanisation: hard impermeable surfaces obviously lead to rapid runoff and accumulation of potential floodwater, with potentially dramatic local scale effects, but this has commonly been taken account of in recent development by engineering local storage. How the overall effects join-up at the catchment scale, particularly for extreme events, is unclear. Neither is it clear the extent to which modifications to urban drainage pathways, through 'sustainable urban drainage systems', for example, can make a difference at the catchment level.

With respect to agriculture as a receptor, farm land is more tolerant of flooding than urban land, and the unit damage costs are much lower. While flooding (and associated waterlogging of soils) in intensively farmed areas can result in significant losses of agricultural output, in many rural, especially grassland, areas in the UK this is not the case. Changing policies on agriculture and environment suggest there could be benefit in 'setting back' some previous agricultural flood defences to restore 'natural' floodplains in ways that provide benefits in terms of flood storage and enhanced biodiversity. Promoted by financial rewards to land managers, these could help to support rural livelihoods.

With respect to alternative futures, the constituents of the driver set are mainly ranked as having a medium impact on future flood risk, although the impact of urban and rural land-use is perceived to be particularly high for the utilitarian world market and national enterprise scenarios. Agriculture as a receptor is shown to exert a medium relative influence under most scenarios: although the reason for this assessment varies among scenarios due to differences in land-use, damage costs, and degree of exposure to flooding. For rural land-use as a pathway and a receptor, flood risk is mainly a function of societal preferences evident in agricultural and environmental policy drivers. Similarly, the contribution of urbanisation to flood risk is influenced by social and economic factors as these shape the nature and rate of urban development.

The possibilities identified here are obscured by uncertainty and gaps in knowledge concerning the relationship between land-use and the accumulation of floodwater at the catchment scale. None the less, the analysis presented here identifies a key role for catchment land-use drivers within strategies for management of flood risk. The implications for 'responses' to future flood risk are addressed in Chapter 16.

References

Bird, S.B., Emmett, B.A., Sinclair, F.L., Stevens, P.A., Reynolds, B., Nicholson, S. and Jones, T., 2003. *Pontbren: Effects of Tree Planting on Agricultural Soils and their Functions*. Final Report to National Assembly of Wales/Countryside Council for Wales/ Forestry Commission, Centre for Ecology and Hydrology, Wallingford.

Boardman, J., Ligneau, L., Deroo, A. and Vandaele, K., 1994. 'Flooding of property by runoff from agricultural land in northwestern Europe', *Geomorphology*, 10 (1–4), 183–196.

Burt, T.P., 2001. 'Integrated management of sensitive catchment systems', *Catena*, 42 (2–4), 275–290.

Calver, A. and Wheater, H.S., 2002. *Scoping the Broad Scale Modelling Hydrology Programme*, Defra/Environment Agency Flood and Coastal Defence R&D Programme Project FD2104 Final Report.

Castle, D.A., McCunnel, J. and Tring, I.M., 1984. *Field Drainage Principles and Practice*, Batsford, London.

Crooks, S., Cheetham, R., Davies, H., Goodsell, G., 2000. *EUROTAS (European River Flood Occurrence and Total Risk Assessment System)*, Final Report, Task T3: Thames Catchment Study. EU Contract ENV4-CT97-0535.

Dunderdale, J.A.L. and Morris, J., 1996. *River Maintenance Evaluation*, R&D Project 317, R&D Note 456, National Rivers Authority (now Environment Agency), Bristol.

Dunderdale, J.A.L. and Morris, J., 1997. The benefits and costs analysis of river maintenance, *Journal of Inst. of Water and Environmental Management*, 11 (6), 423–430.

Environment Agency, Department for Environment, Food and Rural Affairs and National Assembly for Wales, 2002. *Catchment Flood Management Plans: Guidelines: Vol. 1 Procedures* (3rd Draft), Environment Agency, Bristol.

EPSRC, 2002. *Flood Risk Management Research Consortium*, Joint R&D Programme on Flood and Coastal Erosion Risk Management, Engineering and Physical Research Council, Swindon.

Evans, R., 1996. *Soil Erosion and its Impacts in England and Wales*, Friends of the Earth Trust, London.

Gowing, D.J.G., Spoor, G., Mountford, J.O. and Youngs, E.G., 1994. *The Water-Regime Requirements of Lowland Wet-grassland Plants*, Report to Ministry of Agriculture, Fisheries and Food, Flood and Coastal Defence Division, London, Cranfield University, Bedford.

Hall, M.J., 1984. *Urban Hydrology*, Elsevier, London.

Hall, M.J., Hockin, D.L. and Ellis, J.B., 1993. *Design of Flood Storage Reservoirs*, Construction Industry Research Association, Princess Risborough.

Hess, T.M. and Morris, J., 1988. 'Estimating the value of flood alleviation on agricultural grassland', *Agriculture Water Management*, 15, 141–153.

Holman, I.P., Hollis, J.M. and Thompson, T.R.E., 2000. *Impact of Agricultural Soil Conditions on Floods – Autumn 2000*, R&D Project W5C (00) 04, Environment Agency, Bristol, Cranfield University, Bristol.

Institute of Hydrology, 1999. *Flood Estimation Handbook*, Centre for Ecology and Hydrology, Wallingford.

MAFF, 1999. *Flood and Coastal Defence Project Appraisal Guidance 3, Economic Appraisal*, (FCDPAG3), Ministry of Agriculture, Fisheries and Food (now Defra, Department for Environment, Food and Rural Affairs), London.

Morris, J., 1992. 'Agricultural land drainage. land use change and economic performance: experience in the UK', *Land Use Policy*, 3(9), July, 185–198.

Morris J., Hess, T.M., Ryan, A.M. and Leeds-Harrison, P.B., 1984. *Drainage Benefits and Farmer Uptake*, Four volumes, Report to the Severn-Trent Water Authority, Cranfield University, Bedford.

Morris, J., Hess, T.M., Gowing, D.G., Leeds-Harrison, P.B., Bannister, N., Vivash, R.M.N. and Wade, M., 2004a. *Integrated Washland Management for Flood Defence and Biodiversity*. *English Nature Research Report*, 598, English Nature, Peterborough.

Morris, J., Hess, T., Gill, A., Howsam, P. and White, S., 2004b. The Water Framework Directive and Flood Management – a missed opportunity? *Proceedings of 39th Defra Flood and Coastal Management Conference*, 28 June–1 July, Department for Environment, Food and Rural Affairs, London.

Morris, J., Hess, T.M., Gowing, D.G., Leeds-Harrison, P.B., Bannister, N., Vivash, R.M.N. and Wade, M., 2005. 'A framework for integrating flood defence and biodiversity in washlands in England', *International Journal of River Basin Management*, IAHR & INBO, 3 (2), 1–11.

O'Connell, P.E., Beven, K.J., Carney, J.N., Clements, R.O., Ewen, J., Fowler, H., Harris, G.L., Hollis, J., Morris, J., O'Donnell, G.M., Packman, J.C., Parkin, A., Quinn, P.F. and Rose, S.C., 2004. *Review of Impacts of Rural Land Use and Management on Flood Generation. Part A: Impact Study Report*, Draft Report to Defra/Environment Agency R&D Technical Report (FD2114).

ODPM, 2005. Planning Policy Guidance 25: Development and Flood Risk, Office of the Deputy Prime Minister, London, available online http://www.odpm.gov.uk

Penning-Rowsell, E., Johnson, C., Tunstall, S., Tapsell, S., Morris, J., Chatterton, J., Coker, A. and Green, C., 2003. *The Benefits of Flood and Coastal Defence, Data and Techniques for 2003*, Flood Hazard Research Centre, Middlesex University.

Robinson, M., 1986. 'Changes in catchment runoff following drainage and afforestation', *J. Hydrol.*, 86, 71–84.

Robinson, M. and Rycroft, D.W., 1999. 'The impact of drainage on streamflow', in *Agricultural Drainage*, eds Skaggs, W. and van Schilfgaarde, J., Agronomy monograph 38, *Soil Sci. Soc. Amer.*, 753–786.

Smedema, L.K. and Rycroft, D.W., 1983. *Land Drainage*, Batsford, London.

Thorne, B., 2003. 'Farming water on the Parrett Catchment Project', *Proc. Land Use and Flood Management Conference*, Institution of Civil Engineers, January (Abstract).

van Ek, R., Witte, J.P.M., Runhaar, H. and Klijn, F., 2000. 'Ecological effects of water management in the Netherlands: the model DEMNAT', *Ecological Engineering*, 16, 127–141.

Wheater, H.S., 2002. 'Progress in and prospects for fluvial flood modelling', *Phil. Trans. R. Soc. Lond. A*, 360, 1409–1431.

Wheater, H.S., Shaw, T.L. and Rutherford, J.C., 1982. 'Storm runoff from small lowland catchments in South West England'. *J. Hydrol.*, 55, 321–337.

6 River processes

S.N. Lane and C.R. Thorne

Introduction

The river network comprises the pathway by which surface water drains through the basin and the processes operating in that network have both direct and indirect impacts on the water level associated with a given flood discharge. In this context, we have grouped river processes into three functional driver sets:

1. morphology and sediment supply;
2. conveyance;
3. environment, ecosystems and habitats.

River pathways have a direct bearing upon flood risk because they influence the speed and attenuation of the flood wave as it passes through the drainage network and control the local relationship between discharge and water level during a flood event. For example, it is the morphology (dimensions and geometry) of the channel-floodplain landform that controls its conveyance (capacity to convey water downstream), and hence the elevation of the water surface for a particular discharge. In this respect, it may seem odd to treat conveyance separately from morphology, as the shape of the channel and topography of the floodplain are major factors affecting their conveyance. However, the role of morphology as a flood risk driver is not limited to its effect on conveyance and, hence, it is dealt with separately. This recognises that future flood risk will be conditioned not only by changes in conveyance, but also by morphological instability that occurs in response to changes in river flow regime and/or sediment supply. Erosion and deposition processes associated with channel instability and floodplain adjustments may drive channel aggradation/degradation, channel narrowing/widening and/or floodplain sedimentation/scouring that impact both natural functions of the channel-floodplain system in conveying or storing floodwater and the standard of protection and condition of any structural flood defences.

The environment, ecosystems and habitats driver group is also treated separately because the nature of ecological communities associated with a river, as well as their management through operational maintenance within the riparian corridor, commonly influence the relationship between discharge and water level through their effects on conveyance and by influencing patterns of erosion and sedimentation. The extent to which present-day management activities will continue to be acceptable in the future will vary across scenarios, depending on the emphasis placed on conserving or enhancing river environments, ecosystems and habitats relative to that placed on providing a specified standard of service for flood defence. In this context, uncertainty clouds our ability to predict the degree to which past and present tensions between environmental regulation and flood management activies reliant on structural defences will be resolved as flood risk management and environmental conservation become increasingly embedded within holistic catchment planning.

Morphology and sediment supply

Definitions

Changes in river morphology and/or sediment supply lead to adjustments of multiple aspects of the river channel and floodplain system which, in turn, affect both flood storage and conveyance. To understand the operation of this driver, it must first be recognised that changes in channel morphology and sediment supply affect the fluvial system, which is an important pathway in the source-pathway-receptor model. The difficulty with this driver is that river morphology and sediment supply can act not only together as an independent driver (a controlling variable that influences flood risk) but also as two interdependent variables. For example, the existing morphology of a river will control its sediment transport carrying capacity but, in time, that morphology will respond to changes in the sediment supply from upstream. The degree to which morphology and sediment supply behave in inter-dependent or independent ways depends primarily on the *catchment context*. That is, the location of the reach of river that is under consideration within the wider catchment, and the topographical, hydrological, geological and management characteristics of that catchment. This makes it notoriously difficult to generalise on how a particular reach of river will interact with the other source, pathway and receptor drivers in the flooding system.

Second, given the 100-year timescale over which the definition of future flood risk is being considered and the spatial resolution of the risk assessment methods employed in the Foresight FCD Project (see Chapter 13), it is appropriate to consider the operation of this driver in relation to the longer-term process-response mechanisms acting in rivers that are affected by secular environmental change. These longer-term adjustments of the fluvial system differ substantially from the dramatic, short-term morphological responses exhibited by river reaches that are subject to a high magnitude event. Specifically, the latter are characteristically localised and recoverable, while over the long term it is relatively frequent events of intermediate magnitude that condition progressive evolution of the river network at the system scale (Hey, 1997). This leads to consideration of the morphology and sediment supply driver in terms of adjustment of the fundamental properties of channel-floodplain system to changes in the regimes of both flow and sediment. In this respect, it should be emphasised that many sedimentary features of the UK landscape are linked to the legacy of quaternary deglaciation and the history of human land-use, notably deforestation, which may have sensitised the landscape to both historic and future climate change (Macklin *et al.*, 2000). This emphasises the importance of the morphology and sediment supply pathway drivers and emphasises that models of river channel adjustment must be treated with some caution.

Mode of operation

This driver operates in two ways. First, flow regime and sediment supply influence river processes and, hence, flood levels and, second, these direct influences on flood level are subsequently modified by morphological responses in the channel-floodplain system (which depend on these controlling variables, but which themselves also drive changes in flood levels).

*Table 6.1. Modified from Schumm (1969) for a UK context. The response of four key morphological variables to changes in the discharge of sediment (Q_s) and water (Q_w). + indicates increase, ++ a strong increase, − a decrease, −− a strong decrease, · a negligible change and * an unpredictable response*

Driver	Adjustment	Example of change	Relationship to RASP Flood Risk in terms of standard of protection and condition (Chapter 22)
$Q_s.,Q_{w++}$	$\rightarrow$ s_-, D_+, d_+, w_{++}	Long-term effect of urbanisation is an increased frequency and magnitude of runoff, generally leading to channel erosion	Widening and deepening of the channel will lead to a degradation in condition (i.e. defence failure)
$Q_s.,Q_{w+}$	$\rightarrow$ s_-, D_+, d_+, w_+	Initial response to increase in catchment vegetation cover through afforestation. Land preparation generally increases discharge but may either increase or decrease sediment delivery according to nature of management. May lead to widening of channel as mean discharge and/or frequency of bankfull channel increases. No necessary increase in sediment delivery, which is why only a small increase in Q_w may increase w	Widening and deepening of the channel may lead to a degradation in condition (i.e. defence failure)
Q_{s--},Q_{w-}	$\rightarrow$ s_-, D_+, d_+, w^*	Longer term response to increase in catchment vegetation is a net negative effect on water balance and a major reduction in sediment delivery. Effect on width determined by the relative effects of reduction in sediment discharge and water discharge	Difficult to be certain of RASP implications as it depends on relative magnitudes of driver effects, which will be catchment specific
$Q_s.,Q_{w+}$	$\rightarrow$ s_-, D_+, d_+, w_+	Increase in runoff due to more frequent extreme events. System is supply limited, so the amount of sediment delivered does not change excessively. In this case, the increase in Q_w will dominate and both d and w will increase	Widening and deepening of the channel may lead to a degradation in condition (i.e. defence failure)
Q_{s+},Q_{w+}	$\rightarrow$ s_-, D_*, d_-, w_*	Increase in runoff due to more frequent extreme events. Overland flow increases erosion of surface sediment (e.g. observations for the Yorkshire Ouse system suggest a rapid increase in sediment delivery above a critical surface erosion threshold). Thus, system is transport limited and an increase in Q_s will dominate over the increase in Q_w. Generally, d will decrease. w may increase or decrease depending upon the nature of the river bank. Feedback effects of D and s may make both of these responses difficult to predict. The response of D is also difficult to predict as it depends on the type of sediment delivered to the reach of river under consideration	Difficult to be certain of RASP implications as it depends on relative magnitudes of driver effects, which will be catchment specific. However, reduction in depth is likely to reduce standard of protection. If sediment aggradation leads to channel widening (notably in situations where there are high rates of gravel delivery leading to mid-channel bar development), then there may be degradation in condition

RASP = risk assessment of flood and coastal defence for strategic planning

The morphological characteristics of a river system respond to changes in the input regimes of sediment (Q_s) and water (Q_w) (Schumm, 1969). Table 6.1 shows that river response is sensitive to how changes in the water and sediment regimes relate to each other.

Channel response to an increase in the frequency of bankfull discharge coupled to a possible increase or decrease in sediment delivery can be expressed in terms of the degrees of freedom of channel response. Hey (1997) identifies the following degrees of freedom of a river response:

1. average bankfull width (w);
2. average bankfull depth (d);
3. maximum depth (d_{max});
4. bedform height (Δ);
5. bedform wavelength (λ);
6. bed slope (s);
7. velocity (v);
8. sinuosity (p);
9. meander arc length (z).

It is important to add to these changes in surface sedimentology (D), which may also adjust. These degrees of freedom demonstrate why changes in river morphology will influence flood risk. For instance, an increase in average bankfull flood width implies bank erosion, which may lead to fluvial attack and breaching of linear flood defences. Table 6.2 lists the possible range of responses in relation to the above degrees of freedom. However, in most UK catchments, management and engineering constrain the river in some respect and it is unlikely that responses will be distributed between all nine degrees of freedom. Consequently, responses will be concentrated in those dimensions that the river is free to adjust and they may be exaggerated accordingly. In practice, the timing and sequence of morphological adjustments that occur in response to changes in the flow and sediment regime tend to be not only complex (Hey, 1997), but also site specific and

Table 6.2. Possible responses of variables, in relation to differing levels of constraint, to the process drivers Q_w, Q_s and D (modified from Hey, 1982)

Degrees of freedom	Variables that respond	Variables assumed to be fixed	Process drivers	Type of channel
2	v, d	$w, d_{max}, \Delta, \lambda, s, p, z$	$Q_w, (D)$	Fixed bed channel. Adjustment to Q_w through change in flow velocity or water depth
3	v, d, s	$w, d_{max}, \Delta, \lambda, p, z$	$Q_w, Q_s, (D)$	Sediment and mobile bed, with streamwise slope changes as a result
5	v, d, w, d_{max}, s	Δ, λ, p, z	$Q_w, Q_s, (D)$	Possible bank erosion and bar deposition as well as mobile bed and slope change
7	$v, d, w, d_{max}, \Delta, \lambda, s$	p, z	$Q_w, Q_s, (D)$	As above, but with additional changes in bedform properties, but no major planform change
9	$v, d, w, d_{max}, \Delta, \lambda, s, p, z$	–	$Q_w, Q_s, (D, S_v)$	Fully unconstrained channel

context related, making them complex and difficult to predict *a priori* (Richards and Lane, 1997).

There is, however, a wealth of literature (Blench, 1966; Hey, 1982, 1997; Hey and Thorne, 1986) that has established hydraulic geometry relationships between the morphological attributes of the channel once adjustment is complete and the controlling discharge and sediment regimes, represented by the bankfull discharge (Q_b) and associated sediment load (Q_s) (Hey, 1997). Given the importance of bed material size, D, it is common practice to characterise river adjustment to Q_b and Q_s in sand-bed, gravel-bed and cohesive channels, separately. Results are summarised by Blench (1966) for sand-bed channels and Hey and Thorne (1986) for gravel-bed channels. The equilibrium dimensions of channels with cohesive beds are less well-explored, but there has been research into tidal channels, with cohesive boundaries that allows similar relationships to be derived.

Consideration of hydraulic geometry relations for alluvial channels that have adjusted to the prevailing flow and sediment regimes leads to a summary of the mode of operation of this process driver. First, both sand and gravel-bed channels demonstrate a strong dependence of width on bankfull discharge. Thus, if either the climate change or land-use change drivers (see Table 6.1) result in an increase in the magnitude and/or frequency of storm runoff, the eventual outcome will be wider channels, which will tend to increase conveyance capacity, but which may also degrade the condition of flood defence assets along the river. The extent to which the condition of flood defences is impacted depends upon the distance from the river bank to the defence, as well as the degree and rate of widening. For example, Fig. 6.1 shows the results of a geomorphological audit of the non-tidal River Ouse, North Yorkshire. In the upper reach the set-back distance to the flood embankment is small and bank erosion is severe, leading to a higher probability of significant deterioration in defence condition. This finding highlights the advantage of setting back embankments and making space for river adjustments as part of sustainable flood management.

Second, an increase in the magnitude and/or frequency of bankfull discharge will also result in increased channel depths, the effect being greater in channels with finer bed grain sizes. While this will increase conveyance and improve the standard of protection, it may also degrade defence condition through promoting bank failures due to toe scour and by undermining flood defences.

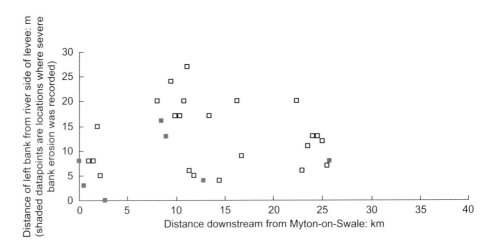

Fig. 6.1. Plot of the distance of the left embankment from the riverbank edge versus distance downstream from Myton-on-Swale, North Yorkshire. Shaded datapoints show locations where severe bank erosion was also noted

However, Table 6.1 also indicates that if an increase in the quantity and/or calibre of sediment delivered to a reach accompanies an increase in storm runoff, this could counteract the expected increase in depth, leading to aggradation, elevated water levels for a given discharge and a marked increase in the probability of flooding. The effect might be exacerbated in channels where the width and planform are fixed by bank protection works, as channel responses will be constrained to adjustments of bed elevation and composition. Historically, little attention has been given to the impact of bed-level adjustments on flood risk (Stover and Montgomery, 2001) but this is now changing. For example, Pinter and Heine (2005) showed that water levels have systematically risen for specific discharges in the lower Missouri River during the twentieth century due to reductions in channel size associated with sedimentation. As a result, discharges that were conveyed within the channel during the early twentieth century now lead to floodplain inundation, and the most extreme floods have stages up to 3.7 m higher than at the beginning of the period of record. Similarly, in the UK, Harvey (2002) reported that long-term morphological response to a major input of sediment to Bowderdale and Langdale Becks in the Howgill Fells, northern England, involved partial stabilisation of associated sedimentation zones rather than downstream progradation/migration of the excess sediment. In the UK, and especially in upland and piedmont zones, this situation may be the norm, as one legacy of quaternary environmental change and human activities during the Holocene is the presence of significant amounts of erodible sediment and catchments with land-uses that have sensitised the landscape to climate change (Macklin and Lewin, 2003). It follows that the sediment supply element of this driver may be equally as important as the component dealing with morphology and that further research is required to elucidate the impacts of climate change and land-use management on upland sediment yields, as well as catchment runoff.

Morphology, sediment supply and foresight scenarios

Table 6.3 shows estimates of driver changes under each of the Foresight scenarios. It is likely that channel widening and deepening will occur in all scenarios, but the extent and severity vary between scenarios depending on upstream sediment supply, prevailing policies with regard to river management and the relative importance placed on channel stabilisation to protect floodplain assets versus allowing fluvial systems to adjust naturally to the changing flow and sediment regimes. These are factors that are strongly related to the Foresight future that is envisaged.

Uncertainty

There is considerable uncertainty surrounding morphology and sediment supply as a driver of flood risk change. In essence, uncertainty stems from four (consecutive) sources:

1. the degree and rate of change in flow and sediment regimes;
2. the nature, extent and rate of morphological response in terms of deepening, widening, etc.;
3. the impact of morphological responses on channel conveyance capacity and hence on flood levels and probabilities;
4. the impact of morphological adjustments on the condition of flood defences and, therefore, on their performance under load.

Uncertainties stemming from these sources are compounded by marked geographical variability in sediment availability, both within and between river catchments, which may be the prime determinant of how sediment supply responds to changes in climate and land-use.

Table 6.3. Driver changes under different Foresight scenarios: morphology and sediment supply

Scenario	Driver change		Comments on trends and degree of driver change and impact
	2050s	2080s	
World markets	Channel widening, limited to undefended sites. Channel deepening throughout, except where major increases in sediment delivery result	Severe channel widening, limited to undefended sites. Channel deepening perhaps reaching maximum levels, except where major increases in sediment delivery result	Channel widening and deepening occurs. For the 2050 time slice, this is likely to be in equal measure. However, there is a limit to the amount of over-deepening that might be expected, and a link between over-deepening and bank instability due to the maximum possible riverbank height before failure occurs. Thus, channel widening is likely to be very serious, channel deepening less so. However, under this scenario, the emphasis on environmental control, and the reduced emphasis on environmental protection, may allow increased protection from bank erosion, provided the trend towards 'individual responsibility' is not too high. This observation is strongly conditional upon how future climate changes impact indirectly upon sediment delivery which may actually result in net channel aggradation if future sediment delivery rates are sufficiently high
National enterprise	Channel widening, limited to undefended sites. Channel deepening except where major increases in sediment delivery result	Channel widening, limited to undefended sites. Channel deepening throughout, except where major increases in sediment delivery result	Strong emphasis upon environmental security means continued use of floodplain defence systems where sites are defended. Undefended sites may become defended where necessary. This is aided by an emphasis upon maintaining, refurbishing and converting existing structures (i.e. through improving standard of protection and condition where necessary)
Local stewardship	Channel widening. Channel deepening except where major increases in sediment delivery result	Severe channel widening in some locations. Channel deepening, except where major increases in sediment delivery result	Local response to local problems means that problems are dealt with in a piecemeal fashion, reinforced by reduced public funding for public services. Lack of system-scale river management leads to progressively more severe river system responses and possibility of serious river management problems in isolated areas
Global sustainability	Channel widening at all sites. Channel deepening at all sites, except where major increases in sediment delivery result	Serious channel widening. Channel deepening at all sites, except where major increases in sediment delivery result	Strong planning controls plus an emphasis on biodiversity mean a progressive retreat from river management as they are allowed to behave in a more natural way, such that widening and deepening are allowed. Effects are progressive in the case of widening due to progressive increase in the frequency of bankfull discharge events

Conveyance

Definitions

Conveyance is an important pathway driver representing the retarding effects of both channel and floodplain vegetation and micro-morphology on the dynamics of inland flood flows. Conveyance in the great majority of river channels in the UK is affected by both vegetation and micro-morphology. Vegetation may be found in any or all of the aquatic, in-stream, riparian and floodplain elements of most fluvial systems. Likewise, local topographic variability in the bed, bank and floodplain surfaces is a feature of all natural and most engineered rivers as a result of grain organisation (e.g. dunes in sand-bed rivers and pebble clusters in gravel-bed rivers), bank irregularities (e.g. scour pockets, failure scars and slump debris) and flood-plain terrain (e.g. sloughs, swales and scroll bars). Fundamentally, vegetation and micro-morphology impact upon flood conveyance in similar ways. First, vegetation and micro-morphology both roughen the surface over which the floodwater flows to increase skin friction, while also introducing form drag. For instance, in relation to flow over a gravel surface, Lane *et al* (2004) show how large gravel particles shift the plane of maximum fluid shearing above the bed, resulting in a net reduction in downstream flux. Second, they further reduce downstream flow momentum by acting as a source and a sink for turbulent velocity fluctuations, which increases the effective drag upon water flow.

Thus, the major effect of vegetation and micro-morphology is to reduce reach-scale conveyance, which has implications for water levels and flood routing. However, these same attributes also significantly enhance river and floodplain habitats, by creating complex flow structures and morphological diversity that provide a range of velocity-depth environments, cover from predators and refugia during floods and droughts. Historically, engineering-led approaches to vegetation management have focused on controlling its spread, cutting its foliage or removing it all together, but the growth of a more holistic approach to river management, coupled with the desire to restore biodiversity and the statutory requirement to attain good ecological status, have led to re-evaluation of operations and maintenance. Current and future developments in river operations delivery are, and continue to be, aimed at making maintenance sustainable: that is cost-effective, environmentally sound and socially equitable. Consequently, there will be strong links between the conveyance driver and process (e.g. climate change), as well as socio-economic drivers (e.g. public attitudes and expectations).

Mode of operation

The mode of operation of this driver is described separately for vegetation and micro-morphology. With respect to vegetation, most research has concluded that flood conveyance capacity is reduced by the presence of vegetation and that this effect can be represented through an increase in either the global flow resistance parameter (Manning's n or Darcy–Weisbach f) or the effective roughness height of the boundary material (k_s). Indeed, it has been suggested that changes in vegetation can have a far greater effect on conveyance than can other components of resistance, such as the bed material size (Kutija and Hong, 1996).

However, the amount by which vegetation increases flow resistance varies with the degree of bending of the plant stems, which leads to vegetative roughness decreasing as flow velocity increases (Wu *et al.*, 1999). This is important as it leads to a non-linear relationship between discharge and resistance, with channels becoming more efficient hydraulically at higher flows due to plants flexing and eventually lying prone.

Empirical approaches have been proposed to describe vegetation roughness (e.g. Wu *et al.*, 1999; Kouwen and Fathi-Maghadam, 2000), but it may be preferable to estimate vegetative roughness using a more physically-based analysis (see Lane and Hardy (2002) for a recent review). The fact is, however, that at present it remains difficult to generalise the effects of vegetation on flood hydraulics, although an increase in vegetation density, extent or stiffness is widely accepted to lead to a decrease in flood conveyance capacity.

Vegetation has links with other drivers that could be potentially important. For example, the density and extent of vegetation in a river is affected by a number of abiotic factors, and notably the concentration of atmospheric carbon dioxide and temperature. It follows that in futures with high CO_2 emissions and a longer growing season, greater amounts of vegetation must be expected. The impact will, however, be somewhat species dependent. Similarly, environmental regulation may be expected to promote the extent and range of vegetation found along the UK's river systems, at least in the more environmentally-aligned futures. Conversely, urbanisation will normally lead to a net loss of riparian and floodplain vegetation. Also, vegetation is itself an important component of the river ecosystem and is, therefore, an important receptor that will in future affect the consequences as well as the probability of flooding.

Micro-morphology affects flow conveyance through its impacts on flow resistance at scales smaller than that represented by the reach-scale morphology. The topography of roughness at the channel boundary is usually represented in terms of skin friction that generates fluid shearing in the boundary layer. To account for the effects of micro-morphology the skin friction term is augmented, normally implicitly, to represent the resistance effects of:

1. details of bed, bank and floodplain geometry that are not represented in surveyed cross-sections;
2. effects of vertical and lateral components of mass and momentum flux on the downstream flux;
3. turbulent velocity fluctuations associated with eddies in extracting momentum from the mean flow and dissipating it at smaller spatial scales.

Terms 2 and 3 reflect the common assumption that three-dimensional flow and turbulence can be treated as a net increase in the effective boundary roughness in a one-dimensional hydraulic model. This is problematical because the effects of micro-morphology in generating flow resistance vary as a complex and non-linear function of the velocity field. However, for practical river risk management purposes it is necessary to predict flood stages on the basis of available data defining channel geometry and bed roughness. Thus, conventional flow resistance parameters, such as Manning's n and Darcy–Weisbach f are, strictly, measures of effective hydraulic resistance rather than boundary roughness itself. Furthermore, both n and f have a strong dependence on the hydraulic radius, R. Knight (2001) notes that this can result in an odd situation when water levels reach bankfull, floodplain flow begins and there is a sudden increase in the wetted perimeter. This results in an effective reduction in R, and hence n or f, when floodplain inundation actually results in a *net increase* in flow resistance due to higher relative roughness on the floodplain and lateral shearing between the channel and the floodplain flows. Thus, using the conventional Manning or Darcy–Weisbach equations may be inappropriate when accounting for micro-morphology on the relationship between flood discharge, conveyance and water level.

An alternative approach to specification of global values of n or f is based upon the concept that roughness derived from multiple sources is *additive*. For example, Cowan (1956), suggested supplementing the roughness due to the skin friction of individual grains (n_0) with that due to bed geometry (n_1), cross-section morphology (n_2), obstructions in the flow, such as boulders or islands (n_3) and vegetation (n_4). These values may then be scaled by m to represent the effects of channel curvature to produce:

$$n = (n_0 + n_1 + n_2 + n_3 + n_4)m \tag{1}$$

This expression recognises that the effective roughness of a river depends upon the scale over which it is measured. However, the question remains of how this approach can be used to estimate the contribution of a given source of flow resistance (such as micro-morphology) on n.

The current approach to answering this question rests on calculating cumulative resistance for different parts of the river-floodplain cross-section separately and then introducing appropriate interfacing between them to account for lateral transfers of water and momentum. Thus, cross-sections are divided into sub-areas termed panels and the discharge of each sub-area is calculated and then summed to give the total discharge, e.g. Knight (2001). This approach is especially useful in the case of over-bank flood flows, when there is water in both the main channel and on the floodplain, and where retardation of flow on the floodplain surface is significantly greater than that in the channel due to the presence of vegetation on the floodplain and/or the greater relative roughness due to the shallower floodplain flows. A little recognised drawback of the approach is, however, that, due to non-linearity in the relation between flow resistance and hydraulic radius, when used in a hydraulic model, the sum of the panel discharges may not actually match the total discharge in-coming from upstream, leading to models that fail to conserve the mass of water in the system (Garbrecht and Brown, 1991). It may be concluded that, while the nature and spatial distribution of micro-morphology between the channel and its floodplain are unlikely to change radically in the future, achieving a better understanding of flow resistance due to micro-morphology and developing improved ways of accounting for its affects on flood conveyance will remain important research goals.

In acting as a factor affecting the conveyance driver of changes in future flood risk, the importance of micro-morphology is closely related to its role in providing river habitats (Crowder and Diplas, 2000), and the emphasis that is placed on promoting improved habitats and biodiversity relative to that placed on using structural solutions to flood problems, which involve increasing conveyance by reducing flow resistance, enlarging the channel or embanking the floodplain. Micro-morphology is a natural attribute that is ubiquitous to most rivers and floodplains, but structural flood management approaches either reduce local morphological diversity or isolate the channel from its morphologically-contrasting floodplain to damage or eliminate in-stream, riparian and floodplain habitats in ways that are likely to be unacceptable in the more environmentally aligned futures. For this reason, there will also be interaction with the environment, eco-systems and habitats driver. Conversely, climate-related changes in rainfall and runoff are unlikely to result in significant changes in micro-morphology and, hence, climate-related impacts on flood risk by way of changes in micro-morphology are likely to be minor relative to those of changes in vegetation.

This treatment of the mode of operation of the conveyance driver has made no distinction between instream and floodplain conveyance. However, this distinction is important within the context of flood management using structural defences. In protected reaches, the key issue is the extent to which conveyance between the defences changes, as this will affect the standard of protection. Where linear defences are located adjacent to the channel, the standard of protection will be particularly sensitive to the effects of instream vegetation and micro-morphology in reducing conveyance. Conversely, floodplain vegetation and micro-morphology will become the crucial factor affecting coneyance where defences are set back. In the latter case, the conveyance driver interacts strongly with the rural land-use management driver.

Conveyance and Foresight scenarios

Table 6.4 summarises how the water levels may respond to changes in conveyance under the four Foresight scenarios. In general, reductions in conveyance will lead to increased flood probabilities as a result of increases in the water levels associated with events of a given return period. The driver impact will be greatest under the global sustainability scenario, where a strong emphasis on promoting biodiversity may lead to marked loss of conveyance. At the other extreme, under the national enterprise scenario, the emphasis placed on environmental security may result in river management strategies to maintain or increase conveyance through vegetation control, up to a level that is limited only by financial constraints.

Uncertainty

The conveyance driver is associated with uncertainty because the way that vegetation and micro-morphology affect flow resistance varies between different river contexts, making it difficult to predict future impacts on flood probability (scientific uncertainty), and because changes in this driver are indeterminate due to their heavy scenario dependency and the fact that they are strongly influenced by the

Table 6.4. Driver changes under different Foresight scenarios: conveyance

Scenario	Driver change		Comments on trends and degree of driver change and impact
	2050s	**2080s**	
World markets	Small increase in water levels	Increase in water levels	The progressive rise in temperature will lead to a related increase in growing season length. The reduced requirement to protect the environment will allow for greater maintenance of channel conveyance to counter this. However, the shrinking emphasis on the community may transfer costs to the individual, which will counter the growing freedom that people have to maintain the rivers that pose flood risks
National enterprise	Neutral	Slight increase in water levels	Strong emphasis upon environmental security means that maintenance of conveyance is largely achieved up to the point at which it becomes prohibitively expensive. This is facilitated by reduced supranational legislation but limited by a strong voice for local pressure groups
Local stewardship	Variable, with a tendency to slight increase	Increase in water levels	Environmental concerns are brought into people's activities, but this can lead to conflict with an individual's perceived need for protection from flooding. Conflict at the local level results in variable attitudes to maintaining conveyance. In some situations active management and maintenance remain acceptable but in others it is not. In general, a progressive reduction of conveyance occurs in line with decreasing emphasis on flood risk reduction at national and regional levels
Global sustainability	Increase in water levels	Large increase in water levels	Strong emphasis on promotion of biodiversity probably means reduced ability to maintain rivers and floodplains to maximise conveyance. Progressively increasing impact on flood risk through time due to trend of conveyance reduction, especially in previously maintained reaches

unknown (and unknowable) impacts of changes in several other important drivers (true uncertainty).

In relation to future flood risk impacts, it is possible to divide uncertainty into that associated with:

1. the probability of a specified flood level being reached due to conveyance changes;
2. the probability of a given conveyance change occurring as a function of changes in other drivers;
3. the potential of a given conveyance change occurring within the context of a given future scenario;
4. uncertainty in these uncertainties, and its change as a function of the amount of conveyance change: it is quite possible that as the amount of conveyance change increases, uncertainty also increases (e.g. depending on how river managers wish or are allowed to respond to changes in flood risk driven by changes in river conveyance).

Uncertainties stemming from these sources are compounded by the system-specific nature of flow partitioning and exchange between the channel and its floodplain, and the degree to which channel–floodplain interaction may be impeded, constrained or blocked by linear flood defences. Both these factors vary within and between river catchments and they may be key determinants of how conveyance responds to future changes in climate, catchment runoff regime, and river management policies and priorities.

Environment, ecosystems and habitats

Definitions

Environment, ecosystems and habitats is the functional label given to an increasingly important pathway/receptor driver. This reflects the fact that the last 20 years has witnessed two fundamental shifts in management priorities and policies for UK rivers. First, management priorities have shifted from anthropocentric, utilitarian needs centred using river engineering to deliver high levels of flood defence, land drainage and navigation towards achieving multi-functional goals that place these longstanding functions alongside new objectives, including those for conservation, recreation, fisheries, national heritage and ecological status. Consequently, as management priorities have evolved, the range of disciplines and specialisation directly involved in the management process has widened, and the way management performance is judged has expanded to embrace multi-criteria analyses.

Second, river management policies in the UK have come to recognise that rivers have multiple users and that the legitimate needs of all users and stakeholders must be accounted for when identifying optimal solutions to management issues and problems. This policy shift, which has been underway for some years, has recently been reinforced by the European Water Framework Directive (WFD) and the switch from flood defence to flood risk management that is promulgated through discussion documents such as 'Making space for water'. In the context of flood risk management, the drive to produce catchment flood management plans (CFMPs) for all major river basins is indicative of the holistic approach that now pervades all aspects of river management policy.

Nested within this shift in policy is explicit recognition that the fauna and flora making up the river's ecosystem constitute a valid and clearly defined 'user group'. The effect is to sharpen stakeholder appreciation of the fundamental importance of the river environment and its ability to provide the quality and range of habitats required to support the target ecosystem. This requirement is also increasingly legislated, for example under UK Habitat Regulations (1994), to protect sites of nature conservation interest, and the trend for river management to be directed by statutes designed to protect or enhance environments, ecosystems and habitats seems likely to continue.

It follows from these arguments that river environments, ecosystems and habitats have the potential to be important as a driver of future flood risks.

Driver operation

This driver directly affects an important flood pathway through its close coupling with flood dynamics in the channel, riparian corridor and the wider floodplain. It also constitutes an important receptor, as the aquatic, riparian and floodplain habitats and the ecosystems that occupy them benefit from the flood pulse advantage during moderate events, but may be damaged or destroyed by the most extreme floods. The environment, ecosystems and habitats driver also has indirect impacts on flood risk as policies and laws governing environmental regulation have important implications for the morphology and sediment supply and conveyance drivers described earlier. Thus, this driver acts to influence multiple aspects of river and floodplain management, with direct and indirect implications for future flood risk.

To understand the operation of this driver it is necessary to examine each of these three aspects of driver change and impact. The first aspect deals with institutional and legislative changes that will directly affect the degree to which future river and floodplain management can make reducing the probability of flooding its primary purpose. The second aspect deals with the indirect flood risk impacts of changes in river environments, ecosystems and habitats that act by way of changes in the river morphology and sediment supply driver. The third aspect concerns indirect flood risk impacts that act by way of their effects on Conveyance.

Future regulatory changes that influence this driver are likely to be derived from both EU and UK legislation. For instance, the UK's biodiversity action plan identifies five different floodplain habitats as priority restoration targets (lowland raised bogs, fens, reedbeds, wet woodland and grazing marsh) and lists no less than 500 existing sites of special scientific interest that require high water levels to sustain their ecosystems. Under the EU Water Framework Directive and associated laws in the UK, river basin management plans must be developed in order to meet environmental objectives for surface water, groundwater and protected areas. Each surface-water body will have hydro-morphological, ecological and water quality objectives, and these will condition management activities and constrain the engineering interventions (such as dredging or embanking) that can be invoked. While the trends established by current legislation look set to continue (and are likely to accelerate under the more environmentally aligned futures) the problem with assessing the impacts of future environmental regulation on flood risk is that they will be strongly dependent on the geographical context within which regulations are enacted. For instance, an imperative to restore wetland habitats could be achieved through a stand-alone programme aimed at protecting sites of special scientific interest (SSSIs) or it could be nested within a much broader programme of land-use change related to reform of the common agricultural policy (CAP) and a move away from intensive agriculture. While such a programme would dovetail naturally with plans to reduce downstream flood risk through increased use of catchment-wide storage, other aspects of habitat protection could exacerbate flood risk by reducing the scope for flood risk management using structural flood defences wherever they are believed to degrade the river environment – either directly through habitat loss, or indirectly through adverse impacts on reach or system-scale hydro-morphology.

In practice, consideration of issues concerning the environment, ecosystems and habitats driver will in future become inseparable from all other water resource issues, irrespective of how future scenarios unfold and, hence, this driver is a node in the framework that will link together a multitude of watery concerns. The importance of this node in terms of the priorities and practical outcomes of water resource management in the UK will, however, be expressed through environmental regulation, which is certain to vary markedly between foresight scenarios. Hence, the only sure conclusions that can be drawn regarding the operation of this driver are that its changes will be steered and conditioned by multiple issues that extend far beyond flood risk management and that it has the potential to increase or decrease flood risk, depending on the degree of integration between flood management and wider societal values, articulated through environmental regulations.

Environment, ecosystems and habitats and Foresight scenarios

Given the nature of this driver and its reliance on environmental regulation as an activating agent, it is not surprising that it is sensitive to the type of future envisaged (Table 6.5). As this driver operates in part through environmental management and its governing legislation, it is highly sensitive to future environmental values and priorities in the UK, which are heavily scenario specific. In some futures, planning for flood risk management will become fully integrated with management of environmental assets but, in others, over-reliance on providing adequate flood protection through structural defences may lead to situations where the need to conserve and enhance environmental assets is perceived as a serious constraint on the choice of flood management options that can be adopted. For example, under the world markets scenario there is a presumption that government will keep regulation to a minimum, facilitating development on floodplains and encouraging the use of structural defences to protect flood-vulnerable areas. Conversely, the presumption under the global sustainability scenario is that strengthening of trans-national and domestic legislation puts the needs of the environment ahead of those of flood defence.

However, in considering the impacts of these driver changes on national flood risk, it must be stressed that sustainable flood risk management need not necessarily require a trade-off between flood defence and environmental protection. Indeed, assuming that such a trade-off is unavoidable can give a false impression and misses the point that the two interests can interact symbiotically.

Uncertainty

This driver interacts with the morphology and sediment supply and conveyance pathway drivers, which are both associated with significant uncertainty, as described earlier. These uncertainties feed through to amplify uncertainty concerning how the indirect impacts of changes in environments, ecosystems and habitats will influence future flood risk.

Uncertainty is also high with respect to how environmental regulation will impact flood risk during the second half of the twenty-first century. Not only are impacts strongly scenario dependent, but also decisions on the implementation of environmental protection are likely to continue to be negotiated within the context of individual situations, with environmental capital often traded off against other interests in the more market-orientated scenarios. While national and trans-national regulations will be stronger and more stringently enforced in the future if sustainability is the major policy goal in river management, this may not *necessarily* constrain effective flood risk management so long as that management is properly embedded within a holistic and multi-functional catchment plan.

Uncertainty specific to the issue of environmental regulation arises because the driver assessment presented here is bound by the Foresight baseline assumption that future flood management policies, investment levels and technologies remain unchanged. The baseline assumption does not allow for the fact that more environmentally aligned approaches to flood management should emerge naturally as part of integrated catchment planning, independently of any conscious response to

Table 6.5. Driver changes under different Foresight scenarios: environment, ecosystems and habitats

Scenario	Driver change		Comments on trends and degree of driver change and impact
	2050s	**2080s**	
World markets	Reduction in environmental regulation	Reduction in environmental regulation	Reduced concern for intangible environmental benefits leads to decreased environmental regulation and greater potential for use/maintenance of structural protection from flooding, linked to development of floodplains and greater emphasis on environmental control. These trends may be countered by a growing emphasis upon the individual to provide flood protection, meaning only commercially viable types of development can occur
National enterprise	Neutral to slight increase in environmental regulation	Neutral to slight increase in environmental regulation	Regulation of the environment follows national priorities which, from past experience in the UK, means less change (recent environmental legislation in the UK has derived largely from the EU). Regulation switches towards market-based implementation with a strong regional influence. The outcome mixes a broad move towards protecting built-up areas while preserving key habitats perceived to be national assets, where environmental regulation should be enforced
Local stewardship	Variable increase in environmental regulation	Variable increase in environmental regulation	Environmental concerns are integral to all activities, but with a strong emphasis upon local planning control. Thus, while strong regulation is available, the decision whether to enforce it is taken at the local level. This leads to widespread variability in environmental regulation, with some communities stressing environmental protection and others allowing development and structural defence in the floodplain in order to promote economic growth
Global sustainability	Increase in environmental regulation	Marked increase in environmental regulation	Global sustainability implies increased supranational regulation of the environment, including protection of the global commons, maintenance of biodiversity and promotion of sustainability principles in all aspects of water resource planning and management. The outcome is for all flood alleviation schemes to be integrated into broad-scale catchment plans that prioritise environmental values and limit the scope for structural defences

increases in future flood risk, in some if not all of the futures examined in Tables 6.3 to 6.5. It is therefore by no means certain that the association between increased environmental regulation and increased flood risk implicit in the baseline assumption will persist in future, even in futures unfavourable to adoption of integrated responses to rising flood risks.

Case example: sediment delivery, morphological response and flood risk

In this section a case example from the River Wharfe in North Yorkshire is used to illustrate the potential of the morphology and sediment supply driver to increase flood risk. The example demonstrates that short-term morphological changes

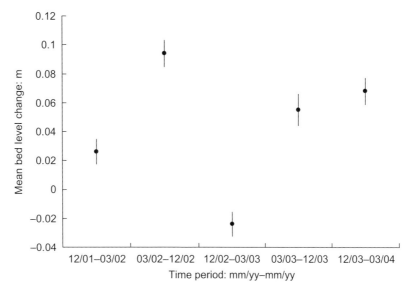

Fig. 6.2. Changes in reach- and width-averaged mean bed level from December 2001 to March 2004

involving bed aggradation due to increased sediment supply can generate increases in flood risk comparable to those expected to result from climate change up to 2050 (Lane *et al.*, in press).

Aggradation along a 6 km-long study reach of the Wharfe is apparent in both short- and long-term records of bed level (Fig. 6.2). Lane *et al.* (in press) coupled a one-dimensional hydraulic model of flow in the main channel to a two-dimensional, diffusion wave model of flow on the floodplain (after Yu and Lane, 2006a, 2006b) to simulate the effects of aggradation between December 2002 and March 2004 on the extent of inundated areas associated with the one in 0.5-year and one in two-year floods. They then compared the impacts of these bed-level changes (associated with just 16 months of morphological change through aggradation) with those expected due to climate change. For the 0.5-year event, the inundated area increased by almost 50% of the increase resulting from climate change up to the 2050s.

When the observed bed-level change was combined with forecast climate changes, the increases in inundated area were amplified over the increases associated with each change in isolation. In other words, in-channel sedimentation not only increases flood probability through its impacts on morphology and conveyance, it also increases the sensitivity of the flood system to the impacts of climate change. This occurs despite the fact that Lane *et al.*'s analysis does not account for any increases in sediment supply associated with climate change. In the upper Wharfe basin, tributary sediment supply is expected to increase markedly (Reid *et al.*, in review), constituting a powerful, positive feedback loop between the climate change and morphology and sediment supply drivers that would amplify the effects of aggradation in increasing the severity of flooding.

While this case example comes from an upland basin, the findings should be relevant to the flood risk impacts of aggradation and elevated sediment supply in UK fluvial systems more generally.

Conclusions

The two salient points to emerge from this chapter are that river processes have the potential to act directly and indirectly as significant drivers of future flood risk, and that river process drivers are associated with substantial uncertainty in terms of their modes of operation and flood risk impacts.

This chapter has highlighted that flood risk impacts arise from river processes directly, through the effects of sediment erosion, transport and deposition in altering the dimensions, geometry, and planform pattern of the channel, the relationship between the channel and its floodplain, and the likelihood of failure under load of flood defences in or adjacent to the river. The chapter has also explained that river processes can act indirectly to change flood risk through the effects of vegetation and micro-morphology on the conveyance capacity of the channel and surrounding flood-plain or engineered floodway. Consideration of the river environment, its ecosystems and habitats established that environmental regulation is likely to be expanded and strengthen in the future and put forward the argument that this could drive increases in those flood risks in futures that rely heavily on structural flood defences. In practice, tensions between environmental regulation and effective flood risk management can be avoided, provided that both are embedded within holistic catchment planning. In context of the analysis presented here, this possibility is ruled out under the baseline assumption, which makes no allowance for the evolution of more sustainable approaches to flood risk management that may occur independently of the responses to increases in future flood risk dealt with later in this volume.

Uncertainty concerning the impacts of river processes on future flood risks associated with rivers in the UK is high due to lack of knowledge (scientific uncertainty) concerning the complex interactions that exist between changes in runoff and sediment delivery, the nature of morphological responses, accurate representation of flow resistance functions and the relationship between environmental regulation, flood dynamics and flood management. In addition, the location-specific nature of detailed relationships between river processes, morphological responses and management contexts (true uncertainty) makes it extremely difficult to make general predictions of the flood risk impacts of river process drivers.

A case example from the River Wharfe demonstrates that the flood impacts of short-term morphological changes can be of the same order as those associated with climate change up to 2050, even without allowing for the amplifying affects of climate change in boosting sediment delivery.

The arguments and findings presented here emphasise the need to situate river process drivers more centrally within flood risk management, at least in terms of mapping out where in the UK issues related to morphology, sediments and ecosystems will impinge significantly on flood risk. The uncertainties revealed and discussed in this chapter also underline the need for concerted research into the river process drivers and to elucidate there impacts on future flooding.

References

Blench, T., 1966. *Mobile-bed Fluviology*, University of Alberta Press, Edmonton.

Cowan, W.L., 1956. 'Estimating hydraulic roughness coefficients', *Agricultural Engineering*, 37, 473–475.

Crowder, D.W. and Diplas, P., 2000. 'Using two-dimensional hydraulic models at scales of ecological importance', *Journal of Hydrology*, 230, 172–191.

Garbrecht, J. and Brown, G.O., 1991. 'Calculation of total conveyance in natural channels'. *Journal of Hydraulic Engineering*, 117(6), 788–798.

Harvey, A.M., 2002. 'Effective timescales of coupling within fluvial systems'. *Geomorphology*, 44, 175–201.

Hey, R.D., 1997. 'Stable river morphology', in *Applied Fluvial Geomorphology*, eds Thorne, C.R., Hey, R.D. and Newson, M.D., Wiley, Chichester, 223–226.

Hey, R.D., 1982. 'Design equations for gravel-bed rivers', in *Gravel-Bed Rivers*, eds Hey, R.D., Bathurst, J.C and Thorne, C.R., Wiley, Chichester, 553–574.

Hey, R.D. and Thorne, C.R., 1986. 'Stable channels with mobile gravel beds', *Journal of Hydraulic Engineering, American Society of Civil Engineers*, 112, 671–689.

Knight, D.W., 2001. *Conveyance in 1D River Models*, Report to HR Wallingford and the Environment Agency.

Kouwen, N. and Fathi-Maghadam, M., 2000. 'Friction factors for coniferous trees along rivers', *ASCE Journal of Hydraulic Engineering*, 126, 732–740.

Kutija, V. and Hong, H., 1996. 'A numerical model for assessing the additional resistance to flow introduced by flexible vegetation', *Journal of Hydraulic Research*, 34, 99–114.

Lane, S.N. and Hardy, R.J., 2002. 'Porous rivers: a new way of conceptualising and modelling river and floodplain flows?', in *Transport Phenomena in Porous Media, 2*, eds Ingham D.B. and Pop, I., Pergamon/Elsevier, Oxford, 425–449.

Lane, S.N., Hardy, R.J., Ingham, D.B. and Elliott, L., 2004. 'Numerical modelling of flow processes over gravelly-surfaces using structured grids and a numerical porosity treatment, *Water Resources Research*, 40, W01302.

Lane, S.N., Tayefi, V., Reid, S.C., Yu, D. and Hardy, R.J., in press. 'Interactions between sediment delivery, channel change, climate change and flood risk in a temperate upland environment', *Earth Surface Processes and Landforms*.

Macklin, M.G. and Lewin, J., 2003. 'River sediments, great floods and centennial-scale Holocene climate change', *Journal of Quaternary Science*, 18, 101–105.

Macklin, M.G., Taylor, M.P., Hudson-Edwards, K.A. and Howard, A.J., 2000. 'Holocene environmental change in the Yorkshire Ouse Basin and influence on river dynamics and sediment fluxes to the coastal zone', in *Holocene Land Ocean Interaction and Environmental Change around the North Sea*, ed. Shennan I. and Andrews, J.E., Geological Society, London. Special Publication 166.

Pinter, N. and Heine, R.A., 2005. 'Hydrodynamic and morphodynamic response to river engineering documented by fixed-discharge analysis, Lower Missouri River, USA', *Journal of Hydrology*, 302, 70–91.

Richards, K.S. and Lane, S.N., 1997. 'Prediction of morphological changes in unstable channels', in *Applied Fluvial Geomorphology*, eds Thorne, C.R., Hey, R.D. and Newson, M.D., Wiley, Chichester, 269–292.

Reid, S.C., Lane, S.N., Montgomery, D.R. and Brookes, C.J., in review. 'Climate change impacts upon coarse sediment sources and delivery within an upland catchment', paper submitted to *Earth Surface Processes and Landforms*.

Schumm, S.A., 1969. 'River metamorphosis', *ASCE Journal of the Hydraulics Division*, 95, 255–273.

Stover, S.C. and Montgomery, D.R., 2001. Channel change and flooding, Skokomish River, Washington', *Journal of Hydrology*, 243, 272–286.

Wu, F., Shen, H., and Chou, Y., 1999. 'Variation of roughness coefficients for unsubmerged and submerged vegetation', *Journal of Hydraulic Engineering*, 125, 934–942.

Yu, D. and Lane, S.N., 2006a. 'Urban fluvial flood modelling using a two-dimensional diffusion wave treatment: 1. Development of a sub-grid scale treatment', *Hydrological Processes*, 20, 1567–1583.

Yu, D. and Lane, S.N., 2006b. 'Urban fluvial flood modelling using a two-dimensional diffusion wave treatment: 1. Mesh resolution effects', *Hydrological Processes*, 20, 1541–1565.

7 Human behaviour

David J. Ball and Colin H. Green

Introduction

From a social science perspective our primary interest is in the nature of, and relationships between, individuals and groups, where those relationships notably include power and the roles of each group. It is through these relationships in particular by which we attempt to understand the world.

Thus, from a social science perspective, the Foresight 'Future Flooding' exercise is itself worthy of study as a social experience, and as an expression of the clash of what Braudel (1995) would describe as 'civilisations'; the Foresight process sought to reconcile the two quite different understandings of the world represented by the physical sciences and the social sciences. As a social process, it expressed quite different understandings of such concepts as risk, uncertainty, vulnerability and the future.

Of these two conflicting worldviews, that of the physical sciences dominated and while the determinism was reassuring we nonetheless experienced a degree of discomfort in seeking to fit our understandings into a strong physical science framework. But the challenge laid down by the physical scientists, namely, how can we predict the future and how, consequently, can we choose the future, is one which social scientists should welcome, not least because it is revealing of one's own preconceptions and assumptions.

The approach taken by the Foresight programme on flood risk management and coastal defence was anchored in an essentially deterministic worldview. This is readily apparent from the way in which the process of risk change is seen to result directly from an array of factors, physical, climatological, and even social, termed 'drivers,' whose effects on the socio-environmental system can be modelled to predict consequences.

The power of this type of approach is that change can be simulated, by computer if necessary, predictions made on the state of the future, and if the predictions are not liked, then the effect of hypothetical interventions of various kinds can be simulated by adjusting the model accordingly. Such systems, if they work, are invaluable to decision makers. Of course, it is now recognised that even those processes which are outwardly deterministic are not entirely certain or predictable, as chaos theory and even experience demonstrate. For example, the Pioneer 10 spacecraft which was launched in the 1970s and is now far beyond the orbit of Pluto, has steadily deviated by some 400 000 km from its predicted course. No one has so far been able to explain this curious behaviour (Anon., 2005). Hence, even in the presence of a seemingly deterministic system, uncertainties are present and estimating these constitutes an important element of any study including the Foresight one.

However, while the above classical worldview, which some call the Rational Action Worldview (or Paradigm, hence *RAP*) (Jaeger *et al.*, 2001), is more or less a taken-for-granted of Western thought and provides the foundation for a wide variety of institutions – markets, governments, international security, industrial management, healthcare – it is not the only conceivable theoretical approach. Indeed, behavioural and social science usually has more modest, or at least different, ambitions, recognising that human behaviour is a rather complex business and subject to influence by a vast array of factors, only some of which are amenable to deterministic-style forecasting (Eiser, 2004).

Thus, the world is taken to exist 'out there' whereas the social science approach both tends to see the world as being constructed and as being constructed through human interaction. From this viewpoint, floods are not simply extreme physical events inflicting themselves upon innocent and unsuspecting people, but highly interactive processes that involve inputs from both nature and society. As such, the very definition of a 'flood' becomes problematic. Within this framing, such complex systems are arguably more readily analysed by recourse to alternative sociological models, some of which are located in Fig. 7.1, but these could not be expected to produce the kinds of outputs demanded by the Foresight methodology. This figure can be contrasted to the models presented elsewhere in this volume.

For this reason, while bearing in mind the inevitable shortcomings of any model, an attempt was made to fashion an approach which would lend itself to Foresight as originally envisaged by its designers. In particular, in each of the four scenarios adopted in the Foresight study, the social scientist is inclined to the view that each then determines how floods will be understood, how decisions will be made, and how the flood risk will be managed. Thus, concepts such as 'vulnerability' and

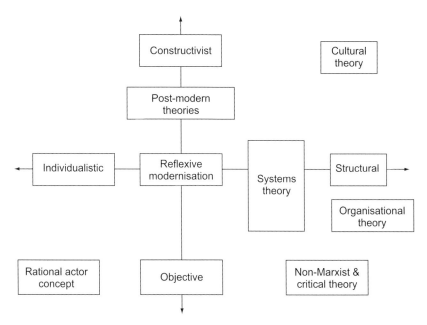

Fig. 7.1. Renn (1994) has classified the major sociological perspectives on risk according to their anchorage in a) an individualistic versus structural dimension and b) an objectivist versus constructivist dimension. The Rational Actor Paradigm of the Foresight programme inhabits the bottom left (individualistic-objective) quadrant of this classification

'risk' will be defined uniquely by each society in different ways. Rather than it being possible to define such terms as vulnerability, risk and uncertainty in ontological terms, they must then be understood epistemologically.

So, for example, a probability is a claim as to what we can know and how or why we can know it, and a claim which can properly be expressed in terms consistent with Kolmogorov's mathematics of probability. In that there are competing theories of probability, there are different claims as to what we can know and the basis upon which we can know it. In short, if we could determine which form of society would exist, then there would be no choices left to make except in that each society would be faced with resolving its own internal contradictions. Similarly, the distinction between society and technology should be regarded a false dichotomy.

The human behaviour drivers

With the above important caveat in mind, human behaviour was deemed for the purposes of this study to comprise two drivers, denoted as 'stakeholder behaviour' and 'public preferences' (attitudes and expectations). These were defined as follows.

Stakeholder behaviour

Stakeholders include any group, cohesive or dispersed, with a direct or indirect interest or influence on flood risk and its management. The public is clearly an important stakeholder but is not seen as having a single opinion. Stakeholder behaviour, expert or lay, is seen as motivated by numerous factors besides risk. These include beliefs, values, ways of working, and perceived fairness of decision processes.

Public attitudes and expectations

In line with cultural theory (Douglas, 1985; Schwarz and Thompson, 1990) the public is not regarded as a single entity with one position on matters related to flood risk. Attitudes and expectations are seen to be determined by multiple factors including actual and perceived risk, equity concerns, issues of process (i.e. the means and manner by which risk management decisions are made) and world view.

It is self-evident that these drivers are closely inter-related. The 'public' has been singled out as one stakeholder group in terms of its preferences, and is clearly one contributor to 'stakeholder behaviour' overall, which will be driven partly by public preferences. Social impacts (see Chapter 8) will clearly influence preferences, especially those of the public, and hence behaviour. Other stakeholder groups – farming, insurance, etc. – will have their own strong preferences too. Because the ways in which the livelihoods of these latter communities are linked with flood risk management are better defined, it may be expected, though is not guaranteed, that their preferences will be less diverse within their own group than those of the public at large.

This framing positions people and groups as though they were physical phenomena to be taken into account in decision making. But people differ from physical phenomena in two key aspects. First, people are the decision makers; it is out of the cognitions and relationships between individuals and groups that decisions will emerge. Second, if research is about learning, when the researcher seeks to learn about the physical world the physical world does not learn anything about the researcher. But when the researcher seeks to learn about the social world, the people studied are changed to a greater or lesser extent by the experience.

Hence, the main impact of these drivers upon flood risk is likely to be by way of their influence upon other actors, such as regulators. Thus there will be strong feedback loops, e.g. between stakeholder behaviour and regulation and other drivers. Regulators will be tuned in to stakeholder behaviour and public expectations in deciding on risk management interventions. But stakeholder behaviour and public expectations will in turn be influenced by the ways in which regulators make choices, as well as actual choices made. In turn, the roles of individuals and groups, and the inter-relations between them, are both defined by and define the society and can be taken to reflect the worldview of that society.

The concept of 'regulators' is itself predicated upon the existence of a particular form of society, being most closely associated with the form of society defined as 'national enterprise'. In the world markets model, with its emphasis upon both the market and individualism, and a desire to minimise the scope of government, the emphasis would be on the use of prices and formal regulation would be minimised. Under the purist form of cultural theory (Adams, 1995), once the nature of the society is determined, there are no choices left to make.

Overall feedback is thus strong, complicated, and perhaps even unfathomable. Furthermore, the stakeholder groups that have the most influence upon regulatory decisions, and who are therefore most likely to feel enfranchised and therefore satisfied, will vary from one Foresight scenario to another, though not in a simple or predictable way. This is because it is as much the 'fine structure' of the scenarios which will be important as their broad brush nature. Self-interest, beliefs, (dis-) satisfaction and ways of working will provide the energy to drive the stakeholder behaviour-regulation cycle, and this energy will in turn be topped up by, among other things, that stakeholder group denoted as 'the public' in the driver listing. 'Public preferences' will in turn be fuelled as much if not more by perception of the regulatory process than the actual risk, and this in its turn will be fed by other drivers such as 'institutions', 'science, engineering and technology' and 'risk compensation and insurance' through their attitudes to the public and the public's then view of their rights to involvement and say in regulatory choice.

In view of the large number of stakeholders, there are inevitably other kinds of stakeholder behaviour which will impinge on other drivers. Agricultural practices, for example, could clearly have a big impact on runoff. Similarly, the insurance industry can be regarded as a separate player or the actions of the insurance industry can be understood in relation to the actions of other players (Green and Penning-Rowsell, 2004). Notably, flooding is seen as uninsurable risk except through some form of public–private partnership (Gaschen *et al.*, 1998).

Likewise, the behaviour of the insurance sector – an essentially free market – will have an effect on what is demanded of flood risk managers. Already there is speculation that the insurance sector, faced with rising flood-related claims, might opt for novel risk-transfer or hedging instruments such as catastrophe bonds which transfer the risks to global capital markets (Linnerooth-Bayer and Amendola, 2003).

Mitchell (2003) gives the following salutary example of the complexity of stakeholder behavioural impacts, this in the context of the selection of port locations for industries:

> ... the burgeoning emphasis on port locations for industries is facilitated by changes in a complex web of factors that includes, among other things, marine transportation, navigation, and dredging technologies; shipboard labor practices; vessel registration and regulation rules; the acquisition of new electronic skills by mariners; the profitability of the shipping industry; and the state of competition between different transportation modes. In turn these components are embedded in a dominant consumer-oriented economy that is made possible by fluid supplies of investment capital and preferences for entrepreneurial risk-taking, coupled with precisely segmented and targeted marketing strategies that rely on vast quantities of timely and comprehensive information about consumer tastes and surplus income.

As Mitchell (2003) concludes, this list only begins to scratch the surface of the process that is impinging on flood and coastal processes, but it is still sufficient to demonstrate that hazard analysts and risk managers must look far beyond changes in the physical environment when contemplating effective responses to the flood-hazard conundrum.

Stakeholder behaviour

As above, stakeholders are defined as all those individuals, groups, parties or institutions with a direct or indirect, witting or unwitting, interest in or influence upon flood risk. So far as flood hazards are concerned they include an enormously wide array of public and private institutions. The professions – ranging from engineering to agribusiness, law, insurance and far beyond – also manifest as important stakeholders as they bring their own sets of interests, beliefs, values and ways of working to bear (Ball, 2000).

All stakeholder behaviour, lay and professional, will be fashioned by concerns that may be motivated by any of a variety of factors ranging from true concern about flood risk to peripheral affairs, matters of process, or old-fashioned vested interests (Ball and Boehmer-Christiansen, 2002). Behaviour will also be fashioned by beliefs and values as much if not more so than by evidence or perceived evidence (Seedhouse, 2002).

More importantly, stakeholder behaviour at the group or institutional level will have significant implications for flood risk, even though actions may apparently be far removed from the domain of flood risk and its management. Thus, competition between supermarket chains affects food-purchasing policy, which in turn affects agricultural land-use patterns and hence runoff.

'Risk' itself could even be defined in terms of the understood relationships between the different stakeholders. Rather than there being some level of 'acceptable' or 'tolerable' risk, tolerability is heavily dependent upon the way in which the risk has been managed and communicated, and certainly by the presence or absence of what have loosely been termed 'outrage' factors and the manner by which these have been dealt (Sandman, 1993; Fischhoff, 1995).

In summary, stakeholder behaviour in response to short- and long-term events will be influenced by multiple factors besides pure risk or evidence of risk of flooding. These include:

- the scope and scoping of risk decision agendas;
- the nature of decision processes;
- the institutional structure through which flood risk management is delivered;
- the forms of the conflicts and crises that confront society;
- the forms of flood risk management (including technological options) preferred and by whom;
- the trade-offs that are made with other policy areas and societal goals;
- the form of conflict resolution adopted;
- considerations of value-for-money and sensible resource allocation.

Furthermore, actions of stakeholders are not independent but permeated throughout by interactions (Jaeger *et al.*, 2001). Each stakeholder's actions will impinge upon others such that they can be expected to adjust their own positions. This could take the form of strategic manoeuvring or simply a response to new circumstances. Table 7.1 lists some of these stakeholders and gives an example of how particular interests, beliefs or values, some of which are not specifically related to flood risk itself but to other entrained aspects of the management of those risks, may figure directly or indirectly in triggering stakeholder responses.

Table 7.1. Illustrating, by way of example only, the diversity of stakeholder motivations and hence complexity of behaviour in response to flood risk management issues

Stakeholder type	Source(s) of influence
The public	Willingness to accept risk; concept of fairness; satisfaction with decision processes; trust in flood risk managing agencies; wider interests affected by flood risk management interventions such as landscape and conservation
Flood risk managers (wherever located)	Ability to communicate effectively with other stakeholders including the public; professional codes of practice (formal and informal); professional beliefs
Insurers	Attitude to flood risk premia and the extent to which these are based, or seen to be based, purely on commercial self-interest
Environmental campaign groups	Through favouring particular management regimes (for reasons only indirectly founded on flood risk concerns); exploitation of 'causes' to build solidarity
Legal profession	Promotion of flood-related litigation (in seeking out new markets to increase income generation)
Farming community	Agricultural practices in response to market forces
Media	Reporting style
Engineers	Preference for particular types of flood risk management control systems
Landowners	Willingness to accept risk; priorities that do or do not accommodate inundation
NGOs and local organisations	Specific agenda being pursued; willingness to countenance other agendas

NGO = non-governmental organisation

The importance and uncertainty of stakeholder behaviour as a driver

As a driver, stakeholder behaviour is crucially important. Unfortunately, however, those matters that drive stakeholder behaviour are widely and deeply rooted in society, are subject to disparate pressures, interact strongly with each other, and hence are not easily forecast. For example, at the practical level, the impacts of the USA 9/11 terrorist attack and asbestos-related lung disease are now having an effect upon the price and availability of insurance in totally unconnected markets. It is plausible that the current parlous state of the insurance industry is already impinging on the availability of flood risk insurance and the premia demanded.

At a deeper level, theory suggests that the real problem of risk acceptance is not the substantive issue of flood risk but the wider moral questions regarding the trade-offs involved in any particular decision choice *and* the processes by which those choices are made (Adams, 1995; Douglas, 1985). Discussions both of equity and legitimacy stress that what is understood to be a just decision depends not simply upon the outcome but also upon the process through which that decision is reached (Green, 2004). In turn, the societies in each of the different scenarios can be expected to have different understandings of both what is a just decision and what is a just decision process.

Thus, the issue is one not so much of the presence of flood hazards but of the transgression of norms to which particular social groups subscribe. Hence, to predict the future form of flood risk management would require predicting the moral norms then prevailing which will themselves be contested.

None of this suggests that stakeholder behaviour in respect of flood risks over the long term is amenable to the kind of forecasting that is applied to physical parameters of climate change. What can be said with confidence is that the struggle between competing perspectives will continue. The extent to which this struggle is

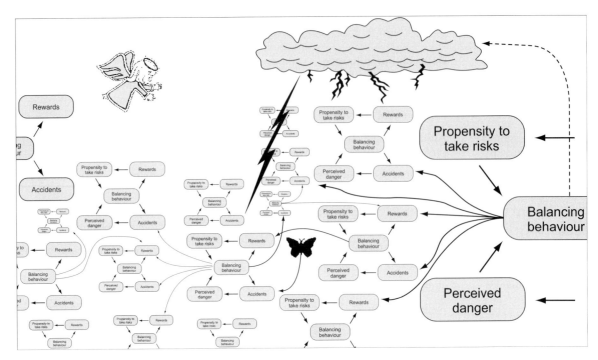

Fig. 7.2. The dance of the risk 'thermostats' (Adams, 1995), a reference to the fact that individual actors, in making decisions about risk, weigh up not just the riskiness of an activity but also its benefits, and that society is composed of countless actors all dancing to their own tunes. Predictability of outcome is therefore a matter of much faith. Hanging over all of this are the forces of nature, the Beijing butterfly (beloved of chaos theorists) and fortune

orderly or fractious, and who comes out 'on top', will depend on the attitudes and interactions of numerous stakeholder groups within each of the four Foresight scenarios. However, while each scenario provides a top-level indication of the kind of world which exists, it provides no detail of the inner-workings which would determine such attitudes. The situation is perhaps summarised by Adams' 1995 depiction of risk balancing behaviour by multiple social actors (Fig. 7.2).

Public attitudes and expectations

Public attitudes and expectations are taken here to signify preferences for particular risk management interventions and associated factors rather than personal preferences as to, for example, the desirability of living in certain types of location.

Public preferences, while originating from the public, are heavily influenced by the stances and behaviour of other stakeholders, and hence cannot be viewed in isolation. Furthermore, it is recognised that 'the public' as such does not exist in the sense of having a single position, and instead different views are to be expected. Since opinions on risk issues are always based as much (if not more) upon beliefs and values as upon facts, something that applies as much to professionals as the public (Seedhouse, 2002), it should also be conceded that multiple rationalities may well have legitimacy. Research on public attitudes to risk confirms that, while public opinions may differ from those of experts, they are nonetheless valid on their own terms (Slovic, 2002).

The most obvious ways in which public preferences are likely to influence flood risk are through public reactions to alternative flood risk management decisions to which they, or people or things they care about, are exposed. In particular, the acceptability of any imposed flood risk management regime, and its associated actual risk, will be a factor of a number of variables including the perceived risk and its tolerability, the cost of intervention and who pays, any equity issues, any undesired consequences of interventions, alternative styles of intervention and their attributes, the process by which choices are made, and trust in the 'system' including the people and institutions involved.

The importance of the latter human factors in risk decisions is high (Sandman, 1993). The fact that they are important means that the position of the public is also determined by the attitudes and behaviour of other stakeholders. Thus, the commonly-held belief that the public are now less accepting of floods than used to be the case might, supposing it is true, stem from limitations of process as much as any real or perceived increase in flood risk or concern about damage.

Public preferences are often characterised as short term, e.g. as provoked by some calamity or the way in which some incident is reported by the media, but quickly forgotten. However, lasting preferences exist too, predicated upon deeply held values changing little over time. Given that the Foresight Project is concerned with a 100-year time horizon it is tempting to consider that it is the more lasting values that are relevant. This is the line taken here. Nonetheless, if society and moral norms are compared between 1905 and 2005, there have obviously been substantial shifts and it would be brave to argue that in 1905 either drivers of those changes could have been defined or the outcome of those conflicting pressures predicted. Rather than the end of history having been reached, there is instead more history happening faster.

Public preferences should be reflected in the types of risk management strategies that are considered appropriate in response to the real and perceived hazards presented by floods and coastal erosion and their full implied range of social, environmental and economic implications. With reference to Fig. 7.3 (a much simplified version of the risk management process), public preferences should exhibit their primary impact through the process of deciding which kinds of response strategies are necessary and acceptable. Those public preferences will be expressed in quite different ways under the different scenarios. Under the world markets scenario, the public are consumers and their preferences are expressed

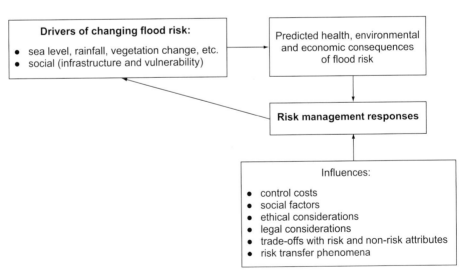

Fig. 7.3. The risk assessment–risk management cycle is subject to influence by public preferences most strongly at the risk management response stage. The degree to which this influence is deemed appropriate by 'risk managers' might differ substantially between the four Foresight scenarios

through money. Conversely, the global sustainability and local stewardship scenarios are more consistent with the current emphasis on stakeholder engagement, partnerships and governance.

Hence, the Foresight scenarios have a very significant bearing upon the kinds of decision-making approach likely to be preferred at the institutional level, and ultimately the risk management interventions deemed as necessary and acceptable. For example, Renn *et al.* (2003) distinguish five types of risk management (decision-making) strategies. These differ according to their methods of selecting objectives, assessing and handling data, and choice of procedures for balancing pros and cons. Each appraisal strategy is seen as having its own niche, depending upon three specific aspects of the hazard described as uncertainty, complexity and ambiguity.

Complexity here refers to the difficulty of identifying and quantifying causal links, especially where many drivers are involved and which may exhibit synergisms, antagonisms, feedback phenomena, long delays between cause and effect, etc. Ambiguity denotes variability of interpretations of identical data and assessments as should be anticipated in a pluralist society. The appraisal strategies are: a presumption of prevention; precautionary appraisal; extended risk assessment; discursive process; and standard risk assessment. The management strategies range from prevention, through ALARP/ALARA (as low as reasonably practicable/achievable) and BATNEEC (best available technology/technique not entailing excessive cost), to unrestricted activity. Uncertainty may be attributable to any or all of the following: variability of responses to identical stimuli (as, for example, in the extreme sensitivity to initial conditions as manifest in chaotic systems), measurement errors (due to imprecision, modelling uncertainty, extrapolation, etc.), indeterminacy and ignorance.

The four Foresight scenarios, embodying significantly different worldviews that are internally coherent, *prima facie* would result in quite different ways of handling these aspects and hence of choosing and managing risk, including both the technical means by which it is managed and the nature of the consultative process (see Fig. 7.4). However, whichever scenario (or hybrid) comes to pass, even though partially determined by public preferences, public preferences will in turn moderate. The different worldviews of the public will continue to exist in whatever future transpires, and will continue to exert their influence. So public preferences are at once a driver and a moderator of change.

The importance and uncertainty of public attitudes and expectations as a driver

This driver is of high importance because of its powerful interaction with the drivers impinging upon Regulation through which it feeds. In turn, Regulation is recognised as of high importance in all the Foresight scenarios. As evidence of the strength of the relationship between these drivers, it is pointed out that in the USA Environmental Protection Agency's (EPA's) own early and ground-breaking study of risk prioritisation, the priorities of the EPA itself were found to be driven more by public perceptions than by the EPA's own risk assessments (see, for example, HSE, 1997).

However, it is perhaps worth reflecting that this driver can act in opposite senses. The attitude of the public to a flood risk will depend on how they perceive it. Ignoring, for the moment, the dominance of outrage factors, a four-fold situation can be envisaged (Eiser, 2004):

	Risk is small	**Risk is not small**
Risk perceived as small	A Not a driver	B Is a driver
Risk perceived as significant	C Is a driver	D Is a driver

World markets

Basis for decision making	Conflict between individual interests
Mode of decision making	Political power – pork barrelling emerges with techniques such as benefit-cost analysis and multi-criteria analysis being used to justify decisions taken upon a political basis. In Reisner's words 'water will flow uphill to the money'. Emphasis on using prices to change people's behaviour
Institutional structure	Ideally, would abolish the Environment Agency but practicalities means continues in a reduced role as an enabler of flood risk management with the increased use of Framework Agreements
Ideal flood risk management option	Ideally, would like to push for flood proofing, but will then have to settle for whatever is the most effective. Minimal land use/building control. Flood management is reactive
Crises and conflicts	Between individualist ethos and economies of scale in collective action; between beliefs in small government and self-interest (i.e. when self-interest served best by collective action); between those at risk and those creating the risk
Conflict resolution	Courts
Resource use	Anything goes, but compensation for flood victims is introduced following the model in the USA and in apparent contradiction in Libertarian ideology

Global sustainability

Basis for decision making	The public good
Mode of decision making	Participatory with extensive use of benefit-cost analysis and multi-criteria analysis. A strong emphasis on communication between stakeholders
Institutional structure	Environment Agency strengthened and takes over from IDBs and also all coast projection
Ideal flood risk management option	Land use control including of agricultural land
Crises and conflicts	Between the public good and local or individual interest; between different definitions of 'equality'
Conflict resolution	The political process
Resource use	Renewable resources and recycling

National enterprise

Basis for decision making	The national interest
Mode of decision making	Technocratic, heavy reliance on mathematical modelling, optimisation, and economic analysis. A belief that the public needs to be 'educated' so as to take on the beliefs attitudes of the technicians, coupled with the use of regulations
Institutional structure	Unchanged
Ideal flood risk management option	The optimal solution
Crises and conflicts	Funding flood and coastal defence. Uncertainty will be experienced as intensely uncomfortable and treated as if it were risk (e.g. extensive use of Monte Carlo simulation) – not least because there is an assumption that reality is objectively determinable
Conflict resolution	Conflict not recognised as a formal concept since it is assumed that the national interest is objectively determinable, consensual and exists over and above individual interests. Disruptive elements will be allowed to have their say at Public Inquiries
Resource use	Availability of imports (e.g. hardwood, aggregate) determined by foreign exchange rate, probable reduction in capacity to import

Environmental imperative plus communal solidarity

Basis for decision making	Environmental imperative plus communal solidarity
Mode of decision making	Discursive; reluctance to accept that choice is inherently about conflict. Emphasis upon building social relationships and communality
Institutional structure	Abolition of the Environment Agency and replacement by local stakeholder groups similar to the Parrett Catchment Project
Ideal flood risk management option	Wetlands, source control (urban and rural), 'room for rivers'
Crises and conflicts	Between need to maintain arable land and desire for managed retreat to allow environmental recovery. Conflict itself will be experienced as intensely uncomfortable since the ethos assumes consensual processes
Conflict resolution	Mediation
Resource use	Local aggregate extraction only and possible problems for the adoption of 'big beaches' and rocky groynes; no imported hardwoods; compensation for flood victims

Fig. 7.4. Matrix summarising plausible flood management characteristics under the four future scenarios

In circumstance A, public preference is not a driver because the risk is perceived as small. In circumstance B, it is a driver of flood risk – it exacerbates it because no action is taken. In C and D, public preference will act to try to reduce risk. There are two possibilities:

1. 'do it yourself' activities;
2. apply pressure to responsible agencies.

The uncertainty associated with this driver is high. The underlying causes of apparent trends in public opinion regarding flooding, for instance, are related to perceived changes in flood risk, opinions on flood risk acceptability, procedural issues of risk management, trust in the system and other factors besides. In a political climate demanding increasing openness (which may or may not continue), greater consultation (extending to partnership in risk decisions), corporate governance and the like, expectations of management standards will increase, irrespective of whether there is demand for greater safety from flooding. Reliable models of social interactions over the long term which can be linked to flood risk preferences would be at least as complex as those established for predicting the physical dimensions of climate change, if possible at all. Such models do not exist although some sociological models are informative.

Although in no case is it easy, it would appear that some drivers (e.g. precipitation, temperature, waves and surges) are, in some sense at least, more amenable to quantification and forecast than others. In part this is because they are less closely coupled with other drivers, particularly socio-economic drivers. This is not to say that no coupling exists but that there is a difference of degree, timescale, or complexity. Furthermore, one can envisage, perhaps, how global CO_2 emissions and hence temperature etc. might vary between the designated scenarios. This suggests that drivers, like temperature, are amenable to ranking and can provide more meaningful inputs to models for each of the scenarios.

On the other hand, social drivers like public attitudes and public expectations are tightly coupled to other drivers. This presents problems, because these drivers cannot then be quantified in isolation. Such feedback phenomena are not unusual. It is well known in risk management circles in general that regulatory interventions for hazard mitigation are often subject to social responses of various kinds (Graham and Wiener, 1995). Feedback loops are also powered by other kinds of social response. According to Sandman's model of risk perception (Sandman, 1993):

$$Risk = Hazard + Outrage$$

In this formulation, 'Risk' means *risk as perceived* by the affected party, whereas 'Hazard' means actual statistical risk, and 'Outrage' is a factor based (in Sandman's account) on Slovic-style (Slovic, 2002) psychometric variables such as voluntariness, controllability, equity, openness of decision makers and characteristics of the decision process itself. Sandman asserts that Outrage factors dominate substantially over Hazard (actual risk) in determining stakeholder response to threats (e.g. exposure to flood risk).

This being the case, the acceptability of any regulatory intervention will be assessed only partially in terms of its ability to manage risk. It will be assessed mainly by the process followed to arrive at that regulatory choice, and by how it matches up against other non-technical factors. This has led some authors to talk in terms of 'procedural rationality' (Shrader-Frechette, 1993) and others to talk of 'procedural equity' (Lind and Tyler, 1988). These reactions, in turn, will fuel or not the demand for new intervention. Because this coupling is tight, it seems that it is not feasible to predict how either public expectations or intervention will affect flood risk in isolation.

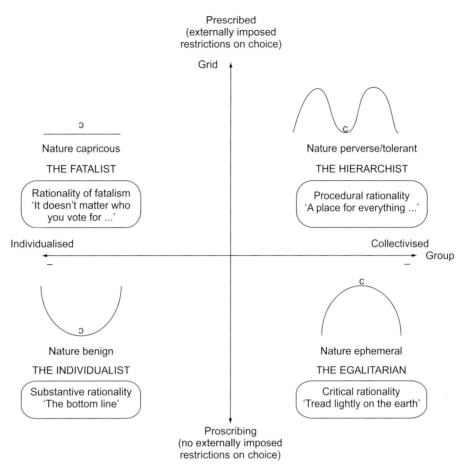

Fig. 7.5. The four cultural theory types mapped onto their views of the world in terms of threat (Schwartz and Thompson, 1990)

Sandman's model is itself an example of a rational action approach and can be contrasted with the worldview model put forward by cultural theory (Fig. 7.5). One does not need to accept cultural theory *in toto* in order to appreciate the power of this model in which risk and uncertainty are variously understood as an expectation of the world. In the bottom-right quadrant, change and risk are dominant and highly threatening; in the bottom-left quadrant, all is well in this best possible of all possible worlds.

From a different perspective, this diagram can be regarded as being underpinned by two dimensions: a vertical dimension of chaos versus optimisation, and a horizontal dimension of stability versus instability. The model in the upper-right quadrant is that of the economist in which markets are both optimising and homeostatic. Second, the other three models can be subsumed as local features within a variant of the model of the upper-right quadrant, a model of chaos and instability, without the symmetry and known topography of all four models shown. The difference between this last variant and the others is that everything is local landscape within it. The Shell approach to scenario generation is an approach based upon this last model, wherein it is recognised that we do not necessarily know even the local landscape, let alone the wider landscape. Thus, Davis (2002) argued that this approach is necessary because: 'We need to do this for a future that is essentially unknowable – but not unthinkable.' Hence, that a scenario approach is intended to explore '... the things we don't know about which might transform our business. And on the things we do know about in which there might be unexpected discontinuities. They help us understand the limitations of our 'mental maps' of the world – to think the unthinkable, anticipate the unknowable and utilise both to make better strategic decisions' (Shell International, 2001). From the Shell approach to scenario generation, the purpose of scenarios is to explore and not to predict.

The four scenarios, while providing an overarching view of society, do not attempt (unsurprisingly) to describe detailed workings, even if that were possible. For example, during the Thatcher era, in the UK, there was a strong emphasis on individual enterprise as opposed to social cohesion, but this seems to have simply polarised society rather than leading to domination by one particular ideology other than, perhaps, temporarily. Cultural Theory (Adams, 1995), which belongs in the top-right corner of Fig. 7.1, offers an explanation for this phenomenon, since it would argue that each of the four cultures depends upon the others for its own existence, and each continually changes its stance according to the stances taken by the others.

The point here is that what actually transpires in a society is not necessarily open to prediction even if the overarching perspective can be identified. The actuality derives from complex interactions between numerous actors, some knowingly in competition and others not even aware of it. This is reminiscent of, and more complex than, the notoriously difficult three-body problem that seeks a solution to the mutual gravitational interaction of three masses moving in a common plane.

In summary there are several common problems with all of the social drivers. These are:

- tight coupling with other drivers leading to;
- 'circular causality'; and
- feedback loops that may be positive or negative, stable or unstable, gently fluctuating or wildly erratic.

For these reasons, quantification of the effects of these drivers on flood risk over the next 100 years is problematic. This means neither that they are unimportant nor undeserving of serious consideration.

Forecasting the effect of the human behaviour drivers on flood risk

The serious complications with these drivers mean that their effects on flood risk cannot be forecast either quantitatively or even qualitatively. The reasons are their complexity, interaction with other drivers and the presence of strong feedback mechanisms leading to 'circular causality'.

Furthermore, each scenario sits within a global future that will influence it. Most obviously, the global markets scenario for the UK depends upon the existence of a global market. Those global forces may dominate forces within the UK. For example, in the course of the Foresight study it was argued that flood losses at any date were critically dependent upon the proportion of household income spent upon food. Hence, that the losses would be dependent upon world prices for basic foodstuffs. Looking forward a century, flood losses in the UK would then be dependent upon food prices denominated in yuan and rupees, the currencies of the then global economic superpowers, and by whether India and China will be net importers or exporters of basic food stuffs (Green, 2003). Making any detailed assessment would require predicting the comparative economic performance of the European economy versus those of India and China – and hence the exchange rate – and also of our capacity to satisfy the very high water needs of crops, together with the degree to which global diets will shift towards a meat-based diet. What

Table 7.2: Speculative driver impact for each scenario in 2050. Refer to key for explanation

Interest group	2050 world markets			2050 national enterprise			2050 global responsibility			2050 local stewardship		
	D	I	ΔR	D	I	ΔR	D	I	ΔR	D	I	ΔR
Trade organisations	↓	–	–	↓	–	–	↓	↑	X1/2	↓	↓	X1
Insurers	↓	↑	X1	↓	↑	X1	–	–	–	–	–	–
Media	↑	↑	X2	↑	↑	X1	–	↓	–	–	↓	–
Pressure groups	–	↑	–	–	↑	–	–	–	–	↓	↓	X1
Community groups	–	↓	–	–	–	–	–	–	–	↓	↑	X1/2
Government and regulators	↓	↓	–	↓	–	–	↓	↑	X1/2	↓	–	–
Operating authorities	↓	↑	–	↓	↑	X1/2	↓	↑	X1/2	↓	–	–
Legal sector	↓	↑	X1/2	↓	↑	X1	↓	–	–	–	–	–
Academia	↓	–	–	↓	↑	X1/2	↓	↑	X1/2	–	–	–
Professions	↓	↑	X1/3	↓	↑	X1/2	↓	–	–	↓	↓	–
Health care	↓	–	–	↓	↑	X1/2	↓	↑	X1/2	↓	–	–
The 'public'	↓	–	–	↓	–	–	–	–	–	↓	↑	X1/2
Food and agriculture sector	↑	↑	X2	↑	↑	X2	↑	–	–	–	↓	–
Indicative trend			X2/3			X1/8			X1/32			X1/4

Key: D = the direction (up or down) in which overall this group could tend to push flood risk compared with baseline; I = the influence this group has in the scenario compared with baseline; ΔR = the estimated risk multiplier (speculative only) compared with baseline. Note: this table includes consideration of feedback responses, e.g. under world markets a backlash can be anticipated from certain groups. As an illustration, under world markets, the professions might be expected to have grown in influence (I increasing) while wishing to improve control of flood risk (D diminishing), suggesting that a significant, downward impact upon flood risk (<1) might be sought

can be said is that the current agricultural and flood risk management policies assume that we will be able to buy foodstuffs very cheaply on the world market. However, it would be unwise to irrevocably convert any high-grade agricultural land to another use on the assumption that it will always be possible to supply our food needs from the world market.

For public expectations and attitudes, the biggest problem is the close-coupling with the regulatory stance taken and how this is perceived both in terms of risk tolerability and potential outrage factors. While it might be surmised that if the flood risk in 2050 increases by say $\times N$, then there will be a tendency to want to reduce this driver by $\sim \times 1/N$ in order to restore risk to a former, customary level (*if* other things are equal), this is not helpful for the deterministic approach followed by Foresight. In any event, this response would be tempered by public perceptions of what is reasonably achievable (the public are not as cavalier with the nation's resources as is often implied) and any other entrained interests, e.g. under a 'Green' scenario there might be a preference for natural river-scapes even if it meant more flooding. It also depends on the state of the economy. In a wealthier era it might be expected that something better than $1/N$ could be achieved and vice versa.

So far as stakeholder behaviour is concerned, the main problem is that there are so many stakeholder groups, each with their own motivational factors. Predicting the 'front runner' from such an array is hardly possible, particularly as the stakeholders interact with one another in constantly changing ways. Perhaps the best that can be done in the absence of some Isaac Asimov vision, is to consider qualitatively how each actor might fare under the different Foresight scenarios in terms of influence and in what direction they might drive flood risk (some actors might increase it, others might diminish it), and then to take an overall view on the combined impact. Table 7.2 provides an illustration based on a small group discussion. At the very least it illustrates the difficulty of the task!

Concluding remarks

The deterministic model adopted by Foresight is arguably more suited to the handling of the 'physical' drivers of flood risk and coastal erosion than it is to the 'social' drivers. This raises the issue of whether, if the policy approach requires accurate prediction, it would not be better to shift to a policy approach that does not rely upon accurate predictions.

The 9/11 Commission in the USA concluded: 'We believe the 9/11 attacks revealed four kinds of failure: in imagination, policy, capabilities and management. Imagination is not a gift usually associated with bureaucracies. It is therefore crucial to find a way of making routine, even bureaucratizing, the exercise of the imagination.' How can we plan for the future if the future is inherently unknowable and when the actions we take now are intended to change that future but will do so in ways that are not always intended?

Here, there is a gap in approach between the physical scientists, engineers – where engineers have been described as people who always have to take decisions on the basis of inadequate information and social scientists, where one engineer memorably described the problem with social scientists being that they always 'kick for touch' (i.e. play safe). Engineers have to do something now about the risk of flooding and coastal erosion while the social scientist tends instead to want just to study it.

While we failed to give the physical scientists the answers to the questions they asked, we question whether they were asking useful questions: those for which there is an answer that can be applied. While the social scientist here tends to talk about learning and adaptive management, the challenge is to convert these concepts into frameworks for action.

References

Adams, J., 1995. *Risk*, UCL Press, London.

Anon., 2005. *New Scientist*, 4 June, 33.

Ball, D.J., 2000. 'Ships in the night and the quest for safety', *J. Injury Control and Safety Promotion*, 7(2), 83–96.

Ball, D.J. and Boehmer-Christiansen, S., 2002. *Understanding and Responding to Societal Concerns*, HSE Research Report No. 34, HSE Books, Sudbury.

Braudel, F., 1995. *A History of Civilisations*, trans. Mayne, R., Penguin, Harmondsworth.

Davis, G., 2002. *Questioning Assumptions – exploring alternative business futures.* London: Shell.

Douglas, M., 1985. *Risk Acceptability According to the Social Sciences*, Russell Sage Foundation, New York.

Eiser, J.R., 2004. *Public Perception of Risk*, Report for Foresight Office of Science and Technology, OST, London.

Fischhoff, B., 1995. 'Risk perception and communication unplugged: twenty years of process', *Risk Analysis*, 15(2), 137–146.

Gaschen, S., Hausmann, P., Menzinger, I. and Schaad, W., 1998. *Floods – an insurable risk*, Swiss Re, Zurich, available online www.swissre.com

Graham, J.D. and Wiener, J.B., 1995. *Risk versus Risk – tradeoffs in protecting health and the environment*, Harvard University Press, Cambridge, MA.

Green, C.H., 2003. 'Change, risk and uncertainty: managing vulnerability to flooding', paper to 3rd Disaster Risk Management Conference, Kyoto, available online http://idrm03. dpri.kyoto-u.ac.jp/proceedings.htm

Green, C.H., 2004. *Water, Economics and Ethics*, UNESCO, Paris.

Green, C.H. and Penning-Rowsell, E.C., 2004. 'Flood insurance and government: "parasitic" and "symbiotic" relations', *The Geneva Papers on Risk and Insurance – Issues and Practice*, 29(3), 518–539.

Health and Safety Executive (HSE), 1997. *Risk Ranking*, Report No. 131/1997, HSE Books, Sudbury.

Jaeger, C.C., Renn, O., Rosa, E.A. and Webler, T., 2001. *Risk, Uncertainty and Rational Action*, Earthscan, London.

Lind, E.A. and Tyler, T.R., 1988. *The Social Psychology of Procedural Justice*, Plenum, New York.

Linnerooth-Bayer, J. and Amendola, A., 2003. 'Introduction to special issue on flood risks in Europe', *Risk Analysis*, 23(3), 537–543.

Mitchell, J.K., 2003. 'European river floods in a changing world', *Risk Analysis*, 23(3), 567–574.

Renn, O., 1994. 'Concepts of risk: a classification', in *Social Theories of Risk*, eds Krimsky, S. and Golding, D., 53–79, Praeger, Westport, CT.

Renn, O., Stirling, A., Muller-Herold, U., Morosoni M. and Fisher, E., 2003. *The Application of the Precautionary Principle in the European Union: Regulatory strategies and research needs to compose and specify a European policy on the application of the precautionary principle (PrecauPri)*, Centre for Technology Assessment, Stuttgart, available online www.sussex.ac.uk/spru/environment/precaupripdfs.html

Sandman, P.M., 1993. *Responding to Community Outrage: Strategies for effective risk communication*, American Industrial Hygiene Association, Washington, DC.

Schwarz, M. and Thompson, M., 1990. *Divided we Stand: Redefining politics, technology and social choice*, Harvester Wheatsheaf, New York.

Seedhouse, D.F., 2002. *Total Health Promotion – Mental health, rational fields and the quest for autonomy*, Wiley, Chichester.

Shell International, 2001. *Energy Needs, Choices and Possibilities: Scenarios to 2050*, Shell, London.

Shrader-Frechette, K.S., 1993. *Burying Uncertainty*, UCLA Press, Los Angeles, CA.

Slovic, P., 2002. *The Perception of Risk*, Earthscan, London.

8 Socio-economic drivers, cities and science

Colin H. Green and Edmund C. Penning-Rowsell

Introduction

In many senses socio-economic forces and factors are not true drivers of flood risk in that they principally affect receptors, rather than sources. Also, it is difficult to see the economy or social aspects as factors that are autonomous from responses, in that these impacts reflect a lack of response. Moreover, it would take a great deal of research and effort to determine fully the effect of social processes on flood risk, society being more unpredictable than, say, channel flow.

Given this, we have looked at just three areas where aspects of social process affect flood risk. These are social impacts of floods on people (Tapsell et al., 2002), the economic impacts on different sectors (Penning-Rowsell and Chatterton, 1977; Parker et al., 1987; Penning-Rowsell et al., 2003) and the questions of urban impacts and infrastructure development and their effects on flood risk (Parker, 1995a).

Social impacts

Definition and operation

The 'social impacts of flood risk' is something of a catch-all term. It embraces the risk to life, being the conditional chance of death should a flood occur which varies dramatically between contexts from around 1 in 10 000 in most floods to roughly 1 in 10 in other circumstances (Bennet, 1979). It can also include all of the unpriced or 'intangible' impacts of flooding on households, specifically to include the stress, the damage to health and quality of life, and the sheer disruption caused by flooding (Tapsell et al., 2002). In particular, it is used to include the variations in the vulnerability of different community groups (RPA/FHRC, 2004). In addition, the term also can be used to describe the impact on the long-term viability of a community if some activities permanently leave the area as a result of a flood problem (Thompson et al., 1991).

In terms of how this driver operates, the impacts of flooding on the population are entirely irrelevant in the world markets scenario: in the libertarian worldview, individuals are solely responsible for taking action to manage risks (Landes, 1998). Given also that 'nature' is seen as both there for human exploration and as to be conquered, those who fail are morally inferior. Those who are flooded and do not recover rapidly and easily will thus be regarded both by others and themselves as moral failures.

In practice, there is likely to be a split between the 'deserving' and 'undeserving' poor. The former are those who have fallen on hard times through no fault of their own; in the latter, poverty is a sign of a lack of moral worth since all, it is believed, could succeed if they really tried. The defining characteristic of the deserving poor is then that they have identifiable physical or mental restrictions that limits their capacity. The government will be expected to provide this group with aid and support. Hence, the aged and those with relatively common disabilities, particularly those associated with degenerative diseases, are likely to be provided with help.

This help is likely to be in the form of helping hands such as soft loans and medical care (North, 1990). Support through charities will also be available. Since there is no necessary relationship between the scale of the problem and the income of a charity, help will be very unevenly distributed: furry pets and children are likely to be particular beneficiaries. The political influence of those charities will also influence the nature and targets of what government help is available. However, most voluntary bodies, such as the Red Cross, will lose support as the sense of community weakens.

Single parents, those with low incomes, and the poorly educated will be seen as the undeserving poor; as being poor as a result of their moral failings. There is likely to be some latent if not explicit racism. However undeserving these poor are, and the expectation is of a widening underclass, fears of riots are likely to result in a minimum safety net being provided. This will be in the form of means tested aid.

The existence of a large underclass will be accepted. This underclass will be poor, poorly educated, have low self-esteem, weak kinship links and very little in the way of community organisation. Indeed, the strongest form of community organisation will probably be gangs. A significant proportion of this population will have a criminal record. Loosening labour laws will mean that those in this underclass who have jobs will probably lose them in a flood. While the broad ideology in the national enterprise scenario is similar, the practicalities differ in details. Pressure groups will be more likely to capture government policy and help will be provided through bureaucratic social services.

The ethos of communal solidarity, in the face of natural disasters, that characterises the global sustainability scenario results in efforts to identify those who are most vulnerable, those who are least able to cope with both the risk of flooding and the occurrence of flooding. Whereas, in the former two scenarios, vulnerability is defined solely in terms of personal characteristics and in moral terms, in this scenario vulnerability will be defined in social terms and by their conditions more than by individual characteristics. While under the two previous scenarios, single parents will be regarded, particularly if the children were not born in an apparently stable relationship, as morally defective, here they will be seen as victims of their former partner or the conditions under which they were brought up. Therefore, those who are socially disadvantaged will be defined as the 'vulnerable' with both disaster relief and action to reduce the risks being targeted at them.

At the same time, the stress on a communitarian ethos will result in an emphasis on developing informal communal organisations. Some of these organisations will be 'virtual', existing as electronic communities. One outcome is that friendship links are maintained even though mobility is high. These informal and virtual communities will assist in disaster relief and the emphasis on communal solidarity is likely to result in some form of voluntary disaster relief corps being established. Overall, the impacts of floods on people will be less, both because they are more able to cope with those floods and because they receive more effective recovery assistance.

Regional patterns, exceptional locations and driver importance

The risk to life in a flood is largely determined by the velocity of flow (Jonkman *et al.*, 2002; Penning-Rowsell *et al.*, 2005) so the risk to life is greatest in small, flashy catchments and behind fixed defences if those defences fail. In addition, occupied areas below ground level obviously pose a potentially catastrophic risk; underground stations are an obvious example but so too are retail and leisure areas below ground level.

Vulnerability is greatest for those communities or individuals that have the least coping capacity where, conceptually, this coping capacity is a function of the degree of individual and collective resources that they can mobilise and how effectively these can be mobilised. Identification of the most important resources and determinants of the effectiveness of mobilisation remains somewhat tentative. Areas in need of social and economic regeneration are known, and the issue is especially of concern when a particular area is short of readily developable land.

The flood management community will want to promote improvements in flood management primarily to reduce the risk to life and reduce the suffering that flooding causes those affected by flooding.

'Intangible' social impacts

Those who are flooded almost invariably report that the 'intangible' impacts of the flood were much more severe than financial losses they experienced (Fig. 8.1), with between 40 and 70% reporting that their health has been affected.

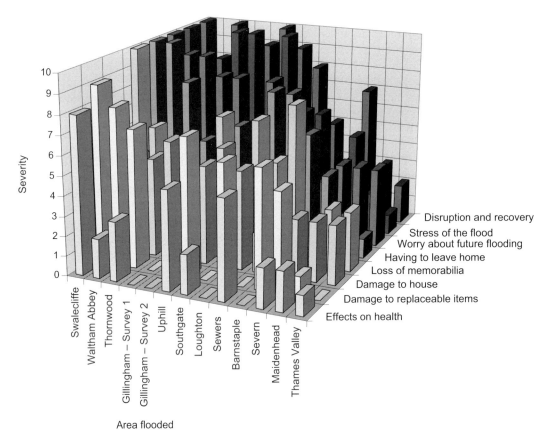

Fig. 8.1. Subjective assessments by flood victims of the relative severity of the different impacts of flooding

Flood and coastal defence are then justified in terms of the reductions in the losses to property that will result. The reason for this apparent paradox is that to date it has not been possible to estimate with any reliability the risk to life presented by a specific flood. Equally, it has not yet been possible to identify unambiguously who are most vulnerable to the 'intangible' impacts of flooding and under what conditions. However, recent research will hopefully resolve this problem and provide a basis for the economic evaluation of these effects (RPA/FHRC, 2004).

With regard to uncertainty, flood victims always report that the degree of social support they received was very important to them in recovering from their flood. It is reasonable, therefore, to expect that the extent and nature of social support, and related parameters such as social capital, should be expected to differ between the Foresight scenarios. Equally, that it will vary between ethnicities. However, it has never been possible to show statistically that social support has any effect in ameliorating any of the effects of flooding.

Looking to examples, one woman interviewed following a flood at Uphill, Somerset, said that her adopted son had died when he was 18; the flood destroyed all the photographs she had of him and she said that it was as if she had 'lost him twice'. Another woman lost all of the handwritten recipes she had been collecting throughout her marriage and said that 'it was her whole life gone'.

Economic and sectoral impacts

These impacts are the damage to buildings and their contents (Tables 8.1 and 8.2) including to production and household durables as well raw materials, intermediate goods and consumption, together with the costs of flood recovery and the disruption caused to others in consequence of those properties being flooded.

Elaboration and operation

For industrial losses, changes in the magnitude of direct damages are a function of:

- the relative returns to capital and labour, and changes in the capital invested per employee;
- consequently, the rate of investment in production durables;

Table 8.1. Projected household contents in the Foresight scenarios (all changes relative to time of writing)

	World markets	National enterprise	Global sustainability	Local stewardship
Income growth	Highest	Moderate	Moderate	Low
Percentage of income spent on household durables	Constant	Constant	Up	Up
Susceptibility of household contents to flood damage	Up	Up	Up	Down
Life expectancy of durables	Down	Down	Up	Up
Real flood losses (£)	Up	Up somewhat	Marginally increased	Falls
Rate of change in loss relative to change in GDP/income	Above	Above	Below	Below

Table 8.2. Domestic buildings: projected damages to building fabric in the Foresight scenarios (all changes relative to time of writing)

Losses	World markets	National enterprise	Global sustainability	Local stewardship
Income growth	Highest	Moderate	Moderate	Low
Percentage of income spent on dwellings	Up	Constant	Up	Up
Susceptibility	Up	Up	Up	Down
Real loss (£)	Up	Up	Up	Down
Rate of change in loss relative to change in GDP/income	Above	Above	Above	Below

- the susceptibility of the technologies and built forms adopted;
- the rate of replacement of existing production durables (e.g. expected life).

Changes in the scale of indirect losses are a function of:

- the degree of specialisation and concentration within industrial sectors;
- the dependency upon 'just in time' (JIT) deliveries of intermediate and finished goods;
- the time taken to repair or replace equipment and buildings affected in a flood (including cleaning up the building).

The world markets scenario is characterised by a high rate of investment and, in turn, the mean life of production durables is likely to fall. Industrial and commercial activities are anticipated to be focused on the 'high tech' activities including biotechnology and nanotechnology. The global nature of the economy will be accompanied by increasing specialisation and concentration. In addition, there will be a high degree of shipping of partially finished goods between countries. Within the industrial sector, potential flood losses should be expected to increase ahead of the change in the GDP and at a greater rate than in the other three scenarios, because:

- electronic equipment is more susceptible to flood damage than the traditional mechanico-electrical equipment and there will be rapid replacement of the existing stock of production durables by more modern equipment;
- equipment takes longer to repair or, more usually, replace;
- under this scenario the greatest development of biotechnology and nanotechnology will occur; both require ultra-clean conditions and the clean-up after a flood will be longer than in the old 'dirty' industries;
- the adoption of JIT techniques so that any disruption has extensive effects;
- the degree of concentration and specialisation means that products cannot be sourced from other firms.

Of particular concern under this scenario is the potential loss of research and trials material; already one of the multi-national pharmaceutical firms has looked closely at the level of flood defence of one of its UK sites. Concentration means that large sites are likely to be required and hence there is likely to be further development on floodplains (Parker, 1995b). This tendency will increase as different countries compete for inward investment and the interests of multi-nationals dictate development.

Two potential problems under this scenario require investigation:

1. The impact of floods on fields of genetically modified (GM) crops and the potential GM contamination of other areas.

2. Ensuring that high security biological and chemical laboratories are not exposed to flood risk.

The overall pattern under the national enterprise scenario is similar to that under the world markets model but the pressures are less intense. And government will be even more inclined to agree to the demands of multi-nationals offering inward investment and this will be an important influence on national flood risk management policy. In real terms, the potential flood loss will tend to increase, but at a lower rate than in the world markets scenario. Even in a national economy, economies of scale are likely to dictate further specialisation and concentration.

Under global sustainability there is likely to be a rapid growth in the use of 'packaged' water management systems. The water industry will shift from bulk transmission of water and wastewater towards offering specialised design, construction and management systems for the larger-scale industrial, commercial and residential developments. These packages will potentially include rainwater harvesting, demand management and wastewater treatment, allowing a significant degree of water re-use.

Logically, these solutions will also involve energy management. The result will be to increase the average value at risk of flooding. The chemical industry will continue to require large coastal sites as there will be a need either to import basic chemicals or to produce chemical feedstocks from non-fossil sources (e.g. plant material). The most noticeable change is likely to be a somewhat more uniform distribution of flood loss potential across urban areas.

The regionalisation of the economy under local stewardship will mean that local areas will be more seriously affected by a flood, with fewer alternative sources of goods, but the indirect impacts of a flood on the national economy will be proportionately lower than now. Similarly, infrastructure will be even more spread out than it is under global responsibility; again, vehicles will be fewer in number and less susceptible than under the world markets scenario. More generally, the susceptibility of buildings will depend upon what is the nature of a sustainable building resource strategy, but we should expect a strong tendency either to re-use existing buildings or to re-use materials from those buildings. Flood losses will, on average, be somewhat less than they are now.

In terms or household losses, the changes in the real loss to households from floods depend upon the ratio of spending for immediate consumption to that on durables (e.g. televisions, cookers). Although the prices of individual items should continue to fall in real terms, it is the ratio of spending upon immediate consumption to that on durables that determines the magnitude of flood losses. At present, the ratio of household expenditure on durables (including the dwelling itself) to flows is roughly 1 to 2 but since durables have a relatively long life, potential losses to durables are greater than the destruction of immediate consumption items (e.g. food, drink).

The changes in flood losses to households (Green *et al.*, 2000) thus depend upon:

- changes in real income;
- the relative real prices of immediate consumption and durables, with immediate consumption items typically having a price inelastic demand;
- the life expectancy of durables;
- changes in the susceptibility to flood damage of durables.

Table 8.3 estimates how the shares of household income could change. This is very tentative: we are not certain that the changes in different forms of expenditure are sufficient to balance out. Changes in real income mean that the absolute totals of expenditure can increase even when the share of household expenditure shows a slight fall.

Table 8.3. Changes in household expenditure in the Foresight scenarios (all changes relative to time of writing)

	World markets	National enterprise	Global sustainability	Local stewardship
Taxes	Down	Down	Up	Up
Education and health	Up	Up	Down	Down
Food	Down in short term and up in the long term – shift to world markets	Up slightly in short term, up in longer term	Up – shift to sustainable world production, large reduction in subsidies	Up – shift to organics, local production
Clothing	Constant	Constant	Up	Up – shift to natural materials
Personal items including drink and tobacco	Constant	Constant	Down	Down
Leisure and recreation	Down (as in the USA)	Constant	Down – less travel	Down – less travel
Energy and other utilities	Down	Down	Up – shift to renewables	Up
Transport	Constant – real energy costs stay constant, real costs of vehicles fall, demand up but expenditure constrained by increased expenditure on health etc.	Up	Down – less travel although real costs per unit distance increase	Down – less travel
Household durables	Up – demand for increase in quality outweighs reductions in real costs	Constant – change in performance matches reductions in real costs	Up – shift to energy efficiency and sustainability	Up – stress on life-cycle performance and sustainable production
Housing	Constant	Constant	Up – improved energy and water efficiency	Up – attempt at closed cycle buildings
Savings	Down	Down	Up	Up

Historically, buying food took 60–70% of household income, and it is the real fall in the price of food that has freed income to buy household durables, including the dwelling itself. In turn, this means that the price of food has a very significant impact on flood losses in households.

Regional patterns, exceptional locations and uncertainty

Geometry is important in flood management; it is the density of value at risk per unit area that is important. Moreover, given that a significant proportion of flood interventions are along the length of the river (e.g. channel improvements, flood embankments), it is the density of value per unit length that is critical. Hence, wide flat areas that are densely developed are those where the losses are likely to be greatest. In steep-sided valleys, losses are generally low.

Elsewhere, flood potential is rising. The extensive use of electronics in cars now means that car parking and storage areas result in very high densities of loss, with underground car parks potentially yielding the highest density of loss. For household losses, the critical uncertainty turns out to be the world price of basic food-stuffs denominated by foreign exchange rates against the then dominant economic power. Those prices are determined, first, by the regional balances in supply and demand for food and, second, by the comparative economic performance of the UK economy relative to those of the major food exporters and importers. If these prices are high, then household flood losses will fall simply because households have less money to spend on household durables.

Two examples of the consequences of industrial concentration are that, in 1953, the Unilever plant that produced 60% of the UK's margarine was flooded; similarly, the factory that now produces a similar proportion of baker's yeast for the UK lies on the floodplain. Making up the shortfall in production would be difficult. An example of the consequence of specialisation is a plant that produced refuelling gantries for nuclear power stations on a one-off basis, with the equipment being manufactured in a pit. The consequence of a flood would then have been to delay the completion or operation of the nuclear power station.

Urban impacts

These impacts result from the development of land, including the form of building layout and resulting densities of development, building form and nature of land-use.

Driver operation and importance

Urban land-uses are both the generator of flooding, since most people are flooded by someone else's runoff, and the primary way in which flood losses are generated. These consequences are then influenced by which land is developed and the way that it is developed.

The primary factors affecting the patterns of urbanisation are:

- the rate of change in population;
- the age structure of that population;
- the rate of household formation;
- internal mobility;
- the net rate of migration;
- the rate of replacement of the existing building stock;
- the density of development.

Under world markets, the rates of internal mobility and emigration and immigration will be greatest. People will move to work where countries and regions compete to attract multi-nationals (Fig. 8.2). In turn, this movement means that

Interdependence

Wherever you like, e.g. Houston and other cities in the USA that have no zoning control at all	Similar to the French system: marked conflict between interests of central government and those of autonomous municipalities. Use of whole series of plans and techniques including strategic environmental assessment. Lots of plans, not necessarily very much achieved

Individual   **Community**

Strong planning controls set by central government based upon control of externalities (e.g. common law of nuisance) and on maximising the national interest where this over-rides individual or local interest	Theory is of 'zero impact' development (e.g. including source control), no development should cause any environmental harm or any unavoidable harm must be compensated by environmental enhancement. In principle, no development on floodplains but other environmental constraints may be more important. Acquisition and demolition of existing development on floodplains

Autonomy

Fig. 8.2 Development and Foresight scenarios

significant fractions of the existing stock of buildings will be located in the wrong places and it will be necessary to chase the apparent demand in areas that are attractive to multi-nationals. The emphasis on individualism promotes the early formation of independent households, although many of the young must, for financial reasons, share properties with friends. Rates of immigration and emigration are high, with both skill shortages and low-skilled work sucking in migrants. Those areas with significant numbers of immigrants create cosmopolitan cultures that attract further inward investment by multi-national companies and then further immigration.

There is some change in the traditional British preference for a house with a garden, particularly among the young who want to be close to the night-time street scene. A preference here is for new construction over old buildings so that building replacement increases. Hence, urban centres attract population and population densities increase here. The traditional British semi-detached house becomes the refuge for an increasingly aged population. At the same time, the spread of 'tele-working' increases diffusion of work out from urban centres.

The absence of any land-use control means that development takes place where developers expect to make the most profit (cf. Pottier *et al.*, 2005). While this is partly dependent upon demand, it also depends on the developers' skill in assembling land packages at the lowest possible cost. Under this scenario, the consequence is the greatest degree of development, concentrated in the south-east, and including both floodplains and 'greenfield' sites.

Under global sustainability, a sustainable resource policy becomes important. The importation of timber from unsustainable sources will be banned, energy life-cycle costing will apply to building materials, and the 'best environment aggregate policy' will prevail (Holling, 1978). It is not clear what would be the resulting resource policy and, hence, the outcome in terms of built form. The overall result is likely to be some limited development, with a strong preference for redevelopment of existing sites, with floodplains being avoided.

These trends are greater under local stewardship (Global Water Partnership/ WMO, 2002). This society will minimise development on greenfield sites, and require a sustainable resources policy but emphasise community and equity. The result should be a variant on the regional building styles that existed prior to the railway age. However, when each of the alternative resources for construction is considered on a life-cycle basis, some inter-regional transfers of building materials may be the most sustainable option.

Given these wider issues, the emphasis will be on re-using existing buildings and, where this is not possible, re-using the building materials. Second, there will be an emphasis on quite high density, low-rise development where the feasible density, and hence land take, will depend upon the constraints of sustainability (e.g. the need to allow space for solar power, source control and rainwater harvesting).

A fairly critical question, then, is whether this density exceeds or is less than existing densities; if it is less then there will be pressure to convert further land. The emphasis will be on locating redevelopment and any new development close to public transport linkages. But it may be that the ethos of this society leads to a significant number of people to want to abandon urban areas and return to a life closer to nature, and lives of near-complete self-sufficiency. Hence, there may be quite strong pressures towards de-urbanisation and a decline in the size of major cities. The emphasis on community and equity also implies that there will be some development around small villages and towns to the population levels necessary to support community facilities, such as shops, schools and health care.

Given the shift under this scenario towards a vegetarian diet, the likelihood is of some improved grazing land being converted to urban uses but avoiding the flood-plains. Land will be under acute pressure in this scenario and there will be great difficulties in reconciling the conflicting requirements of environmental needs with arable food production, afforestation for sustainable timber production, industrial crop production and urban uses.

Regional patterns, exceptional locations and driver importance

The south-east region already has a population density greater than that of the Netherlands and has a population equal to 75% of the Netherlands. Future migration is expected to be towards this area. In general, the lower the population density and the lower the intensity of economic activity (measured as GDP per square kilometre), the easier it is to manage floods and water in general (Global Water Partnership/WMO, 2002). However, even in less-densely populated areas, there will be local problems, particularly in the hilly areas where land suitable for development is relatively scarce.

The rates of land-take predicted in the Foresight scenarios are comparatively small and the critical questions are whether the current very low rate of replacement of existing building stock will increase and whether there will be a change in preferences for dwellings. Hence, under the best estimate, the effects of urbanisation will be small but potentially they could be very large: if the annual rate of replacement of stock increased to 1%, then by 2080 the effects of new urbanisation will be very significant.

In terms of uncertainty, currently the rate of construction of dwellings is less than a third of its post-1939/45 peak: the rate of replacement has fallen to less than 0.1% per annum. A major uncertainty is then whether there will be a change in preference in favour of a new dwelling, with a consequent increase in the replacement rate. In general, it is easier and cheaper to build-in higher standards, such as source control or flood proofing into new construction, than into existing stock. Managed retreat will also be easier if the property in that area is seen as time-expired.

There are uncertainties about three other forms of preferences for housing: first, a possible switch to a preference for high-density urban living and consequently an increase in demand for city centre apartments. Or, conversely, particularly under the global sustainability and local stewardship scenarios, for a desire to live in small, rural or semi-rural communities. One consequence of the latter would probably be a reversal of the direction of migration back to the north and west. Any such changes would have major implications. A third possible change would be a switch from regarding a dwelling as an asset, to regarding it as a consumer durable as it is in some other European countries.

Case examples

Prior to the privatisation of the water and wastewater industry, the local authority's engineers were often appointed as agents of the water authority. Consequently, when a planning application was received by the planning department it was sent down the corridor to the engineering department for comment.

In Bournemouth, the engineering department had a special stamp prepared 'NOT approved by the Dept of Engineering', which was used on the majority of planning applications passed to it for comment. Many of these involved the redevelopment of sites for higher-density use. The Planning Department then almost invariably recommended planning approval on the principle that development was a planning issue, whereas flooding was a water authority problem. The resulting increase in impermeable area, and therefore in runoff, resulted in a major problem of flooding from a combined sewer system, which at one time was expected to cost £35 million to resolve.

Conversely, at about the same time, Loughborough Council undertook flood alleviation works along the Black Brook, a minor watercourse, in order then to develop the floodplain with around 2000 new homes and associated facilities. Given other environmental constraints, it feared that otherwise development pressures would overwhelm Charnwood Forest, an Area of Outstanding Natural Beauty.

The Wentlooge Levels, between Newport and Cardiff, lie below high-tide level and it might be expected that managed retreat, so as to reduce coastal squeeze on the offshore mudflats, would be the appropriate option. But, in the 1990s there was heavy inward investment both for housing and industry. However, when the area was examined more closely, the reason why this investment was being made on the Levels seemed to be the same reason why the area had been reclaimed in the Romano-British or the Medieval periods, and heavy investment during Victorian times: an absence of flat, developable land elsewhere in the area.

Infrastructure impacts

Driver definition and operation

Urban infrastructure is the physical services, in the form of networks of nodes and connecting linkages, that support and enable the economy to transform raw materials into production durables, intermediate goods and final consumption. The effects of flooding on parts of these networks can then have consequences that spread far outside of the area directly affected by flooding (Parker *et al.*, 1987).

Infrastructure functions as networks; the effect of a flood is then to cut some of the links or affect some of the nodes. Where these effects then extend outside of the area flooded depends partly upon the topological characteristics of the network and also on the degree of surplus capacity in the network. Traditionally, landline telephone systems were highly susceptible to flood-induced disruption because they are tree-like in form, with flooding of a main exchange potentially cutting off a large part of the network. Conversely, except on the geographical periphery, other networks typically include redundant paths between different nodes.

Usually it is therefore disruption to the nodes that can cause the greatest disruption. What has generally been happening is a trend towards thinning down the networks and particularly the nodes; for example, the signalling requirements of the railway networks have moved from many local mechanically operated signal boxes to a few electronically driven centres controlling trains over a large area. Those signal boxes are both more susceptible to flood damage and the consequences of flooding are greater.

The shift to 'just in time' supplies obviously increases the susceptibility of the economy to flood-induced transport disruption. A critical issue in the effects of infrastructure flooding is the duration of both the flood and the time taken to get back into normal service following the flood.

Bridges and culverts are both potentially at risk as a result of flooding and a potential cause of flooding. Bridges are pinch points both in the transport (and sometimes also a utility) network and, as are culverts, also in flood management systems. At the same time, a number are scheduled either for their archaeological importance or because of their heritage value. This limits what can be done to increase the flow capacity of those bridges and culverts.

In extreme cases, bridges may fail as a result of flooding from scouring of the foundations – a few years ago, a railway bridge in the UK collapsed while a train was passing across it. In catchments where flow velocities are high, debris (e.g. tree trunks, vehicles, etc.) can block a bridge creating a dam which then may fail catastrophically, as was the case in the 1952 Lynmouth flood.

More generally, the capacity of the bridge opening or the culvert may be exceeded by the volume of flow. What then happens depends upon the context; initially, upstream storage is likely, then either the bridge will fail (a large number failed in the Oder floods in Poland) or flood water will find a bypass channel around the bridge. Where a watercourse is culverted for part of its route, then the flow channel is usually over the top of the culvert – in a significant number of old urban areas, parts of the watercourses are culverted in this way.

Culverts are also designed to protect road and railway embankments by allowing flood waters to pass through them. In some circumstances, these embankments may form a useful element in flood management either to retain flood waters in storage or to protect areas lying behind them. However, unless the embankment is designed to retain water, it may fail either when water starts to weir over the crest of the embankment or as a result of failure before that point.

Under the world markets scenario, UK industries will become progressively more exposed to disruption as a result of natural disasters in other countries, a potential competitive advantage of the UK now being the relative absence of natural hazards. Therefore, within the UK it is the nodal points connecting the UK to the global economy from which the greatest disruption could be expected as a result of flooding.

The spread of competition will act somewhat to reduce vulnerability but conversely the drive to economies of scale and scope will tend to introduce more centralised control rooms, which may themselves be at risk of flooding. A broadly similar pattern can then be expected under the national enterprise scenario.

Under the global sustainability scenario, we should expect to see a switch to a hydrogen economy and the use of biofuels; the implications in terms of flood risk require examination. We should also expect to see the greater use of low-head or micro-hydro schemes which may have implications for flood management.

Local stewardship will see less transport of goods and raw materials, and less travel overall: the effects of a flood on the national economy as a whole will be less. Water management will be complicated by the increased importance of rivers and floodplains for power generation, fish production and the production of vegetative material.

Regional patterns, exceptional locations and importance

Because a key determinant of the effects of flooding is the local topology of networks, and the degree of redundancy and diversity in the local network, the effects are locally determined.

Even where in the centre of the network there is a higher degree of inter-connectivity, on the peripheries there are usually fewer redundancies and the disruption to a single link or node is more likely to have widespread effects. Equally, the lower the density of development, the more sparse tends to be the network and hence both the lower the degree of surplus capacity and the greater the difficulty of working around local problems. Essentially, looking for the impacts of flooding on the infrastructure involves looking at the different networks with a saboteur's eye, of seeking to identify where the greatest disruption can be caused with the least effort and hence flood management concerns overlap with wider security concerns.

Generally, the losses associated with damage and disruption to infrastructure constitute only a small proportion of total flood losses. The real importance of infrastructure is then the high accumulated value of these assets (e.g. £7000 per household for sewers alone), and the slow rate of their replacement. In turn, this means that both the rate of change to risk and the rate at which these systems can be adapted in response to changes in risk will both be low.

Uncertainty and case studies

In the Oder floods in Germany, a major problem was the contamination of flood waters by domestic heating oil. It is not clear whether a switch to biofuels, such as ethanol, would increase the present low risk presented by gas-fired heating systems. The risk from floods to the components of the infrastructure for a hydrogen-based economy require investigation.

Until the middle 1990s, York was served by a single water abstraction and treatment plant on the Ouse, and there was very limited capacity to transfer water to the city from other areas. In 1947, the Coopermills water treatment plant was flooded, disrupting water supply to the whole of the east side of London. Further afield there is a classic example of an explosion at the single gas plant serving New South Wales, Australia, which meant the entire state was almost entirely without gas for some weeks. Power stations have traditionally been located close to water in order to minimise the costs of abstracting and discharging cooling water; consequently, over significant parts of the coast, we are locked into maintaining existing coastal defences in order to protect nuclear power stations until such time as it is safe to remove their cores.

Another example of a major secondary risk presented by flooding was revealed in the first quantitative risk assessment undertaken on the petrochemical installations on Canvey Island. This found, first, that the highest probability initiating event was a flood, since the chance of a flood overtopping defences was 1 in 1000. Second, at that time, British Gas stored in the region of 10 000 tonnes of natural gas in liquid form in holes in the ground. In the event of a flood, the higher temperature of the sea water would cause this gas to boil off with the likely result of a large-scale explosion.

The North Circular road at Brent Cross has historically been prone to flooding, with the congestion causing gridlock over a large area of north-west London. Underground railways are obviously potentially highly susceptible to flooding; the 1911 flood in Paris closed parts of the network for some months and the recent flooding in Prague caused disruption for some weeks.

Science and technology

Driver definition

The research for the Foresight reports (Hall *et al.*, 2003; Evans *et al.*, 2004a, 2004b) did not in the end rank and further quantify these variables, as we did not have sufficient insight into their detailed operation, but we know that they are important.

Indeed, we can summarise the output (O) of an economy as being:

$$O = NE * T * H * X$$

Where:

NE is the natural endowment
T is technology
H is human inputs of labour and capital
X is some other factor, which may include, pace (North, 1990), institutional form as well as other factors as social capital and social adaptability

Hence the role of $T * X$ is to maximise the ratio of O to $NE * H$ given that NE is fixed and H is relatively fixed in the short term (North, 1990; Landes 1998). In terms of driver operation, science and technology act in two opposite directions:

1. Usually to increase flood losses as technological advance seems typically to increase susceptibility to flood damage.
2. To improve our capacity to manage floods successfully so as to increase the overall ratio of O to $NE * H$. Our objective in flood risk management is to increase this ratio rather than to minimise flood losses *per se*.

The implication is, therefore, that the form of scientific and technological advance will vary according to the Foresight scenario, so that in any scenario the areas in which innovation will take place are largely predetermined. Thus, for example, under the local stewardship scenario, since fossil-fuelled driven vehicles will have been banned, there will be no significant development in fuel efficiency of these engines. Similarly, under the local stewardship scenario, there also will be no attempt at research on the control of precipitation as to do so would be completely contrary to their concept of a respect for nature.

In the other scenarios, there would also be differences in the focus and nature of the research undertaken and also in the funding of research. So, for example, in the world markets scenario health research will concentrate upon that which can be marketed, notably pharmaceuticals and capital equipment, whereas under the global sustainability scenario, it will concentrate on means of reducing the risk of disease, injury and decay. But, irrespective of the scenario, technological advance would seem to be associated with increased susceptibility to flooding with the character of technological advance resulting in smaller, purer, more intricate products which in turn are more susceptible to both water damage and also to the contaminants carried by the flood water.

Regional patterns, importance, uncertainty and examples

In terms of regional patterns, knowledge now diffuses at a very rapid rate both into and out of the country and throughout the country, so there is no apparent reason to expect significant differences across the country. But the driver is important and clearly it outweighs any other factor since it is this combination of $T * X$ that generates the anticipated increase in real national income that drives our society to the scenarios that Foresight presents. But uncertainties here are necessarily very large and paradigmatic shifts entirely unforeseeable; it is the nature of science to discover things that we didn't know that we didn't know.

The rate at which knowledge and understanding develops is relatively unconstrained but the rates at which changes in technology can be diffused are necessarily dependent upon the rate of change in the stock of ideas and assets. An important question is then: what is the rate at which such new concepts will be adopted throughout the flood risk management community (Green *et al.*, 2000)? What then are the rates at which professions and institutions can change their paradigms?

In terms of examples, consider what is now in the basements of large office buildings. They tend to be full of banks of flood-susceptible computer servers, whereas fifty years ago the areas were full of flood-resilient coal-driven heating equipment. Also a different but obvious comparison is between two bypass channels; the River Wey scheme from the 1960s and the recently completed Jubilee River. The former is essentially a concrete canal whereas the latter is a multi-form channel designed to have a significant environmental and recreational value. It is unlikely that it would have been possible to design the Jubilee River when the River Wey scheme was being designed because of the limited computing capacity with which to analyse flood flows in complex channels.

Conclusions

The Foresight Future Flooding Project analysed future flood risk in a scenario framework predicting substantially increased flood risk unless current flood risk management policies and investment levels are changed, with an increase of up to 20-fold in economic risk by the 2080s (Evans *et al.*, 2004a and b).

The overall results (Hall *et al.*, 2003; Evans *et al.*, 2006) show that greater climate change by the 2080s, together with increased floodplain occupancy, mean that the world markets and national enterprise scenarios will see more than a doubling of the number of people at high risk from flooding. In all scenarios, other than the relatively low-growth local stewardship scenario, annual economic flood damage is expected to increase considerably over the next century under the baseline flood risk management assumption, owing to a combination of increased economic vulnerability – partly driven by technological change – and increasing flood frequency.

Change in the ratio of flood risk to per capita GDP provides an indication of how harmful (in economic terms) flooding will be to the UK. In the world markets and national enterprise scenarios, flooding is expected to remove a greater proportion of national wealth than it currently does (and thus merit a greater investment to reduce risk). In the local stewardship and global sustainability scenarios, flooding is predicted to remove a lesser proportion of national wealth since these scenarios will tend to be less vulnerable to flood damage and are expected to be subject to somewhat less climate change.

The increase in flooding in the final Foresight results is attributable to a combination of climate change and increasing value of household, industrial and infrastructure assets (Evans *et al.*, 2006). A very important contribution came from these last three sets of variables, as described in this chapter. Indeed what began – in the Foresight Future Flooding research – as having all the hallmarks of a climate change project, evolved into a project quite unambiguously about social futures.

References

Bennet, G., 1979. 'Bristol floods 1968: controlled survey of effects on health of local community disaster', *British Medical Journal*, August 21, 454–458.

Evans, E.P., Ashley, R., Hall, J.W., Penning-Rowsell, E.P., Saul, A., Sayers, P.B., Thorne, C.R. and Watkinson, A., 2004a. *Foresight Future Flooding, Scientific Summary: Vol. 1: Future risks and their drivers*, Office of Science and Technology, London.

Evans, E.P., Ashley, R., Hall, J.W., Penning-Rowsell, E.P., Sayers, P.B., Thorne, C.R. and Watkinson, A., 2004b. *Foresight Future Flooding, Scientific Summary: Vol. 2: Managing future risks*, Office of Science and Technology, London.

Evans, E.P., Hall, J.W., Penning-Rowsell, E.C., Sayers, P.B., Thorne, C.R. and Watkinson, A.R., 2006. 'Drivers, responses and choices for future flood risk management', *Proceedings, Institution of Civil Engineers, Water Management*, 159, 53–61.

Global Water Partnership/World Meteorological Organisation (WMO), 2002. *Flood Management in the Context of Integrated Water Resource Management*, World Meteorological Organisation, Geneva.

Green, C.H., Parker, D.J. and Tunstall, S.M., 2000. *Assessment of Flood Control and Management Options*, World Commission on Dams, Cape Town.

Hall, J.W., Evans, E.P., Penning-Rowsell, E.C., Sayers, P.B., Thorne, C.R. and Saul, A.J., 2003. 'Quantified scenarios analysis of drivers and impacts of changing flood risk in England and Wales: 2030–2100', *Environmental Hazards*, 5, 51–65.

Holling, C.S., 1978. *Adaptive Environmental Assessment and Management*, Wiley, Chichester.

Jonkman, S.N., van Gelder, P.H.A.J.M. and Vrijling, J.K., 2002. *Loss of Life Models for Sea and River Floods*, Paper presented at the 2nd International Symposium on Flood Defence, Beijing.

Landes, D., 1998. *The Wealth and Poverty of Nations*, Little, Brown and Co., London.

North, D.C., 1990. *Institutions, Institutional Change and Economic Performance*, Cambridge University Press, Cambridge.

Parker, D.J., 1995a. 'Floodplain development policy in England and Wales', *Applied Geography*, 5(4), 341–363.

Parker, D.J., 1995b. 'Floods in cities: increasing exposure and rising impact potential', *Built Environment*, 21(2/3), 114–125.

Parker, D.J., Green, C.H. and Thompson, P.M., 1987. *Urban Flood Protection Benefits: A project appraisal guide*, Gower, Aldershot.

Penning-Rowsell, E.C. and Chatterton, J.B., 1977. *The Benefits of Flood Alleviation: A manual of assessment technique*, Gower Technical Press, Aldershot.

Penning-Rowsell, E.C., Floyd, P., Ramsbottom, D. and Surendran, S., 2005. 'Estimating injury and loss of life in floods: a deterministic framework', *Natural Hazards*, 36, 43–64.

Penning-Rowsell, E.C., Johnson, C., Tunstall, S., Tapsell, S., Morris, J., Chatterton, J., Coker, A. and Green, C., 2003. *The Benefits of Flood and Coastal Defence: Techniques and Data for 2003*, Middlesex University Flood Hazard Research Centre, London.

Pottier, N., Penning-Rowsell, E.C., Tunstall, S.M. and Hubert, G., 2005. 'Land use and flood protection: contrasting approaches and outcomes in France and in England and Wales', *Applied Geography*, 25, 1–27.

RPA/FHRC, 2004. *The Appraisal of the Human-related Intangible Impacts of Flooding*, R&D Project FD2005/TR, Defra/Environment Agency, London.

Tapsell, S.M., Penning-Rowsell, E.C., Tunstall, S.M. and Wilson, T.L., 2002. 'Vulnerability to flooding: health and social dimensions', *Phil. Trans. Royal Society of London A*, 360, 1511–1525.

Thompson, P.M., Wigg, A.H. and Parker, D.J., 1991. 'Urban flood protection post-project appraisal in England and Wales', *Project Appraisal*, 6(2), 84–92.

9 Coastal processes

Claire Hinton, Ian H. Townend and Robert J. Nicholls

Introduction

The coastal process driver set is composed of four separate drivers, three of which represent sources and one a pathway:

- relative sea-level rise (source). The local change of sea level relative to the land;
- surges (source). A temporary change in sea level resulting from meteorological forcing of the ocean surface;
- waves (source). A wind-induced disturbance of the sea surface that propagates across the surface; and
- coastal morphology and sediment supply (pathway). Changes in the form of the seabed, shoreline and adjacent coastal land, coastal inlets and estuaries.

These drivers are strongly coupled, for instance:

- Positive surges combine with high astronomical tides to produce the extreme water levels that cause most coastal floods.
- Over time, relative sea-level rise also contributes to an increase in extreme water levels.
- High waves and surges often coincide, resulting in overtopping of defences and, more seriously, breaching and failure of defences, allowing the extreme water levels to propagate inland.
- Coastal morphology can be an important buffer against these three drivers, but due to sediment starvation (resulting from the exhaustion of Quaternary deposits and a century of coastal defence) and climate change, erosion dominates around much of the UK coast (see Chapters 16 and 17), further increasing the risk of coastal flooding.

In this chapter, each driver is discussed in detail and driver ranking is considered in Chapter 12.

Coastal process driver set

Relative sea-level rise

It is well known that global sea levels rose during the twentieth century and it is probable that this trend will accelerate in the twenty-first century due to human-induced

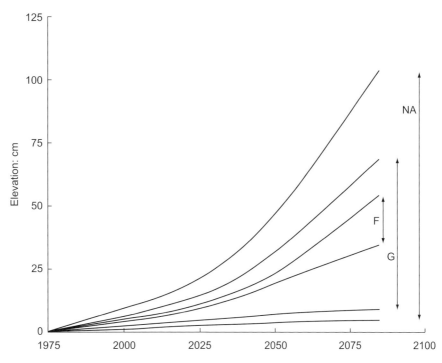

Fig. 9.1. The possible range of sea-level rise 1975 to 2085 from the UKCIP02 scenarios (data from Hulme et al., 2002). G = the range of global mean rise; NA = the range of North Atlantic rise; F = the range of the Foresight scenarios (see Table 9.1); uncertainty due to Antarctica is not included

global warming (Church *et al.*, 2001; Hulme *et al.*, 2002). Figure 9.1 shows the range of global-mean sea-level projections, ranging from a 90 mm to 880 mm rise from 1990 to 2100. However, when considering the potential impacts of this global change, we need to consider relative sea-level (RSL) rise (or more strictly change), which is the sum of the global rise, plus regional and local factors. Hence, global-mean sea-level rise does not simply translate into a uniform rise in sea level around the world. Over the twenty-first century, RSL change will be the sum of several components (Church *et al.*, 2001):

- Global mean sea-level rise: an increase in the global volume of the ocean due to several processes, e.g. thermal expansion, which are mostly a response to human-induced climate change. The contribution of the Greenland icecaps is uncertain, while Antarctica is expected to expand, producing a sea-level reduction for this component (Church *et al.*, 2001). In addition, the collapse of the West Antarctic Ice Shelf (WAIS) could contribute enormously to sea-level rise (Mercer, 1978; Oppenheimer, 1998). According to the most recent estimate, there is a 5% chance that the WAIS will contribute more than 0.5 m of sea-level rise during the twenty-first century (Vaughan and Spouge, 2002). Direct human influence is also likely due to modifications to the hydrological cycle, such as increased terrestrial storage of water (sea-level fall), versus increased groundwater mining (sea-level rise), but the magnitude of the net change is uncertain.
- Regional meteo-oceanographic factors: examples are spatial variation in thermal expansion effects, and mean changes to wind fields, atmospheric pressure and ocean circulation (e.g. Gregory, 1993). This contributes to inter-annual and inter-decadal sea-level variability and long-term change.
- Vertical land movements (subsidence/uplift) due to a range of geological processes. In addition to tectonic and neotectonic changes, land movements

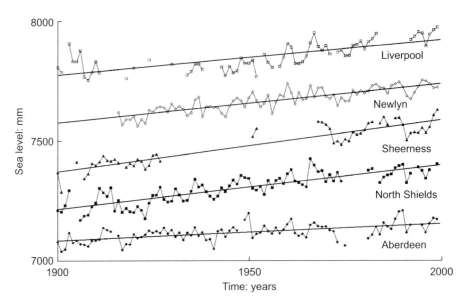

Fig. 9.2. Relative trends in mean sea level for Great Britain during the twentieth century (taken from de la Vega-Leinert and Nicholls, accepted for publication)

due to glacial-isostatic adjustment (GIA) are important contributors to relative sea-level rise (Douglas, 2000). GIA is still occurring due to the unloading of melting ice sheets from the end of the last glacial epoch, 18 000 to 6000 years ago. In addition to natural changes, groundwater withdrawal and artificial land drainage have enhanced subsidence (and peat destruction by oxidation and erosion) in many coastal lowlands.

Direct measurements of sea-level changes in Britain have been available since the eighteenth century, but most records originate from the twentieth century (Woodworth *et al.*, 1999). The five longest relative sea-level records compiled during the twentieth century all show long-term rising trends of varying magnitude (Fig. 9.2). Annual to decadal variations in sea level, due to regional meteo-oceanographic processes, are also apparent around the UK. In terms of changing flood risk, it is the long-term trend in sea level that is most important. To characterise this underlying long-term trend, it is essential to secure tide-gauge continuous data that are, ideally, more than 50 years in length (Douglas, 2000).

Figure 9.3 indicates that RSL rise is occurring at all the stations around the coast of Great Britain. Shennan and Horton (2002) suggest that net uplift of the land is occurring north of a line from the Mersey to the Tees due to isostatic rebound, with maximum rates of up to 2.0 mm/yr in parts of Scotland. South of this line subsidence is occurring, with the greatest rates in Devon and Cornwall of, approximately, 1 mm/yr. This uplift/subsidence data provides a sound basis for developing quantitative regional scenarios for future RSL rise.

Within coastal lowlands, such as the Norfolk Broads, the Lancashire coastal plain and the Fens, draining and consolidation, as well as oxidation and subsequent peat loss, has produced substantial declines in land elevation. This is illustrated by a 4 m decline in land levels recorded at Holme Fen Post in Cambridgeshire since 1851. Consequently, most of the Fens now lie below high-tide levels and significant areas are below mean sea-level. However, the extent and rate of future changes resulting from local drivers are difficult to predict and future scenarios for these sub-regional changes are not considered here.

Relative sea-level rise has a wide range of effects on coastal processes and it influences coastal flood probabilities in a number of discrete ways (Woodworth

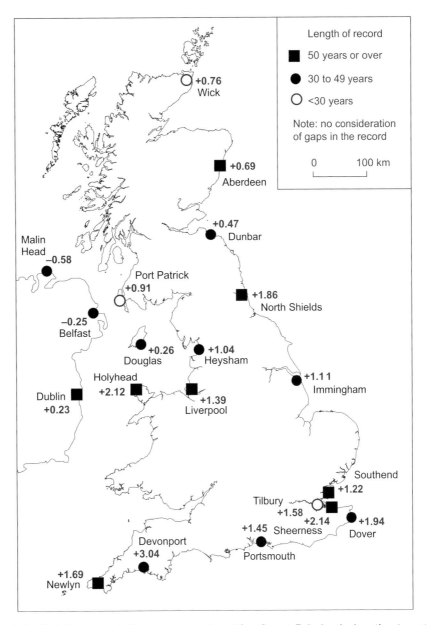

Fig. 9.3. Relative trends in mean sea level for Great Britain during the twentieth century expressed in mm/yr (from de la Vega-Leinert and Nicholls, 2006)

et al., 2004). In addition to raising water levels, rising sea level also elevates all the coastal processes that operate at or around sea level. For example, with a RSL rise of 710 mm for East Anglia, the return period for the 100-year flood elevation is reduced to between two and eight years, depending on local conditions. For a more extreme RSL rise of 960 mm, the 100-year extreme water elevation becomes the annual flood level (Nicholls and Wilson, 2001). Consequently, the most immediate effect of a sea-level rise is to increase the probability of inundation. Longer-term effects include morphological adjustments to higher and more frequent water levels, particularly through beach erosion and saltmarsh decline, as the coastline responds to the new environmental conditions and driving processes (see Chapters 16 and 17). These erosional changes exacerbate the increases in flood probability triggered by the more immediate effects of sea-level rise (see 'Coastal morphology and sediment supply' later in this chapter).

Table 9.1. Foresight relative sea-level rise scenarios

Region	Mean uplift/ subsidence: mm/yr	Relative sea-level rise scenarios to the 2080s: mm – relative to 1990	
		Low emissions	High emissions
East Scotland (Inverness to Border)	1.0	340	550
North-east England	0.2	410	620
Yorkshire	−0.5	480	690
East Midlands	−0.6	490	700
East England	−0.7	500	710
London	−0.7	500	710
South-east England	−0.5	480	690
South-west England	−1.0	530	740
Wales	−0.4	470	680
North-west England	0.7	360	570
South-west Scotland (Border to Fort William)	1.3	310	520
North-west Scotland (Fort William to Inverness)	0.7	360	570
Orkney and Shetland	0.0*	430	640
Northern Ireland	*na*	430	640

* In the absence of good regional estimates of uplift/subsidence, this is assumed to be zero.

Scenarios of relative sea-level rise for the UK were developed using the information provided by Hulme *et al.* (2002) and the new information on uplift/subsidence provided by Shennan and Horton (2002) (see Table 9.1). The global scenarios are derived directly from the Intergovernmental Panel on Climate Change (IPCC), Third Assessment Report (Church *et al.*, 2001). By the 2080s, the overall range for projected global-mean sea-level rise is 90 to 690 mm, relative to 1990. For each emission scenario there is a substantial range of uncertainty in terms of sea-level rise (Nicholls and Lowe, 2004) and, hence, there is considerable overlap between the predictions for the four global-mean scenarios. For each emissions scenario, the median estimate of global sea-level rise for the 2080s (as reported by Hulme *et al.*, 2002) was increased by 50% to account for regional sea-level rise around the UK and then combined with the regional uplift/subsidence component to predict the regional predictions for RSL listed in Table 9.1.

Under all scenarios, predicted changes in RSL mean that the frequency of extreme water levels would be significantly increased around the entire British Isles, even if all other drivers were to remain unchanged.

The range of RSL scenarios that are predicted here is quite large, because it is based on a range of climate models and, therefore, encompasses much of their uncertainty (see Hulme *et al.*, 2002). However, in future analyses of flood and coastal defence, it would be beneficial to consider an even wider range of sea-level rise scenarios covering a wider range of the possible rises. As sea-level rise is likely to continue beyond the 2080s, coastal flood risk will probably continue to increase for centuries and, thus, extending the timespan of assessment might also be advisable.

Surges

Surges are one of the various 'non-tidal' effects superimposed on the regular, tidal behaviour of the sea, that may occur to create an extreme water level. Many of these non-tidal effects originate from meteorological phenomena; for example, persistent winds can generate wind-driven currents, set-up water levels and develop sea states that lead to the generation of large wind waves. Therefore, future increases in extreme water levels could result from the effects of changes in meteorological events (including surges), combined with changes in relative sea level and superimposed on well defined astronomical cycles.

Surges are caused by meso-scale changes in atmospheric pressure due to the inverse relationship between air pressure and sea level, i.e. low atmospheric pressure raises the water surface elevation (positive surge) and high atmospheric pressure depresses the water surface elevation (negative surge). These effects can cause water levels to fluctuate considerably above or below the predicted tidal level.

A good rule of thumb is that an atmospheric change of 1 mb results in a sea-level change of 10 mm. Hence, a deep depression with a central pressure of 960 mb will cause the sea level to rise 0.5 m higher than would have been the case had air pressure been at its average value of 1013 mb. In the case of mid-latitude depressions, pressure effects make a slowly varying contribution to the development of a surge event. Consequently, it is the wind effects associated with the depression that have the more significant influence on surge affected extreme water levels around the UK coast. The combined effect of a strong onshore wind and very low pressure can result in extreme water elevations around the coast of eastern England rising by over 2 m above normal levels. Fortunately, the largest positive surges typically coincide with low- to mid-tidal levels, due to interactions between the surge and the tide.

The distribution of the storm surge sea-level elevation for an event with a return period of 50 years is shown in Fig. 9.4. Around the English and Welsh coastlines, the key surge features are:

- the highest surge elevations are found along the East Anglian shoreline (2.5 m) and on the west coast in Liverpool and Morecambe Bay (2 m);
- most of the rest of the UK is subjected to smaller but still significant surges (<1.5 m).

Water levels in the North Sea are particularly susceptible to storm surge effects and there is a long history of such events, with recorded evidence dating back to at least the thirteenth century (Lamb, 1991; van Malde, 1997). The most intense surge in recent history took place between 31 January and 2 February 1953. This event elevated water levels by up to 3 m above the astronomical tidal level and was caused by an externally generated surge event propagating through the North Sea and becoming enhanced by an internally generated surge due to intense winds.

Areas of England and Wales that are at risk from coastal flooding under present hydrodynamic conditions are presented in Fig. 9.5. For those areas at risk from coastal flooding, the area of the floodplain was delineated by either the one in 200-year event or the highest ever recorded flooding event, whichever was the greatest. It is clear that these areas are mainly located along the North Sea coast. It follows that increases in surge activity and associated wind–wave energy that reaches the shoreline will have the greatest impact on these areas.

Changes in the track, intensity and/or frequency of storms around the UK will change the frequency of storm surges of a given height at a particular coastal location; mainly through the action of strong winds. Future changes in storm surge levels may be important to the probability of coastal flooding as there is, in fact, evidence to suggest that surge activity has increased over the past 100 years (OSPAR Commission, 2000). Future changes in the 50-year return-period water level, including storm surge and change in relative sea level, have been modelled. The model employed different rates of sea-level rise for different scenarios, as given in Table 9.2. The results (Table 9.3) show that, for the high emissions (world markets) scenario, the greatest increase in surge height is 1.5 m at Canvey Island, in the Thames Estuary (Hulme et al., 2002). It should, however, be noted that there are large uncertainties in these results (see Lowe and Gregory, 2005).

One hundred-year projections from the storm-surge model plus RSL also illustrate the potential impact on more extreme high-water levels. In the case considered

Fig. 9.4. Storm surge elevation with a return period of 50 years (from UKDMAP, 1998)

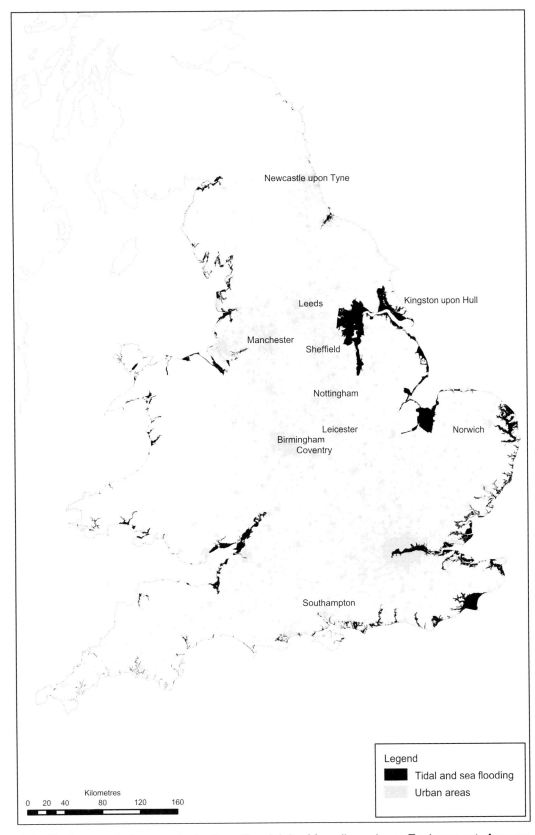

Fig. 9.5. Environment Agency Indicative Floodplain Map (based on Environment Agency data published in 2000)

Table 9.2. Sea-level rise values included in the UKCIP02 modelling work to predict surges under different future scenarios

UKCIP02 scenario	Foresight scenario	Sea level rise value: mm
Low emissions	Global sustainability	90
Medium-low emissions	Local stewardship	200
Medium-high emissions	National enterprise	300
High emissions	World markets	690

here, on the north-east coast of England, the one in 120-year storm-surge event could increase in frequency 17 fold under a medium-high emissions (national enterprise) scenario (assuming a rise in mean sea level of 300 mm). The return period for this event would therefore be only about seven years by the 2080s. Furthermore, the extreme high-water level that presently has a return period of 50 years might have a return period of only three years by the end of this century.

Quantification of changes in storm-surge frequency and intensity requires the use of a storm-surge model which, in turn, uses inputs of changes in storm activity (winds and pressures) from a regional climate model. There are significant uncertainties in both of these models. It is certainly true that projections, such as those reported here from the UKCIP02 scenarios, are model dependent and confidence in the projected patterns and the likely frequencies and magnitudes of storm surges at particular locations around the coast of England and Wales is low.

Waves

Waves can be defined according to the water depth in which they occur:

- the offshore wave height is dependant upon the wind speed and the length of time the wind has been acting upon the sea surface (which, close to the coast, can be affected by the fetch length); and
- the wave form in the nearshore coastal waters is dependent upon the propagation of the waves, which is primarily under the control of the bathymetry, assuming that the energy source (i.e. the wind) remains available.

Severe wave action can not only overtop or cause damage to structural defences but may also cause considerable erosion to intertidal and backshore landforms. Such erosion can, in extreme cases, lead to breaching of artificial and natural

Table 9.3. Potential changes in the 1:50 storm surge level

Location	Current 1:50 event: m[*]	Global sustainability: m[**]	Local stewardship: m[**]	National enterprise: m[**]	World markets: m[**]
Sunderland	1.50	1.60	1.80	1.90	2.30
Flamborough Head	1.75	1.95	2.05	2.15	2.55
Sheringham	2.25	2.75	2.85	2.95	3.35
Canvey Island	2.50	3.40	3.70	3.90	4.00
Dover	2.50	3.20	3.50	3.70	3.80
Isle of Wight	1.00	1.20	1.40	1.50	1.80
Lands End	0.75	0.95	1.05	1.15	1.55
Blackpool	1.75	1.85	1.95	2.05	2.45

[*] UKDMAP (1998).
[**] Factors to convert current levels were taken from available data within UKCIP02 and interpolated for the local stewardship case.

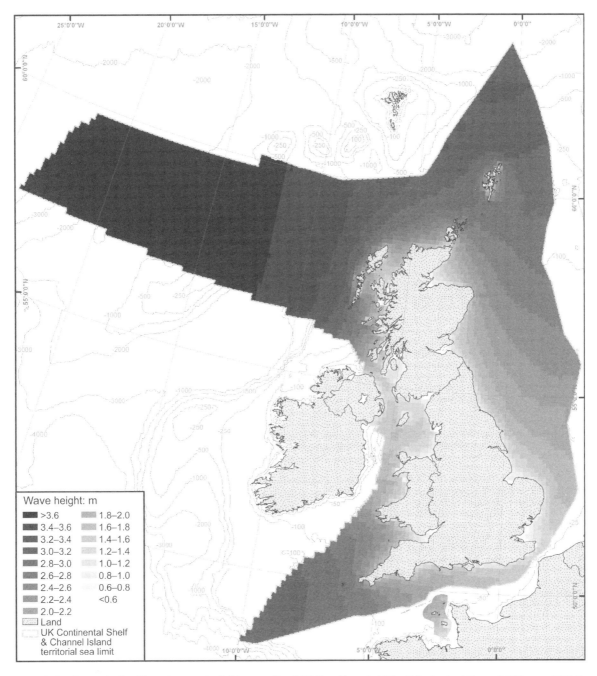

Fig. 9.6. Annual significant wave height over the UK Continental Shelf (adapted from ABPmer, 2004)

defences (e.g. shingle barriers, dune ridges), enabling tidal waters to flood low-lying hinterland.

The dominant offshore wave directions and heights (assuming a 10% exceedance) around the UK are shown in Fig. 9.6. This pattern is replicated for the results for more extreme waves. The key characteristics are:

- the greatest wave heights (2 to 2.5 m) occur on the west coast;
- the dominant wave directions are from the west and south-west on the west and south coasts;
- the dominant wave directions are from the north-north-east on the east coast;

- in parts of the southern North Sea the dominant wave directions are from both the south-west and north-east.

Change in the track, intensity and/or frequency of storms around the UK will, through the action of strong winds, change the frequency of waves of a given height at a particular location on the coast. Work to date suggests that for the national enterprise scenario, the number of winter depressions will increase from approximately five (present-day) to eight (Hulme *et al.*, 2002). This results from a southward shift in the depression track. However, the actual impacts on wave heights will depend on variations in storm, wind and sea-level characteristics. The probability of coastal flooding associated with increased wave heights is also dependent upon the sea-level state. Higher waves are likely to cause the greatest impact when sea-level states are highest (see 'Relative sea-level rise', earlier in this chapter). This effect will be accentuated if relative sea-level rise reduces or negates the protection currently provided by natural nearshore (e.g. barriers, ridges) or offshore (i.e. sandbanks) features.

An investigation reported in the Futurecoast Report (Defra, 2002) considered the impact of changing wave conditions on the shoreline, looking specifically at effects on the net longshore energy and, thus, potential littoral transport. The wave conditions that were investigated ranged from changes in wave direction (of the order of 1 to 2°) to increased Atlantic storminess. It was concluded that, for the ten scenarios tested, there would be little effect on littoral transport. Confidence in these results could be increased if investigations into larger directional changes were undertaken.

Increases in coastal wave height and direction will cause more wave energy to be transmitted to the shoreline at some locations and less energy at others. Where there is an increase in wave energy, there will be an increased probability of breaching and/or overtopping of structural coastal defences. Studies to examine the likely impact of such change under the different future scenarios, suggest that some significant strengthening or raising may be required (Townend and Burgess, 2004). However, the uncertainty in future wave climate alluded to above, means that it is difficult to identify the likely implications for flood probability in any detail.

Changes in the prevailing tracks and directions of major storm events have the potential to alter coastal morphology and hence significantly alter the pattern of erosion and accretion around the coast. In future, morphological changes in response to climate change will also become important at locations that are presently protected from offshore conditions. While there is a negative feedback mechanism between seabed features and wave dynamics (cf. de Vriend and Hulscher, 2003), this feedback may not be sufficient to prevent large areas of the coastline from being destabilised by future changes in wave activity. In addition, if the sea level rises at a faster rate than the coastal morphology can adjust, then natural features (banks, barriers, bars) may become relict and so provide little or no protection. Changes in these features may, in turn, result in changes to the way wave and surge energy is focused at the shoreline, driving further morphological responses that are difficult to predict in detail.

Studies of changes in offshore waves are currently very limited. They have either used simple point models or dynamic models of a region for only a short time or with inadequate driving data. Quantification will require longer simulations using a high-resolution dynamic wave model driven by output from a regional climate model, preferably for the same scenario as the surge predictions. Church *et al.* (2001) also suggest that there is, at present, little agreement between models predicting changes in mid-latitude storm intensity, frequency and variability.

It has been shown that the non-linearity in the coastal system can lead to difficulty in understanding long-term coastal behaviour. However, the appropriateness of extrapolating observed non-linear trends (e.g. exponential trends) to predict future behaviour is fundamentally dependent upon the uncertainty within these trends. Uncertainty also exists with the trends being observed from field data, which are in turn fed into models of coastal behaviour. The example used here is of the future wave climate in the North Sea. The hydrodynamic climate of the North Sea has been shown to have been changing during the latter half of the twentieth century, with waves increasing in height as a result (Carter and Draper, 1988) as a consequence of increasing wind velocities (Hoozemans, 1990). This is supported by data from two wave stations in the north-east Atlantic, which show an increase in the median wave height by 11% and 27% over a ten-year period (Carter and Draper, 1988). However, despite the increase observed in recent years, wave heights are still generally comparable to those at the beginning of the twentieth century (WASA, 1998). Indeed, the IPCC report (Church *et al.*, 2001) states that there is no compelling evidence to indicate that the characteristics (i.e. intensity and frequency) of storms have changed in recent decades. Studies also reveal disagreement concerning the variability of the climate between years. For example, Lamb (1985) states that, 'the North Sea ... is liable to bigger variations of its climate than have hitherto been appreciated', whereas Houghton (1991) concludes that 'there is no firm evidence that the global climate has become more variable over the last few decades'. The fact is that, where annual variation in wave heights has been recorded, the trends are unclear. For example, the largest change in significant wave height at Seven Stones Light Vessel, Lands End, UK, between 1960 and 1990 was recorded from 1971/1972 to 1972/1973, when a decrease of 17% occurred (Carter and Draper, 1988). The high degree of uncertainty suggests that the return periods of wave heights for present climate are poorly understood, with consequential implications for future predictions in coastal areas.

Coastal morphology and sediment supply

The coastal morphodynamic system is complex, involving feedback between three main sub-systems: hydrodynamics, sediment regime and morphology. Essentially, water motion is induced by energy in the form of waves and currents. Water motion results in sediment transport and, hence, morphological change. Within the sediment system, spatial and temporal patterns and gradients link coastal morphology with nearshore hydrodynamics. A close mutual dependence also exists between the hydrodynamics and the large- and small-scale morphological features of the seabed and the shore (Van Rijn, 1993; de Vriend and Hulscher, 2003).

Viewed in this context, coastal morphology includes all landforms present in the following coastal areas:

- nearshore seabed, i.e. pits, sandwaves and sandbanks. An example of a sand-bank is Haisborough Sand, located 14 km to 16 km offshore, which forms part of a series of banks representing the Norfolk Banks;
- shoreline, i.e. headlands, pocket beaches and log-spiral bays. Headlands are less erodible lengths of coast such as St Govans Head, Pembrokeshire. On exposed coasts, such as Devon and Cornwall where there is limited sediment supply, pocket beaches form between rocky headlands. Where there is greater distance between headlands and the shoreline is erodible, log-spiral bays will tend to form, as, for instance, in Bracklesham Bay in Hampshire;
- coastal margin, i.e. saltmarsh, mudflat and lagoon systems. An example is The Fleet, Dorset which is a brackish lagoon enclosed by a long linear shingle beach (Chesil Bank). The Fleet is the largest example of a barrier-built saline lagoon in the UK and Chesil Bank is one of the three major shingle structures in the UK;
- coastal inlets, e.g. Portsmouth, Langstone and Chichester Harbours, Hampshire/West Sussex; and

- estuaries, e.g. the Humber Estuary, Yorkshire/Lincolnshire. The Humber Estuary is one of the largest estuaries in England, receiving drainage from approximately one-fifth of the country.

As a driver, coastal morphology is defined as a change to the landforms in any of the areas listed above. Morphological changes result from variations in the sediment supply to the coast, which, in turn, is a direct response to changes in:

- sediment availability;
- external forcings (e.g. hydrodynamics, relative sea-level rise); and
- anthropogenic activities (e.g. coastal defence, dredging, reclamation and managed realignment).

It can therefore be seen that this driver has strong linkages to the other drivers in the coastal processes driver set.

The morphological consequences of material erosion from the seabed and shore, its movement and subsequent accretion include:

- removal, movement and creation of banks and channels;
- changes in the elevation and geographical position of the coastal profile;
- landward movement of eroding coastal features, such as cliffs and headlands;
- changes to sedimentary features, such as beaches, pits, bars and berms;
- changes from one type of coastal form to another.

In general, coastal erosion is more likely than coastal accretion. Flood probability is increased by coastal erosion in two ways:

1. directly: shoreline erosion leads to loss of land and flood defence assets; and
2. indirectly: loss of foreshore material increases the exposure of the shoreline to waves and surges that could potentially lead to an increase in flooding and/or undermine existing flood defences.

Such is the potential for changes in sediment supply and coastal morphology to impact coastal flood risk that they may, over the next 100 years, be a more significant driver than climate change. Whether this is the case in practice depends on the strategies adopted in coastal defence and coastal management. Under the baseline assumption that the current coastal flood defence policy is continued into the future, it is the failure, abandonment or realignment of coastal defences due to other driver changes that would condition the behaviour of this driver. For example, the sediment supply in some coastal zones may increase in future due to the breaching or removal of defences in response to changes in the wave/surge climate. This is the case because breaching or removal of defences may allow material behind the defence line to be mobilised through shoreline erosion. The resulting increase in sediment availability may have positive (i.e. accretional) impacts downdrift through sediment accumulation. However, the possibility also exists that breaching may create a new sediment sink behind the failed defences, resulting in sediment starvation downdrift. This single example serves to demonstrate the complex nature of morphological response in the coastal system, which precludes detailed morphological predictions over anything longer than a few months or years.

The amount of change to the coastal morphology and sediment supply is dependent, to a lesser degree, upon the changes occurring in the other drivers linked to it within this driver set. Examples of driver interactions are:

- with a rising relative sea level, increasing rates of littoral drift and an insufficient supply of sediment from the existing sources to balance the volume of material transported in the longshore, erosion could be expected on the beach and upper shoreface (Stive *et al.*, 1990). Hence, driver interaction will promote accelerated retreat of the shoreline;

- rising relative sea level will also enhance the degree to which the energy supplied by the storms and associated surges and waves reaches the coast. For example, if sea level rises faster than the morphodynamic system can adjust, then offshore sandbanks may be destroyed, removing the protection they currently provide to the shoreline;
- changing patterns of littoral drift or sediment supply could result in the extension and/or retreat of barrier beach/spit systems across estuary mouths. This, in turn, could result in the partial closure or opening of the estuary or the movement of the river (e.g. the River Alde, Suffolk). The outcome would be to radically alter the flow and flood regime in the estuary through interaction with drivers of river and inland flooding.

While our ability to model morphological change at the scales relevant to the Foresight Project (years to decades and more) is, at present, severely limited, it is improving significantly and this improvement is likely to accelerate in the future. Present research is striving to develop practical methods of making morphological predictions, with one promising line of research being through the use of theoretical behavioural system models (Townend, 2003).

Nevertheless, as with many areas of coastal research, our ability to make morphological predictions is hampered by a lack of good quality, long-term data sets, which means that the observation of long-term trends and the calibration and validation of long-term models are both difficult to achieve with the required degree of accuracy. In addition, large uncertainties exist in predicting coastal morphological behaviour beyond the period represented in the data. For example, processes of granular motion can be used to determine sediment transport at local scales and over short periods but, because sediment motion is inherently indeterminate over large spatial and temporal scales, processed-based models cannot be used to predict the sediment transfer dynamics responsible for change and evolution of coastal morphology (de Vriend and Hulscher, 2003).

Essentially, uncertainty in the future form of geomorphological features arises from the limited predictability of the exchanges taking place and the dependence of these exchanges on future (and uncertain) variations in the forcing conditions, e.g. hydrodynamics. In more detail these arise from:

- uncertainty in model parameters: if uncertainty exists concerning which processes are significant over the scale of interest, then it follows that there are uncertainties concerning those parameters required in the model;
- uncertainty in the relative significance of forcing parameters at different scales. For example, Wright *et al.* (1985) have shown that the characteristics of the beach and surf zone system result from the time-integration of numerous processes that have different spatial- and temporal-scales;
- interactions between external forcing parameters, e.g. hydrodynamics, and internal coastal dynamics, i.e. morphodynamics. While most predictive models assume that the coastline evolves towards an equilibrium condition, this type of non-linear, dissipative system can be maintained in states far-from-equilibrium, due to self-organisation. This implies that the way the system responds to perturbations about a given state is controlled by the internal dynamics of the system, rather than the applied forcing;
- variations in external forcing parameters have and will continue to occur: as outlined in the waves and surges driver description, uncertainty exists regarding the future state of the climatic and hydrodynamic conditions responsible for forcing future changes in sediment supply and coastal morphology.

In conclusion, this driver is of great significance to coastal flooding (n.b. coastal erosion is dealt with in Chapters 16 and 17), but when compared to the other drivers, uncertainties are high, the predictive capability of models is more limited and more expert judgement has been required in terms of assessing its relative importance.

Future risk of coastal flooding

Analysis of the four coastal process drivers and their potential to produce changes in the frequency and extent of coastal flooding under the four future scenarios has been scaled to provide an indication of future changes in local flood probability. In performing the analysis, an assessment of the uncertainty associated with each driver has been undertaken, as described in the previous sections.

With information taken from previous studies, it has been possible to quantify the potential changes to relative sea level and surge events for the various scenarios (Tables 9.1 and 9.3). The results largely reflect the different emission scenarios that are assumed for each of the Foresight Futures (Table 9.2). For RSL this leads to a notable variability between scenarios that is somewhat larger than the spatial variability. A similar variability is observed in storm surge levels, although this is superimposed on the inherent spatial variability of this variable, where the largest events are likely to occur on the east coast (Table 9.3).

There are, as yet, no quantitative predictions for future wave conditions. From the available evidence it seems likely that higher emissions may result in storms becoming more frequent. Whether they also become more extreme remains an area of significant uncertainty. However, given the increased potential for large-scale changes in the Atlantic climate, under the more extreme emission scenarios, there is a strong possibility that storm tracks may be altered; this will be particularly the case if the overturning circulation in the North Atlantic, that gives rise to the Gulf Stream, should weaken or alter (Bryden et al., 2005). Consequently, the uncertainty and potential risk increase substantially with increasing emission scenarios. This implies that there is a greater risk of this type of change under world markets than global sustainability.

The response observed on the coast, in terms of sediment transport and the evolution of morphological features will, to a large extent, reflect the changes in forcing conditions outlined above. Thus, once again, more dramatic impacts may be expected under the more extreme emission scenarios. In particular, changes in storm tracking and, hence, wave characteristics (notably direction) could re-distribute sediments on the coast and so substantially change mobile features such as sand banks, spits and beaches. However, this sort of change is dependent on a series of complex interactions and so is difficult to predict, and remains highly uncertain at this stage.

It is important to recognise that the morphology of the coast will also be influenced by developments and other human activities that take place there. This implies a very significant feedback with the particular future scenario. For instance, under local stewardship one might anticipate limited funds for the provision and maintenance of defences, coupled with a desire for less intervention. As a result, in some areas this is likely to lead to increased sediment availability as, for instance, cliffs are allowed to erode, whereas in other areas failed seawalls may lead to low-lying land acting as a sink for sediments. In complete contrast, under world markets, the demand for development land (particularly at the coast) will increase the need for high-quality defences, leading to ever greater protection of our coast. Holding the line against rising sea levels may lead to progressive degradation of our beaches and, at least in some areas, this is likely to be addressed by an ongoing programme of replenishment. Thus, how we choose to manage the coast will itself alter the form and character of our coast and this is likely to be different under the various future scenarios, as discussed further in Chapter 23.

References

ABPmer, 2004. *Atlas of UK Marine Renewable Energy Resources*, Report for the DTI.

Bryden, H.L., Longworth, H.R. and Cunningham, S.A., 2005. 'Slowing of the Atlantic meridional overturning circulation at 25° N', *Nature*, 438(7068), 655–657.

Carter, D.J.T. and Draper, L., 1988. 'Has the north-east Atlantic become rougher?', *Nature*, 332, 494.

Church, J.A., Gregory, J.M., Huybrechts, P., Kuhn, M., Lambeck, K., Nhuan, M.T., Qin, D. and Woodworth, P.L., 2001. 'Changes in sea-level', in *Climate Change 2001. The Scientific Basis*, eds Houghton, J.T., Ding, Y., Griggs, D.J., Noguer, M., van der Linden, P.J. and Xiaosu, D., Cambridge University Press, Cambridge, 639–693.

Defra, 2002. *Futurecoast Final Project Report and CD-ROM*, Department of Environment, Food and Rural Affairs, London.

de la Vega-Leinert, A.C. and Nicholls, R.J., 2006. 'Potential implications of sea-level rise for Great Britain', *Journal of Coastal Research* (in press).

Douglas, B.C., 2000. 'Sea-level change in the era of the recording tide gauge', in *Sea-Level Rise: History and consequences*, eds Douglas, B.C., Kearney, M.S. and Leatherman, S.P., Academic Press, London, 37–64.

Gregory, J.M., 1993. 'Sea-level changes under increasing atmospheric CO_2 in a transient coupled ocean-atmosphere GCM experiment', *Journal of Climate*, 6, 2247–2262.

Hoozemans, F.M.J., 1990. 'Long term changes in wind and wave climate on the North Sea', *Proceedings of the 22nd International Conference of Coastal Engineering*, ASCE, New York, 1888–1894.

Houghton, J.T., 1991. 'Scientific assessment of climate change: summary of the IPCC working group I report', in *Climate Change: Science, impacts and policy*, eds Jager, J. and Ferguson, H.L., Cambridge University Press, Cambridge, 23–40.

Hulme, M., Jenkins, G.J., Lu, X., Turnpenny, J.R., Mitchell, T.D., Jones, R.G., Lowe, J., Murphy, J.M., Hassell, D., Boorman, P., McDonald, R. and Hill, S., 2002. *Climate Change Scenarios for the United Kingdom: The UKCIP02 Scientific Report*, Tyndall Centre for Climate Change Research, School of Environmental Sciences, University of East Anglia, Norwich.

Lamb, H., 1985. 'Climate and its variability in the North-Sea–Northeast Atlantic region', in *The North Sea – A highway of economic and cultural exchange*, 27–38.

Lamb, H., 1991. *Historic Storms of the North Sea, British Isles and NW Europe*, Cambridge University Press, Cambridge.

Lowe, J.A. and Gregory, J.M., 2005. 'The effects of climate change on storm surges around the United Kingdom', *Philosophical Transactions of the Royal Society A*, 363, 1313–1328.

Mercer, J.H., 1978. 'West Antarctic ice sheet and CO_2 greenhouse effect: A threat of disaster', *Nature*, 271, 321–325.

Nicholls, R.J. and Lowe, J.A., 2004. 'Benefits of mitigation of climate change for coastal areas', *Global Environmental Change*, 14, 229–244.

Nicholls, R.J. and Wilson, T., 2001. 'Integrated impacts on coastal areas and river flooding', in *Regional Climate Change Impact and Response Studies in East Anglia and North West England (RegIS)*, eds Holman I.P. and Loveland P.J., Final Report of MAFF Project No. CC0337, 54–101.

Oppenheimer, M., 1998. 'Global warming and the stability of the West Antarctic ice sheet', *Nature*, 393, 325–332.

OSPAR Commission, 2000. *Quality Status Report 2000: Region II – Greater North Sea*, OSPAR Commission, London.

Shennan, I. and Horton, B., 2002. 'Holocene land- and sea-level changes in Great Britain', *Journal of Quaternary Science*, 17, 511–526.

Stive, M.J.F., Roelvink, J.A. and De Vriend, H.J., 1990. 'Large-scale coastal evolution concept', *Proceedings of the 22nd Coastal Engineering Conference*, ASCE, New York, 1962–1974.

Townend, I.H., 2003. 'Coast and estuary behaviour systems', in *Coastal Sediments '03: Crossing disciplinary boundaries – Proceedings of the 5th International Symposium on Coastal Engineering and Science of Coastal Sediment Processes*, East Meets West Productions (EMW) Inc., Corpus Christi, USA, 1–14 (online at www.estuary-guide.net).

Townend, I.H. and Burgess, K., 2004. 'Methodology for assessing the impact of climate change upon coastal defence structures', in *Proceedings of 29th International Conference on Coastal Engineering*, ASCE, New York, 3953–3966.

UKDMAP, 1998. CD-ROM produced by British Oceanographic Data Centre. Windows 95/ NT version, third edition, British Oceanographic Data Centre, Liverpool.

Van Malde, J., 1997. 'Historical extraordinary water movements in the North Sea area', *Hydrographic Journal*, 86, 17–24.

Van Rijn, L., 1993. *Principles of Coastal Morphodynamics*, Aqua Publications, Amsterdam.

Vaughan, D.G. and Spouge, J.R., 2002. 'Risk estimation of collapse of the west Antarctic ice sheet', *Climatic Change*, 52, 65–91.

de Vriend, H.J. and Hulscher, S.J.M.H. (eds), 2003. 'Predicting aggregated-scale coastal evolution', *Journal of Coastal Research*, 19, 755–866.

WASA, 1998. 'Changing waves and storms in the northeast Atlantic?', *Bulletin of the American Meteorological Society*, 79(5), 741–760.

Woodworth, P.L., Gregory, J.M. and Nicholls, R.J., 2004. 'Long term sea-level changes and their impacts', in *The Sea, Vol. 13*, eds Robinson, A.R. and Brink, K.H., Harvard University Press, Cambridge, MA, 715–753.

Woodworth, P.L., Tsimplis, M.N., Flather, R.A. and Shennan, I., 1999. 'A review of the trends observed in the British Isles mean sea-level data measured by tide gauges', *Geophysical J. Int.*, 136, 651–670.

Wright, L.D., May, S.K., Short, A.D. and Green, M.O., 1985. 'Beach and surf zone equilibria and response times', *Proceedings of the 19th International Conference of Coastal Engineering*, ASCE, New York, 2150–2164.

10 Urban change

Adrian J. Saul and Richard M. Ashley

Background

Urban floods have significant impacts in terms of flood damage, disruption to essential services and transport, and frequently cause a pollution hazard together with an associated risk to human health. The risk and consequences of urban flooding are therefore of major concern to the majority of UK stakeholders and, in particular, to the public.

This chapter specifically addresses urban pluvial and fluvial flooding with a specific emphasis on the performance of the local drainage and sewerage systems within the integrated intra-urban area. The chapter does not address the flooding of urban areas due to rivers overtopping their banks, coastal breaches due to surges, waves and sea-level rise and the impact of coastal erosion on the flooding of coastal urban areas.

Issues are addressed that have the potential to create significant changes in present-day urban flood risk and which create new challenges beyond those that are currently covered by present strategies. The scope of the research has therefore been set against the background of existing policies, technical capabilities, and investment and management strategies, together with current research and new developments in urban flood risk management.

The Foresight research in the intra-urban area had the following objectives:

- To identify the drivers that influence a change in future urban flood risk.
- To deepen the analysis of the impact of the drivers for the timescale 2030–2100, using the Foresight futures scenarios (world markets, global responsibility, national enterprise and local stewardship).
- To rank the drivers in terms of their importance to influence a change in flood risk within the urban environment.
- To determine the extent to which the impact of the drivers on flood risk is amenable to high-level quantification for urban and peri-urban environments and, where possible, quantify and analyse the resulting future flood risk for each of the Foresight futures scenarios.
- Assess the uncertainty in the flood risk estimates associated with the drivers.
- To inform of the need for future work.

The extent of the urban flooding

Urban flooding occurs at different spatial scales within the intra-urban area and these are highlighted in Fig. 10.1. Currently, the principal assets for the conveyance of surface water runoff in the urban areas of the UK are drains and sewers. Each property typically has arrangements for managing surface water using roof collection and conveyance systems, usually in the form of gutter and downpipe systems that transport the surface water from the roof to the ground level.

Once at ground level, storm water from buildings is conveyed, usually below ground, in private drains that usually connect to public sewers. Alternatively, use may be made of local measures termed 'sustainable urban drainage systems' to either temporarily store the surface water for subsequent return to the sewer system or to infiltrate the surface water into the ground. Such systems are becoming more common (CIRIA, 2000), but their installation is a function of the ground conditions, the layout of the urban development, issues surrounding the planning and adoption consents, and their acceptance by all stakeholders, particularly the public.

In older urban areas the public sewer systems are mainly 'combined', where domestic and industrial effluents and storm water are conveyed in the same pipes of the system. Combined sewer overflows (CSOs) (Balmforth *et al.*, 1994; Saul *et al.*, 2003b) are constructed to relieve the system of the excess flows that cannot be accommodated by the downstream sewers or the treatment works, thereby reducing the risk of surcharge and surface flooding in the catchment upstream of the CSO. Similarly, storage tank structures are commonly employed to retain the effluents in the system for subsequent treatment. Separate drainage systems are also

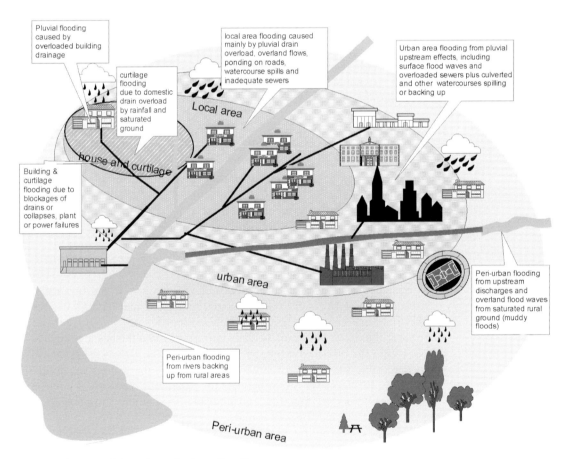

Fig. 10.1. The spatial scales of urban flooding

used, particularly for new developments, in which the foul effluents are conveyed in one set of pipes (directly to the treatment works) with the surface water discharged directly to receiving waters (inland or coastal) by way of a second set of pipes.

Between the 1960s and 1990s, flooding impacts have increased significantly (Crichton, 2002) due to population growth, increased urban development (some in flood-prone areas) and increased wealth. In England and Wales, incidents of flooding from sewers are reported to the Office of Water Services (OFWAT) and are recorded on one of the three registers:

- DG5 – Properties at risk of flooding more than twice in ten years at the end of the year.
- DG10 – Properties at risk of flooding more than once in ten years (but less than two in ten) at the end of the year.
- OFA (other flooded areas) – Flooding that only affects areas outside properties, for example gardens, footpaths, roads and fields.

Properties at risk are then defined as properties that have suffered or are likely to suffer internal flooding from public foul, combined or surface water sewers due to overloading of the sewerage system more frequently than the relevant period (either once or twice in ten years). Internal flooding is defined as flooding which enters a building or passes below a suspended floor. For reporting purposes, buildings are restricted to those normally occupied and used for residential, public, commercial, business or industrial purposes.

Of concern is the mixture of foul sewage and stormwater that enters buildings as this has a potential impact on health (Defra, 2003, 2005b; Tapsell and Tunstall, 2003; Reacher *et al.*, 2004) and, in England and Wales, properties at risk of sewer flooding once and twice in ten years currently stand at 20 368 (0.091%) and 5644 (0.025%) respectively.

However, in 2001 OFWAT reported that 7100 properties in England and Wales were flooded internally with sewage and of these properties some 55% of incidents were due to 'causes other than hydraulic overload'. These figures do not include internal flooding due to severe storm events but, in contrast, the autumn 2000 floods resulted in the flooding of 10 000 properties at a cost of c. £1 billion (EA, 2001; Penning-Rowsell *et al.*, 2002).

Flood mechanisms in the intra-urban zone

Within the urban area there are several mechanisms that may cause surface flooding (Fleming, 2002). These will also be influenced by the way in which future climatic conditions may change the rainfall inputs, due to possible changes in the physical infrastructure of a catchment, including urbanisation and new development, due to the implementation and wider use of new and newly established sustainable technologies, and of the changes that are made to the management and operation of the drainage system (Lancaster *et al.*, 2004; CIRIA, 2003).

Similarly, the management of the runoff within the intra-urban area, e.g. the culverting of watercourses or the construction of flood control structures, has important implications for the management of flood risk within the urban area.

Primary flood mechanisms

Surface runoff from slopes draining to urban areas

Here the flooding is remote from the cause and occurs due to a rainfall event on the rural or peri-urban area that surrounds or is adjacent to the intra-urban area.

The runoff from these surrounding areas, often referred to as 'muddy flooding' (Boardman *et al.*, 2003), is a function of the size, the ground characteristics (cover and soil type) and the slope of the upstream catchment. It is feasible for the intra-urban area to be flooded because there is no sewer system where the flow immediately enters the area, or due to the fact that there are insufficient or inadequate gulley entry points to the underground drainage system or that the underground system is hydraulically overloaded.

Urban pluvial (rainwater) flooding

This occurs primarily when the volume of rainwater that falls on the urban area cannot enter the underground drainage system sufficiently quickly or due to the fact that the below-ground drainage system is hydraulically inadequate.

At the most upstream part of the urban drainage system (Fig. 10.1), flooding may occur due to inadequate roof drainage. This may be caused by poor original design and installation, or the lack of maintenance and repair. Where the building is a large asset – like an office building – it is likely that the rainwater goods will be properly managed and that failure would only occur due to overload in high rainfall. Once removed from the roof, rainwater may be dealt with by local source control and storage (e.g. rainwater butts, storage under driveways or in-sewer flow control, Faram *et al.*, 2004), local disposal using sustainable urban drainage systems (e.g. soakaways, infiltration systems, porous pavements, swales, wetlands, CIRIA, 2000; EA, 2004; Wong, 2004), or by discharge into a drain or sewer (BS EN 752; CIRIA, 2005).

Where the drainage system is within the private curtilage of a property the operation and maintenance of that system is the responsibility of the property owner. It is believed that much of this type of property drainage in the UK is poorly maintained, primarily due to a lack of awareness and, as a consequence, the failure of private drains is a major cause of local internal flooding. Clearly, in future, if climate change results in an increase in rainfall runoff, the risk of flooding from private drains is likely to increase. There is therefore a need to plan for this impact of climate change (ODPM, 2004).

In the main sewer network, flooding may occur where the pipes in the system have a hydraulic capacity that is less than the flows that enter the pipes due to a rainfall event. Hydraulic inadequacy results in pipe-full flow and a backup of the excess flow in the system. This results in a surcharge of the system that may lead to the flooding of basements or the flooding of the catchment surface by way of any access point from the sewer system, usually manholes.

Where flows pass on to permeable areas, there is the potential for the runoff to infiltrate into the ground, subject to the type of cover and soil and the extent of soil saturation (HRW, 1983; FWR, 1998). Future climate change across much of the UK is expected to result in longer wetter periods in winter (Hulme *et al.*, 2002), which will result in a reduction of the capacity of soil to accept infiltrating flows at such times. Hence, in parts of the UK, it may be anticipated that local flooding due to a reduction in infiltration capacity is likely to increase in the winter months.

Flooding of properties may also occur due to the flood waves that are generated over the catchment surface, when the height of the flood wave is greater than the protection level of the property. It is not yet possible accurately to determine the pathways of such overland flood flows with any certainty but advances in knowledge are currently being made, e.g. Jain *et al.* (2004), Lhomme *et al.* (2004) and Chen *et al.* (2005).

Flooding due to asset performance and failure

Sewer flooding is also caused by the lack of effective performance of the system assets and due to asset failure. Currently, at the time of flood events, the UK sewerage undertakers have only a vague idea of the level of service (OFWAT, 2004a) and level of performance that are achieved by their urban drainage systems. This is one of the reasons why attention has recently focused on the need for enhanced serviceability indicators for sewerage assets (e.g. OFWAT/EA, 2001; Fenner, 2002; Heywood *et al.*, 2002; Matos *et al.*, 2003; UKWIR, 2002; Water UK, 2004). Of particular relevance to the intra-urban area is the need for performance measures that describe the incidence of flooding from sewers due to the following processes:

- sewer blockages;
- sewer collapses;
- the presence of sewer sediments;
- mechanical and electrical plant failure;
- pumping station operation;
- inadequate hydraulic access pathways;
- sewer pipe hydraulic inadequacy.

At the present time there is no consistent approach to predict the way in which urban flood risk changes as a function of changes in asset performance and deterioration. Such approaches are the subject of current research, e.g. Sægrov *et al.* (2004), Cashman *et al.* (2004). The problem is further compounded when repair, rehabilitation and replacement interventions are made to the system (Montero and Villanueva, 2004) as these changes modify the status of the condition of the pipes and their future deterioration rate (Baik *et al.*, 2006; Micevski *et al.*, 2006; Savic, 2005).

In respect of sustainable urban drainage systems, a further problem is the clogging of infiltration systems caused by high sediment loads conveyed typically across catchment surfaces and within sewer systems during storm events (Siriwardene *et al.*, 2004). Such clogging results in a gradual reduction in the hydraulic capacity of the system and often leads to unexpected flooding that is caused by relatively small storms. The need to maintain such systems is now well understood (e.g. EA, 2004; Jefferies *et al.*, 1999; Schluter and Jefferies, 2004).

Flooding in the urban area caused by a back-up from urban streams

Sewer capacity may also be compromised where the sewer is interconnected with a river or coastal system. The performance may be hindered by a back-up of flow in the sewer system due to increased river depth or coastal water levels that inundate the discharge outlets of the sewer system. The consequence of such a back-up of flow is a function of the extent of the water depth and of the layout and elevation of the sewer system. This may result in the flooding of basements and the catchment surface with sewage alone or with a mixture of sewage and fluvial-derived flows. Low-lying areas of the intra-urban area are particularly prone to this type of flooding.

Co-incident flooding

Co-incident flooding is of major concern as it combines the influence of pluvial and fluvial flooding, and hence potentially presents the worst-case scenario in respect of the extent of the impacts on the urban area.

Flooding due to fluvial and coastal inundation

Inundation of the intra-urban catchment surface can be caused by the failure, overtopping or bypassing of the flood defences (Christensen and Christensen, 2003; Hrabak *et al.*, 2004; ICE, 2001). This results in an inundation of the sewer system that becomes full and subsequently less operable due to the extremely slack hydraulic gradients that occur due to the ponding effect of the flood on the catchment surface.

Secondary factors that increase or reduce flood risk

Urbanisation and urban creep

Any increase in the extent of urbanisation of the peri-urban area that drains to the existing drainage system of an intra-urban area (ODPM, 2001, 2002, 2003a; HRW, 2005) or due to urban creep, i.e. any increase in the impervious area within an existing intra-urban catchment, for example the construction of patios, extensions to property, etc., may result in an increase in surface runoff that exceeds the design flowrate for the existing sewer system. The effect of such urbanisation is to increase flood risk.

A critical aspect of such urbanisation is the level of density and the potential for the proliferation of high-density developments that may occur under some of the scenarios (ODPM, 2003b).

Culverting of natural watercourses

There are many examples where the natural watercourses within the intra-urban area have been culverted, primarily to afford additional land area for development (Akornor and Page, 2004). Clearly, such culverts have a finite hydraulic capacity and, as a consequence, they suffer from the same hydraulic limitations as the pipes in the drainage system, and due to the fact that they are also prone to collapse, blockage, deterioration, etc. Hence, should a fluvial flood flow exceed the design capacity of a culvert, or should the hydraulic performance of the culvert be impaired, the excess flood flow usually has no alternative other than to inundate the catchment surface of the intra-urban area that surrounds the culvert. This problem is further compounded when the entrance to the culvert incorporates a trash rack or safety screen. These are prone to partial blockage by debris with the result that the hydraulic capacity of the culvert system is impaired.

Groundwater infiltration into sewers

While drainage systems are constructed as watertight structures very few mature systems remain completely watertight. Minor movements at joints or cracks, e.g. caused by ground movements, can result in the pipe system beginning to leak. Hence, if the groundwater table is above the crown of the pipe, groundwater will infiltrate into the sewer (Bertrand-Krajewski *et al.*, 2004a; CIRIA, 1997). The capacity taken up by the infiltration-related flows is not available at the time of storm events and will, in effect, reduce a sewer system's capacity to accept storm flow. This will increase the risk of flooding.

Technological change

The future is likely to see the increased use of water recycling systems, water re-use systems, sustainable urban drainage systems and local flood prevention intervention structures (e.g. Allbee, 2005; Blanksby *et al.*, 2004; Dixon *et al.*, 2001; USEPA, 2002; ODPM, 2003c; Kellagher and Lauchlan, 2005). The use of sustainable drainage systems (SUDS) in new developments is endorsed by the UK Government's Planning Policy Guidance Note PPG25 (ODPM, 2001) and in Part H of the Building Regulations and in *Sewers for Adoption* (5th edition) (WRC, 2001). Emphasis is now given to the sustainability of systems and guidance is provided by Ashley *et al.* (2004b), Foxon *et al.* (2002) and ODPM (2005). The impact of such technological change should usually result in a reduction in flood risk within the intra-urban area.

Sediments in sewer systems

Sediments are known to deposit in sewer systems and they are known to impair hydraulic capacity and contribute to the creation of high pollution loads (Ackers *et al.*, 1996; Saul *et al.*, 2003a). The maintenance of sediments is a key performance issue and research has shown that street sweeping, gully emptying and sewer-cleaning activity all have the potential to minimise the impact of sediment entry into systems (Ashley *et al.*, 2004a; Bertrand-Krajewski *et al.*, 2004b). However, should maintenance activity not be practised, there is the potential for sediments to build up leading to a potential increase in flood risk.

Future change in dry weather flow

There are many other factors that may influence a future change in the dry weather flow (CIRIA, 1998). On the one hand, a year-on-year increase in per capita water consumption and an increase in population will result in an increase in the volume and magnitude of the dry weather flow with the consequent reduction in the available capacity of the pipe to accommodate wet weather flow. Conversely, the implementation of water saving, water re-use and source control technology will result in a reduction in the dry weather flow, leading to an increase in the available hydraulic capacity of the system at the time of storm events and a consequent reduction in flood risk. Conversely, a reduced dry weather flow will result in an increase in the potential for sediments to deposit due to a reduction in the self-cleansing velocity at the time of peak dry weather flow thereby resulting in a potential increase in flood risk.

Urban channel pathways

Road systems may be used to channel and transfer floodwater from one part of the urban system to another. In the case where the floodwater is transferred to green areas or rivers, the flood risk will be reduced but if the flood flows are delivered to dense urban areas these will cause a great deal of damage. The future planning of such drainage features is likely to become a key and fundamental aspect of flood risk management.

Public attitudes and stakeholder behaviour

Given the size of the investment required to address and mitigate the impacts of urban floods, a likely response is adaptation, whereby there will be a shift of the burden and responsibility on to the individual and away from the state, increasing the role of private-sector provision. Such trends are already emerging with respect to insurance. The corollary of this would be a continued growth of a compensation culture as members of the public have increasingly to pay for individual flood protection. The increasing proportion of income required will have social implications linked to ability to pay and may further entrench areas of social deprivation.

It is also anticipated that there will be a continuation of the legislative and regulatory response. This will involve the introduction and extension of planning and building standards and controls, and the more extensive use of regulatory instruments. Here the role, influence and expectations of business and industry will be important, but it is likely that there will be some centralisation of flooding policy and a strengthening of the central role of the Environment Agency.

Such centralisation could create a disjuncture between local communities and local representation and appointed agencies. Moves, such as the disconnection of sewage and storm drainage, the managed retreat from certain urban areas (likely to be those experiencing a range of social problems), may well result in increased social tensions, with implications for commerce and business as well as local public-service delivery and the ability of local authorities to cope. What might be portrayed as 'sustainable solutions' may become increasingly resisted at a local level, primarily as they are seen as infringements on civil liberties and human rights.

At the same time there will be an increased emphasis on the provision of improved information to a wide range of stakeholders, such that all stakeholders make better and informed decisions (Defra, 2004, 2005a). At the community level there will be investment in community capacity building, which will complement and, to some extent, underpin the expectations and therefore investment decisions of the business community, especially the services-related industries. There will be improvements in information and data collection and collation, and an increasing use of 'real-time' information as a primary response to reduce vulnerability.

Summary of factors that influence urban flood risk

In summary, there are many factors that influence flood risk in the urban area. The characteristics of the urban environment are particularly important and this includes the nature, location and characteristics of the drainage network, the inter-action and inter-operation between the permeable and impermeable areas, the groundwater level, the underground drainage system and the fluvial and coastal systems.

In addition, flood risk is also influenced by the performance of the assets in respect of leakage, infiltration, blockage and collapse and of intervention strategies (rehabilitation or replacement of sewer assets, the inclusion of source control and sustainable systems and of changes to river and coastal infrastructure, etc.). Any change to the urban infrastructure for the purpose of flood risk management is the subject of the legislative and planning process. PPG 25 highlights the need for compulsory flood risk assessment and hence there is a need to take regard of all stakeholder attitudes, interests and behaviour, particularly in respect of new legislation, and regulatory and planning guidance.

In respect of the Foresight Futures initiative, these parameters provide the context for the understanding and interpretation of the drivers that influence a change in urban flood risk.

Identification of relevant drivers

A driver was defined in this research as 'any phenomenon that may change the state of the flooding system' over the next 30–100 years. The drivers previously described at the catchment scale were adapted for the intra-urban zone and these are described in Table 10.1. The source, pathway, receptor concept was again used and driver groups were adapted to climate change, runoff, urban conveyance systems and processes, human behaviour and socio-economics. A pathway driver was also included specifically to describe the performance and deterioration of the underground assets of the urban drainage system.

Driver ranking and uncertainty

Objectives

For the intra-urban area, the objective was to determine how the 'native parameters' are likely to change between the present-day and the 2050s and 2080s, and to determine how drivers are likely to contribute to changes in flood risk (in the 2050s and 2080s). To do this, a scenario analysis was completed using the same climatic and socio-economic scenarios as identified for the fluvial catchment scale analysis. Current flood risk management policy and philosophy and flood management investment and expenditure was used in the assessment and, in a similar way to the methodology described in Chapter 2, *a priori,* in that the ranking of the drivers was an estimate of the driver impacts on flood risk.

Table 10.1. Drivers of flood risk in the intra-urban area

Driver group	Driver	SPR classification	Explanation
Climate change	Precipitation	Source	Changes in short-duration precipitation – amount, intensity, duration, location, seasonality and clustering
Runoff	Urbanisation	Pathway	A change in land management with greenfield and pervious surfaces covered by less-pervious materials (buildings and infrastructure) and associated new conveyance systems
	Management of peri-urban rural land	Pathway	Changes in the management of land adjacent to the urban area that influence runoff Into the urban area, e.g. 'muddy floods'
Urban conveyance systems and processes	Environmental management and regulation	Pathway	The management of the green areas within the urban landscape, including flora and fauna
	Urban watercourse conveyance, blockage and sedimentation	Pathway	Processes associated with above-ground overland surface flow in natural watercourses and man-made systems, including performance, maintenance and operation
	Sewer conveyance, blockage and sedimentation	Pathway	As above, but associated with processes that occur in below-ground drainage systems
	Impact of external flooding on intra-urban drainage systems	Pathway	Loss of conveyance and serviceability in below-ground drainage systems due to flooding from external sources
	Intra-urban asset deterioration	Pathway	Changes in the performance, condition and serviceability of urban drainage assets (ageing, performance wear-and-tear and rehabilitation management)

Driver impacts were assessed on the basis that source and pathway drivers alter flood risk through their impact on the probability of flooding while receptor drivers alter flood risk through their impact on the consequences of flooding. Driver impacts were expressed as a multiplier of the flood risk, with multipliers greater than unity indicating an increase in flood risk, while those less than one indicated a reduction in flood risk.

Approach and summary results

To estimate the changes in flood risk and to assess the impact of the drivers, two approaches were adopted. First, the drivers were scored, ranked and assessed for uncertainty by a large number of individual experts who subsequently brain-stormed the findings to produce a final ranking of the drivers. A series of multipliers was applied to the current flood risk and used to change the risk associated with that driver under each scenario and time slice.

Similarly, the flood risk impacts of the drivers in each functional driver set were scored, ranked and assessed for uncertainty.

The results of the exercise to assess flood risk impacts are shown in Table 10.2 while the outcomes of the ranking and uncertainty analysis are shown in Tables 10.3 and 10.4 for the 2080 time slice. The drivers were colour-coded according to the modulus of their level of impact. Drivers with risk multipliers (M) greater than 2 were coded red and correspond to high-increase drivers.

Table 10.2. Summary results for driver impacts on flood risk: the numbers are multipliers on current flood risk in the intra-urban area

Climate change

Driver type	Name	World markets		National enterprise		Local stewardship		Global sustainability	
		2050s	2080s	2050s	2080s	2050s	2080s	2050s	2080s
S	Precipitation	1.8	2.6	1.7	2.5	1.6	2.4	1.5	2.2
Runoff									
P	Urbanisation	1.4	2.0	1.2	1.7	1.1	1.5	1.0	1.4
P	Management of peri-urban rural land	1.2	1.4	1.0	1.0	0.9	0.7	0.9	0.8
Urban conveyance systems and processes									
P	Environmental management and regulation	1.0	1.0	1.0	1.0	1.4	2.8	2.0	4.0
P	Urban watercourse conveyance, blockage and sedimentation	1.6	2.0	1.1	1.2	1.0	0.9	1.0	1.1
P	Sewer conveyance, blockage and sedimentation	2.0	3.0	1.6	2.0	1.0	0.9	1.0	1.1
P	Impact of external flooding on intra-urban drainage systems	1.4	1.8	1.2	1.4	1.6	2.0	1.0	1.0
P	Intra-urban asset deterioration	2.5	4.0	1.8	2.5	1.0	1.0	1.1	1.1
Human behaviour									
P	Stakeholder behaviour	3.0	3.0	3.5	4.7	2.2	2.2	2.1	2.1
R	Public attitudes and expectations – known to be important but not quantified								
Socio-economics									
R	Buildings and contents	4.0	6.4	3.2	4.5	0.9	0.7	1.5	1.9
R	Urban impacts	1.6	2	1.4	1.6	1.0	1.0	1.1	1.1
R	Infrastructure impacts	4.7	9	3.2	5.2	0.9	0.7	1.5	1.5
R	Social impacts	6.0	19.8	2.2	3.6	3.0	6.1	2.2	3.2
R	Science and technology – known to be important but not quantified								

Drivers with multipliers (M) between 1.2 and 2 or 0.5 and 0.83 were coded yellow and blue respectively and correspond to medium-increase drivers and medium-decrease drivers, while drivers with multipliers (M) between 0.83 and 1.2 were coded green and classed as low-impact drivers. The analysis highlighted that, within the urban area, there were no high-decrease drivers (M less than 0.5). Similarly, in respect of uncertainty, the colour codes correspond to a measure of the upper- and lower-bound estimates of the flood risk impact multiplier, B, with values of B greater than 3 coded red, corresponding to parameters with high uncertainty, values of B between 3 and 1.5, coded yellow were assessed to have medium uncertainty, while drivers with B values less than 1.5 had low uncertainty.

The ranking of drivers was extremely complex as the boundary between driver impact and response was difficult to define. For example, in respect of urbanisation, an increase in the impervious area may result in an increase in surface runoff and hence an increase in flood risk but, in contrast, the response to adopt new water saving and sustainable technologies may result in a reduction in runoff with a corresponding reduction in flood risk. The ranking of drivers was very much a function of each Foresight scenario but, as expected, the world markets scenario was the highest risk scenario with global sustainability the least risk scenario. For the intra-urban

Table 10.3. Driver ranking for the 2080s in the intra-urban area

	World markets 2080s	National enterprise 2080s	Local stewardship 2080s	Global sustainability 2080s
1	Social impacts	Infrastructure impacts	Social impacts	Environmental management and regulation
2	Infrastructure impacts	Stakeholder behaviour	Environmental management and regulation	Social impacts
3	Buildings and contents	Buildings and contents	Stakeholder behaviour	Precipitation
4	Intra-urban asset deterioration	Social impacts	Precipitation	Stakeholder behaviour
5	Sewer conveyance, blockage and sedimentation	Intra-urban asset deterioration	Impact of external flooding on intra-urban drainage systems	Buildings and contents
6	Stakeholder behaviour	Precipitation	Urbanisation	Infrastructure impacts
7	Precipitation	Sewer conveyance, blockage and sedimentation	Intra-urban asset deterioration	Urbanisation
8	Urbanisation	Urbanisation	Urban impacts	Intra-urban asset deterioration
9	Urban watercourse conveyance, blockage and sedimentation	Urban impacts	Urban watercourse conveyance, blockage and sedimentation	Urban watercourse conveyance, blockage and sedimentation
10	Urban impacts	Impact of external flooding on intra-urban drainage systems	Sewer conveyance, blockage and sedimentation	Sewer conveyance, blockage and sedimentation
11	Impact of external flooding on intra-urban drainage systems	Urban watercourse conveyance, blockage and sedimentation	Management of peri-urban rural land	Urban impacts
12	Management of peri-urban rural land	Management of peri-urban rural land	Buildings and contents	Impact of external flooding on intra-urban drainage systems
13	Environmental management and regulation	Environmental management and regulation	Infrastructure impacts	Management of peri-urban rural land

Science and technology – known to be important but not quantified

Public attitudes and expectations – known to be important but not quantified

Legend

Driver impact category	Risk multiplier (M) range	Tint code
High increase	M > 2	
Medium increase	2 > M > 1.2	
Low impact	1.2 > M < 0.83	
Medium decrease	0.83 > M > 0.5	
High decrease	M < 0.5	

Table 10.4. Driver uncertainty for the 2080s in the intra-urban area

	World markets 2080s	National enterprise 2080s	Local stewardship 2080s	Global sustainability 2080s
1	Social impacts	Infrastructure impacts	Social impacts	Environmental management and regulation
2	Infrastructure impacts	Stakeholder behaviour	Environmental management and regulation	Social impacts
3	Buildings and contents	Buildings and contents	Stakeholder behaviour	Precipitation
4	Intra-urban asset deterioration	Social impacts	Precipitation	Stakeholder behaviour
5	Sewer conveyance, blockage and sedimentation	Intra-urban asset deterioration	Impact of external flooding on intra-urban drainage systems	Buildings and contents
6	Stakeholder behaviour	Precipitation	Urbanisation	Infrastructure impacts
7	Precipitation	Sewer conveyance, blockage and sedimentation	Intra-urban asset deterioration	Urbanisation
8	Urbanisation	Urbanisation	Urban impacts	Intra-urban asset deterioration
9	Urban watercourse conveyance, blockage and sedimentation	Urban impacts	Urban watercourse conveyance, blockage and sedimentation	Urban watercourse conveyance, blockage and sedimentation
10	Urban impacts	Impact of external flooding on intra-urban drainage systems	Sewer conveyance, blockage and sedimentation	Sewer conveyance, blockage and sedimentation
11	Impact of external flooding on intra-urban drainage systems	Urban watercourse conveyance, blockage and sedimentation	Management of peri-urban rural land	Urban impacts
12	Management of peri-urban rural land	Management of peri-urban rural land	Buildings and contents	Impact of external flooding on intra-urban drainage systems
13	Environmental management and regulation	Environmental management and regulation	Infrastructure impacts	Management of peri-urban rural land

Science and technology – known to be important but not quantified

Public attitudes and expectations – known to be important but not quantified

Legend

Uncertainty band category	Uncertainty band width (B) (B = ratio of upper to lower bound estimates of flood risk impact multiplier)	Tint code
High	B > 3	
Medium	3 > B > 1.5	
Low	M < 1.5	

area, precipitation, urbanisation, science and technology, catchment runoff, asset performance and stakeholder behaviour were identified as the important drivers.

Specifically:

- Precipitation, due to the potential impact of climate change, ranked highly under all scenarios.
- Social impacts were ranked high due to the potential health impacts and inconvenience of flooding from sewers.
- Environmental management and regulation was important under the local stewardship and global sustainability scenarios, as these may constrain future flexibility in the response to flooding, but was of little importance under the world markets and national enterprise scenarios.
- The management and performance of assets drivers – intra-urban asset deterioration and sewer conveyance, blockage and sedimentation ranked highly under world markets and national enterprise, but were of less prominence under the local stewardship and global sustainability. This reflects a different emphasis on the importance of operating, maintaining and managing the underground assets of the urban infrastructure.
- Urbanisation and urban impacts were ranked high as these reflect the potential dangers of increased urbanisation and urban creep as the flood risk may not be taken fully into account.
- The socio-economic driver, stakeholder behaviour, was important across all drivers. Buildings contents and infrastructure impacts are important under world markets and national enterprise but less so under the other two scenarios.

Uncertainty, in the prediction of the impact of the drivers on flood risk, was also wide ranging. Stakeholder behaviour, social impact, precipitation, drainage system performance and regulation were identified as the key uncertain parameters.

The next step in the process was to quantify the impact of the physical drivers taking due regard of the uncertainty of prediction.

Quantified flood risk – intra-urban

Analysis methodology

As detailed in Fig. 10.1, intra-urban interactions associated with flood risk management are complex and, in Chapter 2, details of a 'standard' methodology for flood risk assessment of the wider catchment were presented. The outputs from the 'standard' approach include urban areas within a $1 \, \text{km} \times 1 \, \text{km}$ GIS national-grid scale, but these show risk due only to fluvial or coastal inundation, and do not include sewers, drains or small water courses (Sayers *et al.*, 2003; Hall *et al.*, 2003). Hence, at the present time, there is no 'standard' process for flood risk assessment in the intra-urban area.

The investigation of urban flood risk requires modelling at a finer scale and, for individual urban areas, it is necessary to utilise complex models that include very fine landscape topography. Models with this capability are now emerging (e.g. Clarke *et al.*, 2005; Phillips *et al.*, 2004; Rossman *et al.*, 2004; www.dhisoftware .com; www.microdrainage.co.uk; www.wallingfordsoftware.com). The changes in flood risk in the Foresight study were assessed using the MWH flood assessment tool (www.mwhglobal.com; Balmforth *et al.*, 2004). Three catchments were specifically selected to quantify potential changes in specific areas:

- Catchment 1   flooding occuring only within the urban area.
- Catchment 2   coincident flooding involving local river systems.
- Catchment 3   coincident flooding involving tidal effects.

Table 10.5. Details of three representative catchments used to gauge the number of properties in the intra-urban area at risk of flooding now and in the future

Nature of catchment and location	Area: ha	Impervious area: %	Population	Population density: person/ha	Number of properties	Property density: prop/ha
1. Market town (northern England)	1380	29	86 000	62	39 000	28
2. Inland city with major watercourses (Scotland)	3930	34	260 000	67	77 000	20
3. Coastal city (Wales)	2030	21	120 000	60	31 000	15

The characteristics of the test catchments are given in Table 10.5.

The calculations were based on the analysis of changes in the most important physical drivers – precipitation and urbanisation. The models were used to predict the performance of the main drainage system in each catchment and were used to explore the changes in the volume of floodwater, the number of properties flooded and the expected annual damage (EAD).

The results were scaled to the national level and validated by comparing them to published information on recorded flooding. Further scaling was completed, again using published data, to include the impact of other pathways and receptors associated with intra-urban flooding, e.g. drainage structures, private drains and highways. Based on the averaged flood risks for the test catchments, these factors were subsequently used to scale-up flood risk to the national scale.

Quantified flood risk assessment in the intra-urban area

Not all of the Foresight socio-economic scenarios were modelled in depth as reliable estimates of future urban rainfall are extremely uncertain between scenarios. Efforts were concentrated on the National Enterprise (NE) scenario for two reasons:

1. Current approaches using contemporary rainfall estimates as given in the *Flood Estimation Handbook* (Institute of Hydrology, 1999) and socio-economic conditions comply with the NE scenario.
2. Future climate change predictions for rainfall based on UKCIP98 are believed to correspond with NE socio-economic scenarios (Evans *et al.*, 2004).

Subsequently, a simple sensitivity approach was adopted to model the other scenarios. The modelling strategy is illustrated in Fig. 10.2. The test catchments were evaluated for present-day and the future climate change scenarios. The rainfall information used in the study was based on three approaches:

- The UK *Flood Estimation Handbook* for existing rainfall, with 10-, 30- and 100-year return periods.
- UK Climate Impacts Programme (UKCIP98). Rainfalls were based on the medium-high climate change scenario, for which the minimum rainfall duration timestep is 6 hours. Hence, there was a need to downscale these time intervals and to provide intensity and duration data appropriate to the modelling of urban drainage systems. This information on downscaled rainfall uplift data, at short time intervals, was provided for 2080 by UK Water Industry Research Ltd (UKWIR, 2003). These uplifts are shown in Fig. 10.2.
- The UKCIP98 results were scaled to give outputs corresponding to the UKCIP02 predicted changes in rainfall (Hulme *et al.*, 2002). The scaling of the rainfall was a function of the return period of storm, the catchment location and the Foresight scenario. The range of uplifts are also shown in Fig. 10.2. Significantly, the predictions for much of the UK show up to a 50%

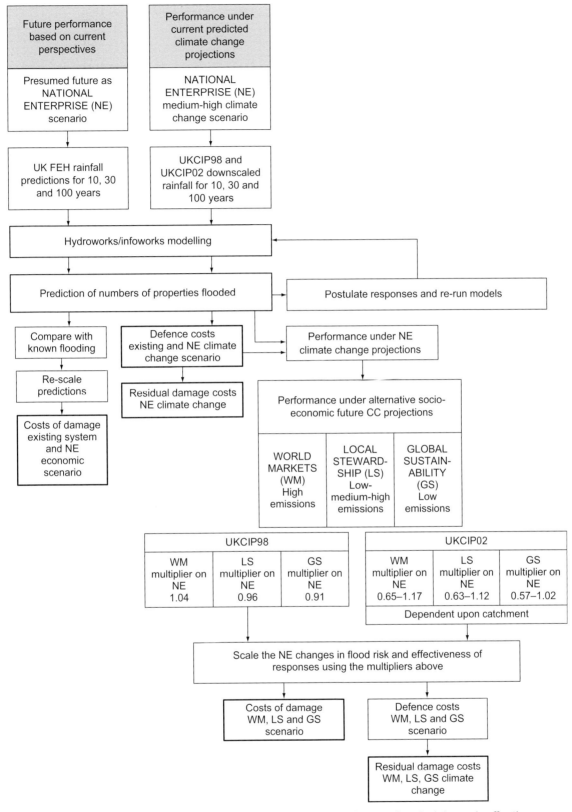

Fig. 10.2. The process used to assess the changes in future flood risk and effectiveness of responses for the four climate change and socio-economic group scenarios – main drainage pluvial flooding only (after Ashley et al., 2005). FEH = Flood Estimation Handbook

Table 10.6. Multipliers of peak rainfall across scenarios to 2080

Flood Estimation Handbook	Scale 1.0
Global sustainability (GS)	Scale 1.05
Local stewardship (LS)	Scale 1.1
National enterprise (NE)	Scale 1.15
World markets (WM)	Scale 1.20

reduction in average rainfall during the summer period for the whole of the UK, whereas the 1998 predictions indicated reductions would only apply to the southern part of the country. These changes are significant when an assessment is made of the performance of urban drainage systems under pluvial extremes, particularly as the summer time is the critical period for intense storms of short duration.

To assess the differences in peak rainfall between each of the socio-economic and climate change scenarios, to 2080, simple percentages were used as precipitation multipliers, as detailed in Table 10.6.

To examine the way in which rainfall uplift changed flood volume, uplifts of 1.2, 1.4 and 1.6 were applied to the test catchments with a one in 30 year return period winter storm event. This resulted in an almost linear uplift in the volumes of water flowing out of the sewers corresponding to the uplift in rainfall. This agreement provides some confidence in the proposed scaling of flood risks, in line with the UKCIP98 increases in rainfall, for the predictions of the impact of other socio-economic scenarios.

The outputs from the performance simulations of each system provided only an estimate of the flood volumes delivered from the sewer system to the catchment surface. To relate these flood volumes to the flooding of individual properties it is necessary to route the flood flow over the catchment surface. Here the local topography and the elevation of property relative to elevation of the pipes of the minor system are important, and were taken into account within the modelling software.

As an example, for the National Enterprise scenario, the FEH and UKCIP98 rainfall was applied to Catchment 1 to estimate the change in the prediction of the numbers of properties at risk of flooding to 2080. The results, shown in Fig. 10.3,

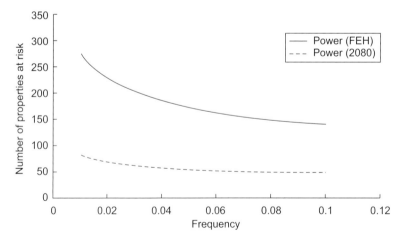

Fig. 10.3. Changes in numbers of properties at risk of flooding to 2080: catchment 1 as a function of FEH or UKCIP98 rainfall

Table 10.7. Properties at risk of flooding due to one in ten-year storm: present-day and to 2080

Flood type	Public sewer	Private sewer	Overland flow	Gutters etc.	Total
Flooding of property	11 600	8850	11 600	30 400	62 500
Flooding adjacent to property	4640	3540	4640	–	12 800
Flooding of highways	2320	1770	2320	–	6410
Total	18 600 (23%)	14 200 (17%)	18 500 (23%)	30 400 (37%)	81 700

highlight that there is the potential for a significant increase (almost a doubling) in flood risk to a large number of properties.

To compare this figure with the outputs of the modelling study, the averaged modelled results from the three test catchments were scaled up to provide an estimate of the total number of properties at risk of flooding once in ten years in England and Wales, based on existing FEH rainfall conditions. Details of the model results are shown in Table 10.7 and highlight a present-day national prediction of 23 000 properties at risk. When scaled using the 2001 census data, the corresponding numbers of properties at risk under the 2080 medium-high emissions scenario is 57 000.

To link the modelling study to published flood risk data, the number of properties currently at risk of sewer flooding in England and Wales were estimated using information from OFWAT (2002a, 2002b, 2004b), Defra (2003) and the English House Condition Surveys (EHCS). Insurance companies also have substantial data related to flood claims but this information was not available to the Foresight team.

Examination of the quality and completeness of this existing data showed that there is a need for improved consistency in data collection (National Audit Office, 2004) and, more particularly, better information is required as to cause and impact of individual flood incidents and as to the distinction between 'sewer' and 'non-sewer' flooding. However, the information showed that, in England and Wales, the present-day numbers of properties at risk of flooding once in ten years was 13 920. As a consequence, the model results of 23 000 were factored down by 0.59 to make the results compatible and such that the three test catchments could be used to predict changes in flood risk under the world markets, local stewardship and global sustainability scenarios.

As shown in Fig. 10.2, the next step was to estimate the expected annual damage (EAD) due to sewer flooding. Details of the scaling of actual recorded events in each catchment are shown in Table 10.8. The numbers were derived using flood damage costings given by Penning-Rowsell *et al.* (2003) and are based on an addition uplift factor of 4.5 for the buildings and contents driver under the national enterprise scenario to 2080. Although subject to modelling and scaling uncertainty, the expected annual damage from sewer flooding alone will be high and potentially in the order of £600 billion.

Other urban flood pathways

Based on recorded data from the English House Condition Surveys (EHCS), the flood risk from main sewerage, as described above, comprises only approximately 17% of the total intra-urban flood risk. Hence, the scaled model simulation results were scaled up by an additional factor of 5.9 to give the total flood risk from all causes in the intra-urban area.

This gave flood risk based on the adjusted model results as some 81 700 properties at risk. This value compares well with the data from EHCS who reported that

Table 10.8. Current and future flood risk from main sewerage, and expected annual damage for the whole of the UK

Test catchment	Population	Present-day			2080s medium-high emissions		
		Properties flooded per year	Properties flooded per 1000 population	Expected annual damage: £	Properties flooded per year	Properties flooded per 1000 population	Expected annual damage: £
1	86 000	5	0.058	110 000	16	0.187	1 600 000
2	260 000	15	0.057	340 000	30	0.114	3 100 000
3	120 000	3	0.024	68 000	5	0.041	510 000
Average for the test catchments	160 000	8	0.046	181 000	17	0.114	1 700 000
National	59 000 000	2900	17	65 000 000	6400	43	598 000 000

the total number of properties at risk in England was 62 458 and nationally, including Scotland, Wales and Northern Ireland, some 77 635 properties. This comparison provided some confidence that the modelling approach applied to the three test catchments could be used to assess the comparative changes in flood risk between the different scenarios.

Other scenarios

The modelling work showed that results were dependent largely on changes in rainfall with the volume and extent of flooding correlating well with rainfall. This meant that the effects of other scenarios could be evaluated with reasonable confidence by scaling from projected rainfall change.

Hence, to predict the total flood risk due to all causes under all scenarios, the uplifts in rainfall presented by UKCIP98, shown in Fig. 10.2, were combined with the catchment specific rainfall uplift for each catchment provided by UKWIR (2003) (Catchment 1, uplift 1.19; Catchment 2, uplift 1.28; Catchment 3, uplift 1.07) and the uplifts from the sensitivity of the scenario analysis (see Table 10.6) to give the multipliers for the numbers of properties at risk. The results of this analysis are detailed in Table 10.9.

The analysis again confirms that, due to precipitation alone, there is the potential for at least a doubling in the number of properties at risk of flooding per year. The differences in the numbers of properties at risk of flooding across scenarios is relatively small and is due to the fact that the rainfall uplift multipliers are also relatively small (c. 20%). When combined with the socio-economic

Table 10.9. Properties at risk of flooding due to all causes of urban flooding

	Present day	World markets	National enterprise	Local stewardship	Global sustainability
Properties at risk of flooding in one in ten-year event	81 700	380 000	340 000	320 000	300 000
EAD: £ million per year	270	7880	5055	740	1870
Uncertainty range – EAD: £ million per year	100–500	2500–15 000	2000–10 000	350–1400	900–3600

Table 10.10. Expected annual damages in £M per year due to all causes of urban flooding across all scenarios

Present day	World markets	National enterprise	Local stewardship	Global sustainability
270	4420	2990	450	1150

multipliers, Table 10.2, the expected annual damage, for all causes of flooding in the urban area, shown in Table 10.10, highlight that there are large differences in EAD due to the large change in the socio-economic multipliers, with EAD, based on a present-day value of £270 million per annum, ranging from £4420 million per annum under the world markets scenario to £450 million per annum under local stewardship.

These predictions are based on UKCIP98 rainfall and UKWIR (2003) predicted uplifts for each catchment in the range 1.07 to 1.28. In contrast, the UKCIP02 predicted uplifts highlight differences in uplift for different parts of the country. In some areas there is a predicted reduction in rainfall. In the Foresight study this differential was not taken into account. Hence, in areas with a high density of properties at risk of flooding, and a predicted uplift in rainfall, there will be the potential for an increase in flood risk with increases in EAD accrued due to increases in flood depth and area of inundation. The converse is true for those areas where the rainfall is expected to reduce. Further research is required to address this issue.

Urbanisation

Future change in urbanisation is potentially a key driver of flood risk in the urban area. This is because the runoff of rainfall from urban impervious surfaces varies almost proportionately with an increase in impervious area. Hence, any increase in impervious area has the potential to increase flood risk.

The current extent of urbanisation in the UK is approximately 7% of land area. Within the urbanised area approximately 23% of the area is open space (Handley *et al.*, 2000). Hence, there is the potential to urbanise both greenfield sites at the perimeter of the urban area and to develop the open space within the urban area. Overall, the national predictions of planned urbanisation suggest very small changes in greenfield land to developed areas, of the order of less than 0.1% per annum, c. 5400 ha per annum (ODPM, 2003a, 2003b). There could, however, be more rapid changes in brownfield areas. In the absence of data, the Foresight Project assumed that development in these areas would occur at a rate some 10 times that for greenfield areas, thereby contributing to an increase in flood risk.

In addition, urban creep by individual properties adding extensions, patios and hard standing has been shown to average some 7% in the UK (Cutting, 2003). Should this trend continue in an uncontrolled way, it is argued that this could have a significant impact on the change in flood risk.

Projected to 2080, it was assumed that greenfield development, the development of open space in urban areas and urban creep would result in a base-case increase in impermeable area of up to 15% (by 2080). The impact of such a change in the urbanisation was predicted across all four of the Foresight scenarios using different rates of urbanisation. Expert judgement was used to predict the scaling factors for urbanisation changes. Values of 2 for world markets, 1.2 for national enterprise, 0.75 for local stewardship and 0.5 for global sustainability were selected. The results of the analysis based on these values, the numbers of properties at risk and the predicted values of expected annual damage, are shown in Table 10.11.

Table 10.11. Urbanisation – changes in properties at risk of flooding and EAD for the UK

	Present-day	World markets	National enterprise	Local stewardship	Global sustainability
Properties at risk of flooding per year per 1000 population	0.16	0.32	0.27	0.24	0.22
Properties at risk of flooding per year	9500	19 000	16 000	14 250	13 100
Properties at risk of flooding in one in ten-year event	81 700	165 000	140 000	125 000	115 000
EAD: £ million per year	270	3460	2065	290	720

These results highlight that the impact of changes in urbanisation on the future change in flood risk is significant and is broadly similar to that due to the projected changes in rainfall.

Future research needs

There were identified limitations in the quantification of the drivers and uncertainty and in the scale-up from local catchment to national scale.

There is an identified need to research future changes in the temporal and spatial scale of rainfall in the intra-urban area, such that improvements in urban flood modelling may be made.

Current computational models are inadequate for predicting urban flooding with any accuracy. There is a particular need to improve the prediction of flood routes across the catchment surface and of the interaction between above- and below-ground drainage components of the minor and major systems.

Summary

Drivers that influence the change in flood risk were identified and these drivers were scored, ranked and assessed for uncertainty by a large number of individual experts. A series of multipliers were applied to the current flood risk to assess the change in urban flood risk for each of the Foresight scenarios and time slices to 2050 and 2080. It is stressed that there was large uncertainty in the prediction of the importance of the drivers and uncertainty.

Flooding of the intra-urban area has been shown to be a function of many complex interactive processes.

For the intra-urban area, precipitation, urbanisation, science and technology, catchment runoff, asset performance and stakeholder behaviour were identified as the important drivers.

Uncertainty in the prediction of the impact of the drivers on flood risk was also wide ranging. Stakeholder behaviour, social impact, precipitation, drainage system performance and regulation were identified as the key uncertain parameters.

High-level quantification of the potential increase in flood risk within the intra-urban areas to 2080, based on the outputs of modelling software applied to three typical catchments for the national enterprise medium to high emissions scenario, showed that there is likely to be a significant increase in urban flood risk and associated expected annual damage across all scenarios.

The impact of future potential changes in precipitation and urbanisation were significant and broadly similar.

References

Ackers, J.C., Butler, D. and May, R.W.P., 1996. *Design of Sewers to Control Sediment Problems*, Report 141, CIRIA, London.

Akornor, O. and Page, D.W., 2004. 'Glasgow strategic drainage plan stage 1 – overview and case study', *Proceedings Scotland Meeting*, available online www.wapug.org.uk

Allbee, S., 2005. 'America's pathway to sustainable water and wastewater systems', *Water Asset Management International*, 1(1), 9–14.

Ashley, R.M., Bertrand-Krajewski, J.-L., Hvitved-Jacobsen, T. and Verbanck M., 2004a. *Solids in Sewers*, IWA Scientific and Technical Report No. 14.

Ashley, R.M., Blackwood, D.J., Butler, D. and Jowitt, P., 2004b. *Sustainable Water Services: A procedural guide*, IWA, London.

Ashley, R.M., Balmforth, D.J., Saul, A.J. and Blanskby, J.D., 2005. 'Flooding in the future – predicting climate change, risks and responses in urban areas', *Wat. Sci. Tech.*, 52(5), 265–274.

Baik, H.S., Jeong, H.S. and Abraham, D.M., 2006. 'Estimating transition probabilities in Markov chain-based deterioration models for management of wastewater systems', *J. Water Resour. Plng and Mgmt*, 132(1), 15–24.

Balmforth, D.J. and Dibben, P., 2004. 'A modelling tool for assessing flood risk', *Proceedings 10ICUD*, Copenhagen, August.

Balmforth, D.J., Saul, A.J. and Clifforde, I.T., 1994. *Design Manual for Combined Sewer Overflow Structures*, WRc Report FR 0488.

Bertrand-Krajewski, J.L., Cardosa, M.A., Ellis, B., Frehmann, T., Guilianelli, M., Gujer, W., Krebs, P., Pliska, Z., Pollert, J. and Pryl, K., 2004a. 'Towards a better knowledge and management of infiltration and exfiltration in sewer systems: the APUSS project', *Proceedings 10ICUD*, Copenhagen, August.

Bertrand-Krajewski, J., Bardin, J.P. and Gilbello, C., 2004b. 'Long term monitoring of sediment accumulation and flushing experiments in a man-entry sewer', *Proceedings 10ICUD*, Copenhagen, August.

Blanksby, J., Ashley, R., Saul, A.J., Cashman, A., Packman, J., Maksimovic, C., Jack, L., Wright, G. and Kay, D., 2004. 'Adaptable urban drainage (Audacious)', Novatech, Lyon, June.

Boardman, J., Evans, R. and Ford, J., 2003. 'Muddy floods on the South Downs, southern England: problems and responses', *Environmental Science and Policy*, 6, 69–83.

Cashman, A., Savic, D., Saul, A., Ashley, R., Walters, G., Blanksby, J., Djordjevic, S., Unwin, D. and Kapelan, Z., 2004. 'Whole life costing of sewers (Cost-S): developing a sustainable approach to sewer network management', *Proceedings Novatech*, Lyon.

Chen, A.S., Hsu, M.H., Chen, T.S. and Chang, T.J., 2005. 'An integrated inundation model for highly developed urban areas', *Water Science and Technology*, 51(2), 221–229.

Christensen, J.H. and Christensen, O.B., 2003. 'Severe summer flooding in Europe', *Nature*, 421, 805–806.

CIRIA, 1997, *Control of Infiltration to Sewers*, CIRIA Report 175.

CIRIA, 1998, *Dry Weather Flow in Sewers*, CIRIA Report 177.

CIRIA, 2000. *Sustainable Urban Drainage Systems – Design Manual for England and Wales*, CIRIA.

CIRIA, 2003. *Sustainable Water Management in Land Use Planning*, Funders Report RP627.

CIRIA, 2005. *Design for Exceedence*, Funders Report RP699.

Clarke, S., Barcock, N. and Page, D., 2005. 'Two-dimensional modelling of overland flow using 2D dynamic modelling to assess overland flood routing and flood depths', WaPUG, Coventry, May, available online www.wapug.org.uk

Crichton, D., 2002. 'UK and global insurance responses to flood hazard', in *Non-structural Measures for Water Management Problems*, Proceedings International Workshop, London, Ontario, Canada, October, ed. Simonovic S.P., IHP-V Technical Documents in Hydrology, No. 56, UNESCO, Paris.

Cutting J., 2003. 'Property Creep', WaPUG, Blackpool, November, available online www.wapug.org.uk

Defra, 2002. *The Review of Existing Private Sewers and Drains in England and Wales*, Consultation Paper, Department for Environment, Food and Rural Affairs and Welsh Assembly Government, London.

Defra, 2003. *The Appraisal of Human-related Intangible Impacts of Flooding*, R & D Programme FD2005, Policy Development Theme, London.

Defra, 2004. *Making Space for Water, Developing a New Government Strategy for Flood and Coastal Erosion Risk Management in England. A Consultation Exercise*, Department for Environment Food and Rural Affairs, London.

Defra, 2005a. *Making Space for Water. Taking Forward a New Government Strategy for Flood and Coastal Erosion Risk Management in England. First Government Response to the Autumn 2004 Making Space for Water Consultation Exercise*, Department for Environment Food and Rural Affairs, London, March.

Defra, 2005b. *Flood Risks to People. Phase 2. The Risks to People Methodology*, FD2321/ TR1, March.

Dixon, A., Butler, D., Fewkes, A., Parsons, S.A., Strathern, M., Stephenson, T. and Strutt, J., 2001. 'Small scale water-recycling systems – risk assessment and modelling', *Wat. Sci. Tech.*, 43(10), 83–90.

EA, 2001. *Lessons Learned Autumn 2000 Floods*, Environment Agency, Bristol.

EA, 2004. *Interim Code of Practice for Sustainable Drainage Systems (SUDS) in England and Wales*, National SUDS Working Group, Environment Agency, available online www.environment-agency.gov.uk/

Evans, E., Ashley, R.M., Hall, J., Penning-Rowsell, E., Saul, A.J., Sayers, P., Thorne, C. and Watkinson, A., 2004. *Foresight Future Flooding. Scientific Summary: Vol. I – Future risks and their drivers*, Office of Science and Technology, London.

Fleming, G. (ed.), 2002. *Flood Risk Management*, Thomas Telford, London.

Faram, M.G., Andoh, R.Y.G. and Williams, C.A., 2004. 'Innovative approaches to urban stormwater management', *Proceedings 10ICUD*, Copenhagen, August.

Fenner, R.A., 2002. 'Performance is your reality, forget everything else', *Urban Water*, 4(2), 119–122.

Foxon, T.J., McIlkenny, G., Gilmour, D., Oltean-Dumbrava, C., Souter, N., Ashley, R., Butler, D., Pearson, P., Jowitt, P. and Moir, J., 2002. 'Sustainability criteria for decision support in the UK water industry', *J. Env. Planning & Management*, 45(2), 285–301.

FWR, 1998. *Urban Pollution Management (UPM) Manual 2nd Edition*, Report No. FR/ CL0009 (available on CD), Foundation for Water Research, Marlow.

Hall, J.W., Dawson, R.J., Sayers, P.B., Rosu, C., Chatterton, J.B. and Deakin, R.A., 2003. 'Methodology for nation-scale flood risk assessment', *Water and Maritime Engineering*, 156(3), 235–247.

Handley, J., Wood, R. and Ruff, A., 2000. 'The Red Rose urban timber initiative: a report on the sampling of street, park and garden tree population', Unpublished report to the Red Rose forest, Salford.

Heywood, G., Lumbers, J., Reid, S., Balance, T., Chalmers, L. and Haywood-Smith, B., 2002. *Capital Maintenance Planning: A common framework*, Vol. 1, UKWIR Report Ref. 02/RG/05/3.

Hrabak, D., Hanak, S., Pryl, K., Kuba, P. and Metalka, T., 2004. 'Sewer system protection against large floods – modelling, evaluation and design – Prague case study', *Proceedings 10ICUD*, Copenhagen, August.

HRW, 1983. *The Wallingford Procedure: Design and analysis of urban storm drainage. Vol. 1: Principles, methods and practice*, Hydraulics Research Ltd, Wallingford.

HRW, 2005. *FD2320 – Flood Risk Assessment for New Developments HR Wallingford*, Defra/EA R&D Programme for Flood and Coastal Defence, Hydraulics Research Ltd, Wallingford.

Hulme, M., Jenkins, G.J., Lu, X., Turnpenny, J.R., Mitchell, T.D., Jones, R.G., Lowe, J., Murphy, J.M., Hassell, D., Boorman, P., McDonald, R. and Hill, S., 2002. *Climate Change Scenarios for the United Kingdom: The UKCIP02 Scientific Report*, Tyndall Centre for Climate Change Research, School of Environmental Sciences, University of East Anglia, Norwich.

ICE, 2001. *Learning to Live with Rivers*, Final Report of the Institution of Civil Engineers' Presidential Commission.

Institute of Hydrology, 1999. *Flood Estimation Handbook*, Institute of Hydrology, Wallingford.

Jain, M.K., Kothyari, U.C. and Ranga Raju, K.G., 2004. 'A GIS based distributed rainfall-runoff model', *Journal of Hydrology*, 299, 107–135.

Jefferies, C., Atkin, A., McLean, N., MacDonald, K. and McKissock, G., 1999. 'Assessing the performance of urban BMPs in Scotland', *Wat. Sci. Tech.*, 39(12), 123–131.

Kellagher, R.B.B. and Lauchlan, C.S., 2005. Use of SUDS in high-density developments, HR Wallingford Report SR 666, June.

Lancaster, J.W., Preene, M. and Marshall, C.T., 2004. *Development and Flood Risk – Guidance for the construction industry (C624)*, CIRIA, available online www.ciria.org.uk/

Lhomme, J., Bouvier, C., Mignot, E. and Paquier, A., 2004. 'One-dimensional GIS based model compared to two-dimensional model in urban floods simulation', *Proceedings 10ICUD*, Copenhagen, August.

Matos, R., Cardoso, A., Ashley, R.M., Molinari, A., Schulz, A. and Duarte, P., 2003. *Performance Indicators for Wastewater Services – IWA Manual of Best Practice*, International Water Association, London.

Micevski, T., Kuczera, G. and Coombes, P., 2002. 'Markov model for storm water pipe deterioration', *Journal of Infrastructure Systems*, 8(2), 49–56.

Montero, C. and Villanueva, A., 2004. 'Rehabilitation techniques within the context of the CARE-S project', *Proceedings 10ICUD*, Copenhagen, August.

National Audit Office, 2004. *Out of Sight – Not Out of Mind. Ofwat and the Public Sewer Network in England and Wales*, HC 161 Session 2003–2004, 16 January, Report by the Comptroller and Auditor General.

ODPM, 2001. *Planning Policy Guidance 25: Development and flood risk*, ODPM, London.

ODPM, 2002. *Planning Policy Guidance (PPG) 3 – Housing*, ODPM, London.

ODPM, 2003a. *Land Use Change Statistics: LUCS18A*, ODPM, London.

ODPM, 2003b. *Housing Statistics: Live set of tables*, ODPM, available online www.odpm. gov.uk/stellent/groups/odpm_housing/documents/page/odpm_house_604023.xls

ODPM, 2003c. *Preparing for Floods (interim guidance for improving the flood resistance of domestic and small business properties)*, ODPM, London, October.

ODPM, 2004. *Planning for Climate Change*, ODPM, London.

ODPM, 2005. *Planning Policy Statement 1: Delivering sustainable development*, ODPM, London.

OFWAT, 2002a. *Flooding From Sewers – A way forward*, OFWAT, London.

OFWAT, 2002b. *Flooding From Sewers, Response to Consultation*, OFWAT, London, September.

OFWAT, 2003. *Assessing the Benefits of Reducing the Risk of Flooding From Sewers*, OFWAT, London.

OFWAT, 2004a. *Levels of Service for the Water Industry in England and Wales*, OFWAT, London.

OFWAT, 2004b. *Survey of Customers Affected by Sewer Flooding. Research by Design Study*, commissioned by OFWAT, London, August.

OFWAT/EA, 2001. *Development of Enhanced Serviceability Indicators for Sewerage Assets*, Report for OFWAT and the Environment Agency, Ewan Associates Ltd, Mott Macdonald Ltd, Ref. 01-g003/02/Ofwat/od/dg/002/63452.

Penning-Rowsell, E.C., Chatterton, J.B., Wilson, T. and Potter, E., 2002. *Autumn 2000 Floods in England and Wales: Assessment of national economic and financial losses*, Flood Hazard Research Centre, Middlesex University.

Penning-Rowsell, E., Johnson, C., Tunstall, S., Tapsell, S., Morris, J., Chatterton, J., Coker, A. and Green, C., 2003. *The Benefits of Flood and Coastal Defence: Techniques and data for 2003*, Flood Hazard Research Centre, Middlesex University.

Phillips, B.C., Yu, S., Thompson, G.R. and de Silva, A.L.L., 2004. '1D and 2D modelling of urban drainage systems using XP-SWMM and TUFLOW', *Proceedings 10ICUD*, Copenhagen, August.

Reacher, M., McKenzie, K., Lane, C., Nichols, T., Kedge, I., Iversen, A., Hepple, P., Walter, T., Laxton, C. and Simpson, J., 2004. 'Health impacts of flooding in Lewes: a comparison of reported gastrointestinal and other illness and mental health in flooded and non-flooded households', *Communicable Disease and Public Health*, 7(1), 39–46.

Rossman, L.A., Dickinson, R.E., Schade, T., Chan, C., Burgess, E.H. and Huber, W.C., 2004. 'SWMM5: The USEPA's newest tool for urban drainage analysis', *Proceedings 10ICUD*, Copenhagen, August.

Sægrov, S., Schilling, W. and Ugarelli, R., 2004. 'Computer aided REhabilitation of sewer and stormwater networks (CARE-S)', *Proceedings 10ICUD*, Copenhagen, August.

171

Saul, A.J, Balmforth, D.J and Morris, G., 2003a. *The WaPUG CSO Design Guide*, available online www.wapug.org.uk

Saul, A.J., Skipworth, P.J., Tait, S.J. and Rushforth, P.J., 2003b. 'The movement of total suspended solids in combined sewers', *Journal of Hydraulic Engineering ASCE*, 129(4), 299–307.

Savic, D., Djordjevic, S., Dorini, G., Shepherd, W., Cashman, A. and Saul, A.J., 2005. 'COST-S: a new methodology and tools for sewerage asset management based on whole life costs', *Water Asset Management International*, 1(4), 20–24.

Sayers, P.B., Hall, J.W., Dawson, R., Rosu, C., Chatterton, J. and Deakin, R., 2003. 'Risk assessment for flood and coastal systems for strategic planning (RASP) – a national application and a look towards more detailed methods', *Proceedings Defra Flood and Coastal Management Conference*, Keele, July.

Schluter, W. and Jeffries, C., 2004. 'The real issues with in-ground SUDS in Scotland', *Proceedings 10ICUD*, Copenhagen, August.

Siriwardene, N.R., Hatt, B.E., Deletic, A. and Fletcher, T.D., 2004. 'Laboratory experiments for predicting clogging in stormwater infiltration systems', *Proceedings 10ICUD*, Copenhagen, August.

Tapsell, S.M. and Tunstall, S.M., 2003. 'An examination of the health effects of flooding in the United Kingdom', *Journal of Meteorology*, 28, 341–349.

UKWIR, 2002. *Capital Maintenance Planning: A Common Framework. Vol. 1–4*, London.

UKWIR, 2003. *Climate Change and the Hydraulic Design of Sewerage Systems, Vol. I – Climate Change Effects on Rainfall; Vol. II – Rainfall Data Production and Analysis; Vol. III – Sewerage System Modelling; Vol. IIIA – Changes in the Performance of Sewerage Networks; Vol. IIIB – Changes in Sewerage Runoff and Water Quality*, London.

USEPA, 2002. *Onsite Wastewater Treatment Systems Manual*, EPA/625/R-00/008.

Water UK, 2004. *Towards sustainability 2003–2004* (UK water industry Sustainability Indicators 2003/2004), Water UK, London.

Wong, T.H.F., 2004. 'An overview of water sensitive urban design', *Proceedings 10ICUD*, Copenhagen, August.

WRc, 2001. *Sewers for Adoption*, 5th Edn, WRc, Swindon.

11 Other flood risks and their drivers

S.N. Lane

Significant flood impacts may be experienced in areas of the UK that are neither within zones indicated on existing floodplain maps nor associated with pluvial flooding problems due to the limited capacity of urban drainage systems. These floods are commonly labelled as 'disconnected' in that they are not linked to a main river or its tributaries. Disconnected flooding results from a wide variety of processes, including:

- flooding due to groundwater table rises in permeable catchments;
- flooding arising in rural areas and at the urban–rural interface linked to rapid surface runoff from agricultural land (sometimes referred to as 'muddy flooding');
- flooding due to small-scale infrastructure failure (e.g. bunds, ponds, etc.) in rural areas;
- flooding related to larger scale infrastructure (e.g. drainage channels and the canal system) that is included in statutory flood risk analyses to a varying degree; and
- flooding that occurs at the boundaries of the indicative flood zones, where those boundaries are in error.

There is no generic mode of operation for disconnected flooding. However, the mechanisms share a number of important characteristics. First, the severity of disconnected flooding (and as many as 40% of the flood insurance claims during the autumn 2000 floods in the UK may have arisen outside the indicative flood plains) arises from impacts upon a large number of people over a wide geographical area. Second, the causes tend to be geographically specific (e.g. linked to isolated springs or local instances of small-scale infrastructure failure). Third, the impacts may be manifest in very different ways (e.g. as rising groundwater levels in the cellars of properties, in surcharging drains or culverts that make rural roads impassable; or as muddy surface runoff from fields into properties). This makes identification of a generic mode of operation difficult, but groundwater flooding, muddy flooding and infrastructure issues are explored in this chapter.

Groundwater flooding in permeable catchments

This is low magnitude and high duration flooding, commonly found in permeable catchments, where groundwater fluctuations can be significant. Typically, it is geographically centred on major aquifer outcrops.

173

Mode of operation

Groundwater is generally distinguished from saturated throughflow in soils by being mainly located in bedrock or sediment (e.g. alluvium) and involving slow flow rates. It is primarily associated with permeable bedrock/sediment and hence sedimentary rocks (e.g. limestone, sandstone), although some sedimentary rocks may still be too impermeable to be associated with groundwater. Rocks that hold and yield significant quantities of groundwater are called aquifers. An unconfined aquifer is one that intersects with the ground surface. A confined aquifer is found between aquicludes, which are bodies of water holding rocks that transmit very little water. However, (hydrostatic) pressure within a confined aquifer can force water upwards to form an artesian spring. The dynamics of groundwater are controlled by recharge, defined by the excess of rainfall over evapotranspiration losses and flow within aquifers as controlled by a piezometric surface. The piezometric surface is a product of the small-scale topography and geology of the system as well as larger scale gradients in rainfall and recharge.

As the amount of water entering the groundwater system through recharge increases: (1) the pressure within confined aquifers may increase, increasing the flow out of and possibly the number of artesian springs; and (2) the elevation of the water table within unconfined aquifers will rise, increasing the extent to which it intersects with the ground surface. The prime loss of groundwater is through either streams fed by unconfined aquifers or artesian springs, and this can be significant in maintaining baseflow in many river catchments.

During the late spring, summer and early autumn months, evaporation and transpiration losses generally exceed rainfall in the UK. Baseflow may continue from some unconfined aquifers and artesian springs. The net result is drawdown of water tables. Groundwater replenishment is generally confined to the late autumn, winter and early spring, when soil moisture deficits are lower or even negative, and recharge occurs. Thus, the magnitude of drawdown in any one year and the magnitude of recharge will be driven by the combination of temperature and precipitation over the year. Low levels of drawdown (e.g. due to reduced evapotranporation losses or high precipitation during the drawdown season) or high levels of recharge (due to high levels of rainfall) can both cause the water table to rise to the surface and groundwater flooding to begin. It should also be noted that there can be persistence from one year to the next, i.e. there can be progressive increases in groundwater levels over a period of time, linked to a series of years with small net positive recharges. This persistence means that conventional linkage of rainfall and annual flood series in groundwater-dominated systems need to be undertaken with caution. There is now guidance for flood estimation in permeable catchments.

Figure 11.1 shows examples of trends in groundwater (from the CEH *Hydrological Year Book 2000*). The dotted line is the long-term expected average, the white band the range of water levels and the black line the actual water levels for 1996 to 2001. These diagrams in this figure are important for a number of reasons. First, they emphasise the very great range in groundwater response modes. Some locations (e.g. Killyglen) are very sensitive to fluctuations in rainfall, with water levels responding more rapidly. These types of systems are most likely to result in short-term groundwater flood events. Dalton Holme (Fig. 11.1), in contrast, is associated with long duration high groundwater levels: wherever these levels intersect the local ground level, there will be sustained discharge of water. These types of situations may lead to prolonged flooding problems (e.g. long-term road closures, flooded cellars) that are very different to both the very short-term, high magnitude flood events associated with pluvial flooding in urban areas and also the relatively short-term high magnitude flood events associated with fluvial flooding from main rivers. Finally, many of the boreholes (e.g. Dalton

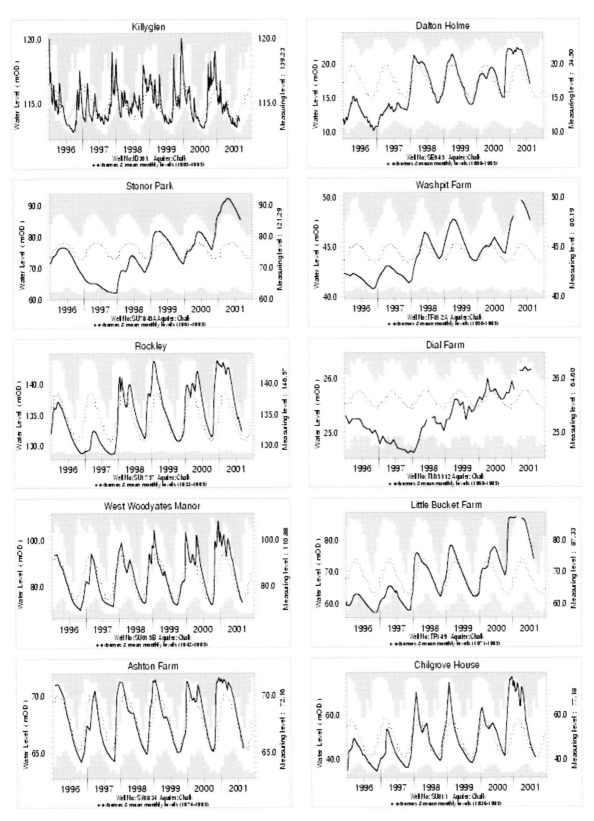

Fig. 11.1. Water levels from selected boreholes between 1996 and 2001 (black lines), long term averages (dotted lines) and maximum and minimum values (defined by the white band) (reproduced from CEH (2001) by permission of CEH (Wallingford) and the British Geological Survey)

Holme, Dial Farm) show persistence, with progressive rises in groundwater levels across many years.

Given the above, we can summarise the operation of groundwater flooding. It is associated with longer-term (as compared to other types of flood events) fluctuation in water tables in autumn, winter and spring periods when either: (1) drawdown rates in the previous summer have been relatively low (due to higher than average effective summer rainfall); or (2), and most importantly, recharge rates have been relatively high. The nature of the flood risk depends upon the nature of the aquifer system, producing both short duration and long duration flood risk. Floods associated with long duration flood risk are very different to those associated with either pluvial or main river fluvial flooding.

Case example: Groundwater flooding in Hambledon, Hampshire

The nature of groundwater flooding is well illustrated by the case of Hambledon in Hampshire (Posford Duvivier, 1995, 2001). Hambledon experiences frequent periods of severe groundwater flooding: in 1960/1, 1962/3, 1974, 1977, 1988, 1990, 1994, 1995 and 2000/1; with the most severe events in 1994 and 2000/1. The village is in the South Downs, in a valley centred on the upper chalk group. The upper chalk is relatively impermeable. However, there are extensive fissures in the rock that provide storage and routing for the passage of groundwater. Groundwater levels respond rapidly to precipitation and there is a regular seasonal variation in water-table levels, in the context of chalk permeability and local topography. Generally, during periods of prolonged heavy rainfall (but not necessarily intense rainfall), there is a progressive rise in the water table within the chalk aquifer. Groundwater starts to have an effect when the water level reaches 50 m ODN (Ordnance Datum Newlyn). When water levels rise above this, springs appear at the base of hillslopes and cellars begin to flood.

In the case of Hambledon, the problem has been exacerbated by the filling in of a ditch and raising of road levels, which prevents some cellars from draining. The ditch used to run the length of Hambledon to accommodate ephemeral flows through the village. This has been piped and filled in through time, with hardstandings over the ditch. The groundwater flood event in 1994 was estimated to have cost £250 000 to the Emergency Services and about the same in private household damages, in a village with fewer than 1000 people (Posford Duvivier, 1995).

Interactions between groundwater flooding and other drivers

Figure 11.2 summarises the source and pathway drivers that may influence the magnitude and frequency of groundwater flooding during the twenty-first century. Precipitation, and notably the magnitude of groundwater recharge (i.e. total annual precipitation, autumn and winter precipitation) is the prime control upon groundwater recharge and hence the precipitation driver is crucial. The temperature driver also matters as this determines the net water balance available for groundwater recharge as well as the water demand that may lead to groundwater abstraction. Thus, in climate change terms, future groundwater flooding will relate to the balance between changes in precipitation and increases in temperature.

Both the land-use and rural land management pathway drivers influence groundwater flooding, but most probably as secondary influences to the prime climatic drivers. The general land-use within a catchment may impact upon groundwater abstraction but, more importantly, will control the partitioning between surface runoff and groundwater recharge. Rural land management appears for the same reasons: it may influence groundwater abstraction and also recharge. Stakeholder behaviour matters as there is evidence that the form of building and infrastructure adoption can influence the flood routing process. The case example for groundwater flooding illustrates how the magnitude and frequency of flooding in the

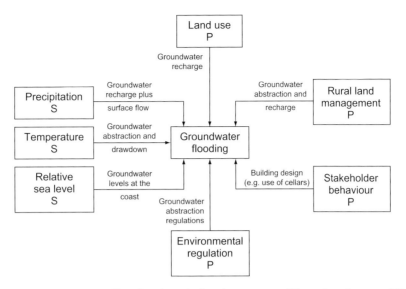

Fig. 11.2. Groundwater flooding in relation to sources (S) and pathways (P)

village of Hambledon may have been exacerbated by road construction. Environmental regulation is potentially a very important pathway driver for groundwater flooding as a result of possible future regulatory controls on groundwater abstraction. Such regulations may reduce the volume of groundwater storage and hence modify flood risk.

In relation to receptor drivers, groundwater flooding impacts can become more significant as a result of a range of socio-economic changes. A progressive increase in consumable goods may require people to make use of all of the space within a house, with more goods stored in cellars and an associated link to the economic and sectoral impact receptor. Growing pressure on space for housing may encourage the conversion of existing properties, including ground floor and below-ground rooms that are most at risk from groundwater flooding. Thus, there is a link to the urban development driver. There are many cases where groundwater flooding impacts upon infrastructure. As groundwater impacts can be of especially long duration, these impacts may become more severe as societies rely more on efficient transport and communications.

Native parameters and groundwater flooding

Representation of groundwater flooding risks represents a challenge in relation to identification of native parameters within a risk analysis framework. In theory, changes in risk could be represented by a change in the standard of protection provided by subsurface and surface drainage infrastructure (i.e. a change in the magnitude frequency of groundwater flooding). However, operationalising this needs some thought, as the risk occurs away from the designated main river and floodplain. We do have a good knowledge of where aquifer outcrops may be found (e.g. Fig. 11.3) and there is generally good local knowledge of both local aquifer characteristics and springs. Thus, it may be feasible to use this information in a strategic risk assessment.

Driver changes and future flood risks

The main drivers relevant to future groundwater flood risk are related to the effects of climate change, under all Foresight scenarios. In general terms, increasing temperature should reduce groundwater recharge, especially if this increases water abstraction due to higher irrigation demand. However, changing precipitation

Fig. 11.3. Many of the main UK aquifers (reproduced from CEH (2001) by permission of CEH (Wallingford) and the British Geological Survey)

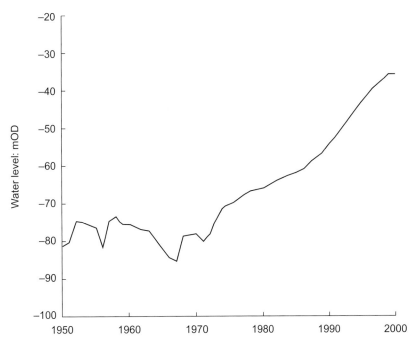

Fig. 11.4. Rising borehole levels at Trafalgar Square since 1950 (reproduced from CEH (2001) by permission of CEH (Wallingford) and the British Geological Survey)

patterns may also influence groundwater recharge. Of particular concern will be: (1) whether or not climate change increases inter-annual variability in precipitation totals; and (2) the extent to which years in which low levels of summer drawdown coincide with high levels of recharge in the subsequent autumn and winter. These changes will be compounded by other driver changes and there is, further, a long-term risk in that over abstraction of groundwater during the twentieth century is now being reversed (due primarily to reduced pumping), leading to long-term rises in groundwater levels in some areas. Figure 11.4, for instance, shows the trend in borehole water levels beneath Trafalgar Square. If these trends continue, and there is evidence from a number of deeper groundwater systems that they may, this implies serious potential groundwater flood risk in relation to infrastructure (e.g. foundations, tunnels, etc.). Thus, in relation to climate change drivers, both land management and regulatory drivers may not only increase flood risk but do so in ways that are very different to pluvial and fluvial flood risk.

Uncertainty and groundwater flooding

Uncertainties associated with this aspect of the flooding system are high and arise for a number of reasons. First, the exact nature of climate change impacts, and the relatively subtle impacts of increases in recharge due to precipitation changes and decreases due to evapotranspiration changes could result in groundwater flood risk either increasing or decreasing. Of particular concern is whether years similar to 2000/1 occur more frequently, not so much in terms of extreme flood events, but more generally wet summer-autumn-winter periods, which are what leads to sustained recharge. The second area of uncertainty is associated with the regulatory environment and issues of water abstraction. This is highly sensitive to the Foresight scenario adopted, as this determines the regulatory framework as well as the agricultural system's demand for water. The third area of uncertainty relates to geographical variation in the nature of the groundwater system, which will produce marked regional variations in groundwater response to climate change that are difficult to characterise and predict.

Muddy floods

Muddy floods are caused by overland flow generated in rural areas where overland flow connects directly with houses and other infrastructure, rather than with the conventional river network. They do not necessarily need to involve significant soil erosion (which is what makes them muddy) but there is a strong link with runoff from fields and small tributaries that also results in soil erosion.

Mode of operation

This type of flood is generally associated with a rainfall event that results in significant overland flow and surface routing of that flow to roads and/or into houses before it can be infiltrated into the soil or enters a drainage channel. Evidence suggests that they can occur due to both infiltration excess and saturated overland flow (Boardman, 2003). Infiltration excess overland flow processes occur either due to extreme intensity rainfall events or due to soil surface processes (e.g. crusting) that lead to reduction in surface infiltration rates. Boardman (2003) notes that soil crusting can occur rapidly in autumn if there is heavy rainfall, and that this may be exacerbated by other aspects of land management such as compaction due to wheelings and rollings. Field observations show that crusting may be sufficient to prevent any rainfall reaching the soil–bedrock interface, with almost all the rainfall becoming overland flow (Boardman, 2003). Surface crusting is a process that tends to occur on bare soil, and Boardman observes that, even during major storms, runoff from grassed area is minimal. However, saturated overland flow can also occur, especially in certain topographic locations (e.g. locations of topographically driven flow convergence) and/or if the soils are thin, and storage capacity is low. There is a linkage here to groundwater rise, which can also result in saturated overland flow.

Chambers and Garwood (2000) identify the factors that affect the probability of muddy flooding: these are sandy and silty soil textures; landform; cropping system; and rainfall. Of particular concern are winter cereals, and Chambers and Garwood estimate that c. 40–65% of fields with this land-use experience erosion (and hence surface flow) of some sort. Boardman and Evans (1991) estimate that the transition from grassland to autumn-sown cereals has lowered the threshold at which flooding took place from one in 100 years to one in three or four years in one location in the South Downs. There is also a strong link to land management: Evans (1990) noted that tramlines, wheelings and downslope cultivation were implicated in 84% of observed erosion events.

However, while rainfall amount is a key factor in muddy flood generation, both long duration low intensity and high intensity rainfall events can result in surface runoff and erosion, depending upon the state of the soil surface, local topography, soil type and the nature of land management (Chambers and Garwood, 2000; Boardman, 2003). For instance, Chambers and Garwood (2000) report that 96% of erosion events studied involved rainfall intensities less than 10 mm/day but greater than 4 mm/hour. Prolonged rainfall, even at low intensities, can generate surface runoff (e.g. Kirkbride and Reeves, 1993), if other conditions are right.

The main issue in relation to this type of flood event is whether or not overland flow can connect to locations where it can do damage. This is partly determined by patterns at the within-field scale and field arrangement scale (i.e. in relation to the land management unit). Runoff pathways are also strongly conditioned by topography and land-use. This was reported by Evans and Boardman (2003), who show that the risk of muddy floods reaching a housing estate in the South Downs was dominated by the extent to which overland flow could travel continuously along the length of the associated drainage path.

In summary, muddy floods are associated with rainfall and land surface characteristics that generate significant, connected overland flow, along drainage pathways that intersect roads, houses and infrastructure, without entering a drainage channel or river. There is a strong land-use and land management linkage. This type of flooding need not always be 'muddy' and not found solely in agricultural areas. It may be found in any environment where there is a very short response time to rainfall events, and is a notable problem in some upland areas.

Case example: Sompting, West Sussex

A good example of flood risk caused by muddy floods is provided by the Sompting catchment, South Downs, West Sussex. The Sompting catchment comprises a series of dry valleys extending to 211 m above mean sea level. The geology is soft, pervious chalk (Evans and Boardman, 2003) with shallow soils (<0.30 m deep). The eastern South Downs have witnessed 138 flood damage incidents in the period 1976 to 2002 (Boardman *et al.*, 2003) and all of these refer to runoff from agricultural land. The prime land-use is winter cereals. Boardman *et al.* (2003) report that the area of the catchment drilled to winter cereals increased from about 15% in 1975, to c. 35% in 1981 and c. 60% by 1988. Boardman and Evans (1991) estimate that this transition from grassland to autumn-sown cereals has lowered the threshold at which flooding took place from one in 100 years to one in three or four years in Sompting and houses have been flooded in 1980, 1987, 1990/1 and 1993/4. Flooding was significantly reduced in the catchment by 2000/1 due to land-use change.

Interactions with drivers

Figure 11.5 shows that one of the primary drivers of future muddy flood risk is changing precipitation, with observations which suggest that the amount of rainfall, its intensity, and its timing can all affect muddy flood generation. Of particular importance is the coincidence of large rainfall amounts with the drilling of winter cereals which commonly takes place in early autumn. Thus, climate changes that increase autumn precipitation may increase the incidence of flood risk. However, and unlike analyses for the effects of rural land management upon main river flood risk, there is a very strong impact from the land-use and land management drivers. There is strong evidence that the incidence of muddy floods in the South Downs can be related to the adoption of winter cereals during the 1980s. Similarly, land management, and notably tramlines, wheelines and ploughing that do not follow contours can significantly increase muddy flood generation. As a result, both the stakeholder behaviour (e.g. farmer decisions over good land management) and environmental regulation (e.g. Common Agricultural Policy

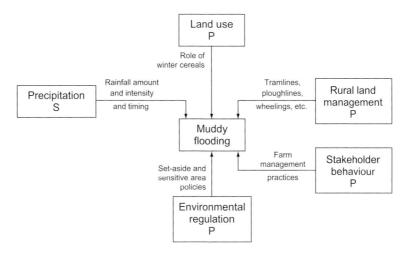

Fig. 11.5. Muddy flooding in relation to sources and pathways.

Reform; Environmentally Sensitive Area Schemes) drivers that impact upon land-use and management will also influence the probability of muddy floods occurring in the future.

Native parameters and muddy flooding

As this is a disconnected flooding problem, there is no explicit method for including it in conventional strategic assessments of future flood risk. However, if areas where this is a flood risk can be identified, then changes in muddy flooding can be expressed as a change in the probability of overland flow being generated in sufficient quantities to cause damage to homes or infrastructure.

Driver changes and future flooding

The driver changes that matter in relation to muddy flooding can be grouped under two main headings. The first is climate change related, and involves possible increases in the amount and/or intensity of early autumn rainfall. This would increase flood risk under all future scenarios. The second group relates to the direct effects of land-use and land management and the indirect effects of stakeholder behaviour and environmental regulation. This group seems to be the prime driver of muddy flood generation. It is strongly sensitive to the Foresight scenario adopted as a result of the changing degree of regulatory influence and prioritisation of agriculture between scenarios.

Uncertainty and muddy floods

There remains a degree of scientific uncertainty regarding the generation of muddy floods. While those associated with the chalk downs of southern England have been studies, the same level of analysis has not been conducted in other parts of the UK. Possibly because it may not be an especially important source of flood risk away from the more developed south coast, where houses have been located very close to areas of muddy flood risk. This uncertainty could be reduced by a more in-depth analysis of insurance industry returns in relation to disconnected flooding, in comparison with other disconnected flood mechanisms. This is mirrored in issues regarding the importance or otherwise of land management practices besides winter cereals. Uncertainty also arises in relation to the possible impacts of future regulatory change and stakeholder behaviour.

Floods related to infrastructure and ordinary water courses outside indicative floodplains

These are flood incidents that are driven by extreme rainfall events but which are linked to infrastructure issues in rural areas. This is a diverse label ranging from the failure of small ponds and bunds through to flooding associated with the network of waterways, where these are not designated as main river and/or not incorporated in flood mapping studies. It should be emphasised that this is a very broad category of flood incidents, related to situations that are not found in river or coastal floodplains.

Mode of operation

Unlike other instances of disconnected flooding, these floods are predominantly related to extreme precipitation events. There are a number of situations where isolated or small groups of properties in rural areas can experience flooding away from the main river due to infrastructure failure or management issues (e.g. ordinary water courses that are not designated as a main river and hence not included in statutory flood risk mapping). Infrastructure failure can take a number of forms.

These include: (1) culvert collapse, blockage or surcharging that causes flow to travel overland according to local topography, including diversion of flow onto roads and hence into properties, damage to vehicles, and, in extreme cases, loss of life; (2) drain blockage or surcharge in non-urban areas, especially those that contain sewerage, or linked to pluvial flooding; (3) any flooding that occurs in ordinary water courses, drains or ditches; (4) failures of small ponds or bunds; (5) failure of pumps associated with internal drainage activities; and (6) flooding linked to the canal network, where either flow into the canal exceeds canal capacity, or where river levels are so high that over flow into the river from the canal cannot occur (this type of flooding is variably dealt with in national level flood risk mapping).

The common characteristic of all of these causes of flooding is that they are associated with ordinary water courses and/or watercourses that come under the responsibility of District Councils, Internal Drainage Boards, individual land owners, the water utilities, Railtrack, the Highways Agency or County Councils (in relation to roads) and British Waterways (in relation to canals). These flood events are problematic in relation to flood risk as they are widely distributed, with many responsible authorities who may not know of the locations of all of the infrastructure for which they are responsible. There is also the issue of ageing infrastructure which may contribute to the problem. However, some of the responsible authorities do have risk management procedures in place in relation to flooding: British Waterways, for example, was actively involved in the management of the 1998 and 2000 floods (Sim *et al.*, 2002). The same is true of local authorities.

Case examples: Carleton-in-Craven and Skipton, North Yorkshire

A very large number of these instances of this type of flooding can be gleaned from the databases of local newspapers. For example, in June 2000, a major summer storm event caused a pond failure in the village of Carleton-in-Craven, North Yorkshire, flooding a small number of properties located well away from the indicative floodplain. In November 2000, extensive parts of the town of Skipton, North Yorkshire, had to be evacuated due to a potential canal failure caused by the towpath being undermined by a tributary of the River Aire. Had the canal failed, the properties that would be affected (c. 700 in total) were not in the indicative floodplain.

Interactions with other drivers

Due to the complex variety of causes of flooding in this category, summarising interactions is difficult. However, the key driver is precipitation, since practically all of the flood types listed above are linked directly or indirectly to the occurrence of extreme precipitation events.

Uncertainty

These flood types are highly uncertain as they are distributed geographically and take on a very wide variety of forms. We know very little about how different flood damages are apportioned between the types identified in the operations section, and there may be other flood types that could be identified. At the earliest opportunity, a detailed analysis of records held by insurance companies would be the first step towards a generic, national management policy for disconnected flooding of this kind.

References

Boardman, J., 2003. 'Soil erosion and flooding on the eastern South Downs, southern England, 1976–2001', *Transactions, Institute of British Geographers*, 28, 176–96.

Boardman, J. and Evans, R., 1991. *Flooding at Steepdown*, Report to Adur District Council.

Boardman, J., Evans, R. and Ford, J., 2003. 'Muddy floods on the South Downs, southern England: problems and responses', *Environmental Science and Policy*, 6, 69–83.

Centre for Ecology and Hydrology, 2001. *Hydrological Year Book, 2000*, CEH, Wallingford.

Chambers, B.J. and Garwood, T.W.D., 2000. 'Monitoring of water erosion on arable farms in England and Wales, 1990–94', *Soil Use and Management*, 16, 93–99.

Evans, R., 1990. 'Water erosion in British farmers' fields – some causes, impacts, predictions', *Progress in Physical Geography*, 14, 199–219.

Kirkbride, M.P. and Reeves, A.D., 1993. 'Soil erosion caused by low-intensity rainfall in Angus, Scotland', *Applied Geography*, 13, 299–311.

Posford Duvivier, 1995. *Investigation and Appraisal of Feasible Options for Flood Alleviation: Location Report Site No. 17, Hambledon*, Report to National Rivers Authority Southern Region, November.

Posford Duvivier, 2001. *Hambledon Flood Investigation Interim Report*, Report to Winchester City Council and Hampshire County Council (Project Code H 604 1/0 1/001).

Sim, S., Morgan, L. and Leftley, D., 2002. 'British Waterways' role in flood mitigation and emergency response', *Proceedings Inst. Civil Eng*, 151, 305–311.

12 Driver impact scoring, ranking and uncertainty

Jonathan D. Simm, Colin R. Thorne and Jim W. Hall

Introduction

The scoring and ranking of drivers of intra-urban flood risk has been dealt with in Chapter 10. This chapter reports how the information provided by the deep driver descriptions was used to score and rank the drivers of catchment and coastal scale flooding presented in Chapters 4 to 9 in terms of their relative importance in affecting future levels of flood risk. Although a quantitative model of future flood risk was constructed in the Foresight FCD Project (see Chapter 13) the model cannot be used to explore the relative importance of the drivers as their effects are integrated in a way that precludes disaggregating them for individual analysis. Hence, it was decided to perform the detailed, qualitative analysis of driver impacts reported here alongside the quantitative work, and reconcile the outcomes of the two approaches later in the project. From the outset, it was recognised that there was bound to be uncertainty in assessing driver impacts and so a band of uncertainty was derived for the flood risk impacts estimated for each driver.

To score and rank the drivers, their future impacts on local flood risk were initially expressed as a multiplier of the current value by small teams of topic specialists, in terms of the change to be expected in each driver on the basis of the deep driver description. The baseline assumption (that flood management policies, investment levels and technologies are unchanged) was applied to all driver impact assessments.

Driver impacts on local flood risk were derived for each of the four socio-economic/climate scenarios and the two time slices described in Chapter 2, yielding a total of eight driver impact scores. As the Foresight FCD Project took a high level, national view of future flooding, the scores representing the local impacts of drivers were then scaled to represent their impacts on national flood risk. The scores for national flood risk under each scenario and time slice were then ordered from highest to lowest to rank the importance of the drivers in impacting national flood risk in the UK under the scenario and at the time slice in question.

To support uncertainty analysis, the deep driver descriptions were additionally used to make upper and lower bound estimates for each driver impact score. The ratio of the upper to the lower bounds defines a geometrically scaled band of uncertainty in the estimate of driver impact for the scenario and time slice specified.

Uncertainty band widths for the drivers were tabulated to highlight those drivers that have both a strong impact on flood risk and a high degree of uncertainty associated with those impacts.

The Foresight approach placed great importance on stakeholder involvement and the preliminary driver scores and ranks derived by the topic specialists were subject to revision following intensive consultation, refereeing and peer review. In a related exercise, the authors reconciled the driver impact scores for the 2080s with the outcomes of quantitative modelling (see Chapter 13) to ensure consistency across the various components of the Foresight FCD Project. It was only after completion of the consultation and reconciliation exercises that the final driver scoring, ranking and uncertainty tables were confirmed.

Driver impacts on local flood risk

The approaches employed to assess future flood risks and elicit flood risk multiplier scores from experts were based on a range of multi-criteria techniques developed by the lead author in studying flood risk in river and coastal environments (Mockett and Simm, 2002; Mockett *et al.*, 2002). In this approach, the topic specialists for each functional driver group (Table 12.1) assigned initial flood risk impact scores to each of the drivers in their group for the Foresight FCD socio-economic/climate change scenarios:

- world markets/high emissions
- national enterprise/medium-high emissions
- local stewardship/medium-low emissions
- global sustainability/low emissions

with respect to the UK as it would exist according to those scenarios in the 2050s and 2080s (see Chapter 2 for a fuller description of the future scenarios and time slices).

In the Foresight FCD Project, flood risk is defined as being the product of the probability and consequences of flooding. In this context, source and pathway

Table 12.1. Topic specialists responsible for scoring driver impacts in each functional driver set

Driver set	Topic specialists	
	Name	**Affiliation**
Climate change	Simon Brown	Hadley Centre
	Nick Reynard	Centre for Ecology and Hydrology
Catchment land-use	Joe Morris	Cranfield University at Silsoe
	Howard Wheater	Imperial College
Fluvial processes	Stuart Lane	Durham University
	Colin R. Thorne	Nottingham University
Coastal processes	Claire Hinton	ABP Marine Environmental Research
	Ian Townend	ABP Marine Environmental Research
	Robert Nicholls	Southampton University
Human behaviour	David Ball	Middlesex University
	John Chatterton	Independent Consultant
Socio-economics	Colin Green	Middlesex University
	Edmund Penning-Rowsell	Middlesex University

drivers were considered to affect the *probability* of flooding, while receptor drivers were taken to affect its *consequences.*

Thus, when envisioning flood risk changes for a given driver in the 2050s and 2080s, topic specialists considered how either the probability or consequence of a flood event may change due to the impact of a particular driver. For example, if precipitation (a source driver) is expected to lead to a one in 20-year event becoming a one in ten-year event in the 2080s, then this would represent a doubling of flood probability (and hence risk). Conversely, if urban impacts (a receptor driver) are predicted to lead to the damages caused by a one in 20-year event in the 2050s being ten times greater than they are now, then this would represent a ten-fold increase in flood consequence (and hence risk).

Topic specialists expressed local driver impacts as a multiplier of the present-day risk associated with the area affected by that driver. Thus, precipitation change that increased the frequency of flooding by a factor of 1.9 would be scored as having an impact of 1.9 on the probability of river flooding. A driver that increased the value of assets at risk from flooding by a factor of 1.6 would be scored as having an impact of 1.6 on the consequences of flooding. These scores are *local* in as much as they represent the changes of flood risk experienced by a stakeholder (an individual or an organisation) located in a particular geographical area or involved in a particular sector of the economy.

For receptor drivers, the Foresight FCD Project recognises three dimensions of flood risk:

- economic;
- health and social;
- environmental.

The environmental context of flood risk was evaluated and dealt with separately (see Chapter 3) and, consequently, in this exercise topic specialists considered the impacts of receptor drivers only as they would affect the economic and health and social consequences of flooding.

With respect to the economic consequences of flooding, topic specialists were given clear direction with regard to the underlying economic assumptions they should make to ensure that future estimates were consistent with UK Government Treasury protocols. Hence, it was decided that:

- Inflation should be excluded.
- Prices should not be discounted to a present value, since all analyses should be undertaken as if they were being performed in the 2050s or 2080s, as appropriate.
- The distribution and types of assets at risk vary between future scenarios. An inventory of assets and their values was projected to the 2050s and 2080s for each scenario by the Foresight team. This enabled the losses associated with a given depth of flooding to be established in a way that varied appropriately between scenarios.
- The value and availability of subsidies is expected to vary between scenarios and, hence, the associated losses associated with flood damage to subsidised assets may also vary. For example, a reduction of 35% in national economic damages associated with losses in agricultural production is currently applied to account for the influence of the Common Agricultural Policy. Hence, in estimating future agricultural damages, allowance was made for scenario-specific changes in the level of agricultural subsidies consistent with the trade, governance and world view dimensions of each scenario.
- Only national economic losses should be considered.

With respect to the health and social consequences of flooding, damages were taken to include:

- pain, grief and suffering;
- loss of quality of life or general welfare;
- anxiety through fear of being flooded;
- physical and mental harm associated with actual harm or exposure to the risk;
- disruption of life style.

Flood risk is often expressed as expected annual damages (also referred to as average annual damages), where the damage is measured on an appropriate scale. Economic damages are usually expressed in monetary units (£), while health and social damages may be represented by a suitable measure such as quality adjusted life years (QALYs) (BMA, 1998; Towse *et al.*, 2002). For comparative purposes, one QALY is currently valued at about £30 000 (HM Treasury, 2003). As in this exercise driver impacts were expressed as a multiplier of current flood risk, the units of future risk remained unchanged from those they are currently expressed in.

To assist topic specialists in assigning scores to drivers, a range of possible risk multipliers was defined and described in terms of the equivalent qualitative descriptors (Table 12.2). Multipliers were scaled geometrically to ensure that they covered the entire range of possible impacts and intermediate risk scores (multipliers) were allowed (e.g. a multiplier of 11.3, which is geometrically midway between 8 and 16, could be allocated to a driver).

In assigning a flood risk multiplier to a driver, scenario and time slice, topic specialists assessed the likely change in the driver they had identified through their deep driver description (see Chapters 4 to 9), allowing for the sensitivity of flood risk to a change in the driver in question. The resulting flood risk multiplier score then represented their *best estimate* of change in national flood risk due to that driver.

To account for uncertainty in their estimates of driver impacts on future flood risk, topic specialists also made *upper* and *lower bound estimates* of each driver impact score to create a band of uncertainty around their central or *best estimate*. The width of the uncertainty band was expressed geometrically as the ratio of the upper to the lower band.

Elicitation of risk multiplier scores began with the preparation and circulation of a detailed protocol explaining the scoring methodology to each of the experts on the topic specialist teams. Initially, teams of two or more specialists assigned preliminary upper bound, best estimate and lower bound scores to the drivers in each functional group. These scores were then presented, explained, discussed and challenged at a 'buy in' meeting that was attended by the specialists responsible for all the functional

Table 12.2. Geometrically scaled multipliers for future flood risk and equivalent qualitative descriptions

Risk as a multiplier of nationally averaged risk under current conditions	Qualitative description
32×	Exceptional increase in flood risk
16×	Extreme increase in flood risk
8×	Very large increase in flood risk
4×	Large increase in flood risk
2×	Significant increase in flood risk
1×	No change
×0.5	Significant reduction in flood risk
×0.25	Large reduction in flood risk
×0.125	Very large reduction in flood risk
×0.0625	Extreme reduction in flood risk
×0.0312	Exceptional reduction in flood risk

driver sets, plus representatives of a wide range of key stakeholder groups and senior Foresight staff, and which was moderated by the authors of this chapter. The meeting first considered the scores for each driver individually before looking across the driver groups to compare how the scores within each functional set related to each other and to check for consistency in the approach and logic underpinning them. The meeting also reviewed draft driver rankings based on the preliminary driver scores. Following the 'buy in' meeting, topic specialists reflected on the challenges posed to their preliminary scores and then confirmed or amended their scores as appropriate.

Process support using electronic spreadsheets

A series of linked, electronic spreadsheets was used to facilitate the compilation and ranking of driver impact scores. The master spreadsheet listed all 22 drivers discussed in Chapters 4 to 9, with a linked sub-spreadsheet created for each of the six functional driver sets. The topic specialists for each functional driver set were provided with the sub-spreadsheet corresponding to the driver set for which they were responsible. This sub-spreadsheet contained a list of the drivers in the functional set, with blank cells into which could be added the upper, best estimate and lower bound scores (that is flood risk multipliers) for each driver. The scoring cells were contained in an array (page) that was repeated eight times, for each combination of scenario and time slice. Following the 'buy in' meeting, when the sub-spreadsheet entries had been revised and agreed, they were saved and submitted to the core team for compilation in the master spreadsheet.

In the case of source and pathway drivers, there was only the one set of upper, best estimate and lower bound scores to enter – corresponding to the driver impact on the probability of flooding. In the case of receptor drivers, two assessments had to be performed, the first dealing with the economic damages and the second with health and social damages. Within the spreadsheet, these two sources of expected annual damage were combined on an equal weighting basis.

The core team copied the completed sub-spreadsheets into an electronic folder within the master spreadsheet, this master spreadsheet being accessible to the core team only. The first page of this master spreadsheet compiled all the results provided in the sub-spreadsheets. Subsequent adjustments to the scores in the sub-sheets (in response to peer review and reconciliation of the results of qualitative and quantitative studies performed within the Foresight FCD Project) led to automatic updating of the master spreadsheet whenever it was opened.

Subsequent pages of the master spreadsheet transposed the flood risk multiplier scores for ranking and uncertainty analyses. Ranking was performed for each scenario and time slice by pressing the 'order' button at the bottom of each table.

Consultation and elimination of two drivers from the scoring exercise

Initial driver descriptions, scores and rankings benefited from wide peer review that was obtained from two specialised workshops (with 21 and 34 stakeholder attendees, respectively), refereeing commissioned by the Foresight team and conducted by independent experts, an open meeting attended by 131 people, and electronic dissemination of draft results for comment.

The response of stakeholders and expert referees to the deep driver descriptions and the initial outcome of the initial driver scoring and ranking exercise was overwhelmingly positive, but it was to be expected that there would also be constructive criticism. In the event, the deep driver descriptions were all accepted, but in finalising the outcomes of the analysis, the Foresight team accepted the consensus of stakeholder and expert opinion that two of the 19 drivers should be neither scored or ranked in the final tables.

This decision was made because it emerged during review that the attempt to be inclusive in considering drivers that might affect flood risk had led to some ambiguities in the driver scoring process. Problems stemmed from the fact that high-level drivers (that is, drivers that act through their influence on governance to affect flood risk indirectly by way of other, lower level drivers) were mixed in with lower level drivers that directly affect local flood risk themselves. The result was a lack of clarity in defining how the influence of the higher level factors could be separated from issues of governance (that were intrinsic to the scenario and which were, therefore already accounted for in the scenario) and how experts could avoid 'double counting' given that the indirect impacts of these drivers should already be represented in the scores for lower level, direct drivers. Also, the difficulty of evaluating the impacts of high level drivers under the baseline assumption became apparent as, at a national level, it was not always clear which changes should be considered as drivers (and so be included in the analysis) and which should be considered as responses (and so be held constant until assessment of responses later in the project). After a great deal of discussion it was, therefore, decided not to proceed further with scoring and ranking two drivers, although it was agreed by all parties that they should be left in the driver tables so that their importance would not be forgotten. The detailed reasoning is given below.

Public attitudes and expectations

This driver is one of two in the human behaviour driver set. During the consultation exercise it became clear that this was an important driver that was tightly coupled with issues of governance, and which acted indirectly through its influence on a number of other, lower level drivers. The defining characteristic of this driver is that public attitudes to flooding are voiced through a third element of flood risk, defined broadly as 'outrage' (see Chapter 7). For example, increased public concern about flooding often follows a serious event and the influence of public opinion on elected representatives and decision makers can be difficult to resist. The effect is to make public attitudes and expectations, in a sense, a virtual driver – reflecting the public's demand that 'something must be done to reduce flooding'. It follows that, while public attitudes and expectations can be highly effective in altering future flood risk, the flood risk impacts of this driver are (1) realised solely by way of the stakeholder behaviour driver and (2) likely to involve changes in flood management that are precluded in this assessment under the baseline assumption. Consequently, it was decided to designate this driver as 'Known to be important but not quantified', while leaving it in the driver scoring and ranking tables. The effect of this driver is not lost in the Foresight FCD Project, however, as its impacts on future flood risk are accounted for in the stakeholder behaviour driver and a number of the response measures included in the managing flood events and managing flood losses response themes.

Science and technology

Science and technology is certain to be an important driver of flood risk through its impacts on the consequences of flooding. However, during the scoring exercise, divergent opinions emerged regarding how technological advances would map onto the different Foresight futures. For example, it could be argued that greater exposure of high technology equipment to damage by flooding in homes and businesses might markedly increase the risk associated with this driver under the world markets scenario, while losses might not increase so much under local stewardship as there would be a move towards 'intermediate technologies' that were more flood tolerant. However, counter arguments that can be put forward include the propositions that, in a high technology future, more advanced satellite based and wireless systems would reduce the flood risk associated with home, office and business equipment, and that intermediate, land-based technologies would actually be more vulnerable to disruption or destruction by flooding. Two points became clear through debate. First, that the characteristics of the science and technology driver and its role in society were largely subsumed within the scenarios and so its effects should not be duplicated when considering driver impacts. Second, that impacts like those in the example above would act through and be covered by other drivers such as buildings and contents, urban impacts and infrastructure impacts. Methodologically, there was, therefore, a real danger of double counting these effects. As with public attitudes and expectations, a decision was made to designate this driver as 'Known to be important but not quantified', while leaving it in the driver scoring and ranking tables. This introduced the possibility that some of the elements of science and technology as a driver of future flood risk are under-represented in the analysis, but the team concluded that, weighed against the danger of double-counting, this was the lesser of two evils.

Multipliers of local flood risk – results

The agreed flood risk multiplier scores for driver impacts on local flood risk are listed in Table 12.3.

Table 12.3. Flood risk multiplier scores for the future impacts of drivers on local flood risk (Evans et al., 2004)

Climate change

Driver type	Name	World markets		National enterprise		Local stewardship		Global sustainability	
		2050s	2080s	2050s	2080s	2050s	2080s	2050s	2080s
S	Precipitation	4	5.7	2.8	4	2.8	4	2	2.8
S	Temperature	1	1	1	1	1	1	1	1
Catchment runoff									
P	Urbanisation	2.8	4	2.8	4	0.7	0.5	0.7	0.5
P	Rural land management	1.4	2	1.4	2	0.7	0.5	0.7	0.7
R	Agricultural impacts	0.7	0.7	1.2	1.7	1	0.85	0.7	0.5
Fluvial process									
P	Environment, ecosystems and habitats	1	1	1	1	1.4	2.8	2	4
P	River morphology and sediment supply	1	2	1	1	2	4	1.4	2.8
P	River vegetation and conveyance	1	1.4	1	1.4	1	2	2	5.7
Coastal processes									
S	Waves	3	10	2	5	1	3	1	2
S	Relative sea-level rise	5	20	4	13	3	10	3	7
S	Surges	5	20	3	9	2	5	1	2
P	Coastal morphology and sediment supply	5	10	4	7	3	4	2	2
Human behaviour									
P	Stakeholder behaviour	2	2.8	0.5	0.33	0.25	0.2	0.25	0.2
R	Public attitudes and expectations	Known to be important but not quantified							
Socio-economics									
R	Buildings and contents	6.0	17.0	2.2	3.1	3.0	4.8	2.5	4.8
R	Urban impacts	5.0	19.8	1.8	3.6	3.0	4.8	2.2	3.9
R	Infrastructure impacts	7.1	24.0	2.2	3.6	3.0	4.8	2.5	3.9
R	Social impacts	6.0	19.8	2.2	3.6	3.0	6.1	2.2	3.2
R	Science and technology	Known to be important but not quantified							

National driver impact scores

While the local impacts of the drivers are important, in a high-level analysis of flood risk it is their impacts on national flood risk that are most relevant. The national impacts of some drivers differ markedly from their local impacts in a particular geographical area or within a particular sector of the economy, because of variability in the distribution of these impacts across the UK.

Two types of adjustment were made to the local impact scores in Table 12.3 to convert the scores from local to national multipliers of future flood risk. Adjustments for spatial distribution were applied to drivers in the climate change, catchment runoff, fluvial processes and coastal processes driver sets. Local scores were reduced to account for the fact that climate change, catchment runoff and fluvial processes only affect inland flooding, while coastal drivers only affect coastal and estuarial flooding. Sectoral scaling was applied to local scores for the impacts of drivers in the socio-economic driver set (buildings and contents, agriculture, urban

Table 12.4. Flood risk multiplier scores for the future impacts of drivers on national flood risk (Evans et al., 2004)

Climate change

Driver type	Name	World markets		National enterprise		Local stewardship		Global sustainability	
		2050s	2080s	2050s	2080s	2050s	2080s	2050s	2080s
S	Precipitation	3	3.6	2.2	2.7	2.2	2.7	1.7	2.0
S	Temperature	1	1	1	1	1	1	1	1
Catchment runoff									
P	Urbanisation	2.2	2.7	2.2	2.7	0.8	0.7	0.8	0.7
P	Rural land management	1.3	1.6	1.3	1.6	0.8	0.7	0.8	0.8
R	Agricultural impacts	1	1	1	1	1	1	1	1
Fluvial process									
P	Environment, ecosystems and habitats	1	1	1	1	1.4	2.8	2	4
P	River morphology and sediment supply	1	1.6	1	1	1.7	2.7	1.3	2.0
P	River vegetation and conveyance	1	1.2	1	1.2	1	1.6	1.7	3.6
Coastal processes									
S	Waves	1.7	5.1	1.3	2.8	1	1.9	1	1.5
S	Relative sea-level rise	2.4	9.6	2	6.4	1.7	5.1	1.7	3.7
S	Surges	2.4	9.6	1.7	4.6	1.3	2.8	1	1.5
P	Coastal morphology and sediment supply	2.4	5.1	2.0	3.7	1.7	2.4	1.3	1.5
Human behaviour									
P	Stakeholder behaviour	2	2.8	0.5	0.3	0.3	0.2	0.3	0.2
R	Public attitudes and expectations	Known to be important but not quantified							
Socio-economics									
R	Buildings and contents	4.0	6.4	3.2	4.5	0.9	0.7	1.5	1.9
R	Urban impacts	1.6	2.0	1.4	1.6	1	1	1.1	1.1
R	Infrastructure impacts	4.7	9.0	3.2	5.2	0.9	0.7	1.5	1.5
R	Social impacts	6.0	19.8	2.2	3.6	3.0	6.1	2.2	3.2
R	Science and technology	Known to be important but not quantified							

impacts and infrastructure impacts) based on the proportion of each sector within the UK economy.

Scores for drivers in terms of their impacts on national flood risk are listed in Table 12.4.

Ranking driver impacts on future flood risk

Results

The aim of the driver scoring exercise was to support ranking of the drivers in terms of their potential for generating future changes in flood risk, so that consideration of the possible responses (see Part 5) could concentrate on reducing the potential impacts of the most important drivers. Given the high degree of uncertainty associated with many of the drivers (see the next section of this chapter) it was decided to group the drivers in the ranking tables (Tables 12.5 and 12.6) according to the type of impact they produce using the following tiers:

- high increase drivers – with flood risk multiplier scores greater than 2;
- medium increase drivers – with flood risk multiplier scores between 1.2 and 2;
- low impact drivers – with flood risk multiplier scores between 0.83 and 1.2;
- medium decrease drivers – with flood risk multiplier scores between 0.5 and 0.83;
- high decrease drivers – with flood risk multiplier scores less than 0.5.

Commentary

Social impacts dominate the ranking tables and the results listed in Tables 12.5 and 12.6 suggest that, under the baseline assumption, the future with regard to the social consequences of flooding is bleak, with serious increases in the consequences of flooding to people and communities expected under all scenarios. The effect of the social impacts driver would be manifest in marked rises in the health and social costs of flooding (in addition to economic losses). Severe impacts on individuals, households and communities result from societal changes that tend to increase the number and/or vulnerability of people at risk, coupled with the increased frequency and severity of flooding due to climate change. The nature and extent of social impacts will be partly determined by political, cultural, public health and social factors, which will be realised differently under different scenarios. Consequently, social impacts rank first under the world markets and local stewardship futures, which are less socially resilient. There are, however, factors responsible for increased social impacts under all scenarios, such as an ageing population, that will become increasingly susceptible to distress due to flooding.

Drivers related to different aspects of climate change produce high or medium increases in flood risk in Tables 12.5 and 12.6. The precipitation driver generates high increases in flood risk under all scenarios, generally ranking just below drivers in the stakeholder behaviour and socio-economic driver sets. Precipitation impact scores are greatest under the world markets scenario due to its high emissions of greenhouse gases, and least under the low emissions, global sustainability scenario (Table 12.4). To gauge the significance of the scores and ranks for precipitation as a driver of future flood risk, it is salutary to note that the risk of inland flooding in the 2080s is predicted to increase by between approximately 4 and 6 times over the present levels due to the impact of this driver (Table 12.3). The effect in an urban conurbation protected by linear flood defences would be to reduce the standard of protection (SoP) from one in 100 years to just one in 17 years under the world markets scenario. This corresponds to a doubling of national flood risk.

Drivers related to the coastal aspects of climate change such as relative sea-level rise, coastal morphology and sediment supply, and surges and, to a lesser extent,

Table 12.5. National ranking of catchment and coastal scale drivers for the 2050s (Evans et al., 2004)

	World markets 2050s	National enterprise 2050s	Local stewardship 2050s	Global sustainability 2050s
1	Social impacts	Buildings and contents	Social impacts	Social impacts
2	Infrastructure impacts	Infrastructure impacts	Precipitation	Environment, ecosystems and habitats
3	Buildings and contents	Social impacts	Relative sea-level rise	Relative sea-level rise
4	Precipitation	Precipitation	Coastal morphology and sediment supply	Precipitation
5	Relative sea-level rise	Urbanisation	River morphology and sediment supply	Vegetation and conveyance
6	Coastal morphology and sediment supply	Relative sea-level rise	Environment, ecosystems and habitats	Infrastructure impacts
7	Surges	Coastal morphology and sediment supply	Surges	Buildings and contents
8	Urbanisation	Surges	Waves	Coastal morphology and sediment supply
9	Stakeholder behaviour	Urban impacts	Urban impacts	River morphology and sediment supply
10	Waves	Rural land management	Vegetation and conveyance	Urban impacts
11	Urban impacts	Environment, ecosystems and habitats	Temperature	Surges
12	Rural land management	Vegetation and conveyance	Agriculture impacts	Waves
13	Vegetation and conveyance	River morphology and sediment supply	Infrastructure impacts	Temperature
14	River morphology and sediment supply	Waves	Buildings and contents	Agriculture impacts
15	Temperature	Temperature	Urbanisation	Urbanisation
16	Agriculture impacts	Agriculture impacts	Rural land management	Rural land management
17	Environment, ecosystems and habitats	Stakeholder behaviour	Stakeholder behaviour	Stakeholder behaviour

Science and technology – known to be important but not quantified

Public attitudes and expectations – known to be important but not quantified

Legend

Driver impact category	Risk multiplier (M) range	Tint code
High increase	$M \geq 2$	
Medium increase	$2 > M \geq 1.2$	
Low impact	$1.2 > M \leq 0.83$	
Medium decrease	$0.83 \geq M \geq 0.5$	
High decrease	$M < 0.5$	

Table 12.6. *National ranking of catchment and coastal scale drivers for the 2080s (Evans et al., 2004)*

	World markets 2080s	National enterprise 2080s	Local stewardship 2080s	Global sustainability 2080s
1	Social impacts	Relative sea-level rise	Social impacts	Environment, ecosystems and habitats
2	Relative sea-level rise	Infrastructure impacts	Relative sea-level rise	Relative sea-level rise
3	Surges	Surges	Environment, ecosystems and habitats	Vegetation and conveyance
4	Infrastructure impacts	Buildings and contents	Surges	Social impacts
5	Buildings and contents	Coastal morphology and sediment supply	Precipitation	Precipitation
6	Coastal morphology and sediment supply	Social impacts	River morphology and sediment supply	River morphology and sediment supply
7	Waves	Precipitation	Coastal morphology and sediment supply	Buildings and contents
8	Precipitation	Urbanisation	Waves	Infrastructure impacts
9	Stakeholder behaviour	Waves	Vegetation and conveyance	Coastal morphology and sediment supply
10	Urbanisation	Urban impacts	Urban impacts	Surges
11	Urban impacts	Rural land management	Temperature	Urban impacts
12	Rural land management	Vegetation and conveyance	Agriculture impacts	Waves
13	River morphology and sediment supply	Environment, ecosystems and habitats	Infrastructure impacts	Temperature
14	Vegetation and conveyance	River morphology and sediment supply	Buildings and contents	Agriculture impacts
15	Temperature	Temperature	Urbanisation	Rural land management
16	Agriculture impacts	Agriculture impacts	Rural land management	Urbanisation
17	Environment, ecosystems and habitats	Stakeholder behaviour	Stakeholder behaviour	Stakeholder behaviour

Science and technology – known to be important but not quantified

Public attitudes and expectations – known to be important but not quantified

Legend

Driver impact category	Risk multiplier (M) range	Tint code
High increase	$M \geq 2$	
Medium increase	$2 > M \geq 1.2$	
Low impact	$1.2 > M \leq 0.83$	
Medium decrease	$0.83 \geq M \geq 0.5$	
High decrease	$M < 0.5$	

195

waves, also result in high or medium increases in risk under most scenarios. However, Tables 12.5 and 12.6 reveal that the impacts of these drivers are much worse under the world markets and national enterprise scenarios due to their high emissions and they suggest that the impacts will intensify after the 2050s, as the effects of climate change become more apparent. These same drivers are also responsible for worsening coastal erosion risks (see Part 4). The outcome under the baseline assumption would be that, if the current expenditure on coastal defences were continued, a time would come when it would not be possible to maintain the present SoP provided by coastal defences, unleashing the potential for up to a 20-fold increase in local flood risk in the coastal floodplain. This scales to nearly an order of magnitude increase in the national risk in the 2080s.

The stakeholder behaviour driver promotes large reductions in flood risk under all but the world markets scenario by bringing about decreases in the exposure to and consequences of floods. The impacts and ranking of stakeholder behaviour under the global sustainability, national enterprise and local stewardship scenarios suggest that a high priority will be given to actions to reduce flood risk (excluding changes to flood defences, which are held constant under the baseline assumption). In part this stems from the fact that this driver incorporates the effects of the public attitudes and expectations driver in persuading and empowering stake-holders to act to avoid flood risk by altering their behaviour. Conversely, its rank as producing a high increase in flood risk under the world markets scenario illustrates the way that risk can spiral upwards when the attention of stakeholders and the wider public is focused on other priorities.

Drivers in the socio-economic and catchment runoff functional driver sets include buildings and contents, infrastructure impacts, urban impacts, urbanisation and rural land management. The scores and ranks of these drivers are very strongly scenario dependent. Under the two consumerist scenarios (world markets and national enterprise), weak planning allows urban sprawl and rural land management is inattentive to runoff control. The result is increased runoff that increases the probability of flooding in floodplains further downstream in the fluvial system. At the same time, new developments and weak planning controls on the types, densities and numbers of new buildings that are not resilient to flooding increase losses in those floodplains. Conversely, under global sustainability and, particularly, local stewardship futures, strong urban planning laws, the application of sustainable urban drainage systems (SUDS) and high levels of land stewardship act to reduce catchment runoff. Also, lower numbers of new properties and schemes that avoid placing developments in areas at risk from flooding are capable of combining to produce marked reductions in flood losses. The diverging flood risk outcomes of the different possible futures for these drivers are made clear by high to medium increases in flood risks associated with world markets and national enterprise futures that contrast with low impacts and even flood risk reductions indicated under the global sustainability and, particularly, local stewardship scenarios.

It should be noted when considering the scores and ranks for the buildings and contents, infrastructure impacts and urban impacts drivers that these incorporate the effects of the science and technology driver, which acts by way of these drivers and so was not scored separately. The results suggest that, in the high-technology world markets, national enterprise and (to a lesser extent) global sustainability futures, the vulnerability of electronic, electro-mechanical and computer-controlled assets to damage by flooding could lead to very large increases in risk. For example, the late twentieth century witnessed transformations in the numbers and complexity of telecommunication, transportation and computer systems and these trends are set to continue for at least the first half of the twenty-first century. This is likely to generate the potential for major increases in losses related to science and technology. These will be due not only to direct damage but also to wider disruption of integrated networks, the efficient operation of which relies on remotely sensed data and centrally controlled and coordinated operation of complex systems. The impacts of science and technology are therefore partly responsible for the high scores recorded for the buildings and contents, infrastructure impacts and urban impacts drivers. However, this trend may not continue, and flood resilience should eventually increase as data-collection and system-control mechanisms become wireless and/or satellite based.

Drivers in the fluvial processes driver set (environment, ecosystems and habitats, river morphology and sediment supply, and vegetation and conveyance) produce low impacts and cluster around the middle of the ranking table under the consumerist scenarios (world markets and national enterprise). However, they score and rank much higher under the two more environmentally oriented scenarios, global sustainability and local stewardship, owing to regulatory frameworks that restrict the use of rivers for flood-defence purposes and promote restoration of their natural attributes, including the natural process of flooding. In this analysis, the baseline assumption precludes the possibility that evolving flood risk management would take advantage of a growing emphasis on improving river environments and ecosystems through innovative developments in non-structural flood defence (involving, for example, expansion of wash lands and enhanced wetlands) to increase off-line storage for flood waters. The message that emerges here from the scoring and ranking of these drivers is that in practice, to avoid increasing flood risk, care would have to be taken to factor in the flood-defence function of rivers in futures where environmentally led river management is the norm and channel restoration is commonplace.

Two drivers, temperature and agricultural impacts, have low impacts across all scenarios. The effects of temperature on flood risk are important but mainly operate indirectly through the precipitation driver (see the deep driver description in Chapter 4). National risk scores of unity for agricultural impacts stem from scaling local impacts sectorally. This reflects the small proportion of gross domestic product (GDP) generated by agriculture in the UK as a whole. This is not to say that local impacts are insignificant. For example, under national enterprise, the push for national self-sufficiency in food would have impacts on risk within the farming sector through increasing the exposure of crops to damage and livestock to flooding (see Table 12.3). Conversely, reductions in agricultural losses in Northern Ireland under world markets and global sustainability scenarios (see Chapter 15), are significant not only because they indicate the ameliorating effect of restricting farming to grade 1 and 2 land, but because they signal the vulnerability of farming communities to the loss of subsidies under reforms of the Common Agricultural Policy (CAP).

Uncertainty assessment

In this element of the analysis, an assessment was made of the range of uncertainty associated with each of the driver scores, based on the uncertainty tracking exercise described in the deep driver descriptions (see Chapters 4 to 9).

It was recognised throughout the Foresight FCD Project that uncertainty in assessing the future impacts of drivers was unavoidable and that this must be accounted for in the driver scoring and ranking exercise. However, the approaches used by topic specialists to identify the sources of uncertainty and track their effects during driver scoring, varied widely between functional driver sets, reflecting the different cognitive bases and processing techniques that were employed in assessing the impacts of the drivers. In some cases, a rich picture was used to visualise and

Table 12.7. Uncertainty sources and tracking for the catchment runoff driver set (Evans et al.*, 2004)*

Driver		Linking components	
Description of source or uncertainty	Quantification of uncertainty	Description of source or uncertainty	Quantification of uncertainty
Rural land management (pathway)			
Impact of soils and land management practices on runoff	High: high uncertainty at local and catchment scale	Research and testing of effective and suitable land management practices	Moderate to high, dependent on funding and research products
Willingness of land managers to adopt land-use and management practices to control runoff (also see reference to wetland/washland options under agriculture receptor)	High: depends on acceptability and incentives to land managers	Extension services and incentive schemes to promote adoption Use of regulation or compliance requirements	High: dependent on funding and willingness to adopt, and on use of regulatory methods/ compliance requirements
Urbanisation (pathway)			
Precision in the estimation of catchment scale effects	High: precision of estimates currently varies according to scale, surface and event characteristics. Precision depends on proportion of urban area in catchment, catchment size, drainage design and location aspects	Urban growth and regulation Aggregate catchment scale effects	High: dependent on social and economic drivers affecting urbanisation, and regulation of urban development
Estimation of future storm water management solutions	High: uncertainty regarding performance of storm water solutions for different scales and pluvial events	Effective storm water solutions Adoption of storm water solutions	High: dependent upon funding and research products and voluntary or compliance-driven implementation of solutions
Agriculture (receptor)			
Estimation of flood (and waterlogging) damage costs by frequency, duration, seasonality and depth of inundation (and excessive soil water)	Low to medium: Water regime requirements of commercial crops relatively well known and observable, but knowledge gaps given new technologies, farming practices and systems	Prediction of land-use, management practices and farming systems (linked to agriculture as a pathway) Strategic food security issues	Low to medium: function of agricultural and related policies, markets and prices, including agri-environmental options, land tenure systems, and response/coping strategies of land managers Potential damage to strategic assets
Feasibility of integrated wetland/washland land management options which deliver flood management, bio-diversity and rural livelihood benefits by making flood vulnerable areas into flood suitable areas	High: limited empirical or research evidence to support potential opportunities for integrated rural land management	Integration of policy objectives and instruments: agriculture, agri-environment, flood management Development, testing and guidance on interventions and management practices to achieve potential synergy	Medium to high: need to develop and test new land-use and management practices which seek to promote multi-functional floodplain land-use Feasibility of 'joined-up' floodplain management strategies Willingness of land managers to engage

synthesise how uncertainty was propagated as drivers operated and interacted, while in others a table was used to trace uncertainty in conjunction with a flow chart of driver interactions. For example, Table 12.7 presents the uncertainty table for the catchment runoff driver set while Fig. 12.1 illustrates the flowchart of driver operation and interaction used to track uncertainty for the drivers in this set.

The aim of the uncertainty analysis was not only to make clear the uncertainties associated with the scoring and ranking exercise, but also to allow experts and stakeholders to identify drivers that are both important in terms of their impacts on future flood risk and uncertain in terms of our capability to characterise their future impacts with confidence. In the analysis, the degree of uncertainty associated with each driver, scenario and time slice combination was expressed using a geometric band width, B, defined by the ratio of the upper to the lower bound estimates for the flood risk multiplier score.

Given the high degree of uncertainty involved in the scoring, ranking and uncertainty analyses, it was decided to group the drivers in the uncertainty ranking tables (Tables 12.8 and 12.9) according to the width of the uncertainty band using the following tiers:

- High level of uncertainty – band width greater than 3.
- Medium level of uncertainty – band width between 1.5 and 3.
- Low level of uncertainty – band width less than 1.5.

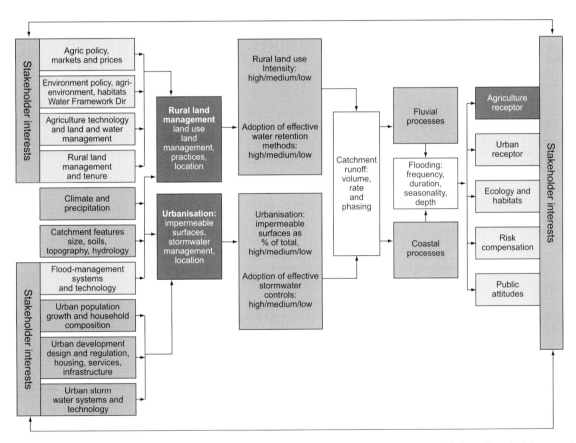

Fig. 12.1 Driver operation and interaction flowchart for the catchment runoff functional driver set. This driver set includes the drivers: rural land management, urbanisation and agriculture (as a receptor) (Evans et al., 2004)

Table 12.8. Uncertainty in catchment and coastal drivers ranked by impact on national flood risk for the 2050s (Evans et al., 2004)

	World markets 2050s	National enterprise 2050s	Local stewardship 2050s	Global sustainability 2050s
1	Social impacts	Buildings and contents	Social impacts	Social impacts
2	Infrastructure impacts	Infrastructure impacts	Precipitation	Environment, ecosystems and habitats
3	Buildings and contents	Social impacts	Relative sea-level rise	Relative sea-level rise
4	Precipitation	Precipitation	Coastal morphology and sediment supply	Precipitation
5	Relative sea-level rise	Urbanisation	River morphology and sediment supply	Vegetation and conveyance
6	Coastal morphology and sediment supply	Relative sea-level rise	Environment, ecosystems and habitats	Infrastructure impacts
7	Surges	Coastal morphology and sediment supply	Surges	Buildings and contents
8	Urbanisation	Surges	Waves	Coastal morphology and sediment supply
9	Stakeholder behaviour	Urban impacts	Urban impacts	River morphology and sediment supply
10	Waves	Rural land management	Vegetation and conveyance	Urban impacts
11	Urban impacts	Environment, ecosystems and habitats	Temperature	Surges
12	Rural land management	Vegetation and conveyance	Agriculture impacts	Waves
13	Vegetation and conveyance	River morphology and sediment supply	Infrastructure impacts	Temperature
14	River morphology and sediment supply	Waves	Buildings and contents	Agriculture impacts
15	Temperature	Temperature	Urbanisation	Urbanisation
16	Agriculture impacts	Agriculture impacts	Rural land management	Rural land management
17	Environment, ecosystems and habitats	Stakeholder behaviour	Stakeholder behaviour	Stakeholder behaviour

Science and technology – known to be important but not quantified

Public attitudes and expectations – known to be important but not quantified

Legend		
Uncertainty band category	**Uncertainty band width (B) (B = ratio of upper to lower bound estimates of flood-risk impact multiplier)**	**Tint code**
High	$B \geq 3$	
Medium	$3 > B \geq 1.5$	
Low	$1.5 > B$	

Table 12.9. Uncertainty in catchment and coastal drivers ranked by impact on national flood risk for the 2080s (Evans et al., 2004)

	World markets 2080s	National enterprise 2080s	Local stewardship 2080s	Global sustainability 2080s
1	Social impacts	Relative sea-level rise	Social impacts	Environment, ecosystems and habitats
2	Relative sea-level rise	Infrastructure impacts	Relative sea-level rise	Relative sea-level rise
3	Surges	Surges	Environment, ecosystems and habitats	Vegetation and conveyance
4	Infrastructure impacts	Buildings and contents	Surges	Social impacts
5	Buildings and contents	Coastal morphology and sediment supply	Precipitation	Precipitation
6	Coastal morphology and sediment supply	Social impacts	River morphology and sediment supply	River morphology and sediment supply
7	Waves	Precipitation	Coastal morphology and sediment supply	Buildings and contents
8	Precipitation	Urbanisation	Waves	Infrastructure impacts
9	Stakeholder behaviour	Waves	Vegetation and conveyance	Coastal morphology and sediment supply
10	Urbanisation	Urban impacts	Urban impacts	Surges
11	Urban impacts	Rural land management	Temperature	Urban impacts
12	Rural land management	Vegetation and conveyance	Agriculture impacts	Waves
13	River morphology and sediment supply	Environment, ecosystems and habitats	Infrastructure impacts	Temperature
14	Vegetation and conveyance	River morphology and sediment supply	Buildings and contents	Agriculture impacts
15	Temperature	Temperature	Urbanisation	Rural land management
16	Agriculture impacts	Agriculture impacts	Rural land management	Urbanisation
17	Environment, ecosystems and habitats	Stakeholder behaviour	Stakeholder behaviour	Stakeholder behaviour

Science and technology – known to be important but not quantified

Public attitudes and expectations – known to be important but not quantified

Legend

Uncertainty band category	Uncertainty band width (B) (B = ratio of upper to lower bound estimates of flood-risk impact multiplier)	Tint code
High	B ≥ 3	
Medium	3 > B ≥ 1.5	
Low	1.5 > B	

Table 12.10. *Priorities for research to improve our capability to predict future flood risk due to catchment and coastal flooding in the UK (Evans et al., 2004)*

Priority	Driver	Disciplinary area
1	Public attitudes and expectations	Humanities and social sciences
2	Stakeholder behaviour	Social sciences
3	Science and technology	Engineering, physical and biotechnical sciences
4	Surges	Natural environment, engineering and physical sciences
5	Precipitation	Natural environment
6	Waves	Natural environment, engineering and physical sciences
7	Relative sea-level rise	Natural environment
8	Coastal morphology and sediment supply	Natural environment, engineering and physical sciences
9	Social impacts	Social sciences and public health medicine
10	Infrastructure impacts Buildings and contents	Engineering, economic and and physical sciences

In the uncertainty tables, the order of the drivers is the same as that used in Tables 12.5 and 12.6, so that the drivers with the greatest potential to increase flood risk are at the top.

Two points emerge from the uncertainty analysis. First, there is great uncertainty concerning many of the drivers that are most important in increasing future flood risk. Second, when coupled with the driver scoring exercise, the uncertainty analysis provides an objective basis from which to prioritise research intended to improve our capability to predict the trends and changes in future flood risk in the UK.

Hence, a research priority factor (RPF) was defined by:

$$RPF = FRI \times UBW$$

where, FRI = mean flood risk multiplier score and UBW = mean uncertainty band width. The means of the flood risk impact scores and uncertainty band widths were used by averaging the scores for each driver across all four scenarios in the 2080s. This was done so that research priorities would be independent of the choice of future scenario. On this basis, the top ten priority drivers for further research are listed in Table 12.10, with the public attitudes and expectations, and science and technology drivers included (even though their scores and ranks were omitted from Tables 12.3 to 12.6) due to their undoubted importance and very high degree of uncertainty.

Reconciliation of driver scores with the results of quantitative assessment of flood risk drivers

Once descriptive treatment of drivers reported in Chapters 4 to 12 and the quantitative analysis of drivers reported Chapters 13 to 15 had both been completed, a comparative analysis was performed to reconcile the results of the driver description and quantitative risk assessment components of the Foresight study as they apply to England and Wales in the 2080s. This exercise could not be performed nationally as lack of data prevented quantitative risk analysis for Scotland and Northern Ireland (Hall *et al.*, 2003).

The exercise suggested that corrections should be applied to the scores for some receptor drivers, related to the consequential element of flood risk. Here, qualitative analyses performed by topic specialists in writing their deep driver descriptions were enhanced and updated using quantitative data which only became available

Table 12.11. Reconciled driver impact scores for the 2080s

Driver	Driver type		Factor by which flood risk is multiplied in 2080s under each Foresight scenario			
			World markets	National enterprise	Local stewardship	Global sustainability
Precipitation	F	P	2.1	1.9	1.8	1.5
Temperature	F	P	1.0	1.0	1.0	1.0
Land use	F	P	1.7	1.9	0.9	0.9
Rural land management	F	P	1.2	1.3	0.9	0.9
Environment and ecosystems	F	P	1.0	1.0	1.5	1.8
River morphology and sediment supply	F	P	1.2	1.0	1.8	1.5
Vegetation and conveyance	F	P	1.1	1.1	1.3	2.2
Waves	C	P	1.6	2.2	1.7	1.2
Surges	C	P	2.3	3.5	2.5	1.7
Relative sea level	C	P	1.1	1.3	1.4	1.4
Coastal morphology and sediment supply	C	P	1.4	1.8	1.7	1.1
Stakeholder behaviour	B	P	1.0	1.1	1.0	0.9
Social impacts	B	C	1.6	1.7	0.8	1.9
Economic and sectoral	B	C	6.4	4.5	0.7	1.1
Urban impacts	B	C	2.0	1.6	1.0	0.9
Infrastructure	B	C	1.7	1.4	0.6	1.0
Agriculture impacts	B	C	1.0	1.0	1.0	1.0
Maximum – dependent case			6.4	4.5	2.5	2.2
Product – independent case			1170	1666	7.4	46
RASP total risk multiplier			21.0	15.7	1.6	4.9

Key: F = fluvial driver; C = coastal driver; B = driver affecting both fluvial and coastal flood risk; P = driver affecting flood risk probability; C = driver affecting flood risk consequence

later in the Foresight Project, having been generated using the risk analysis for strategic planning (RASP) tool (see Chapter 13). Scores for four of the six receptor drivers were adjusted using RASP data, with those for the 'stakeholder behaviour' and 'social impacts' drivers remaining unchanged (Table 12.11).

The drivers whose flood risk multiplier scores have been adjusted are:

- *Urbanisation*: scores were adjusted using quantitative data for the increased numbers of properties in floodplains and the associated annual economic damages predicted using the RASP tool for each scenario in the 2050s and 2080s. However, it should be stressed that, as the estimates of the increases in properties in the floodplain used in RASP modelling were originally provided by the topic specialists for the socio-economic driver set, the only affect of this correction was to make the expert judgements used in Foresight internally consistent.
- *Buildings and contents*: scores were reviewed in light of the RASP results for increases in annual economic damages in the 2050s and 2080s. This was another internal correction as the estimates of changes in buildings and contents in the floodplain used in RASP were based on guidance provided by the driver set experts. The final score agreed for this driver was also re-evaluated on the basis that it should correspond to the composite outcome of RASP modelling reflecting the proportions of domestic (70%), high technology (10%) and commercial (20%) properties in the floodplain.
- *Infrastructure impacts*: during their deep assessment of drivers, topic specialists developed a ratio between losses due to damage to buildings and contents, and those due to damage to infrastructure in the floodplain. In reconciling the

results of the qualitative and RASP analyses, this ratio was used to adjust RASP results for buildings and contents. The scores were therefore mediated to ensure internal consistency across the Foresight Project.

- *Agriculture impacts*: RASP analysis of agricultural losses indicated that future economic losses due to flood damage will amount to no more than 4% of GDP under the local stewardship scenario and less than 1% for all other scenarios. While agricultural losses will continue to be serious, locally and regionally, when considered in terms of national flood risk, future impacts due to changes in agricultural losses are likely to be small. After discussion with experts in rural policy and agricultural economics it was agreed that the flood risk multiplier scores for agricultural losses should be set at 1.0 for all scenarios.

The final row in Table 12.11 gives the overall risk multiplier for each scenario derived using the RASP tool. This represents the integrated effect on flood risk of all the drivers combined. Unfortunately, there is no simple or explicit relationship between the overall risk multiplier derived using the RASP tool and the risk multipliers for individual drivers. If all the drivers were statistically dependent upon each other, the overall risk multiplier should be the same as that for the driver having the highest individual score (see the 'maximum' row in Table 12.11). Conversely, if all the drivers were statistically independent of each other, then the overall risk multiplier should be equal to the product of the scores of all the individual drivers (see the 'product' row in Table 12.11).

As the overall risk multiplier scores obtained from RASP modelling of the world markets, national enterprise and global sustainability futures are close to but somewhat higher than in those for the driver with the highest individual score, the data in Table 12.11 suggest that, in practice, there is a fair degree of dependence between the drivers although this dependence is incomplete. There is, however, one anomaly in the results, in that the scores for the local stewardship future the overall flood risk multiplier derived from RASP modelling (1.6) is *lower* than the highest individual driver score estimated through qualitative analysis (M = 2.5, for surges). This anomaly is probably a result of flood risk multipliers scores for this scenario being low generally and it may reflect the limiting accuracy of the scoring and modelling methods employed in these high level assessments.

Concluding remarks

The processes by which long-term environmental and socio-economic changes influence future flood risk are highly complex. New understanding of these processes was arrived at in the Foresight Project through a combination of qualitative analysis by teams of experts and quantitative analysis, as described in more detail in Chapters 4 to 11. This chapter has explained the process, based primarily on expert judgement but grounded firmly in the underlying evidence base, by which the importance of drivers was evaluated and compared.

As is well known (Cooke, 1991; Vick, 2002), the use of expert judgement in quantified risk analysis raises considerable methodological challenges if the potential biases of individual and group elicitation processes are to be avoided. This study therefore provided opportunities for experts to review their own judgements and challenge those of their peers. It also included an external peer review. Finally, the process by which the results of the elicitation were reconciled with the results of model-based quantified risk analysis has been described. In documenting the series of methodological choices that have been made, this chapter provides a starting point for future studies to build upon and refine the methodology.

References

British Medical Association (BMA), 1998. *Health and Environmental Impact Assessment*, Earthscan, London.

Evans, E., Ashley, R., Hall, J., Penning-Rowsell, E., Saul, A., Sayers, P., Thorne, C. and Watkinson, A., 2004. *Foresight Future Flooding. Scientific Summary: Vol. I – Future risks and their drivers*, Office of Science and Technology, London.

Cooke, R.M., 1991. *Experts in Uncertainty: Opinion and Subjective Probability in Science*, Oxford University Press, New York.

Hall, J.W., Dawson, R.J., Sayers, P.B., Rosu, C., Chatterton, J.B. and Deakin, R., 2003. 'A methodology for national-scale flood risk assessment', *Water and Maritime Engineering*, 156, 235–247.

HM Treasury, 2003. *The Green Book: Appraisal and evaluation in central government*, TSO, Norwich.

Mockett, I.D. and Simm, J.D., 2002. *Risk Levels in Coastal and River Engineering – A guidance framework for design*, Thomas Telford, London.

Mockett, I.D., Simm, J.D., van Gelder, P., Schoustra, F. and Hall, J.A., 2002. 'A risk framework for integrating multi-attribute problems in coastal engineering decision making', *Proceedings International Coastal Engineering Conference (Cardiff)*, Am. Soc. Civ. Engrs.

Towse, A., Pritchard, C. and Devlin, N., 2002. *Cost-effectiveness Thresholds: economic and ethical issues*, Office of Health Economics, London.

Vick, S.G., 2002. *Degrees of Belief: Subjective probability and engineering judgement*, ASCE Press, Reston, VA.

Part 3
Assessment of drivers and risks

13 Quantitative assessment of driver impacts on future flood risk in England and Wales

Jim W. Hall, P.B. Sayers, Mike Panzeri and Rob Deakin

Introduction

In recent years, thanks to the availability of remotely sensed data and other national datasets, it has become possible to conduct national-scale flood risk assessments in England and Wales. The results of this type of risk analysis have been used to inform policy making and prioritisation of resources for flood management. In the Foresight study, national-scale quantified risk assessment was adapted to examine scenarios of future flood risk in order to generate estimates of how much risk might change in the future.

National-scale risk assessment is by no means straightforward, because of the need to assemble national datasets and then carry out and verify very large numbers of calculations. Increasingly, however, national-scale datasets are becoming available. Aerial and satellite remote sensing technologies are providing new topographic and land-use data. Commercial organisations are generating and marketing increasingly sophisticated datasets of the location and nature of people and properties. In 2002 the Environment Agency, the organisation responsible for operation of flood defences in England and Wales, introduced a National Flood and Coastal Defence Database (NFCDD), which for the first time provides in a digital database an inventory of flood defence structures and their overall condition. Together, these new datasets now enable flood risk assessments to be carried out that incorporate probabilistic analysis of flood defence structures and systems. Once the necessary datasets are held in a geographical information system (GIS) they can then be manipulated in order to explore the impact of future flood management policy and scenarios of climate change.

In this chapter an overview of the national-scale flood risk assessment methodology for flood risk analysis is provided. Results are presented and discussed both for an application of the methodology to all of England and Wales in 2002, and for projections of flood risk under scenarios of climate and socio-economic change. The analysis was applied only to England and Wales because the necessary data to run the model were not available in Scotland and Northern Ireland. Flood risks in Scotland and Northern Ireland are discussed in the following two chapters.

Overview of the methodology

Flood risk is conventionally defined as the product of the probability of flooding and the consequential damage, summed over all possible flood events. It is often quoted in terms of an expected annual damage, which is sometimes referred to as the 'annual average damage'. There are many possible dimensions of flood damage, including economic damage, harm to people and damage to the environment. For a national assessment of flood risk, expected annual damage must be aggregated over all floodplains in the country. An overview of the methodology by which this can be achieved is given in Fig. 13.1 and described in outline below. Further details can be found in Hall *et al.* (2003).

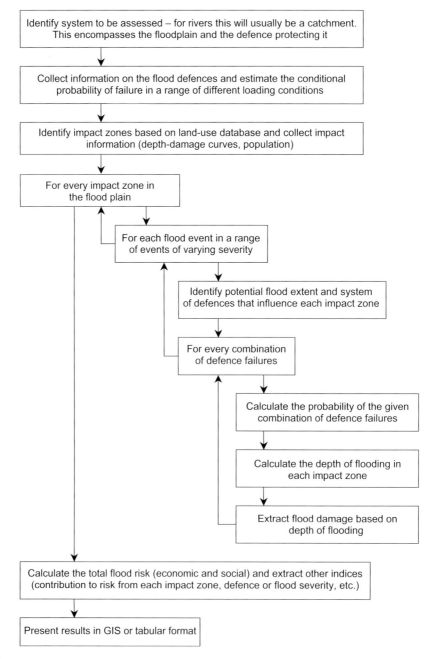

Fig. 13.1. Overview of the national flood risk assessment methodology (Hall et al.*, 2003)*

The most significant constraint on a national-scale flood risk assessment methodology is the availability of data. The methodology presented here has been developed to make use of the following national GIS datasets and no other site-specific information:

1. *Indicative floodplain maps (IFMs)* are the only nationally available information in the UK on the potential extent of flood inundation. The IFMs are outlines of the area that could potentially be flooded in the absence of defences in a one in 100-year return period flood for fluvial floodplains and a one in 200-year return period flood for coastal floodplains.
2. *1:50 000 maps with 5 m contours.* The methodology was developed in the absence of a national topographic dataset of reasonable accuracy, although a higher resolution dataset is now available. At the time of the study, topographic information at 5 m contour accuracy was used to classify floodplain types, as it is not sufficiently accurate to estimate flood depths.
3. *National map of the centreline of all watercourses.*
4. *National Flood and Coastal Defence Database* provides a national dataset of defence location, type and condition.
5. *National database of locations of residential, business and public buildings.*
6. *Land-use maps and agricultural land classification.*

The 34 000 km of flood defences in England and Wales protect areas most at risk from severe flood damage. An essential aspect of flood risk analysis is therefore to assess the reliability of the flood defence infrastructure. These defences must be dealt with as systems if the flood risk is to be accurately estimated. In the absence of more detailed information on flood extent, in the current methodology the indicative floodplain is adopted as the maximum extent of flooding and is further sub-divided into impact zones, not greater than 1 km × 1 km. Each flood impact zone is associated with a system of flood defences which, if one or more of them were to fail, would result in some inundation of that zone.

Reliability analysis of flood defences potentially requires a huge quantity of data, which is not available for all of the flood defences in England and Wales. An approximate reliability method has therefore been developed that makes use of the so-called Standard of Protection (SoP), which is an assessment of the return period at which the defence will be significantly overtopped. Flood defence failure is addressed by estimating the probability of failure of each defence section under a given load (relative to SoP) for a range of load conditions. Generic versions of these probability distributions of defence failure given load, have been established for a range of defence types for two failure mechanisms: overtopping and breaching.

Having estimated the probability of failure of individual sections of defence, the probabilities of failure of combinations of defences in a system are calculated. To do so, it is assumed that the probability of hydraulic loading of individual defences in a given flood defence system is fully dependent. The probabilities of failure of each of the defences in the system, conditional upon a given load, are assumed to be independent. For each failure combination an approximate flood outline, which covers some proportion of the IFM, is generated using approximate volumetric methods. These methods estimate discharge through or over the defence and inundation characteristics of the floodplain, based on an assessment of floodplain type.

In the absence of water level and topographic data, estimation of flood depth has been based on statistical data. These data were assembled from 70 real and simulated floods for a range of floodplain types and floods of differing return periods. These data were used to estimate flood depth at points between a failed defence and the floodplain boundary, in events of a given severity. While flood inundation modelling is not directly employed, the statistical method is a better representation of flood depths than a simple 'bath tub' assumption. Flood depth

estimates from a range of floods were used to construct an estimate of the probability distribution of the depth of flooding for each impact zone (Fig. 13.1).

The numbers of domestic and commercial properties and area of agricultural land
in each impact zone were extracted from nationally available databases. These data
were combined with relationships between flood depth and economic damage that
have been developed from empirical analysis of past flooding events (Penning-Rowsell
et al., 2003a). For a given impact zone the expected annual damage R is given by

$$R = \int_0^{y_{max}} p(y)D(y)\,dy \qquad (13.1)$$

where y_{max} is the greatest flood depth from all flooding cases, $p(y)$ is the probability
density function for flood depth and $D(y)$ is the damage in the impact zone in a
flood of depth y metres. The total expected annual damage for a catchment or
nationally is obtained by summing the expected annual damages for each impact
zone within the required area.

In addition to economic damage, the following metrics were analysed:

- The population at risk was estimated from the number of inhabitants within
  an impact zone using 2001 census data. The Social Flood Vulnerability Indices
  (SFVI) (Tapsell *et al.*, 2002) were used to identify communities vulnerable to
  the impacts of flooding.
- Social vulnerability was ranked from 'very low' to 'very high' and is based on
  a weighting of the number of lone parents, the population over 75 years old,
  the long-term sick, non-homeowners, unemployed, non-car owners and over-
  crowding, obtained from census returns. The risk of social impact is obtained
  as a product of probability of flooding to a given depth and the SFVI,
  providing a comparative measure for use in policy analysis.
- Agricultural damage was based upon agricultural land classification data and
  empirical damage functions (Penning-Rowsell *et al.*, 2003b).

Methods for scenario-based future flood risk assessment

The national-scale flood risk analysis model outlined above was used to analyse
long-term change by making appropriate changes to the model parameters to
reflect the time and scenario under consideration. The four scenarios introduced in
Chapter 2 were analysed for the 2080s:

- world markets/high emissions;
- national enterprise/medium-high emissions;
- local stewardship/medium-low emissions;
- global sustainability/low emissions.

In addition, to investigate the evolution of risks over time, the world markets/
high emissions scenario for the 2050s has also been analysed.

The input data required by the risk analysis model do not correspond exactly to
the information provided either in climate change or socio-economic scenarios. It
was therefore necessary to construct approximate relationships between the
variables for which scenarios information was available and the variables required
for flood risk analysis. A summary of the relationships adopted in the analysis of
risks from river and coastal flooding is provided in Table 13.1. A quantified
estimate was made of the effect in each scenario that a given change, for example
urbanisation, would have on the relevant variables in the risk model (Table 13.1).
The cumulative effect of each of the changes in the given scenario was then calculated. Where feasible, regional variation was applied to these adjustments in order
to take account of, for example, regional differences in climate or demographic

Quantitative assessment of driver impacts on future flood risk in England and Wales

Table 13.1. Representation of future scenarios in risk model

Variable used risk model	Explanation	Changes that may be represented with this variable
Standard of Protection (SoP) of flood defences	The return period at which the flood defence (or where none exists the riverbank) is expected to overtop	Climate change[a] Changes in land-use management (which may change runoff and hence river flows and water levels) Morphological change (that may also influence the conveyance of the river and hence water levels)
Condition grade of flood defences	An indicator of the robustness of the defences and their likely performance when subjected to storm load	Morphological changes Maintenance regimes
Location of people and properties in the floodplain	Spatially referenced database of domestic and commercial properties. Census data on occupancy, age, etc.	Demographic changes Urbanisation Commercial development
Flood depth–damage relationships	Estimated flood damage (in £ per house or commercial property) for a range of flood depths	Changes in building contents Changes in construction practices
Social flood vulnerability indices[b]	An aggregate measure of population vulnerability to flooding, based on census data	Changes in demographics (e.g. age) Changes in equity
Agricultural land-use classification in the floodplain	Agricultural land grade from 1 (prime arable) to 5 (no agricultural use)	Changed agricultural practices Agricultural land being taken out of use
Reduction factors	Measures that will reduce total flood damage, e.g. flood warning and evacuation can be reflected by factoring the estimated annual average damage	Flood warning (including communications technologies) and public response to warning Evacuation Community self-help

Notes

a. For example, a scenario in which if climate change is expected to increase water levels by 20% is represented by reducing the SoP of flood defences by an appropriate increment

b. Tapsell *et al.* (2002)

projections. There is no unique mapping between a scenario, which is an inherently vague entity, and a realisation of the risk model. In other words, there is not a unique representation of the scenario in the risk model. The quantified analysis presented here is one of many equally plausible representations of the same four scenarios. While no claim is made to the uniqueness of these results, they do illustrate some striking contrasts between different scenarios of change and provide the basis for exploring responses to flood risk that are robust across plausible futures.

Future flood risk is greatly influenced by flood management policy and practice, perhaps more so than it is by changes outside the control of the flood manager, such as climate change or economic growth. However, in the analysis described in this chapter, current flood defence alignment and form, as well as the levels of investment in maintenance and renewal, were kept the same across all scenarios (see Chapter 2). Changing scenarios were super-imposed on this fixed flood defence policy (including the current pattern of expenditure and technical approach), in order to assess the capacity of the current policy to cope with long-term changes.

This might at first appear to be at odds with scenario analysis in that we might expect the approach to flood management to differ in each scenario. However, it is particularly informative to today's policy makers in identifying the vulnerabilities of present-day approaches. It provides a baseline against which to judge the effectiveness of different flood management programmes. The risk that actually prevails in the future will be further modified by flood management activity, which will itself be a reflection of society's values and expectations. The quantified analysis of changing flood management policies and practices, in the context of the four scenarios, is discussed in Chapter 25.

Results for the present situation

The national-scale risk assessment methodology described above was applied to all of England and Wales in 2002 in the Environment Agency's National Flood Risk Assessment. The results are reported on a 10 km × 10 km grid (though, as described above, the analysis was conducted on the basis of impact zones not greater than 1 km × 1 km). Figure 13.2 shows the proportion of each 10 km × 10 km grid cell

Fig. 13.2. Proportion of land in indicative floodplain (fluvial flood plains correspond to the 1:100-year flood outline; coastal floodplains to the 1:200-year outline, in both cases in the absence of flood protection) (Evans et al., 2004)

Fig. 13.3. Classification of floodplain types (Evans et al.*, 2004)*

that is occupied by floodplain. It indicates the very high proportions of floodplain around the Wash and the Humber estuary on the east coast of England and in several other coastal areas. Figure 13.3 shows a morphological classification of floodplains, revealing the preponderance of steeper floodplains in the north and west of England and Wales and flatter floodplains in the south and east.

Comparison of the extent of the indicative floodplain with residential, commercial and land-use databases revealed that in England and Wales there are 1.61 million residential properties and 131 000 commercial properties in the indicative floodplain, together with 1.43 million hectares of agricultural land. Comparison on census data with the indicative floodplain yields an estimated 4.47 million people resident within the indicative floodplain. The total value of residential property at risk is £208 billion.

The national-scale risk analysis yielded an estimated expected annual damage due to flooding for England and Wales in 2002 of £1.0 billion, with an uncertainty range between £0.6 billion and £2.1 billion. The uncertainty range was calculated by examining the plausible bounds on the most uncertain quantities in the analysis, the probability of flood defence failure being among the most important. Highest economic risk is located in floodplain areas of high economic value, notably Greater London, despite very high standards of flood protection. A number of areas of high coastal flood risk are located along the south, east and north-west coasts of England. The expected annual damage to agriculture is estimated to be £5.9 million, accounting for only about 0.5% of economic damage due to flooding. This loss is very small in economic terms, but can represent considerable impact on the rural economy.

The risk analysis has been compared with recent flood events to assess the dependability and uncertainties in the methodology (HR Wallingford, 2003). The annual average flood damage estimate of roughly £1 billion is of the same order as, but somewhat larger than, annual losses due to flooding experienced in recent years. For example, floods in autumn 2002 resulted in economic losses of the order of £750 million (Penning-Rowsell *et al.*, 2003a). Some of the inconsistency is explained by reporting of recent flood events and by assumptions in the model (particularly the exclusion of emergency repair works). Although a single event provides only limited basis for validation of annual average risk estimates, the reasonably good correspondence between model and observations indicates that the model does provide a reasonably sound basis for policy appraisal and comparative evaluation of future scenarios.

The method is computer-intensive, and 2002 analysis took several weeks to compute, with separate computers being dedicated to each region of the Environment Agency of England and Wales. The computational aspects, in particular the interaction with the GIS database, was subsequently refined, so that each scenario analysis reported here took about a week to compute.

Results for future scenarios

The results of the flood risk scenarios analysis are summarised in Table 13.2. No discounting or inflation is applied to economic risks. Risk is estimated at time points in the future using today's prices.

Large increases in the number of people occupying the floodplain in the UK are envisaged in the relatively loosely regulated world markets and national enterprise scenarios (Fig. 13.4). Most of this increase is predicted to occur by the 2050s,

Table 13.2. Summary of flood risk scenarios

	2002	World markets 2050s	World markets 2080s	National enterprise 2080s	Local stewardship 2080s	Global sustainability 2080s
Number of people within the indicative floodplain: millions	4.5	6.2	6.9	6.3	4.5	4.6
Number of people exposed to flooding (depth >0 m) with a frequency >1:75 years: millions	1.6	3.3	3.5	3.6	2.3	2.4
Expected annual economic damage (residential and commercial properties): £ billions	1.0	14.5	20.5	15.0	1.5	4.9
Annual economic damage relative to GDP per capita	0.10%	0.15%	0.14%	0.31%	0.05%	0.06%
Expected annual economic damage (agricultural production): £ millions	5.9	41.6	34.4	41.3	63.5	43.9

Quantitative assessment of driver impacts on future flood risk in England and Wales

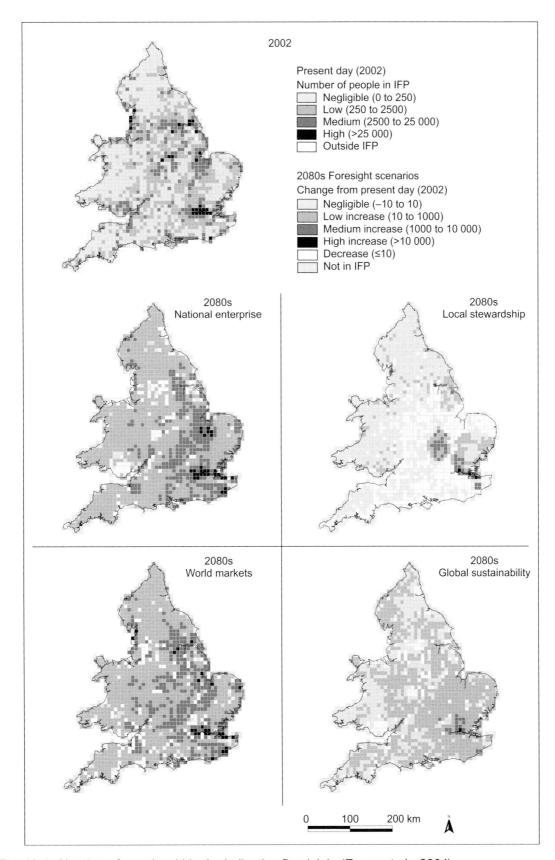

Fig. 13.4. *Number of people within the indicative floodplain (Evans et al., 2004)*

representing predictions of very rapid growth in the first half of this century which is envisaged to approach a limit associated with a fairly stable population and spatial constraints. The Thames Valley, east coast and the area between Lancashire and the Humber, experience growth in population exposure. Although the household occupancy reduces under the world markets scenario to 1.8 (from 2.34 today), the rate of new build of property, particularly in the south (including significant developments in the London Gateway, Ashford and Milton Keynes), increases population density. Floodplain occupancy is kept stable in the global sustainability and local stewardship scenarios but with some ongoing pressure in the south-east.

However, increasing flood frequency (Fig. 13.5), primarily due to climate change, means that even with stable numbers of people in the floodplain, the number of people at risk from flooding more frequently than 1:75 years will increase in all scenarios (Fig. 13.6), assuming that current flood defence systems are continued into the future. The coastal floodplains of the south-east and east coast experience the greatest increase in probability of flooding, reflecting the effect sea-level rise can have on the performance of coastal defences where wave heights are, at present depth, limited. A small increase in mean sea level can lead to increased wave impacts and hence significant reductions in the standard of protection defences afford. Other areas, such as the coastline of north Norfolk, south Wales and along the outer Humber estuary, also exhibit significant increases in flood frequency. The gradient in predicted change in rainfall from north Scotland to southern England translates to limited changes in central England. The predicted drier climate in the south-east leads to a reduced exposure to inundation.

Greater climate change by the 2080s, together with the increased floodplain occupancy noted above, mean that the world markets and national enterprise scenarios will see more than doubling of the number of people at risk from flooding more frequently than 1:75 years (Fig. 13.6). Meanwhile, in the global sustainability scenario, although the number of people living in floodplains changes slightly, there are a few areas where the number of people at high risk increases significantly compared to that experienced in 2002. In the local stewardship scenario, the reduced occupancy of the floodplain allied with a more moderate climate change than observed in the world markets scenario leads to a decrease in the number of people at risk across much of the country. Exceptions to this include the south-east coast, and the area between Lancashire and the Humber and the Thames estuary.

In all scenarios, other than the low growth, environmentally/socially conscious local stewardship scenario, annual economic flood damage (Fig. 13.7) is expected to increase considerably over the next century, assuming the current flood defence policies are continued in future. A roughly 20-fold increase by the 2080s is predicted in the world markets scenario, which is attributable to a combination of much increased economic vulnerability (higher floodplain occupancy, increased value of household/industrial contents, increasing infrastructure vulnerability) together with increasing flood frequency. Increasing risk is predicted to be concentrated in broadly the same areas as where it is currently highest. Coastal flooding makes an increasing contribution to total flood risk, increasing from 26% in 2002 to 46% in the 2080s. The largest increases are observed where both housing pressure is greatest and the standard of defence is most susceptible to climate change. This critical combination is most clearly seen in the world markets and national enterprise scenarios around the coastal strip of the south-east, East Anglia and south and north Wales. The area between Lancashire and the Humber, and the Thames Valley also sees a significant increase in exposure to economic loss. The drier climate in the south-east is reflected in reduced economic damage. In the local stewardship scenario, there is a widespread general reduction in the expected annual damage across the majority of England, with the coastal areas in Wales being categorised as negligible to low. This is compensated for by coastal areas,

Quantitative assessment of driver impacts on future flood risk in England and Wales

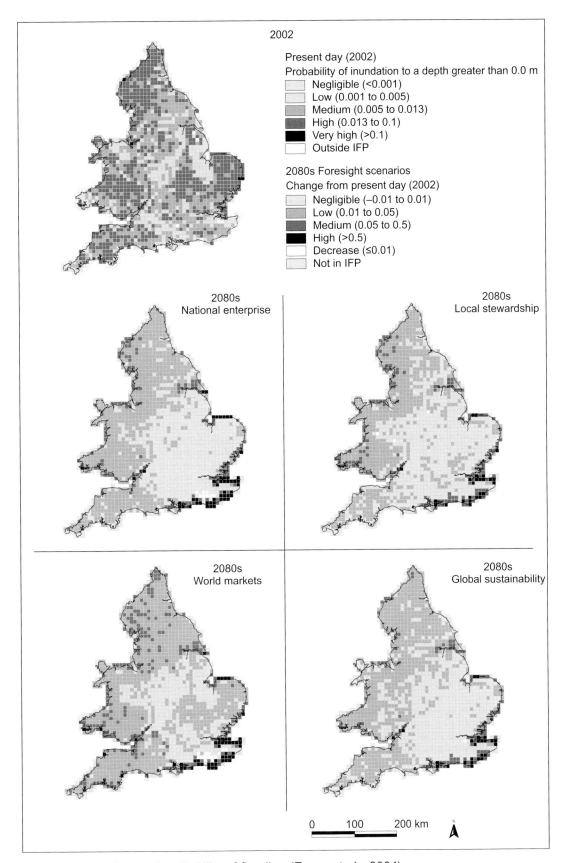

Fig. 13.5. Expected annual probability of flooding (Evans et al., 2004)

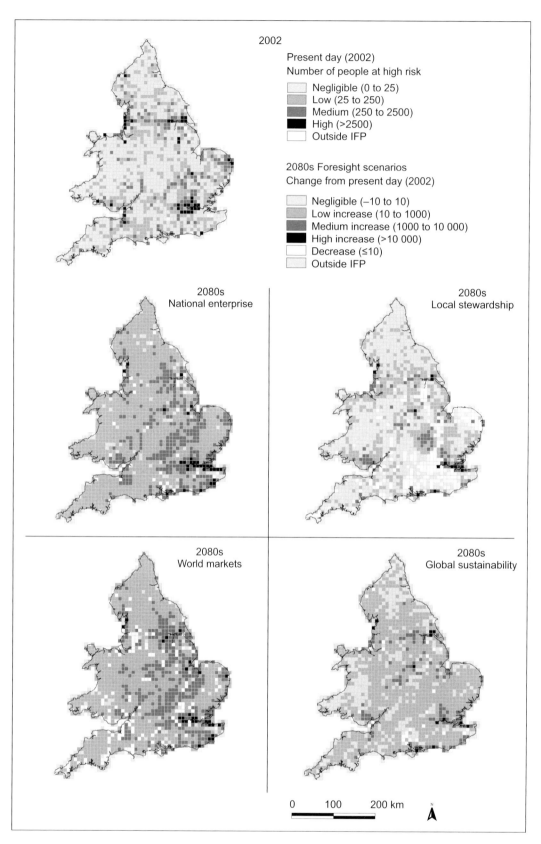

Fig. 13.6. Number of people living with an annual probability of flooding greater than 1:75 (Evans et al., 2004)

Quantitative assessment of driver impacts on future flood risk in England and Wales

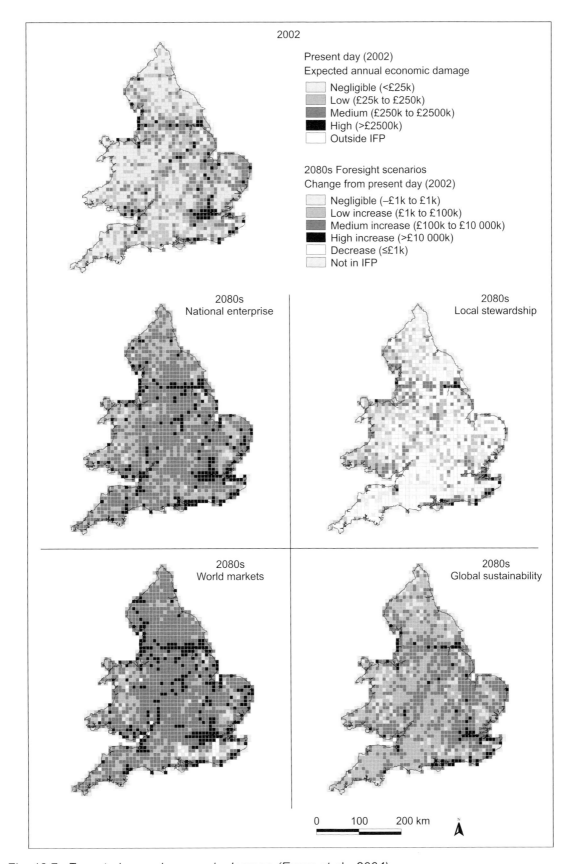

Fig. 13.7. Expected annual economic damage (Evans et al., 2004)

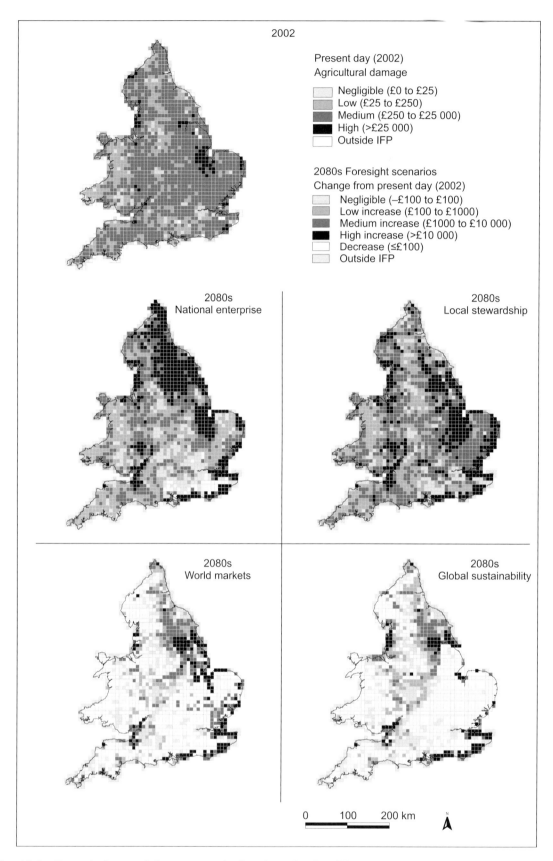

Fig. 13.8. Expected annual damage: agricultural production (Evans et al., 2004)

which experience large increases in the expected annual damage, particularly the south-east coast of England due to the decreasing standard of protection offered by coastal defences, which results in the national increase in expected annual damage by a factor of 1.5.

Change in the ratio of flood risk to per capita GDP (Table 13.2) provides an indication of how severe or harmful (in economic terms) flooding will be when compared with economic growth over the next century. In the world markets and national enterprise scenarios, flooding is expected to remove a greater proportion of national wealth than it currently does (and thus merit a greater investment to reduce risk). In the local stewardship and global sustainability scenarios, flooding is predicted to remove a lesser proportion of national wealth since these scenarios will tend to be less vulnerable to flood damage and are expected to be subject to somewhat less climate change.

The pattern for flood damage to agriculture (Fig. 13.8) is rather different to the pattern from economic damage as a whole. At present, agriculture is relatively evenly exposed to flood risk. The most striking exception to this is the area in the vicinity of the Wash, where significant areas of Grade 1 land lie within the flood-plain and, although well protected, are still at risk. A number of other, smaller areas stand out as exhibiting high expected annual damage associated with agriculture, including parts of the south coast and the north-west. The areas of poorer agricultural land (Dartmoor, West Wales, Pennines, etc.) are categorised as low risk while the major built-up areas (London, Birmingham, etc.) clearly exhibit negligible exposure to agricultural damage, reflecting the limited agriculture in these areas. In the globalised world markets scenario the contribution of agricultural damage to overall economic damage is projected to decrease, with a greater proportion of agricultural products being imported (although the effect of climate change on agriculture globally has not been considered) and low-grade agricultural land being taken out of production. However, where the land is of high agricultural value (Grade 1–3) an increase in economic damage is exhibited. A similar pattern is observed in the global sustainability scenario. Agricultural damage in the more self-sufficient national enterprise and local stewardship scenarios is expected to be more significant.

The influence of global emissions on future flood risk

The future flood risks outlined in the previous section are caused by a combination of climate and socio-economic changes. In order to explore the influence of climate change relative to the influence of socio-economic drivers on flood risk, a fifth scenario was analysed, assuming a high growth economic, equivalent to the world markets socio-economic future in the 2080s, but coupled within a low-emissions future climate. By comparing the results of this fifth scenario with the world markets/high-emissions scenario reported above, insight can be gained into the contribution of global emissions to the increased future flooding. Figure 13.9 illustrates the effect that reduced emission will have on the probability of flooding and number of people at risk in a world markets scenario with low emissions. The expected annual damage in the 2080s is calculated to reduce from an estimated £20.4 billion to £15.1 billion, a very significant reduction compared to today's expected annual damage, but still roughly only a quarter of the total increase, illustrating the importance of socio-economic factors as drivers of future flood risk. Efforts to reduce climate change are expected to yield benefits in terms of flood risk reduction (along with other more significant benefits elsewhere in the environment and economy) but will not on their own resolve the problem of increasing flood risk.

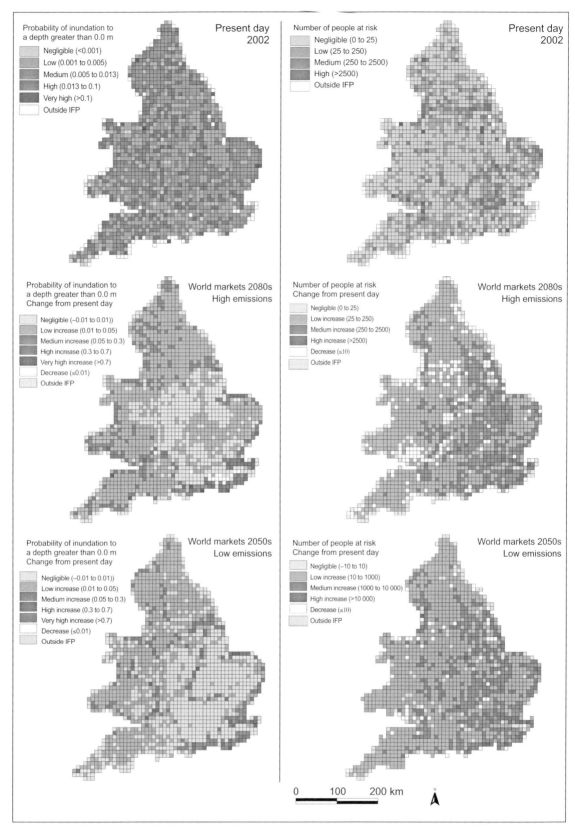

Fig. 13.9. Comparison of flood inundation probability and change in number of people at high risk under world markets high- and low-emissions scenarios (Evans et al., 2004)

Conclusions

A national-scale flood risk assessment methodology, which includes the effect of flood defence systems, was a key component in the quantified analysis of flood risk in the Foresight Project. The analysis was applied only to England and Wales because the necessary data to run the model were not available in Scotland and Northern Ireland. Flood risks in Scotland and Northern Ireland are discussed in the following two chapters. The analysis based on 2002 data estimated an expected annual damage due to flooding of roughly £1 billion, a figure that is slightly higher than, but comparable in magnitude to, economic damage due to flooding in England and Wales in recent years. The largest contribution to this risk is in the Thames Valley and estuary, despite the very high standard of protection from flooding.

Socio-economic and climate scenarios were used in combination in order to generate projections of potential future variation in flood risk, assuming stable flood defence policy. In all scenarios the frequency of flooding is projected to increase, more so on the coast than on rivers. The increase is greatest in high-emission scenarios. The risk of flooding is strongly modified by societal vulnerability and the scenarios analysis demonstrates how widely that vulnerability may vary according to the trajectory of socio-economic change. The risk that actually prevails in the future will be further modified by flood management activity, which will itself be a reflection of society's values and expectations. The potential effectiveness of portfolios of flood risk management measures is analysed in Chapter 25.

Analysis of climate change and socio-economic development over a timescale of 30–100 years in the future involves formidable uncertainties. Model uncertainties in climate projections up to the 2050s exceed the differences between emissions scenarios. There is considerable disagreement about the spatial patterns of climate change down-scaled to the UK. Changes in some climate variables, for example extreme sea levels and short, high-intensity rainfall events, are particularly difficult to predict.

Socio-economic change, which on a global scale leads to changing greenhouse gas emissions trajectories and, on the UK scale, also determines economic and social vulnerability to flooding, is even more difficult to predict and, it is argued, succumbs only to a scenarios-based approach that seeks to illustrate some of the potential range of variation between different futures. Furthermore, the national-scale datasets, while appropriate for high-level analysis, are not consistently of high enough resolution for more detailed local analysis. The results of the analysis at a local scale are therefore considered to be rather approximate, which is one reason why the results were aggregated to a 10 km grid rather than being presented at the 1 km scale at which the analysis was implemented. Nonetheless, use of a quantified model-based approach does enable consistency in the analysis across England and Wales and provides a basis for comparison of scenarios. The results presented contain very considerable uncertainties but have, nonetheless, generated useful new insights.

References

Evans, E., Ashley, R., Hall, J., Penning-Rowsell, E., Saul, A., Sayers, P., Thorne, C. and Watkinson, A., 2004. *Foresight Future Flooding. Scientific Summary: Vol. I – Future risks and their drivers*, Office of Science and Technology, London.

Hall, J.W., Dawson, R.J., Sayers, P.B., Rosu, C., Chatterton, J.B. and Deakin, R., 2003. 'A methodology for national-scale flood risk assessment', *Water and Maritime Engineering*, 156(3), 235–247.

HR Wallingford, 2000. *National Appraisal of Assets at Risk From Flooding and Coastal Erosion*, Technical Report Vols 1 and 2, HR Wallingford Report TR107.

HR Wallingford, 2003. *National Flood Risk Assessment 2002*, HR Wallingford Report EX4722.

Hulme, M., Jenkins, G.J., Lu, X., Turnpenny, J.R., Mitchell, T.D., Jones, R.G., Lowe, J., Murphy, J.M., Hassell, D., Boorman, P., McDonald, R. and Hill, S., 2002. *Climate Change Scenarios for the United Kingdom: The UKCIP02 scientific report*, Tyndall Centre for Climate Change Research, School of Environmental Sciences, University of East Anglia, Norwich.

Penning-Rowsell, E.C., Chatterton, J., Wilson, T. and Potter, E., 2003a. *Autumn 2000 Floods in England and Wales: Assessment of national economic and financial losses*, Flood Hazard Research Centre, Middlesex University.

Penning-Rowsell, E.C., Johnson, C., Tunstall, S.M., Tapsell, S.M., Morris, J., Chatterton, J.B., Coker, A. and Green, C., 2003b. *The Benefits of Flood and Coastal Defence: Techniques and data for 2003*, Flood Hazard Research Centre, Middlesex University.

Tapsell, S.M., Penning-Rowsell, E.C., Tunstall, S.M. and Wilson, T.L., 2002. 'Vulnerability to flooding: health and social dimensions', *Philosophical Transactions of the Royal Society London – Series A, Mathematical, Physical and Engineering Sciences*, 360(1796), 1511–1525.

14 Driver impacts in Scotland

Alan Werritty

Introduction

The history of flood risk management in Scotland has been strikingly different to that in England and Wales. As early as the 1800s, drainage of wetlands, bank revetment and the construction of flood embankments on fertile valley floors by private landowners had reduced flood losses and resulted in the local stabilisation of active gravel-bed rivers (Werritty et al., 2005; Smout, 2000). However, the equivalent of the Internal Drainage Boards in parts of England never developed, as the costs of flooding, while locally significant, only rarely attracted regional or national attention (e.g. the Borders flood of 1948 and the Moray floods in 1956 and 1970) and the post-Second World War drive to drain wetlands and increase arable agriculture productivity was weaker than in other parts of Great Britain. The development of an extensive river gauging network to assist in regulating water quality and sustaining commercial fisheries only became a national priority in the 1950s and flood warning schemes based on this network came much later in the 1980s and early 1990s, following a series of damaging floods.

Reflecting this history, flood risk management in Scotland is less centralised than in England and Wales with duties and responsibilities being distributed as follows:

- the Scottish Executive Environment and Rural Affairs Department (SEERAD) is responsible for developing national policy on flood prevention and flood warning and provides grant aid to local authorities for approved schemes;
- local authorities lead in developing flood prevention schemes, are responsible for planning control and the maintenance of water courses on non-agricultural land, and (with the emergency services) coordinate emergency action during and immediately after floods;
- the Scottish Environment Protection Agency (SEPA) is a statutory consultee on planning applications in flood-prone areas, provides general flood alerts for the whole of Scotland by way of the Floodline service and operates local flood warning schemes in partnership with local councils and the emergency services.

The absence of a highly centralised system for flood management can variously be seen as a weakness (poor strategic planning) or a strength (decentralised, locally-accountable decision making). However, the requirement that Scotland implements 'sustainable flood management' under the Water Environment and Water Services (Scotland) Act 2003 should help deliver a national strategy that is locally delivered. Work currently undertaken under the Scottish Executive's National Flooding Framework and the delivery of sustainable flood management is designed to provide:

> the maximum possible social and economic resilience against flooding, by protecting and working with the environment, in a way which is fair and affordable both now and in the future (Scottish Executive, 2005a)

will see a radical re-appraisal of flood risk management over the next few years (Werritty, 2006).

In this chapter, the same sequence of drivers is followed as in Chapters 4 to 11, but their role is assessed solely as they operate across Scotland. The institutional structure for managing flood risk in Scotland is very different from that for England and Wales, and these contrasts are outlined below in the section on human behaviour.

Climate change

Predicting the impact of climate change on floods in Scotland inevitably draws upon much of the same literature as that already summarised for England and Wales. In particular, future flood flows are derived from UKCIP98 (Hulme and Jenkins, 1998) and UKCIP02 (Hulme *et al.*, 2002) and Hadley Centre global circulation models HadCM2 and HadCM3. To this can be added a study commissioned by the Scottish Executive in advance of the UKCIP02 findings derived from the regional climate model (HadRM2) with a spatial resolution of 50 km (Hulme *et al.*, 2002).

Precipitation

UKCIP02 projected annual changes in precipitation range from 0 to 10% with a stronger seasonal differentiation across all scenarios. The most extreme changes for low emissions (global sustainability) are in the winter, when increases of 10–15% are predicted for eastern Scotland by the 2080s, declining to <10% or even within natural variability for the west. However, in absolute terms the west remains markedly wetter than the east due to the marked west-east precipitation gradient. High emissions (world markets) will accentuate these contrasts by the 2080s with winter increases >25% in the east declining to <15% in the north-west. Again the west will be substantially wetter than the east in absolute terms, and thus more likely to experience winter floods. Summer precipitation decreases of 10–20% in the north and 20–30% in the south are predicted by the 2080s under the low emissions scenario. These shift to decreases of 20–40% in the north and >40% in the south under the high emissions (world markets) scenario.

Floods caused by extreme long duration rainfall are rarely reported in Scotland. More typical are slow-moving frontal systems with embedded high-intensity cells that rarely last more than 48 hours. When associated with an already wet catchment, such frontal systems can generate severe regional flooding (e.g. the Strathclyde floods in 1994). It is likely that the frequency of such extreme 48-hour rainfalls will increase by the 2080s, especially in the west during the winter months, when a stronger westerly airflow over Scotland is anticipated. By the 2080s all of the UK, apart from north-west Scotland, is likely to see an increase in the two-year rainfall according to UKCIP02, this increase exceeding 20% in eastern Scotland under the medium-high emissions (national enterprise) and high emissions (world markets) scenarios. In summer this is predicted to reverse with daily rainfall intensities falling by 10–30%.

Effect of changes in precipitation on floods

The impact of climate change on floods in Scotland has been investigated by Werritty *et al.* (2002). Using UKCIP98 scenarios for future precipitation, values for the 10-, 20-, 50- and 100-year floods were determined for six river basins (Fig. 14.1) using a lumped conceptual rainfall-runoff model (Arnell, 1996) and standard flood frequency analyses. Six of the nine basins reported a marked increase in the size of the t-year flood by the 2080s for the high emissions (world

Fig. 14.1. Location of six basins itemised in Table 14.1 and Scotland's four major cities (adapted from Evans et al., 2004)

Table 14.1. Revised return periods (in years) for selected river basins using four scenarios in the 2050s and 2080s based on the flow for the present-day 50-year flood in each basin (Werritty et al., 2002). For location of river basins see Fig. 14.1

Foresight futures 2002	River Findhorn	River Don	Ruchill Water	River Almond	Lyne Water	River Clyde
2050s						
Global sustainability	46	48	47	45	40	37
Local stewardship	42	46	45	42	36	32
National enterprise	39	44	43	40	33	28
World markets	38	42	43	38	31	26
2080s						
Global sustainability	46	48	47	44	37	34
Local stewardship	40	44	44	40	33	28
National enterprise	32	34	38	32	22	19
World markets	30	32	37	31	20	17

market) scenario: 8–28% for the 50-year and 8–29% for the 100-year flood. The 50-year flood was reduced to within the range of a 17 to 37 year event (Table 14.1).

Temperature

By the 2080s UKCIP02 predicts annual warming of around 3.5°C, with up to 4°C in the summer (in the east) but only up to 2°C in the winter. This implies that the increased soil moisture deficits, which will reduce summer floods in southern England, will not be so highly developed in Scotland. However, the increase in average temperature could increase high-intensity rainfalls, given that the two-year daily precipitation in Scotland is set to rise by 15% for each 1°C of warming in the autumn (Hulme et al., 2001). Given the sensitivity of urban drainage systems to high-intensity storms, even modest increases in temperature could quickly increase the probability of urban flooding.

Snow

Winter floods can have a strong snowmelt component (e.g. the Tay in 1993, Black and Anderson, 1994). Despite a modest increase in winter precipitation in the Scottish mountains under UKCIP02 scenarios, increased winter temperatures mean that more precipitation will fall as rain rather than snow. Harrison et al. (2001), using an analogue model predict that, by the 2080s, the average number of days with snow lying >800 m in the Highlands will be reduced by 8–24% under the medium-high emissions (national enterprise) scenario. In lowland southern Scotland, the risk of snow will almost disappear and even in the north-east, snow cover at 100–400 m will be reduced by 40–70%. This implies a steady reduction in the risk of major snowmelt floods by the 2050s and 2080s.

Catchment land-use

Urbanisation

Scotland is a highly urbanised society with 82% of the population living in settlements of more than 3000 people but occupying only 2% of the land area (SNH, 2002). Scotland's 2002 population of 5.06 million is projected to decline over the next few decades although, in terms of pressure for new housing, this will be moderated by the needs of 150000 extra single-person households, 90000 extra adult only households and 30000 extra single-parent households within the next decade (Scottish Executive, 2002). Despite this pressure, the present policy of favouring brownfield over greenfield sites, means that urban encroachment onto the floodplain should be containable by way of the implementation of national planning guidelines (notably Planning and Flooding SPP7, Scottish Executive, 2004). The requirement to promote 'sustainable flood management' (including sustainable urban drainage systems, SUDS) as part of the process of river basin management planning by 2009 will also assist in protecting floodplains from unwise development. More problematic is managing the anticipated increases in the frequency and severity of urban flooding by the 2050s and 2080s. Holistic flood management, integrating urban drainage with the management of urban watercourses, is the most promising strategy alongside the upgrading of sewerage systems and improved local storage. The emerging Glasgow Strategic Drainage Plan provides a good example of this strategy (Scottish Executive, 2005b).

Glasgow, Edinburgh, Aberdeen and Dundee account for around 30% of Scotland's population and all four cities have coastal or estuarine locations (Fig. 14.1). The complex interaction of increased precipitation combined with rising sea levels and more storm surges could further increase urban flooding by the 2080s.

Rural land-use management

Present-day land cover across Scotland is summarised in Table 14.2. Moorland and rough grazing account for 38% with improved pasture at 13% (especially in the south and west) and arable at 11% (especially in the south and east). All forms of woodland collectively constitute 15% of land cover, with coniferous plantations dominant (at 8%).

The most important trends in land cover since 1950 are (SNH, 2002):

- intensification in agricultural land-use to maximise yields and produce cheap food;
- rapid expansion of coniferous plantations (406% since 1940 mainly in the uplands) with some diversification in species planted in recent years;
- recent promotion of broadleafed forests throughout Scotland (designed to recreate former floodplain forests);
- emergence of peri-urban landscape of new housing and business parks around many towns and cities replacing agricultural land-cover classes.

Given this pattern of land cover and recent trends, the rural land-use management driver in Scotland is complex and multi-faceted:

- *upland land management and grazing*: the driver is broadly similar to that in Wales where increased stocking densities have been linked with compacted

Table 14.2. Scotland's land cover by broad groups (SNH, 2002)

Land cover group	Area: km^2	%
Built	1 914	2
Arable	8 834	11
Grassland	19 847	25
Woodland	11 467	15
Bracken and scrub	522	1
Heather moorland	15 783	20
Peatland	13 922	18
Freshwater	1 669	2
Other	4 864	6
Total	78 822	100

soils and increased runoff. However, these effects are likely to be short-lived in Scotland if subsidies to hill farmers continue to decline.

- *arable agriculture and soil husbandry*: the driver operates in a similar manner to that across much of lowland England. Winter sowing of cereals and oil-seed rape leaves bare soil vulnerable to intense spring rainfall. The ensuing erosion causes blocked drains and culverts, and localised rural flooding to dwellings and roads. With only 11% of land cover classified as arable farming, this is a less significant driver than for much of lowland England.
- *field drainage*: the driver is less significant in Scotland because there is much less arable land on clay-rich soils to be drained. Also, there is less upland drainage of heather moorland than in northern England.
- *afforestation*: the driver is broadly similar to that in the uplands of northern England and Wales where ditching necessary to promote early growth causes accelerated runoff. However, adverse impacts have been reduced since the 1980s through successful implementation of the Forests and Water Guidelines (Forestry Commission, 2003). The area under woodland is likely to expand if hill-farming continues to decline.

Agricultural impacts

Flooding has a differential impact on agricultural and forestry land and wildlife habitats. At present, rural flooding results in only modest losses to the agricultural sector (reduced yields, loss of livestock and localised damage to soil structure). Increased flooding, projected for all scenarios by the 2050s and 2080s, will accelerate these losses if current agricultural activity remains unaltered. However, given further withdrawal of EU subsidies and pressures to use and manage floodplains in a more sustainable manner (including controlled inundation to reduce the need for structural flood defences downstream), agricultural use of floodplains is likely to be reduced over the next half century. The impact of floods on forests varies according to species – while Scot's Pine are damaged, other broadleaf species (such as Alder) thrive under periodic inundation. Projecting current policies forward, water-tolerant broadleaf species are likely to replace more sensitive conifers in an attempt to recreate the former floodplain forests. Wetlands comprising shallow lochs and fens benefit greatly from occasional flooding and this looks set to increase under all four scenarios.

River processes

River morphology and sediment supply

Scottish rivers display a greater range of morphologies than those found across much of the UK. This reflects a higher proportion of active, gravel-bed rivers (many originating in the uplands) with steeper gradients, coarser bed materials and the ability to rework their valley floors unless constrained by bank re-inforcement. Scotland has fewer examples of inactive sand/silt-bedded channels widespread throughout lowland England and often subject to channelisation following land drainage. By contrast, many of Scotland's largest rivers retain their gravel beds to their marine limits (e.g. Tay, Dee, Spey and Tweed) and contribute significant volumes of sediment into their estuaries.

Many gravel-bed rivers in Scotland have recorded significant lateral shifts during 'flood rich periods' since the 1850s which, if continued into the warmer, wetter Scotland predicted for the 2080s under the high emissions (world markets) scenario, could locally place the river outside its indicative floodplain. This behaviour is especially evident in active upland rivers with minimal bank re-inforcement (Werritty and Leys, 2001). Channel migration/avulsion has also been reported on alluvial fans (Werritty *et al.*, 2005) where localised aggradation and channel instability often increase the flood risk. To mitigate these effects, most alluvial fans in Scotland have been subject to dredging, channelisation and bank re-inforcement. This form of river management may become more prevalent in the Scottish uplands if flood flows and sediment yields increase through to the 2080s. While serving to reduce flood risk, these types of river engineering are usually inimical to biodiversity and, on this basis, are often opposed by SNH and environmental non-governmental organisations (NGOs).

Larger rivers, such as the lower Tay and the Aberdeenshire Dee, display a higher degree of stability reflecting, in part, piecemeal river engineering dating back many decades (Smout, 2000; McEwen, 2001). As a result there is no evidence of consistent channel widening on such rivers during the most recent 'flood rich' period (Werritty and Hoey, 2002) comparable to that reported on the non-tidal Yorkshire Ouse (Evans *et al.*, 2004). Despite widespread overtopping and breaching of embankments during recent major floods (e.g. the Tay in 1990 and 1993: Gilvear and Winterbottom, 1992), there is no evidence of either degradation of flood defences by channel widening or an increase in the standard of protection by channel deepening in recent decades.

River regulation and conveyance

Management of seasonal within-channel vegetation to improve flow conveyance (characteristic of fine grained, stable rivers in lowland England) is not a major issue in Scottish rivers. This may reflect the lower levels of eutrophication generally reported for Scottish rivers and lakes (Harriman and Pugh, 1994) with only a few sites reporting significant enrichment by nitrates (Ball and MacDonald, 2001). More significant in terms of potential flood damage is the entrainment of riparian trees (generally alder) into the flow during major floods as the resultant large woody debris can constrict flows through bridges and give rise to local flow surges. The statutory requirement on riparian land owners to maintain watercourses free of such obstacles reflects the potential damage associated with the loss of riparian trees during floods.

Environment, ecosystems and habitats

The EC Water Framework and Habitats Directives and the Water Environment and Water Services (Scotland) Act 2003 are the key items of legislation here. The resulting River Basin Management Plans (due by 2009) will require rivers, lakes, estuaries and coastal waters to achieve good ecological status by 2015. Although at present there is no statutory requirement for catchment flood management plans, 'sustainable flood management' is required under the Act. For some rivers, this may be achieved by restoring wetland habitats and, by enlarging floodplain storage, reducing flood risks downstream. The Scottish Executive endorses a combination of upstream storage and downstream flood embankments (e.g. the Water of Leith scheme being developed by Edinburgh City Council) and this will be strengthened given the need to protect physical habitats under various EC directives and achieving UK targets in terms of biodiversity action plans. Under current legislation, existing flood defences are unlikely to be challenged (using derogation powers or heavily modified waters provisions), but new flood protection schemes may be required to meet more demanding ecological objectives. The link between this driver and regulation makes it very sensitive to different Foresight futures (Evans *et al.*, 2004).

Coastal processes

Waves and surges

Coastal flooding is generally the result of storm surges and waves superimposed on mid-tidal levels. The most severe current storm surge elevations for the 50-year

233

event in Scotland are <1.25 m. Significant wave heights exceeded 10% of the year and capable of breaching structural and natural defences are locally 2–2.5 m on the west coast and 1.5–2.0 m on the east coast (British Oceanographic Data Centre, 1998). In general, storm surges represent a less severe threat in Scotland due to lower levels (0.82 m at Leith in 1953 in comparison with 2.97 m at King's Lynn, Hickey, 2001) and the higher proportion of rocky, hard coasts. Nevertheless, storm surge elevations, when coupled with projected sea-level rise, could increase by up to 0.8 m around Scotland by the 2080s under the UKCIP02 high emissions (world markets) scenario. This could reduce the current 50-year event to a five-year event or even less (Price and McInally, 2001). The impact of such an increase in storm surge activity would be most severely felt in the estuary and river of the lower Clyde, where Glasgow remains highly vulnerable.

Relative sea-level rise

The impacts of thermal expansion of the upper ocean on future British sea levels have recently been estimated for all four scenarios for the 2080s by UKCIP02. When combined with Shennan and Horton's (2002) revised estimate of mean uplift and subsidence during the late Holocene, sea-level rises to the 2080s (relative to 1990) can be predicted for world markets/high emissions and global sustainability/low emissions scenarios (Table 14.3). Given that the IPCC predicted global sea-level rise varies from 90 mm (global sustainability/low emissions) to 690 mm (world markets/high emissions), differential uplift and subsidence around Britain's coast generate significant regional patterns. The east of Scotland (rising at 1.0 mm yr^{-1}) is predicted to have a sea-level rise of 340–550 mm by the 2080s. This slightly reduces to 310–520 mm for south-west Scotland (rising at 1.3 mm yr^{-1}) and increases to 360–570 mm for north-west Scotland (rising at 0.7 mm yr^{-1}). Orkney and Shetland should see sea-level rises of 430–640 mm by the 2080s (but note the absence of published information on isostatic change, Table 14.3). With the exception of Orkney and Shetland, these predicted sea-level rises are much lower than those anticipated for much of England.

Table 14.3. *Relative sea-level rise scenarios to the 2080s and regional uplift/subsidence around the coastline of Great Britain. Subsidence is negative. Based on Shennan and Horton (2002)*

Region	Mean uplift/ subsidence: mm/yr	Relative sea-level rise scenarios to the 2080s: mm (relative to 1990)	
		Global sustainability low emissions	World markets high emissions
East Scotland (Inverness to Border)	1.0	340	550
North-east England	0.2	410	620
Yorkshire	−0.5	480	690
East Midlands	−0.6	490	700
East England	−0.7	500	710
London	−0.7	500	710
South-east England	−0.5	480	690
South-west England	−1.0	530	740
Wales	−0.4	470	680
North-west England	0.7	360	570
South-west Scotland (Border to Fort William)	1.3	310	520
North-west Scotland (Fort William to Inverness)	0.7	360	570
Orkney and Shetland[1]	0.0	430	640
Northern Ireland	*na*	430	640

[1] This is updated to 'no-published estimates' in British–Irish Council (2003), p. 36.

Coastal morphology and sediment supply

Coastal cells define units of shoreline within which natural longshore transport of sediment occurs. Since most cases of severe coastal erosion occur when longshore transport is interrupted, identifying coastal cells is the initial step in seeking to protect a shoreline against erosion or flooding prior to developing a shoreline management plan. This procedure is now well-established for England and Wales (funded by Defra) but has only been applied to Scotland in a piecemeal manner.

The rocky and highly indented coastline of mainland Scotland (especially on the west coast) and fragmented outlines of the Western Isles and Orkney and Shetland make it difficult to define coastal cells using the same criteria adopted for England and Wales (Ramsay and Brampton, 2000). The most recent attempt (Hansom and McGlashan, 2004; Fig. 14.2) identifies seven cells along the mainland reserving a further four coastal cells for the Outer Hebrides and Orkney and Shetland. For the

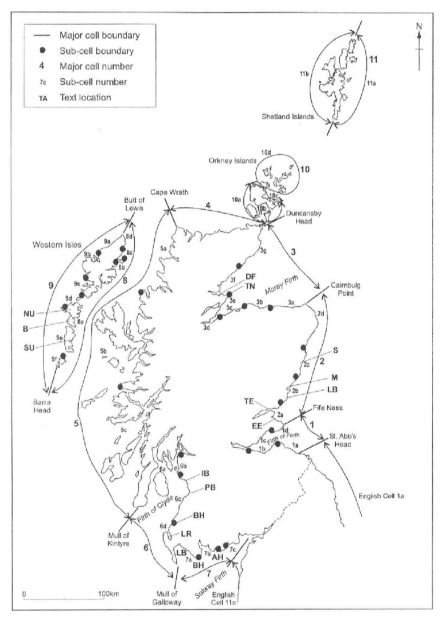

Fig. 14.2. Definition of coastal cells for Scotland (Hansom and McGlashan, 2004)

rocky coasts of the north and west, where sediment is sparse and beaches often confined to deeply indented bays, individual cells are small and numerous. For such lengths of shoreline many small bays (or pocket beaches) are grouped together to form a much larger 'sub-cell' for management purposes.

Within these coastal cells morphology and sediment supply operate to control the long-term patterns of coastal erosion. Quenlenuec *et al.* (1998) characterised some of these coastal cells as follows:

- Berwick to Aberdeen (cells 1, 2a, 2b and 2c): predominantly eroding but stable where there are rocky coasts or coastal defences.
- Aberdeen to Inverness (cells 2d, 2a, 3b, 3c and 3d): mainly eroding but with important river coupling (see below).
- Inverness to Mallaig (cells 3, 4, 5a): stable with eroding pocket beaches.
- Mallaig to Carlisle (cells 6 and 7): predominantly eroding but stable where there are rocky coasts or coastal defences.
- Mull/Islay/Jura/Skye (cells 5b and 5c): predominantly stable but with soft coasts eroding (pocket beaches).
- Orkney (cell 10): stable with eroding pocket beaches.

As in England and Wales, most of the sediment reworked along the Scottish coast is fine grained and of marine origin, and this includes the sandbanks within the outer estuaries of the Solway, Clyde, Forth and Tay. Two exceptions are the inner Tay estuary (dominated by river-derived sands and gravels) and Spey Bay, plus the shoreline to the west (Gemmell *et al.*, 2001). Any reduction in sediment fluxes in the lower Spey would starve Spey Bay and cause immediate erosion along cell 3b. This, however, is a special case and generally there is minimal coupling between fluvial and coastal morphology around the Scottish coast.

Human behaviour

Published work on these drivers in Scotland is, at present, minimal. The following is mainly based on opinions gleaned from experts in the Scottish Executive, Scottish Environment Protection Agency (SEPA), Scottish Water and local authorities. It is anticipated that much more research on these drivers will be forthcoming as sustainable flood management replaces current reliance on structural flood defences (Werritty, 2006).

Stakeholder behaviour

Because of the institutional differences in flood management, the mix of stakeholders in Scotland differs from that in England and Wales. In Scotland the key stakeholders are those whose properties are threatened by floods, the Scottish Executive, local authorities, SEPA, Scottish Water, riparian landowners and environmental NGOs.

The Scottish Executive Environment and Rural Affairs Department is responsible for strategic policy and, following its statutory commitment to sustainable flood management, is actively pursuing this agenda by way of its National Flooding Framework. Under existing legislation, the promotion of flood defence on non-agricultural land is a local authority power for which grant aid may be available from the Executive. With a large increase in the flood defence budget (£89 million over the period 2005–2008) and maximum grants recently increased from 50 to 80%, it is likely that many new schemes will soon be brought forward by local authorities during this budgetary period.

Local authorities have discretionary powers under the Flood Prevention (Scotland) Act 1961 to protect non-agricultural land by way of schemes for which central government grant aid is available. Under the Flood Prevention and Land

Drainage (Scotland) Act 1997, they are also required to maintain urban water courses free of obstructions and to assess flood hazards. Local authorities can also apply for grant aid to undertake coastal defence works to protect properties from flooding. Shoreline management plans are not required under existing legislation, although a few exist on a voluntary basis. However, managed realignment of the shoreline is beginning to emerge as a strategy to help meet UK biodiversity targets under the EC Habitats Directive (Royal Society for the Protection of Birds, 2002).

SEPA is the statutory body for deriving flood warnings, which are then disseminated by the police. Following the introduction of Floodline in Scotland, in November 2001, and the development of Floodwatch, flood warnings are now available across the whole of Scotland. On many of the larger rivers, upstream rainfall and flow levels are modelled and routed downstream to provide warnings. Weather radars are also used qualitatively to improve the flood forecasts. With advances in automatic voice messaging services, flood warnings may soon pass directly from SEPA to local authorities, which will arrange for their wider dissemination. Since 2000, SEPA has also operated one coastal flood warning on the Clyde estuary in response to significant annual flood losses in Saltcoats, Tarbert, Rothesay and Dumbarton (Werritty *et al.*, 2002).

Planning applications for sites potentially at risk must be accompanied by a flood risk assessment undertaken by SEPA following its Planning Authority Protocol (SEPA, 2000) and the Executive's Scottish Planning Policy 7 (Scottish Executive, 2004). Should the planning authority overrule SEPA's recommendation based upon the 2006 second generation indicative flood risk maps, the Scottish Executive retains the power to call in the application. Public awareness is strengthened by Flood Liaison Awareness Groups, which exist in most local authority areas. Meeting several times per year, with members from local authority departments, SEPA, the insurance industry and local developers, the role of these groups is to review possible floodplain developments well in advance of formal planning applications (Tavendale and Black, 2003).

Scottish Water has a duty to provide urban drainage by way of its storm water sewers and combined drainage systems. All new urban developments must also conform to SUDS guidelines and Scottish Water has a duty to maintain such systems once they are operational.

Under the Land Drainage (Scotland) Act 1958, riparian land owners can apply for grant aid for embankments to protect their land against modest floods. Many of these embankments, damaged by major floods in the 1990s, have fallen into disrepair as agricultural subsidies have been eroded and grant aid withdrawn. They are unlikely to be re-instated following future floods, especially given the pressure to increase floodplain storage where possible. Indeed, some local authorities (e.g. Aberdeenshire) are promoting schemes whereby farmers provide flood storage on sections of floodplains which were formerly wetlands (Scottish Executive, 2005c).

Scottish Enviromental NGOs are very active in promoting sustainable flood management in which environmental benefits are privileged (e.g. World Wildlife Fund Scotland, 2002; Royal Society for the Protection of Birds Scotland, 2004). They also advocate a more holistic, catchment-based approach to flood risk management and stress the need for combining this with more effective stewardship of the countryside, especially by way of agri-business schemes.

Public attitudes and expectations

During the 1990s, public attitudes and public expectations have been sharpened following floods in Perth (1993), Strathclyde (1994), Elgin (1997 and 2002), Edinburgh (2000), Glasgow (2002) and Hawick (2005). Although the impacts of these floods were localised, the widespread media coverage heightened the public's general awareness of flooding. This has resulted in increased pressure on local authorities to bring forward new schemes and renewed demands on Scottish Water for the repair or replacement of aging urban drainage systems.

In recent decades Scotland has resisted the imposition of neo-liberal solutions to social problems. This reflects a society in which communal solidarity is still generally fostered and the promotion of unregulated self-interest is questioned. If this social fabric remained in place to the 2100s, the external imposition of a world market scenario would be highly problematic. Indeed, the response of a devolved Scottish Parliament could differ markedly from that which might be adopted in Westminster. The current ethos of Scottish society would certainly engage much more readily with the global sustainability scenario, with its emphasis on a communitarian response to natural disasters. Neither the neo-liberal underpinnings of the national enterprise scenario nor the intense localism and capping of economic growth implicit in the local stewardship scenario attract widespread support across Scotland at present.

Socio-economics

Buildings and contents

Post-flood estimates of flood damage have been variously estimated at £30 million for the Tay/Earn flood in 1993 and £100 million for the Strathclyde flood in 1994 (Werritty *et al.*, 2002; Werritty with Chatterton, 2004). Against a background of average annual flood damages in Scotland in the region of £20 million in 2001, it is estimated that building losses for the 93 000 coastal and 77 000 inland properties at risk may increase by 27% in 2020 by 68% in 2050 and by 115% in 2080, due to climate change. These figures are first-order approximations and take no account of present or future levels of protection offered by flood defences. These estimates of flood losses will be substantially revised once the second generation indicative floodrisk maps become available in 2006 and improved estimates of building losses are incorporated (Black and Evans, 1999).

Urban impacts

Recent intense summer storms (e.g. Glasgow in 2002) have heightened public awareness of urban flooding caused by the surcharging of combined sewer outfall systems. This, in turn, has prompted a more holistic approach to urban flooding illustrated by the emerging Glasgow Strategic Drainage Plan in which Scottish Water, Glasgow City Council, Scottish Enterprise and SEPA are jointly designing a new drainage system. In addition to replacing nineteenth-century sewers, part of the strategy is to introduce SUDS pioneered in Scotland to improve water quality and reducing flooding in new urban areas (e.g. to the east of Dunfermline). This involves the use of detention ponds, permeable surfaces and swales to increase infiltration and attenuate runoff.

Infrastructure impacts

The network of services that enable the economy to deliver goods and services nationally can be impacted within and beyond the immediate areas flooded. These impacts include repairing damaged assets (flood defences, roads and railways), travel disruption and reduced economic activity. Such infrastructure costs are notoriously difficult to estimate but, within the £15 million total economic losses attributed to the summer floods of 2004, £1.3 million was assigned by Perth and Kinross Council for road repairs (JBA Consultants, 2005).

Social impacts

The social impacts of flooding, while recognised, have yet to be systematically evaluated, but following floods in Perth (1993), Strathclyde (1994) and Glasgow

(2002) the highest flood losses occurred within low-income groups, many individual households having no insurance. Higher levels of illness were also registered following the Perth flood and this is likely to be repeated in other areas if urban drainage flooding (such as occurred in Glasgow in 2002) becomes increasingly common. A recent scoping study (JBA Consultants, 2005) following the widespread flooding in the summer of 2004 estimated social costs (anxiety, slight injuries, emergency services and evacuation of properties) of around £2.5 million. In light of these findings, the Scottish Executive has commissioned a major study on the social costs of flooding (Werritty *et al.*, 2006).

Ranking of drivers

This section reports on the ranking of drivers as they operate in Scotland taking into account contrasts in the behaviour of the drivers noted in the previous section. Table 14.4 reports a comparison of driver rankings for the UK as a whole (but operating at a local level – see Table 2.2 in Evans *et al.*, 2004) and for Scotland taken separately. This section provides a commentary on the main contrasts in rankings.

- **Climate change** The precipitation driver is slightly increased under the national enterprise scenario and further increased under the world markets scenario. This reflects the more severe impacts anticipated under these scenarios, especially during the winter flood season. By the 2080s, a stronger westerly circulation is predicted for Scotland generating more storms, higher rainfall and flooding especially in the winter. Daily and short duration rainfall is also set to increase in Highland Scotland at rates up to twice those anticipated in south-east England. Anticipated changes in temperature are more conservative, with Scotland fitting within the 1–5°C range anticipated for the whole of the UK.
- **Catchment land-use** The higher increase in short duration rainfall intensities for Scotland interacts with the land-use driver (especially in terms of urban land-use). Scotland is a highly urbanised society with many ageing nineteenth-century sewerage systems and the risk of urban flooding is likely to increase more rapidly than for England and Wales. By contrast, the agriculture and rural land-use driver has a lower ranking in Scotland than for the UK as a whole. This reflects changes in rural land-use as the Common Agricultural Policy is reformed, stocking densities are reduced, upland woodlands become more extensive, wetlands are re-instated and floodplains are used for controlled inundation. Since Scotland has a higher proportion of upland than the rest of the UK (where many of these changes are focused), this driver is likely to exercise a less important role by the 2080s. Agricultural impacts focused on the lowlands should prove similar to those in the rest of the UK, leaving this driver unchanged.
- **River processes** By contrast with the rest of the UK, Scotland's rivers are potentially more active in reworking their valley floors. Failure to repair existing flood defences for agricultural land could place some rivers beyond their current indicative floodplains by the 2050s, increasing the relative importance of the morphology driver. This would generate a lower standard of protection for agricultural land and small rural settlements. Reduced within channel vegetation and better flow conveyance with lower fertiliser levels under the global sustainability and local stewardship scenarios would offset this. Given less eutrophication in Scotland than across much of southern and eastern England, this effect is likely to be triggered by the 2050s, especially

Table 14.4. Summary results for Scottish driver impacts of flood risk (UK local flood risk values in brackets, from Table 2.2 in Evans et al., 2004). Driver types: S (source), P (pathway) and R (receptor)

Climate change

Driver type	Name	World markets		Global sustainability		National enterprise		Local stewardship	
		2050s	2080s	2050s	2080s	2050s	2080s	2050s	2080s
S	Precipitation	5.7 (4)	8 (5.7)	2	2.8	4 (2.8)	5.7 (4)	2.8	4
S	Temperature	1	1	1	1	1	1	1	1

Catchment land-use

Driver type	Name	World markets		Global sustainability		National enterprise		Local stewardship	
		2050s	2080s	2050s	2080s	2050s	2080s	2050s	2080s
P	Urbanisation	2.8	5.7 (4)	0.7	0.5	2.8	5.7 (4)	0.7	0.5
P	Rural land management	1.4	1.4 (2)	0.7	0.7	1.4	1.4 (2)	0.7	0.5
R	Agricultural impacts	0.7	0.7	0.7	0.5	1.2	1.7	1	0.85

River processes

Driver type	Name	World markets		Global sustainability		National enterprise		Local stewardship	
		2050s	2080s	2050s	2080s	2050s	2080s	2050s	2080s
P	Environment, ecosystems and habitats	1	1	2	4	1	1	1.4	2.8
P	River morphology and sediment supply	1	2	2 (1.4)	2.8	1	1	2.8 (2)	4
P	Vegetation and conveyance	1	1.4	1.4 (2)	4 (5.7)	1	1.4	1	1.4 (2)

Human behaviour

Driver type	Name	World markets		Global sustainability		National enterprise		Local stewardship	
		2050s	2080s	2050s	2080s	2050s	2080s	2050s	2080s
P	Stakeholder behaviour	2	2.8	0.25	0.2	0.5	0.33	0.25	0.2
R	Public attitudes and expectations	NQ	NQ	NQ	NQ	NQ	NQ	NQ	NQ

Coastal processes

Driver type	Name	World markets		Global sustainability		National enterprise		Local stewardship	
		2050s	2080s	2050s	2080s	2050s	2080s	2050s	2080s
S	Waves	3	10	1	2	2	5	1	3
S	Surges	3 (5)	12 (20)	1	2	2 (3)	6 (9)	1 (2)	3 (5)
S	Relative sea-level rise	3 (5)	12 (20)	2 (3)	7 (10)	3 (4)	10 (13)	2 (3)	7 (10)
P	Coastal morphology and sediment supply	2 (5)	5 (10)	1 (2)	1 (2)	3 (4)	5 (7)	2 (3)	3 (4)

Table 14.4. Continued

Socio-economics

Driver type	Name	World markets		Global sustainability		National enterprise		Local stewardship	
		2050s	2080s	2050s	2080s	2050s	2080s	2050s	2080s
R	Building and contents	6.0	17.0	2.5	4.8	2.2	3.1	3.0	4.8
R	Urban impacts	6.0 (5.0)	23 (19.8)	2.2	3.9	2.2 (1.8)	4.8 (3.6)	2.2 (3.0)	3.0 (4.8)
R	Infrastructure impacts	7.1	24.0	2.5	3.0	2.2	3.6	3.0	4.8
R	Social impacts	6.0	19.8	2.2	3.2	2.2	3.6	2.2 (3.0)	4.8 (6.1)
R	Science, engineering and technology	NQ	NQ	NQ	NQ	NQ	NQ	NQ	NQ

NQ – known to be important but not quantified.

under the global sustainability scenario. However, increases in floodplain woodlands could reduce these improvements in flow conveyance, especially under the local stewardship scenario. Given that the EC Water Framework Directive will be fully implemented across the whole of the UK by 2015, the environmental regulation driver is likely to be broadly similar.

- **Coastal processes**   For three of the coastal process drivers the Scottish rankings are consistently lower than comparable values for the whole of the UK across most scenarios. Extreme water levels in Scotland for the 50-year storm are less than 1.25 m compared with 2.5 m along the East Anglia shoreline. Projected relative sea-level rises are also much lower than those in south-east and south-west England due to continued uplift of Scotland's coastline following the melting of the last icesheet. Given the hard, rocky nature of much of Scotland's coastline, coastal morphology and sediment supply operates as a less significant driver than in southern and eastern England, where readily erodible cliffs and major river estuaries provide large volumes of sediment to the near-shore zone.
- **Human behaviour**   Stakeholder behaviour is the only scaled driver in this group with scores identical to those for the whole of the UK. As noted above, the institutional structures governing flood risk management in Scotland differ, but their future patterns of behaviour under the four scenarios are unlikely to diverge significantly from the rest of the UK. Public attitudes and expectations are not quantified in Table 14.4, but there is a clear divergence north and south of the border. The current public ethos in Scotland favours communitarianism and implicitly the global sustainability scenario. By contrast, the national enterprise scenario would more closely mirror the public ethos in England.
- **Socio-economics**   The higher rankings for Scotland for the urban impacts driver under world markets and national enterprise scenarios reflect a highly urbanised society, a marked increase in urban flooding by the 2080s and a presumed reluctance by the private sector to retro-fit existing urban drainage. Given low growth and low consumption, the pressure to develop floodplains and the coastal zone (already lower in Scotland than for much of the UK) will be reduced under the local stewardship scenario.

Overall, the rankings for Scottish drivers differ only slightly from those for the UK as a whole with most of the adjustments being downwards but usually by relatively small amounts. Drivers where this is not true are the precipitation and urban land-use drivers (both higher in Scotland) and those associated with coastal processes (surges, sea-level change and sediment supply) all of which are significantly lower. Scotland's higher levels of social cohesion and lower development pressures on floodplains and coastal lowlands mean that the economic and social costs of future flooding are likely to be proportionately lower than for more densely populated areas of the UK.

References

Arnell, N.W., 1996. *Global Warming, River Flows and Water Resources*, Wiley, Chichester.

Ball, D.F. and MacDonald, A.M., 2001. *Groundwater Nitrate Vulnerable Zones for Scotland*, British Geological Survey Comissioned Report CR/01/50, Edinburgh.

Black, A.R. and Anderson, J.L., 1994. 'The great Tay flood of January 1993', *1993 Yearbook, Hydrological Data UK Series*, 29–34, Institute of Hydrology, Wallingford.

Black, A.R. and Evans, S.A., 1999. *Flood Damage in the UK: New insights for the insurance industry*, University of Dundee, Dundee.

British-Irish Council, 2003. *Scenarios for Climate Change for Islands Within the BIC Region*, available online www.british-irishcouncil.org/climatechange

British Oceanographic Data Centre, 1998. *UKDMAP: CD-ROM*. Windows 95/NT version, 3rd edition, British Oceanographic Data Centre, Liverpool.

Evans, E., Ashley, R., Hall, J., Penning-Rowsell, E., Saul, A., Sayers, P., Thorne, C. and Watkinson, A., 2004. *Foresight Future Flooding, Scientific Summary: Vol. 1 – Future risks and their drivers*, Office of Science and Technology, London.

Forestry Commission, 2003. *Forests and Water Guidelines*, 4th edn, Forestry Commission, Edinburgh.

Gemmell, S.L.G., Hanson, J.D. and Hoey, T.B., 2001. *The Geomorphology, Conservation and Management of the River Spey and Spey Bay SSSIs, Moray*, Scottish Natural Heritage Research, Survey and Monitoring Report No. 57.

Gilvear, D.J. and Winterbottom, S.J., 1992. 'Channel change and flood events since 1783 on the regulated River Tay, Scotland: implications for flood hazard management', *Regulated Rivers: Research and Management*, 7, 247–260.

Hansom, J.D. and McGlashan, D.L., 2004. 'Scotland's coast: understanding past and present processes for sustainable management', *Scottish Geographical Journal*, 120, 99–116.

Harriman, R. and Pugh, K.B., 1994. 'Water chemistry', in *The Freshwaters of Scotland*, eds Maitland, P.S., Boon, P.J. and McClusky, D.S., 89–111, Wiley, Chichester.

Harrison, J., Winterbottom, S. and Johnson, R., 2001. *Climate Change and Changing Snowfall Patterns in Scotland*, Central Research Unit, Scottish Executive, Edinburgh.

Hickey, K.R., 2001. 'The Storm of 31 January to 1 February 1953 and its impact on Scotland', *Scottish Geographical Journal*, 117, 283–295.

Hulme, M. and Jenkins, G.J., 1998. *Climate Change Scenarios for the United Kingdom*, UKCIP Technical Report No. 1.

Hulme, M., Crossley, J. and Lu, X., 2001. *An Exploration of Regional Climate Change Scenarios for Scotland*, Central Research Unit, Scottish Executive, Edinburgh.

Hulme, M., Jenkins, G.J., Lu, X., Turnpenny, J.R., Mitchell, T.D., Jones, R.G., Lowe, J., Murphy, J.M., Hassell, D., Boorman, P., McDonald, R. and Hill, S., 2002. *Climate Change Scenarios for the United Kingdom: The UKCIP02 Scientific Report*, Tyndall Centre for Climate Change Research, School of Environmental Sciences, University of East Anglia, Norwich.

JBA Consultants, 2005. *Scoping Study into the Costs of Flooding: Using the August 2004 event as a case study*, Scottish Executive, Environment Group Research Report, 2005/02.

McEwen, L.J., 2001. *The Geomorphological Character of the River Dee, Aberdeenshire*, Scottish Natural Heritage Report No. F99LF05.

Price, D.J. and McInally, G., 2001. *Climate Change: Review of levels of protection offered by flood prevention schemes*, Central Research Unit, Scottish Executive, Edinburgh.

Quenlenuec, R.E. with collaboration with Uhel, C.O.R. and Devos, W., 1998. *CORINE: Coastal erosion*, European Commission, Brussels.

Ramsay, D.L. and Brampton, A.H., 2000. *Coastal Cells in Scotland: Cell 11 – Shetland*, Scottish Natural Heritage, Edinburgh.

Royal Society for the Protection of Birds, 2002. *Seas of Change: The potential area for intertidal habitat creation around the coast of mainland Britain*, RSPB, Sandy.

Royal Society for the Protection of Birds Scotland, 2004. *Go with the Flow: The natural approach to sustainable flood management in Scotland*, RSPB Scotland, Edinburgh.

Scottish Environment Protection Agency, 2000. *A SEPA-Planning Authority Protocol (Development and Risk of Flooding: Advice and Consultation)*, Policy No. 41, SEPA, Stirling, available online www.sepa.org.uk/policies/pdf/41.pdf

Scottish Executive, 2002. *Review of Scotland's Cities: The analysis*, Scottish Executive, Edinburgh.

Scottish Executive, 2004. *Scottish Planning Policy SPP7: Planning and flooding*. Scottish Executive, Edinburgh.

Scottish Executive, 2005a. *Final Report of the National Technical Advisory Group on Flooding*, Scottish Executive, Edinburgh, available online www.scotland.gov.uk/Topics/Environment/Water/Flooding/16919/ntgfinalreport

Scottish Executive, 2005b. *Sustainable Flood Management Pilot Study*, final report, MWH and Jacobs-Babtie, Scottish Executive, Edinburgh, available online www.scotland.gov.uk/Resource/Doc/1223/0020971.pdf

Scottish Executive, 2005c. *Flood Management and Multifunctional Land Use in River Catchments*, Flooding Issues Advisory Committee, FIAC2005(10), Scottish Executive, Edinburgh, available online www.scotland.gov.uk/Resource/Doc/1223/0019876.pdf

Scottish Natural Heritage (SNH), 2002. *Natural Heritage Futures*, SNH, Edinburgh.

Shennan, I. and Horton, B., 2002. 'Holocene land- sea-level changes in Great Britain', *Journal of Quaternary Science*, 17, 511–526.

Smout, T.C., 2000. *Nature Contested: Environmental history in Scotland and Northern England since 1600*, Edinburgh University Press, Edinburgh.

Tavendale, A. and Black, A.R., 2003. 'Planning Practice under NPPG7: Planning and flooding', *Scottish Planning and Environmental Law*, 95, 11–13.

Werritty, A. 2006. 'Sustainable flood management: oxymoron or new paradigm?' *Area*, 38, 16–23.

Werritty, A., Black, A.R, Duck, R.W., Finlinson, W., Thurston, N., Shackley, S. and Crichton, D., 2002. *Climate Change: Flooding Occurrences Review*, Central Research Unit, Scottish Executive, Edinburgh.

Werritty, A. with Chatterton, J., 2004. *Future Flooding Scotland*, Foresight. Office of Science and Technology, London.

Werritty, A. and Hoey, T.B., 2002. *Trends and Issues: Geomorphological changes and trends in Scotland – trends in river channels and processes*, Report FOOAC107B to Scottish Natural Heritage, SNH, Edinburgh.

Werritty, A., Hoey, T.B. and Black, A.R., 2005. 'The geomorphology and management of a dynamic unstable gravel-bed river: the Feshie/Spey confluence, Scotland', in *Catchment Dynamics and River Processes*, eds Garcia, C. and Batalla, R., Elsevier, Amsterdam, 213–224.

Werritty, A., Houston, D.S., Ball, T., Tavendale, A. and Black, A.R., 2006. *Exploring the Social Impacts of Flood Risk and Flooding in Scotland*, Scottish Executive, Edinburgh.

Werritty, A. and Leys, K.F., 2001. 'The sensitivity of Scottish rivers and upland valley floors to recent environmental change', *Catena*, 42, 2–4.

World Wildlife Fund Scotland, 2002. *Turning the Tide on Flooding*, WWF Scotland, Dunkeld.

15 Driver impacts in Northern Ireland

John Chatterton and Stuart Suter

Background to flood risk in Northern Ireland

Administrative context

One of the functions of the Rivers Agency of Northern Ireland is to manage inland and coastal flooding. The Agency has sole responsibility and discretionary powers for maintaining all designated watercourses as well as designated sea defences. Administratively, the Agency is divided into East and West Regions, with six functional Area Offices. Unlike the English and Welsh Environment Agency, which is quasi-autonomous, the Agency is a Civil Service department within the Department of Agriculture and Rural Development (DARD), equivalent to England's Defra.

Physical backdrop

Northern Ireland experiences high rainfall with 1500–1600 mm and 800–900 mm falling annually in upland and lowland areas respectively. The high precipitation, coupled with soils of low permeability and poor drainage, generates a significant risk of flooding. The Province has a high relief (Fig. 15.1) and is drained by an extensive network of watercourses emanating mainly from the Sperrin and Mourne Mountains. After falling steeply from the uplands, many rivers maintain relatively steep gradients. On reaching the lowlands, rivers drain through Loughs Erne, Foyle, Neagh and Strangford, which provide features unique to Northern Ireland's drainage pattern, before reaching the sea.

Existing fluvial and coastal flood risk context

The Asset Management Unit of the Rivers Agency holds a database of recent flooding. Notable areas of flooding (Fig. 15.2) have included:

a. Strabane on the River Mourne in 1987.
b. Omagh on the River Strule also in 1987.
c. Castlederg on the Derg River, for which a flood protection scheme was completed in 2000.
d. Ballymena, where flooding came from the Braid and Main Rivers.
e. Limavady on the Roe River.
f. Belfast on the River Lagan, where both drainage and flooding are tidally affected.

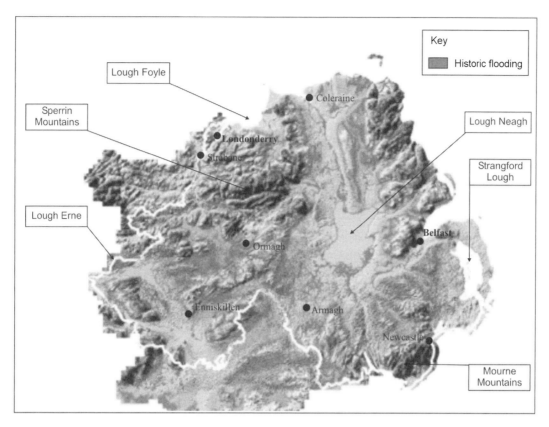

Fig. 15.1. Relief map of Northern Ireland (Rivers Agency, 2002b)

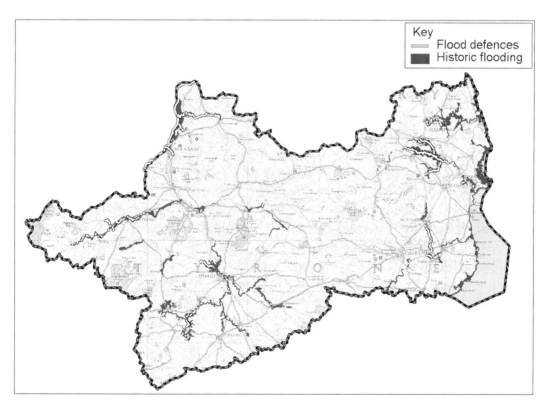

Fig. 15.2. Notable areas of flooding and flood defences in Northern Ireland (Rivers Agency, 2002b)

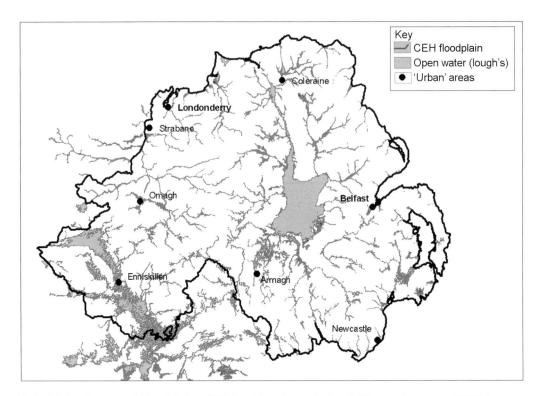

Fig. 15.3. Main rivers and floodplains (CEH) of Northern Ireland (Rivers Agency, 2002b)

The Asset Management Unit are also developing flood risk maps, which include historic and predictive floods, in addition to Indicative Floodplain Maps prepared by the Centre for Ecology and Hydrology (CEH), Wallingford, which were generated from a digital elevation model with flood depths (Fig. 15.3). These maps are used for development control purposes to identify the numbers and types of property at risk during a 1:100-year event (Table 15.1) assuming no flood defence infrastructure is in place.

Flood risk to buildings and infrastructure is not perceived as a major issue by the public and the scale and impacts of historic flooding have received less attention in Northern Ireland than is the case for Great Britain.

CEH flood risk maps are not made available to the public as it is considered this would create unnecessary anxiety, given that the residual risks within defended areas are considered small. The level of risk is low because:

Table 15.1. Properties at risk of flooding <1.0 m depth (CEH flood risk maps)

Area	Number of properties (1:100 years)					
	Public		Industrial/commercial		Dwellings	
	<1.0 m	>1.0 m	<1.0 m	>1.0 m	<1.0 m	>1.0 m
Fermanagh	27	140	183	303	1046	2277
Coleraine	68	156	156	413	1274	2801
Omagh	44	188	135	523	823	2279
Armagh	68	174	62	157	543	1125
Lisburn	76	226	119	306	301	7846
Greater Belfast	458	678	1163	1920	7226	10 842
Total	741	1562	1818	3622	11 213	27 170

a. Flood defence schemes for many towns and other locations have been constructed to high standards of protection over the past 10–15 years.
b. The Agency has successfully worked with the Department of Environment Planning Service to control and limit development in floodplains and consequently, unlike many river catchments in England, there are no real examples of extensive floodplains with large-scale housing development.
c. There is a natural cultural preference manifested in the high proportion (50%) of applications for new residential development to be located in rural, upland (drumlin) areas.

In future, areas where floodplains might come under increased pressure due to urban expansion are thought to be located in the Lough Neagh and Londonderry areas, and along the River Lagan corridor through to Belfast (see Fig. 15.1).

Agriculture plays an important part in the economy of Northern Ireland, principally through milk and beef production. Many grant-aided agricultural drainage improvement schemes were built 10–15 years ago and maintenance of good drainage and flood protection in key agricultural areas is still important. However, no new drainage schemes have been implemented in the past ten years.

The threat of coastal erosion in Northern Ireland is perceived to be minor, partly because the formed coastline is hard rock (predominantly basalt), and partly because the erosion that is currently taking place on the east coast is localised. Land at risk from marine flooding, nominally taken as that lying below the 5 m contour level, generally coincides with the location of existing coastal flood defence works. Coastal areas where future housing development pressure may occur and, hence, where erosion could become a potential issue, include Portrush (mainly second-home development), the Outer Ards peninsula, Rostrevor, and at Newtownards on Strangford Lough, where coastal defences already exist.

Fluvial defence assets

The Rivers Agency is responsible for some 6 792 km of watercourses designated under the Drainage Order 1973 for Northern Ireland. Of these, some 28% are designated 'main' watercourses, 63% are designated 'minor' and 9% are 'urban'.

Asset surveys have been undertaken since 1993 to define the type, location and construction materials of defences, and this information is available as a GIS database. A total of 754 individual reaches of river defence and structures, with a total length of 562 km, are maintained by the Rivers Agency. These defences are mainly earth and clay embankments of 1.5–3 m in height but with occasional masonry, concrete and sheet pile defences. Comprehensive condition surveys for these assets have not yet been undertaken.

The Standards of Protection provided by the fluvial defences are not recorded in asset surveys but, because of the robust design approach used by the Rivers Agency, they are considered to be high, being of the order of 1:50 to 1:100 years for minor and major urban areas, respectively. For agricultural land, the Rivers Agency seeks to provide standards of protection of 1:3 to 1:5 years.

Coastal defence assets

Sea defences around the coast of Northern Ireland include:

a. The Foyle Sea Defences at Myroe, Ballykelly, Longfield and Blackbrae.
b. The Strangford Dyke defences at Strangford Lough.
c. Intermittent but localised defences along the Antrim coast road from Larne to Cushendall.
d. Local railway line defences on the north coast.
e. Port defences such as Newry and Belfast.

Designated sea defences maintained by the Rivers Agency are primarily earth banks with stone pitching or rock armouring on the seaward face, protecting valuable agricultural land, e.g. the horticultural production area of Ballykelly. In comparison with England and Wales these are limited in extent totalling 26.36 km in length and protecting only 2186 ha.

Summary of flooding and coastal risks

The scale and current perception of fluvial flood risk in Northern Ireland is significantly lower than for Great Britain, for a number of physical, institutional and cultural reasons. This has to be seen in the context that the Rivers Agency is currently committed to maintaining an extensive and dense network of rivers and watercourses for land drainage and flood protection, extending to a length of 6792 km over a total drainage area of 12 133 km^2, representing a density of 1 km of channel for every 2 km^2 of catchment.

As well as watercourse maintenance, the Rivers Agency also operates and maintains an extensive system of flood defence assets, which cover some 10% of the total length of all the designated watercourses. Annual expenditure on the operation and maintenance of these assets is of the order of £6.6 million, which is a similar sum to the annual expenditure on capital works programmes.

In future, climate change, with its trend towards wetter winters, more intense rainfall, higher runoff and, hence, higher peak flows, will place even greater emphasis on the need to maintain and operate watercourses and flood defence assets efficiently. The morphological response of rivers to increases in flood peaks and altered flow regimes will be either to widen or deepen their cross-sections, or a combination of both. As the great majority of existing river flood defences are constructed from earth or clay embankments, these will therefore become progressively more susceptible to attack due to morphological changes. Continued and increasing emphasis on maintenance, probably combined with improvement works, will be required if existing standards of protection for fluvial defences are to be maintained into the future.

Areas at risk from coastal flooding due to future climate change accompanied by rising relative sea level are limited, and are restricted to places where coastal defence structures are already in place. However, increased emphasis on maintenance works, together with improvement works to raise defences where necessary, will be required if existing standards are to be maintained.

Institutional aspects

Organisational structure

The Strategic Planning Order enacted in 1999 (following the Good Friday Agreement) created ten departments of government in Northern Ireland.

Flood- and water-related management issues are within the remit of three of these departments:

- Rivers Agency (Department of Agriculture and Rural Development);
- Roads Services and Water Services (Regional Development);
- Planning, and Environment and Heritage Services (Environment and Core Policy Unit).

The Rivers Agency

The Rivers Agency is the statutory land drainage and flood protection authority, with discretionary powers, under the Drainage (Northern Ireland) Order 1973, to:

- maintain watercourses and coastal defences, which have been designated by the Drainage Council for NI;
- construct and maintain land drainage and flood defence structures;

- administer advisory and enforcement procedures to protect the drainage function of all watercourses.

An 18-member Drainage Council represents the interests of stakeholders. Three directors (Corporate Services, Development and Operations) are responsible to the Chief Executive. The Director of Development is responsible for planning, operational support and asset management at the Hydebank, Belfast HQ, while the Director of Operations manages regional operations in the western region (Omagh, Coleraine and Fermanagh) and the eastern region (Lisburn, Greater Belfast and Armagh).

The six areas are largely catchment based. The Rivers Agency employs 425 staff, including approximately 260 direct labour or industrial staff. Resource allocations for 2002/2003 were £11 million for departmental running costs and £10 million of programmed expenditure (capital and current) (Rivers Agency, 2002a). Every year, £6.6 million is spent on watercourse maintenance. The Newry Flood Alleviation Scheme is the largest scheme in progress with £1.0 million of the total scheme costs of £5.4 million committed to the last financial year.

Prioritisation of capital works is based on a four-criteria evaluation system, largely a hybrid of the Defra system in England. All funding is directly allocated by Central Government by way of the Northern Ireland Department of Finance and Personnel, with no land drainage precept being levied by local authorities. The Rivers Agency has delegated responsibilities for all cost beneficial schemes up to a threshold of £3 million, using Defra FDCPAG3-style appraisal methods. Programming of works is controlled by way of the Director of Development.

The Bateman formula (devised in 1967) defines responsibilities for executing coastal flood defence works. At present, any coastal defence not managed by (a) the Rivers Agency for designated defences; (b) Road Services for roads; (c) Port Authorities are taken up by the Construction Services of the Department of Agriculture and Rural Development (DARD). The Rivers Agency has a clear responsibility only for The Foyle and Strangford designated coastal defences.

Water Services

Three agencies form the Inter-Agency Flood Group, which was invoked by Lord Dubbs following urban flood incidents in the greater Belfast Area in autumn 1999. The agencies and areas of responsibility are:

a. the Rivers Agency, with responsibility for fluvial flooding and coastal defences as specified above;
b. Water Services, with responsibility for storm and foul sewers;
c. Road Services, with responsibility for gulleys and road drainage.

A 'hot spots' register was developed and assigned according to these responsibilities. Water Services are responsible for Drainage Area Plans. Although a £50 million upgrade of the Belfast drainage system is planned for 2010, most of the Province's drainage and fluvial systems, when combined, can handle intensive flows and likely levels of pluvial flooding. As provincial towns are small (c. 20–30 000), flood probabilities are low, provided that engineering design is sound and watercourse maintenance is effective. Geography is also a factor, as distances from stream sources to sea are relatively short. Sustainable urban drainage systems (SUDS) are rarely adopted.

Out of a Water Services' annual budget of £110 million, urban drainage maintenance totals £300–400 000 for Belfast, £100 000 for Londonderry, and £25–30 000 for the remaining provincial towns. Priorities for spending are (a) raw water treatment, (b) wastewater treatment, (c) improvements to distribution systems, and (d) improvements to urban drainage.

Road Services

Road Services are considered to be a minor player within the Inter-Agency Flood Group. Their responsibility is limited to cleaning and maintaining gulleys, drains and pipes for rural, minor and trunk roads. If road flooding is judged to come from a designated watercourse, this is taken as the responsibility of the Rivers Agency. If road flooding occurs from a non-designated watercourse, then this is seen as the responsibility of the landowner. The Rivers Agency is seen as the arbiter in the settlement of disputes.

Of the total annual budget of £95 million, only 3% is spent on maintenance of road drainage facilities for the 25 000 km of roads in Northern Ireland (a road density incidentally being two to three times greater than in England).

Environment and Heritage Service (EHS)

The EHS is split into three Directorates: Built Heritage, Environmental Protection and Natural Heritage. EHS is responsible for nature conservation in Northern Ireland and has designated approximately 200 SSSIs and 40 sites designated under the European Habitats legislation. The Conservation Protection and Designation Department declares/designates sites as SSSI, SAC (Special Areas for Conservation), SPA (Special Protected Areas) and provides advice to the Rivers Agency and statutory authorities under the Habitats Order on how development or works will impact on habitat.

Though many sites are located within coastal and estuarine zones, there is no effective strategy in place to manage the coast; with no coastal zone management policy and no shoreline management plans. However, the formation of a coastal forum appears imminent.

Planning service

Planning and controlling future development in the Province falls under the auspices of three departments:

- Department of Rural Development (DRD): responsible for preparing Regional Development Strategy (RDS) including transport strategy, and policy for implementing that strategy;
- Department of Environment (DoE) responsible for operations, i.e. planning applications, preparation of development plans, enforcement of procedures;
- Department of Social Development (Regeneration) (DSD).

DRD and DoE have produced a series of Policy Planning Statements (PPSs). Those with relevance to flood risk include:

- PPS 2: Planning and Nature Conservation
- PPS12: Housing
- PPS13: Transportation and Land Use
- PPS14: The Countryside
- PPS15: Flood Risk
- PPS18: The Coast.

These policy statements will control or manage development within both coastal and fluvial floodplain environments.

Land-use and the planning processes

Agriculture and drainage

Agriculture plays an important part in the economy of Northern Ireland. DARD's rural development programme recognises the importance of an efficient, competitive and diversified agricultural sector and effective land drainage is important to achieving this. Thus, one of the River Agency's principle objectives (through its rural drainage programme) is to achieve high levels of channel maintenance, mainly through clearance of vegetation, to maintain free-flowing watercourses and to provide good drainage for agriculture.

Land drainage has and remains a key policy driver within the Rivers Agency. As a consequence, in the 1970s and 1980s many grant-aided agricultural drainage improvement schemes were built. Such integrated drainage schemes brought about quicker runoff response times and higher peak flows. Grant-aided drainage to farmers is now at its end and, with no new schemes implemented during the past decade, there is evidence of a proliferation of blocked land drains which could exacerbate flooding. Nevertheless, the Ulster Farmers' Union is a key player in lobbying for effective maintenance of arterial drainage.

As in other upland and marginal agricultural regions of the British Isles most farmers are 'envelope farmers' reliant on subsidy from area payments and the Common Agricultural Policy (CAP) for their economic survival. The farming community is ageing and holding sizes are small (the 30 000 farms in the Province have an average size of only 34 ha). Cereal farming is limited, with the focus of efficient production (largely horticultural); coincident with the Foyle and Strangford (Ards) defended coastal flood plains. Schemes by EHS to promote MOSS (Management of Sensitive Sites), which are analogous to Stewardship Schemes in England, provide assistance packages to promote positive management of declared sites.

Housing development

From a planning perspective, housing development in Northern Ireland has always, traditionally and for cultural reasons, focused on upland hilly areas and away from the low-lying inter-drumlin fen areas, particularly in County Down. Potential future areas, where floodplains could come under pressure from housing development, are likely to be limited to around Lough Neagh, Londonderry and the River Bann through to Belfast. Thus, with the possible exception of the Greater Belfast area, pressure on land for development, particularly floodplain land, is minimal. Under the Regional Development Strategy, a total of only 10 000 additional houses per year are predicted for the next 15 years and 5000 of these will be in upland rural areas outside floodplains. This scale of rural development is greater than that projected for the rest of the UK combined. One hundred and fifty years ago the population of what is now Northern Ireland was 2.5 million but now it has fallen to 0.7 million, still with a cultural pattern of dispersal throughout the countryside, as in the Irish Republic.

Planning and development control

Planning to control development in flood risk areas is currently based on the English PPG25 (but with no current statutory base), though the Planning Services of DoE are currently developing a parallel document for the Province entitled PPS (Planning Policy Statement) 15. Planning to control development is now also being based on the use of flood mapping (CEH flood depth maps supplemented by use of hydro-dynamic modelling) and aerial photography. However, parallel principles to those in PPG25 do not exist for coastal areas.

Policy Planning Statement (PPS2), 'Planning and Nature Conservation', will provide guidance on safeguarding environmental assets (e.g. Ramsar sites) and promote wise use of wetlands, but until this policy is in place then the presumption generally is that permission will be given for development. For example, the outer Ards (Strangford Lough) is an SPA but is under pressure for residential development and, if, eventually, a proposal for a sea wall protection is put forward, EHS will have difficulty resisting it.

EHS has developed a River Conservation Strategy, and catchment management plans have been prepared. Where there are judged to be little or no discernible environmental impacts from development, EHS recommend implementation of a SUDS-type approach for runoff control, though the requirement for this is not embedded in legislation. The Environment Protection Department is responsible for catchment management planning and driving sustainable drainage policy. The Rivers Agency has no present remit to produce catchment flood management plans.

Coastal areas, where future housing development pressure may occur, are considered to be Portrush on the north coast (mainly second homes development), the outer Ards, Rostrevor and Newtownards at Strangford Lough, which has its own flood defence works. PPS18 will provide guidelines for determining coastal flood risk and protection requirements, and give DoE the tools to determine planning applications, control future development and raise public awareness.

River basin management plans are to be prepared by EHS by 2009 under the EU Water Framework Directive, and PPS15 will need to incorporate the requirements of these. In the meantime, agencies are less able to apply the precautionary principle to development, and there is less explicit commitment to sustainable development. In fact, there is low awareness of fluvial or coastal flooding (and erosion) as an issue and therefore low public pressure, and consequently less pressure on the preparation of PPS15. A more preventative approach will be required and this may follow from adherence to the requirements of the Water Framework Directive.

In summary, flood problems in Northern Ireland are localised, obvious and therefore easier to address in the planning process than in England, with pressure for flood plain development not being a primary driver.

Climate change

Current climate

Precipitation is the main (source) driver of flooding in Northern Ireland, but to date no specific work has been undertaken for the Province to estimate changes in peak flood flows expected to result from the climate change predicted by UKCIP02 scenarios. Future estimates need to be made using appropriate rainfall–runoff models based on predictions of future temporal and spatial distributions of rainfall and intensity, and catchment physical characteristics, including land-use, soil type (permeability) and topography. Such estimates need to be set within the context of existing long-term climate trends and fluctuations.

Temperature

The longest continuous data records (from 1844) for temperature in Northern Ireland are from the Armagh Observatory meteorological station. Betts (2002a) notes that this site has experienced little environmental change, and there has been little general variation in lowland temperatures since the mid nineteenth century.

Precipitation

Betts (2002b) also reviewed the recent precipitation trends for Northern Ireland. This analysis was based on area-averaging of monthly records for the period from 1931–2000. Conclusions are that from both an annual precipitation perspective, and for winter precipitation on its own, no statistically significant trends are evident. Betts (2002b) notes that summers in Northern Ireland have generally been drier during the past three decades than earlier in the 70-year record, with 1976, 1983 and 1995 being particularly dry years. This has led to an increasing trend in

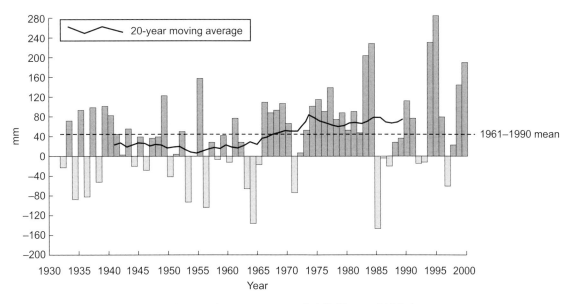

Fig. 15.4. Historical trend in winter minus summer rainfall (Betts, 2002a)

the difference between winter and summer precipitation, measured as proportions of the relatively unvarying (or trendless) total annual precipitation (Fig. 15.4). This trend towards relatively drier summers and wetter winters is consistent with that expected according to the predictions of the UKCIP02 scenarios.

Future climate change for Northern Ireland under UKCIP02 scenarios

Future climate change will alter temperature and precipitation regimes throughout the UK, although it is uncertain how the climate will change in specific areas, and uncertain what precise effects such changes in rainfall will have on the flow regimes and future flood hazards associated with particular rivers.

Temperature

UKCIP02 suggests that the predicted rate of climate warming in Northern Ireland for the four Foresight socio-economic scenarios, annually averaged over all four seasons, could be of the order of 1.5°C per century under low- and 3°C per century under high-emission scenarios respectively. Predictions also include strong seasonal differences, with greater rises of 3.5–4°C for summer and autumn months under the world market scenario, but with lower rises during the winter months of 2–2.5°C. Similarly, higher rises of 1.5°C are predicted during summer and autumn for the low emissions global sustainability scenario, with lower than average rises of 0.5–1.0°C during winter months. These projections are summarised in Table 15.2.

Table 15.2. Predicted rate of climate warming (Northern Ireland) – UKCIP2

Foresight scenario	Temperature increase all seasons	Temperature increase summer/autumn	Temperature increase winter
Global sustainability	+1.5°C	+1.5°C	+0.5–1°C
World market	+3°C	+3.5–4°C	+2–2.5°C

These temperature rises may be significant due to their impact on evapotranspiration rates and, hence, on future water balances within catchments, and surface runoff and flood hazards. Of particular importance will be the impact (in terms of their magnitude and timing) that these temperature changes have on moisture conditions during winter months. Wet antecedent catchment conditions prior to prolonged winter rainfall events, of the order of 50–75 mm, are reported by the Rivers Agency to be a major driver of fluvial flood events in Northern Ireland.

Significantly, while UKCIP02 models predict decreases in soil moisture and hence catchment wetness, during summer and autumn months, this is accompanied by increased soil moistures by up to 4% during winter months for all future scenarios.

Precipitation

The spatial resolution ($50 \, \text{km} \times 50 \, \text{km}$) of UKCIP02 scenarios allows regional differences to be discerned across Northern Ireland for predicted changes in precipitation. On an annual basis and averaged across the Province, precipitation is predicted to decrease under all four future scenarios, by up to 7% in 2050 and 9% by 2080 for the high emission, world market scenario. These decreases are due to large predicted decreases in summer precipitation, which are, in part, offset by slight to marginal increases in both autumn and spring precipitation, and more so by marked increases in winter precipitation.

Summer precipitation is predicted to decrease by 15% by 2050 and by 23% by 2080 under the low-emission, global sustainability, scenario; and to decrease by more than 30% and 40% respectively under the medium- and high-emission scenarios. In contrast, predicted increases in autumn wetness are nominal (1%), although the impact of such increases on runoff and flood flows could be noticeable. Predicted increases in winter rainfall are significant and, for example, are likely to rise by as much as 10% and 20% by 2050 and 2080, respectively under the world markets scenario, with significant implications for increased runoff and peak flood flows.

Winter rainfall, in conjunction with wet antecedent catchment conditions, is considered to be the main driver of flooding in Northern Ireland. It is, therefore, of relevance to consider UKCIP02 predictions for increases in 'intense' winter precipitation, and the corresponding likelihood of increased incidence of flooding. These projections are summarised in Table 15.3.

These factors will have a significant cumulative impact in terms of increased runoff volumes, time to peak and, hence, on peak flood flows in rivers and, therefore, on flood risk. Climate change, in particular precipitation, is therefore predicted to be a progressively more and more important driver of increased flood risk in Northern Ireland in the future, which in time will become the dominant driver of flood risk in the Province. The key measure of increased flood risk associated with this driver will be the increase in peak river flood flows that will occur in response to changed climatological conditions.

Table 15.3. Predicted changes in precipitation (Northern Ireland) – UKCIP2

Foresight scenario	Percentage change summer	Percentage change autumn	Percentage change winter
Global sustainability	−15% (2050) −23% (2080)	Nominal, say 1%	
World market	−30% (2050) −40% (2080)	Nominal, say 1%	+10% (2050) +20% (2080)

River processes

River systems

Introduction

The relief map of Northern Ireland (Fig. 15.1) and the fluvial network (Fig. 15.2) show the dominant fluvial drainage systems of the Province. These include:

- upper and lower Lough Erne system, principally receiving water from the rivers of Fermanagh;
- western rivers of Tyrone and Londonderry, flowing north-west by way of the Mourne and the Strule Rivers to Lough Foyle;
- rivers of Tyrone, Londonderry, Antrim, Armagh and Down, including the Balinderry, Blackwater and Upper Bann, flowing into Lough Neagh;
- east and northward flowing coastal rivers including (a) the Lower Bann which drains Lough Neagh, (b) the Lagan flowing through Belfast, (c) the rivers that drain to Strangford Lough, and (d) the steep coastal rivers of Antrim.

While morphological differences do exist between them (e.g. the Lower Bann and the Lagan and the north-eastern rivers of Antrim), many rivers rise in the uplands before falling steeply for the first 20 km after which their gradients flatten but are still noticeable (1:500) over a distance of 20–30 km to their outfalls at either Lough or sea level. This pattern confirms the view expressed by the Rivers Agency that most rivers are free flowing and provide effective drainage, except in their very lower reaches or where urbanisation has taken place.

Standards of protection

No definitive information is available about the standards of protection provided by existing flood defence assets. Through its recently prepared flood management strategy, the Rivers Agency is currently developing new procedures for flood-flow estimation and identification of appropriate standards of protection. These procedures include the preparation of flood maps, use of simulation models, database development and the application of the FEH approach to flood hydrology for catchments above a specified minimum.

Demand for large-scale flood defence works has diminished in recent years due to scheme implementation in the areas of highest risk, successful control of flood-plain development, and a cultural preference for locating housing in upland, rural areas. Consequently, the Rivers Agency has focused on providing flood protection and land drainage in smaller, and urban and urbanising catchments.

Estimated future peak river flood flows

The assessment of catchment response and the impact of climate change on future peak flows and flood probabilities presents a major challenge (Arnell, 1996). In the Foresight Project on flood and coastal defence, Nick Reynard applied various modelling techniques to estimate percentage changes in peak river flows for several hydrometric regions within England, Scotland and Wales. Reynard's approach and findings are described in some detail in Chapter 4. These estimates represent changes in comparison to a baseline period 1961–1990 and are nominally representative of the 50-year return period peak flow.

The model-based estimates prepared by Reynard (see Chapter 4) using (currently) limited data are estimated within a framework of informed expertise concerning hydrology and modelling, key climate drivers and the requirements for the scaling of runoff response. In the absence of data that are specific to Northern Ireland, transposition of estimates for Wales and Southern Scotland have been

Table 15.4. Estimated percentage increases in peak flows under different Foresight Project data (unpublished Foresight Project data supplied by Dr Nick Reynard, Centre for Ecology and Hydrology)

Hydrometric region	Date	World market	National enterprise	Local stewardship	Global sustainability
N. Ireland	2050	10	8	7	6
	2080	18	15	12	88

judged to be most appropriate in terms of geographical and hydrological similarity. On this basis, percentage increases in peak flood flows could be as high as 10 and 18% for 2050 and 2080 respectively under a future high-emission world market scenario (see Table 15.4).

In addition, Northern Ireland rainfall Statistics for Annual Average Rainfall (SAAR) 1961–1990 shows an average annual variability in rainfall of 800–900 mm and 1500–1600 mm between lowland and upland areas respectively. Superposition of this rainfall map onto the hydrological soils type (HOST) map shows that those areas with the highest soil impermeability coincide with those areas subjected to the highest average annual rainfall conditions, with implications for increases in peak runoff and flood flows.

Influence of soil types

The HOST mapping for Northern Ireland, derived from the National Soil Survey for Northern Ireland, utilises two principal hydrological indices to classify surface soils as an indication of hydrological response: the base flow index (BFI) and the standard percentage runoff (SPR). Superposition of the HOST map onto the physical relief map (Fig. 15.1) of Northern Ireland shows that upland areas almost exclusively comprise soils, such as gleysols, having high SPRs of 60% or higher. This estimate of runoff is an average annual figure, and will be higher under shorter-term rainfall conditions during winter, with consequently higher impacts on runoff and hence peak flood flows.

Estimation of future flood return periods

Flow gauging records from five representative rivers have been selected to estimate the potential reduction in existing standards of protection brought about by increased peak flood flows due to future climate change. They have been selected because between them they:

- capture a large proportion (30%) of the total drainage area of the Northern Ireland (14 133 km^2), and they include the important Lough Neagh and Lough Foyle systems;
- include rivers which typically rise in and drain highland areas, and which have runoff from within their free-flowing middle reaches, as well as flow attenuation from floodplain storage within their lower reaches;
- include rivers which have had a history of flooding, but for which flood defences have been constructed during the last two to three decades.

These selected rivers and gauging stations are:

- the River Mourne, gauged at Drumnabuoy House (1844 km^2);
- the Blackwater River, gauged at Maydown Bridge (972 km^2);
- the Ballinderry River, gauged at Ballinderry Bridge (430 km^2);
- the River Roe, gauged at Ardnargle (364 km^2);
- the Upper Bann, gauged at Moyallen (316 km^2).

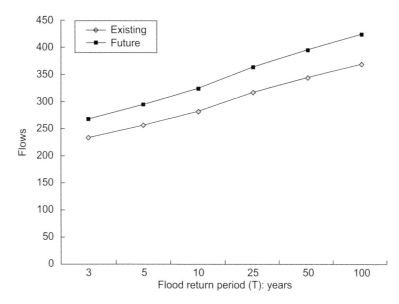

Fig. 15.5. Existing and estimated future flows versus their return periods for rivers in Northern Ireland (Rivers Agency, 2003)

Data on flood flows and return periods for these stations are available from the Rivers Agency Hydrometrics Section. These are based on annual maximum time series analysis.

As a practical approach to estimating increases in future flows, the flows have been aggregated, averaged and plotted against return periods, as shown in Fig. 15.5. Current data are plotted together with increased flows representing a future increase of 15%, corresponding to the estimated long-term (2080) potential increase under medium-high emission, national enterprise scenario. The implication in terms of changes in peak flow return periods, or the increased frequency of higher flows, is shown in Table 15.5.

These predicted reductions in return period are not directly translatable into changes in standard of protection, as flood levels are also related to channel shape, roughness and slope as well as of discharge.

This assessment is based on a limited sample of rivers and a simplified representation of a complex process. For example, research shows that river morphology responds to two changes in the supply of sediment and changes in the flow regime (see Chapter 6). The morphological response to future changes in flow regime and sediment supply will depend upon specific local circumstances, but will be likely to involve a significant period of channel instability and adjustment. These changes in channel geometry will in turn affect water levels for a given flood discharge, and hence affect standards of protection, but the effects are unpredictable at this level of analysis.

Table 15.5. Potential changes in peak flow return periods under a future medium-high emission scenario

Existing peak flow return period: years	Equivalent future peak flow return period: years
100	20
50	15
20	10
5	2

257

Within this context, and while the above assessment is preliminary, it does provide a pragmatic estimate of the possible magnitude of future changes in flood probabilities expressed as return periods.

Climate change and river maintenance

In-stream and river bank vegetation are, together with micro-morphology, important factors affecting channel roughness and, hence, the capacity of a river to convey flood flows, with corresponding implications for water levels and for standards of protection. Micro-morphology is affected by changes in flow and sediment transport regimes but, in comparison with reach-scale morphology, is unlikely to have a particularly major impact on future change in flood risk (Chapter 6).

On the other hand, vegetation can have a major effect upon conveyance, more so than other components of roughness, such as bed material. The amount of vegetation in a river is affected by a number of abiotic factors and particularly by temperature. For instance, the seasonal timing of vegetative growth and die-back depends upon not only daylight hours, but also on ambient soil and water temperatures.

Temperature increases as predicted under UKCIP02 scenarios could lead to:

a. changes of up to a month in when vegetation growth begins;
b. warmer springs, resulting in greater amounts of vegetation;
c. warmer autumns, resulting in longer growing periods.

These changes will all significantly increase flow resistance in rivers and, hence, tend to increase flood levels and reduce standards of protection.

One of the River Agency's principle objectives is to maintain high levels of channel maintenance for all designated watercourses, in order to maintain free-flowing channels, provide high levels of flood defence for urban areas and support good land drainage conditions in important agricultural areas. Maintenance operations include silt and gravel shoal removal, clearance of vegetation (including in-stream weed removal), bank maintenance and, where necessary, brush and tree trimming.

Any future change in vegetation growth brought about by climate change could have significant adverse implications for channel conveyance and hence for standards of protection, unless current levels of maintenance activities are increased proportionately.

Given the heavy reliance on free drainage in the rivers of Northern Ireland, future environmental legislation that limits or inhibits in-channel maintenance operations could potentially lead to increases in flood probability under the more environmentally orientated scenarios (local stewardship or global sustainability).

Coastal processes and climate change

Introduction

Two key factors linked to future climate change over the next 50–80 years will have impacts on coastal flooding and protection. These are:

a. the potential change in relative sea level (RSL);
b. the potential increase in storminess and hence short-term surges in sea level.

Both of these factors will lead to increased probabilities of coastal flooding and erosion, as discussed in SNIFFER 2002 (Orford and McFadden, 2002).

Relative sea-level rise

Changes in absolute sea level will be driven by two key climate-related factors: the expansion of the oceans due to global warming, and an increase in the volume of the oceans due to glacial melting.

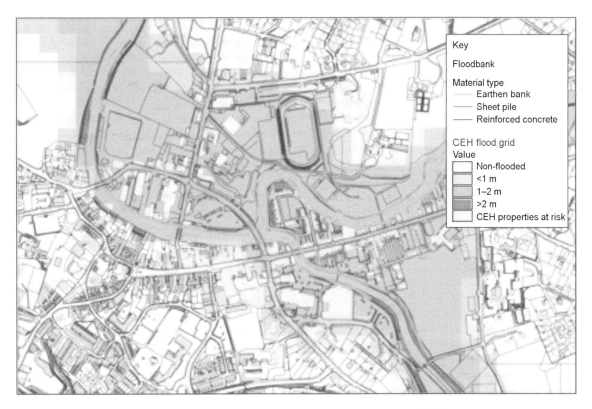

Fig. 15.6. Flood envelope and defences for Omagh (Rivers Agency, 2002b)

Coastal flood risk inventory

The Rivers Agency also analysed the number of properties at 5 m above sea level or lower. The results show that 12 715 properties fall within this 'coastal zone' representing nearly 2.5 million square metres of ground-floor space. By number, 55% are residential properties but 79%, by floor space, are non-residential properties mainly industry and commercial. Few properties at risk are located below the 2.5 m contour.

Of those properties in the <5 m coastal zone, 3686 properties are already counted in the CEH analysis as they are vulnerable to river flooding, with 24% of this 'overlap' in Newry and 6% in Strabane alone. Greater Belfast accounts for over half of the total duplications.

It is recognised in England and Wales that the CEH flood outlines can be inaccurate for determining flood risk at a local level and statistics on flood risk inventory should be used with caution. For the Province, the outlines provide only an overview indicating that about 6% of properties are located in fluvial flood plains, and a further 1.5% within the broadly defined (below 5 m contour) coastal flood zone. This compares with England and Wales, where about 10% of property lies within coastal and fluvial flood zones.

Table 15.6. Residential versus non-residential flood risk (all CEH flood risk bands)

Type	No.	% no.	Area: m^2	% area
Total residential (all depths)	28 981	67.2	2 020 094	36.4
Total non-residential (all depths)	14 166	32.8	3 527 255	63.6
Grand total	43 147		5 547 349	

Valuing the benefits of flood alleviation and continued maintenance (fluvial)

The Atkins report (2003) estimates that $1089 \, km^2$ or 8% of the land area of Northern Ireland is within the indicative flood plain as defined by the CEH analysis. Most of this land is primarily used for grazing livestock. Atkins conservatively estimated that the economic value expressed in terms of loss of agricultural output, if maintenance were not undertaken in rural areas, is in the region of £5.7 million per annum. This report, commissioned by the Rivers Agency, also suggests that about one-quarter of the properties within the CEH indicative flood plain are in rural communities dispersed across the Province. Using FHRC (1990) techniques, Atkins also evaluated annual average damages to built property as £5.8 million in urban areas and £2.0 million in rural areas. These estimates assume that 25 891 properties would be affected by a 50-year flood event and that continued maintenance reduces the number of properties affected by 40%. Without any form of flood protection, Atkins calculated, again from very limited data on existing standards of protection, a maximum annual average estimated damages of £29 million.

For expediency, the estimate of future flood losses presented herein will concentrate on damages to built property. The Atkins study allocated only £3000 per property to reflect flood damages, irrespective of flood frequency or flood stage. The Multi-coloured Manual (FHRC, 2003) is used here to update the potential damages *without the presence of existing flood defences*. It is now widely accepted that the *Flood Loss Assessment Information Report* (FLAIR) (FHRC, 1990) damages (the basis for Atkins' calculations) grossly undervalue realistic flood damages. The flood-depth zones within the CEH floodplains are here used to re-estimate the current 100-year event damages. A total value of damage to built property in the flood plains of £3.15 billion is calculated, with three-quarters of this within the non-residential sectors. This is about 30 times higher than the Atkins (2003) estimate.

The effect of perceived climate change on property damages

The *raison d'être* of the Rivers Agency is to maintain existing standards of flood protection in urban areas and, where cost effective, to improve these standards through rigorous prioritisation procedures in the allocation of funding. As indicated in Table 15.5, the potential changes in peak flow return periods under a future medium- to high-emission (national enterprise or world market) scenario will impact severely on existing standards of protection. In this study, an estimate is made of future increases in annual average damages, assuming maintenance of defences is continued as today and using the Atkins (2003) estimate of properties at risk during a 50-year event as 90% (or 38 837) of the 100-year event. Without other evidence, a figure of 10% of the 100-year property losses is assumed for the 20-year event. The threshold for property damage is taken as five years. Using these assumptions, the current annual average damage estimate for Northern Ireland's built floodplains is around £100 million (about four times higher than the Atkins (2003) figure). Reducing the standard of protection to reflect a future medium-high emissions, national enterprise scenario increases this figure by 60% in 2050. Although the current estimate may be perceived as high, the relative change remains irrespective of the damages estimated for the base condition.

Closure

It is clear that although the flood risk to people and property in Northern Ireland is significantly lower than in other parts of the UK, particularly within coastal zones, the consequences of increased magnitudes and/or frequencies of fluvial flooding would locally be both socially and economically disastrous. Extreme flood risk (flood depths greater than 2 m) is evenly spread throughout the Province's floodplains, but this risk will be exacerbated by the predicted increases in peak flows, such that communities with existing flood protection and communities within Greater Belfast, which have no real perception of existing risk, will, without significantly increased expenditure, become increasingly exposed. The River Agency data suggest increased exposure to risk will be particularly acute in commercial districts.

References

Arnell, N.W., 1996. *Global Warming, River Flows and Water Resources*, Wiley, Chichester.

Atkins, W.S. Ltd, 2003. *Evaluation of Watercourse Maintenance*, Rivers Agency (DARD) Northern Ireland.

Betts, R.A., 2002a. Climate Change in Northern Ireland, in Implications of Climate Change for NI: Informing Development Strategy, *SNIFFER*, Stationery Office, Belfast.

Betts, R.A., 2002b. Water Resources, in Implications of Climate Change for NI: Informing Development Strategy, *SNIFFER*, Stationery Office, Belfast.

Centre for Ecology and Hydrology (CEH), 2003. *Hydrometric Register and Statistics 1996–2000*, CEH, Wallingford.

Flood Hazard Research Centre (FHRC), 1990. *Flood Loss Assessment Information Report (FLAIR)*, FHRC, Enfield.

Flood Hazard Research Centre (FHRC), 2003. *The Benefits of Flood and Coastal Defence: Techniques and data for 2003*, FHRC, Enfield.

Halcrow Group Ltd, HR Wallingford, Flood Hazard Research Centre, 2000. *National Appraisal of Assets at Risk for England and Wales (NAAR)*.

Orford J.D. and McFadden, L., 2002. Coastal and Flood Defence, in Implications of Climate Change for NI: Informing Development Strategy, *SNIFFER*, Stationery Office, Belfast.

Rivers Agency, 2002a. *Corporate Plan 2002/7 and Business Plan 2002/3, 2002/2003*.

Rivers Agency, 2002b. *Northern Ireland Surface Water Hydrometric Review*, from Local Network Review.

Rivers Agency, 2003. *A Flood Estimation Strategy for Rivers Agency*.

Wilson, P. and Orford, J.D., 2002. 'Relative sea-level changes', in *Field Guide to Coastal Environments of Northern Ireland*, University of Ulster, 11–15.

Part 4
Coastal erosion drivers and risks

16 Drivers of coastal erosion

Kevin Burgess, Helen Jay and Robert J. Nicholls

Introduction

Much of the UK's shoreline is currently in a transgressive phase, i.e. moving landwards, in response to an ongoing rise in relative sea level. Along many stretches of the coast this is evidenced by coastal erosion. This process supplies sediment to the shorelines to maintain pace with ever-changing hydrodynamic and climatic conditions. The coasts of Scotland and Northern Ireland are also experiencing erosion but more locally than in England and Wales. Due to the limited understanding, the focus of this chapter is England and Wales.

Coastal change, or evolution, is however also affected by a range of interacting factors, or drivers:

- Natural morphology and processes:

    o existing hydrodynamic forcing (e.g. wave diffraction processes around headlands);
    o new hydrodynamic influences (e.g. interruption of littoral drift by newly created tidal inlets);
    o changes in geological controls (e.g. emergence of headlands within eroding cliffs; recession of existing headlands or exacerbation of embayment curvature due to immaturity of development);
    o sediment transport (e.g. natural changes in the rate or direction of sediment transport);
    o changes in sediment budget (e.g. shorelines switching from drift to swash-aligned tendencies due to exhaustion of relict sediment sources); and

- Human intervention (e.g. coastal defence, reclamation, dredging):

    o defence or intervention at the coast can have considerable impacts upon the operation of coastal systems, e.g. through creating hard points that alter shore alignment or interrupt sediment supply.

- Climate change:

    o climate change may change the forces acting upon the shoreline, such as altered wave or water-level conditions.

Drivers – natural morphology and processes

Natural forces

Although the *rate* of coastal erosion is influenced by many factors, it is largely driven by the natural forces acting upon it. These are mostly hydrodynamic, i.e. waves and water levels, although other forces such as wind and rainfall can be additional causes of erosion of some shorelines such as soft cliffs and dunes. A fuller account of the primary forces acting on the coast is provided earlier in this book, so is not repeated here, although a brief view of the relationship between the primary hydrodynamic drivers and coastal change is worth noting.

Wave action can cause considerable erosion to intertidal and backshore land-forms – either occasionally driving severe events, i.e. storms, or due to the regular exposure to more moderate activity. The level of exposure at the shoreline and the zones subjected to wave action is strongly influenced by tides. Wave heights at the shoreline are a function of water depth, as much of the UK coast is what is known as 'depth limited' conditions. This means that waves are often limited by the depth of water inshore; larger waves will be broken further offshore.

However, the UK also experiences large irregular increases in water levels, called surges, usually produced by in the passage of cyclonic weather systems. These both increase water depth, allowing larger waves to reach the shore, and exposure to more landward sections of the shore to wave attack.

Both waves and water levels are constantly varying forces; therefore our shore-lines will never reach a state of stable equilibrium. Consequently, coastal change is something that we can expect to continue indefinitely.

Natural features

Coastal morphology changes in response to the forces acting upon it, i.e. waves, tides and winds, but the formation and maintenance or growth of some features also depends upon a supply of suitable sediment, which requires a sediment source and a sediment pathway. The coast can be viewed as an open 'system' that has a number of components, which are linked by flows of both energy and sediment. Changes in the coastal zone occur as it moves towards a state of 'dynamic equilibrium' in response to the flows of energy and sediment. However, within the system there can be a number of feedbacks, both positive and negative, which complicate these interactions. The coastal environment is further complicated by the fact that these feedbacks and subsequent responses act on a number of different scales, both spatial and temporal (Stive *et al.*, 2002). Not all processes are operating at the same intensity and they may also be operating in different phases. The coastal response to these processes is also complex and there may be thresholds and lags to this response. In general, coastal change can be considered to occur over three characteristic timescales (Halcrow, 2002):

- macro-scale secular change (centuries to millennia);
- meso-scale cyclic or periodic change (years to century);
- micro-scale episodic or individual event change (days to years).

The present coast is predominately a function of variable timescale changes that have been operating over the last 10 000 years (the Holocene), with certain areas still responding to changes in coastal drivers since the early Holocene (when sea levels rose significantly due to the end of the Ice Age).

The response of the coast to changes in processes and controls is dependent on the coastal morphology and there is interdependence between different geomorpho-logical features that make up the natural system, such that evolution of one particular coastal feature is influenced by evolution in adjacent areas.

Table 16.1. Typical controls on coastal behaviour (Jay et al., 2003)

Headlands	Promontories, often due to more resistant geology, can have a major influence upon the coastal processes and the resultant orientation of the shoreline, in particular the formation and evolution of embayments. These form due to wave diffraction around at least one fixed point (although often between two fixed points); a soft coast between two resistant points will readjust its orientation to minimise the wave-generated longshore energy. Examples include Flamborough Head (a geological headland) and Dungeness foreland (a non-geological and mobile headland).
Shore platforms	Hard rock or armoured foreshores limit exposure of the backshore to wave activity and are resilient to shore lowering, restricting the rate of evolution of the shoreline. Examples of this type of control can be seen on the Cumbrian and Northumbrian coasts.
Offshore banks and features	Accumulations of sand, or submerged headlands, can both shelter areas of the shoreline, and alter the wave regime inshore, which will be influential upon the rate and nature of sediment movement. Notable examples include the sand banks offshore between Great Yarmouth and Lowestoft, and the submerged headland off Selsey Bill.
Estuaries and tidal inlets	Flows from these water bodies can deflect sediment from the shoreline to offshore. The formation of ebb tidal deltas can act as 'soft' shore platforms and headlands, limiting exposure of the backshore and diffracting waves.

Some typical controls on coastal behaviour and response are identified in Table 16.1.

The evolution of hard rock coasts is almost exclusively a function of the resistant nature of the geology, with the influence of prevailing coastal forcing on the orientation of these shorelines only occurring over very long timescales (millennia). Differential erosion may occur along these coastlines to create indentations or narrow pocket beaches where there is an area of softer geology, or faulting, which has been exploited by wave activity.

The evolution of softer shorelines is more strongly influenced by coastal forcing, although geology continues to play a significant role in both influencing this forcing (e.g. diffraction of waves around headlands) and dictating the rate at which change may occur. The plan-form of these shorelines will, over timescales of decades to centuries, tend towards a shape whose orientation is in balance with both the sediment supply and the capacity of the forcing parameters to transport available sediment (Komar, 1976).

There is a huge diversity of coastal environments and morphologies, even when just considering the coastline of England and Wales. Although broad generalisations can be made on the characteristics of each coastal system and therefore the likely response, there are more local and regional perturbations which result in deviations from these generic assessments, such as the interrelationships between morphologies, the variety of sediments and the introduction of artificial controls and hard points through the use of defences and coastal structures, such as ports. In recent years there has been a growing appreciation of the variation in the rate of coastal change (Haslett, 2000).

The resistance of any morphology is dependent upon a number of factors, specific to that feature. Therefore, the sensitivity of coastal morphologies to climate change varies both generically and site-specifically (also see SCOPAC, 2001). The generic sensitivity is relatively simple to define (see Table 16.2), but the site-specific

Table 16.2. Relative sensitivity of coastal landforms to different climate change drivers (Jay et al., 2003)

Landform type	Climate change sensitivity			
	Sea-level rise	**Storm surge**	**Precipitation**	**Wave direction**
Simple cliff	High	Moderate	Moderate	Low
Simple landslide	High	Low	High	Low
Composite cliff	Moderate	Low	Moderate	Low
Complex cliff	Moderate	Low	High	Low
Relict cliff	High	Low	High	Low
Embryonic dunes	High	High	Low	
Foredunes	High	High		
Climbing dunes	Moderate	Moderate	Moderate, impacts on vegetation	Low*
Relict dunes	Low	Low		
Parabolic dunes	Moderate	High	Low	
Transgressive dunes	Moderate	Moderate	Low	
River deltas	High	High	Moderate	Moderate
Tide dominated deltas	High	High	Low	Moderate
Wave dominated deltas	High	High	Low	High
Shore platforms	High	Moderate	Low	Low
Sandflats	High	High	Low	Moderate
Mudflats	High	High	Low	Low
Pioneer saltmarsh	High	High	Moderate, impacts	Low
Saltmarsh	High	High	on vegetation	Low
Sand beach	Moderate	Moderate	Low	High
Shingle beach	Moderate	Moderate	Low	Moderate
Mixed beach	Moderate	Moderate	Low	Moderate
Composite beach	Moderate	Moderate	Low	Moderate
Boulder beach	Low	Low	Low	Low
Barrier island	High	High	Low	High
Barrier beach	High	High	Low	High
Spit	High	High	Low	High
Cuspate foreland	Low	Low	Low	Low

Notes

Sea-level rise = sensitivity to accelerations in the rate of sea-level rise.

Storm surge = sensitivity to changes in intensity/frequency of storm surges (will depend upon exposure of site).

Precipitation = sensitivity to changes in pattern/intensity of precipitation.

Wave direction = sensitivity to changes in wave direction (e.g. changed sediment transport patterns).

* Dunes are likely to be sensitive to changes in wind direction and also wind strength.

nature and therefore actual response is more complex; as illustrated by the four case studies presented later in this chapter.

Drivers – human intervention

Throughout history, man has tried to control the coast and how it behaves. Human interference disturbs the balance of coastal systems, and as interference has increased, so humans have become an important influence on coastal behaviour.

Man causes perturbations in coastal behaviour and these perturbations can range from minor to catastrophic, depending both upon the action undertaken and the affected morphology. If a perturbation is catastrophic it is usually followed by further

Fig. 16.1. Groynes at Whitstable, south-east England

intervention and this may continue until the natural system is almost totally replaced by an artificial one, e.g. along the south-east coast of England. The lag time of the natural system to respond to any disturbance may mean that the consequence of an action is not felt for many years and may be many kilometres downcoast.

Coastal erosion is only considered a problem because of man's presence on the coast, which makes land too valuable to lose. However, under scenarios of sea-level rise, the coastline will become increasingly out of balance with the coastal forcing, resulting in deeper water at the coastline and therefore increased wave energy inshore. This will put greater pressure on existing defences and increase the risk of their failure.

A beach generally provides the interface between the sea and the land and is both a focus for energy dissipation and a primary conveyor of sediment throughout the shoreline. As such it is a key link between process and response, and is both reactive to coastal processes and a control upon the backshore response. Defence of the shoreline almost always involves actions that are influential upon beaches.

Beaches around the coasts of the UK are heavily used and many are artificially maintained through the use of sediment-trapping structures, such as groynes (e.g. Whitstable, south-east coast; see Fig. 16.1), beach stabilisation structures, such as breakwaters (e.g. Sea Palling, north Norfolk; see Fig. 16.2), and beach recharge (e.g. Mablethorpe, Lincolnshire). While beach stabilisation structures and recharge change the natural environment, they do not necessarily restrict the supply of sediment to downdrift areas. However, groynes are specifically designed to control longshore drift and historically the impacts of groyning a beach have been felt several kilometres downdrift, with erosion being caused. In many areas, beaches are also affected by the restriction of sediment supply from cliffs, e.g. due to the construction of a seawall.

Dune systems of varying size occur around the UK and are an integral part of the coastal system. There is significant beach–dune interaction, with dunes releasing sand to the beach during storms, which assists in wave energy dissipation. Therefore they provide an important role in coastal defence. However, they are also a physical barrier to marine inundation and, rather than viewing dunes as a sediment store, man has tended to view them as permanent fixed features, which has led to attempts to stabilise them. This has traditionally been through the use of plants,

Fig. 16.2. Breakwaters at Sea Palling, north Norfolk

such as marram grass, which may restrict the release of sediment during storms, but in more severe cases it has involved the construction of seawalls or revetments in front of the dunes, which effectively separates them from the active coastal system.

Cliffs occur around much of the UK coast, but vary considerably in their composition and morphology. Some of the hardest rocks in the country occur in Cornwall, Wales, Scotland and Northern Ireland and, because of their resistance to erosion, many of these cliffed sections remain unprotected and in a natural form because they pose little risk to cliff-top properties (e.g. Tenby, see Case study 3). In contrast, the cliffs along the Holderness and East Anglia coasts are probably the most rapidly eroding cliffs in England, if not in Europe (French, 1997). As such, they provide high volumes of sediment, some of which is suitable for beach building, with much of the balance maintaining muddy coasts. However, as a result of their rapid erosion rates, properties on the cliff tops are threatened and historically there has been significant loss of property and land. Where there has been economic justification, cliffs around the UK have been protected through use of seawalls, revetments, rock bunds and other defence measures. In a number of cases, this has restricted sediment input locally, and has also had an impact on downdrift beaches. Locally it may also change the plan-form shape of the coast through holding certain sections and allowing adjacent sections to continue to erode (e.g. North Norfolk, see Case study 1), which in turn affects drift rates. In heavily urbanised areas, many cliffs now sit behind defences, effectively separating them from the active coastal system, and many have also been re-graded, thus changing their morphology (e.g. Brighton, see Case study 2).

Some of the most heavily modified coastal environments are the UK's estuaries. The sheltered nature of these environments has often led to them being extensively developed for human activities (see Fig. 16.3). There has also been extensive land reclamation within estuaries to provide land for agricultural, industrial and urban uses. This has resulted in significant modification of the estuary form, morphological components (e.g. area of saltmarsh, mudflats and sandflats) and processes. Many estuaries are now considerably constrained and the natural processes are significantly modified, making it difficult to predict how they are likely to respond to future change.

Fig. 16.3. Portsmouth Harbour – showing the significant changes made to the coastline

Around the coast of the UK, land claim has taken place both within estuarine areas and on the open coast, which has necessitated the construction of sea defences. Land claim has taken place for two main reasons: for the generation of agricultural land and for development (French, 1997). Typically the defences constructed are earth embankments, although occasionally seawalls are used, and are there to protect the reclaimed land from flooding by the sea. There is often a differential in height between the claimed land and the saltmarsh level seaward of the defence, due to dewatering and compaction, which means that the flood defences become even more important. These areas are particularly vulnerable to sea-level rise (see Case study 4) as the natural response of the saltmarsh to trans-gress landward and maintain the same position relative to the tidal frame is constrained and the saltmarsh is therefore subject to higher-energy wave attack. This results in coastal squeeze and saltmarsh erosion. It also increases the threat of overtopping of defences and subsequent flooding as the protection function of the saltmarsh declines. The presence of the defence also means that sediment has been removed from the coastal system.

Drivers – climate change

The potential influences of climate change upon changing the hydrodynamic parameters that are of relevance to coastal erosion are explored in earlier chapters of this book, which conclude that although there are close connections between the drivers, 'over a timescale of 100 years, sediment supply and coastal morphology will tend to have more significant impacts as a function of management strategies than climate change'. It is also apparent that little reliable information or confidence exists with regards to long-term future changes in waves, storminess or surge conditions; indeed the predictions of changes within these parameters tend to be within the limits of uncertainty that currently exist with assessments of present-day conditions. As such, inter-relationships between these parameters are not well established, and differences in response between the four UKCIP future climate change scenarios are not quantifiable to an acceptable degree of accuracy.

Sea-level rise is the only parameter where there is a reasonable degree of information and agreement with respect to the four future climate scenarios. This would also appear to be the parameter of most significance with respect to shoreline erosion. While there is no evidence of combination of changes in different parameters, the potential for greater surge height and increased wave activity at the shoreline is dependent to some extent upon an increase in sea level (as a function of increased water depth).

Furthermore, it should not necessarily be assumed that increases in erosion will lead to more substantial beaches and better natural defences. While more sediment will be delivered to the coastal system, the shoreline is also experiencing a vertical adjustment in position resulting from the rise in sea levels, i.e. much of this sediment may be transported and deposited offshore to form the submerged coastal slope. Where this is not occurring, wave energy at the shoreline would increase as a result of deeper water, which will produce more volatile shorelines that are less conducive to sediment retention. Despite this, compared to the present situation, any increase in erosion due to defence failure may feed beaches both locally and downdrift, which could increase the ability of the system to keep pace with rising sea levels. Beaches may therefore be maintained but, for the reasons stated above, it is unlikely that they would significantly build in size. So, we should not expect erosion rates to reduce in the future.

Case studies

Four cases studies from England and Wales are presented below which discuss potential coastal response to future drivers. Locations have been chosen to reflect both different morphologies and different management policies:

- Case study 1: north Norfolk – this is a soft-cliffed, high-erosion risk coastline, where defences are restricted to the major towns and villages.
- Case study 2: Brighton – this is an example of a heavily modified coastline, where major assets are being protected.
- Case study 3: Tenby – this is an example of a hard-rock coastline, where tourism is a key asset and there are only localised defences.
- Case study 4: Bradwell Power Station, Essex – this is an estuarine coastline, where defences relate to historic reclamation of low-lying land, which is now very vulnerable to sea-level rise.

Box 16.1

Case study 1: North Norfolk coast

Coastal characteristics

This is a predominately soft-cliffed coastline composed of unconsolidated glacial sediments, which are currently experiencing high erosion rates. There are no hard geological control points along this frontage, but seawalls and groynes exist in front of all of the towns and larger villages (i.e. Sheringham, Cromer, Overstrand, Trimingham, Mundesley and Bacton), which have resulted in these areas developing as promontories, while adjacent cliffs are eroding.

The cliffs are an important source of beach sediment both locally and to downdrift areas. There is a time lag of approximately 40 to 50 years between erosion of the cliff releasing sediment and this sediment reaching beaches as far south as Lowestoft.

Coastal evolution

Present-day benchmark: the coastal system is in a natural state of retreat as it is still responding to the rise in relative sea level since the last glaciation. The unconsolidated nature of this shoreline makes it highly susceptible to coastal erosion; cliff erosion varies along the coast, with the rate of retreat dependent in part on the cliff height and composition. As the cliffs erode there is potential for beach building, but wave energy rapidly moves this material away resulting in a translation or steepening of the beach profile as the shoreline retreats. At the towns and villages, defences restrict the amount of erosion taking place, resulting in the development of promontories as undefended cliffs on either side continue to erode.

Future climate change: erosion of the soft, unconsolidated cliffs is by both marine and sub-aerial processes; therefore this coastal system is sensitive to changes in both precipitation and sea-level changes. A rise in sea level raises all the coastal processes, thus resulting in greater attack by wave action at the cliff and therefore increased cliff erosion. Increased erosion of the cliffs would result in the increased release of some beach-building materials, however it is unlikely that this would build the beaches sufficiently to result in an overall reduction in cliff erosion. Therefore, the high-emissions scenario is likely to have the most detrimental impact in terms of shoreline erosion rates, however all climate change scenarios will induce the same type of change, if not the same magnitude. The soft nature of the cliffs means that it is likely that the cliffs will keep pace with the rate of sea-level rise, with beaches tending to translate shoreward.

At the town and village locations where there are seawalls, the shoreline position would be held and artificial hard points would develop as promontories for as long as the seawalls remain. At these locations the natural response of the shoreline to move landward would be inhibited, resulting in narrower, steeper beaches. Either side of the seawalls, retreat of the profile would continue resulting in cut-back and erosion on the downdrift side (to the south) but stabilisation on the updrift side (to the north). Over time this would result in large embayments forming between these man-made 'hard points', which would restrict any feed of sediment to the south, with possible impacts being felt as far south as Lowestoft.

Under all four climate change scenarios, these hard points will become increasingly difficult to maintain due to deeper water at the shoreline, and the expense of doing so will be in excess of current expenditure levels.

Box 16.2

Case study 2: Brighton

Coastal characteristics

In contrast to Case study 1, this is a predominately relict sediment system, with few new sources or stores of beach material. The entire length of the coastline is developed and the shoreline is characterised by long, thin shingle barriers that are backed by a heavily modified shoreline, consisting of promenades and seawalls, which front re-graded cliffs. The contemporary longshore transport is from west to east, but at present is limited both by the relatively small volume of sediment available and the defences.

The key control on future evolution of the shoreline is man's intervention and the maintenance of existing defences. The continuous seawalls/revetments along the frontage hold the shoreline position, while other management interventions attempt to hold shingle on the beaches due to the scarcity of contemporary sediment input.

Coastal evolution

Present-day benchmark: the behaviour of this shoreline is heavily controlled by management intervention, which restricts both alongshore sediment transport and coastal retreat. The almost ubiquitous presence of seawalls and revetments prevents tidal inundation of low-lying backshore areas, but also restricts the natural tendency of the shingle barriers to roll back in response to sea-level rise; this prevents material presently being stored within backshore raised beaches from being released to contribute to the foreshore stock and prevents the existing beach from moving back and developing an extended dissipative foreshore width. There has been a relatively low rate of foreshore retreat and beach steepening, with recent local shingle accumulation to the west of Brighton Marina.

Future climate change: the heavily modified nature of this shoreline means that a key control on its future evolution is the man-made defences, as natural evolution of this coastline is prevented. The shoreline will therefore remain at its present plan-form position, for as long as defences remain, but will experience progressive beach steepening with sea-level rise, under all four scenarios, as the beach is prevented from moving landwards and developing an extended dissipative foreshore width. Sea-level rise will result in a deepening of the nearshore water, so that larger waves can break on the shore, which will accelerate erosion and beach draw-down. The defences also prevent material presently being stored within the backshore from being released to contribute to the foreshore stock, thus exacerbating the problem of beach volume; this will have a knock-on impact on life-span of the defences. In the short term (decades), the high-emissions scenario is likely to have the greatest impact on the coastal change, assuming that there is no change in the management practice, but all four climate change scenarios will induce a similar response and, over time, the net impact will be similar, with eventual submergence or loss of the beach. Eventually the backshore slope will be under attack from waves, with an increase in overtopping likely, which will have an impact on the Brighton frontage properties.

Under increased wave attack and frequency of overtopping, the defences will become increasingly difficult and expensive to maintain.

Box 16.3

Case study 3: Tenby, south Pembrokeshire

Coastal characteristics

This is a hard-rock cliffed coastline, which has tourist developments along the cliff-tops. The cliffs are fronted by a rock platform, which is covered by gravel and sand to form pocket beaches.

The hard, rock cliffs are resistant to erosion and are therefore the dominant control on the shoreline position, with the shoreline platform being a governing factor on beach level. There is very little littoral drift along the beaches and the pocket beaches tend to be self-contained microcells. Material supplied by cliff erosion is very small and does not build the beaches. This coastal stretch sits within Carmarthen Bay, which is effectively a closed system, which contains a fairly constant volume of sediment, with neither significant contemporary supply into the Bay or significant losses.

Due to the resistant nature of the cliffs, much of the open-cliffed coastline is undefended, but there are localised defences at the cliff toe.

Coastal evolution

Present-day benchmark: due to their resistant nature, there are very low rates of cliff retreat, although, locally, rock falls can cause faster retreat. The beaches are generally tending towards swash-alignment to the wave fronts diffracted around Caldey Island. The cliffs themselves are a natural constraint on shoreline retreat.

Future climate change: similar to Case study 2, a key control on coastal evolution is the constraint of beach retreat. However, unlike the Brighton frontage, here the constraint is natural and is due to the resistant nature of the backing cliffs.

The natural response of the beach to sea-level rise would be to translate landward, commensurate with the tidal levels, but this is prevented by the cliffs which are more resistant to wave attack and therefore will not retreat at a similar rate. Thus, under all four climate change scenarios, sea-level rise will result in deeper water and great waves attacking the beach, which will cause beach draw-down and loss of the sandy sediment. Beaches will narrow and, under the more severe scenarios (i.e. high and medium-high emissions), could disappear or become submerged. This would result in an increased attack on the cliffs, but with erosion dependent upon their geological composition, recession rates are still likely to be low. Therefore, the net impact of all four scenarios is likely to be similar in the longer term.

The existing defences are unlikely to have a major impact on the coastal evolution. The main settlement of Tenby is situated at the top of the cliffs and is therefore unlikely to be significantly affected, but there would be considerable loss of the recreational beach.

Box 16.4

Case study 4: Bradwell Power Station, Essex

Coastal characteristics

This is an area of low-lying reclaimed land, fronted by large widths of intertidal flats and salt-marshes. Clay embankments used to reclaim the land now protect extensive areas of low-lying land and the power station site from regular tidal inundation. These defences prevent the supply of sediment to reclaimed areas, while vertical accretion of sediment continues on the tidal flats and marshes to seaward. This intervention has resulted in considerable topographic differences either side of flood embankments.

Coastal evolution

Present-day benchmark: despite slow vertical accretion of fine sand and mud, progressive net loss of intertidal area has occurred due to coastal squeeze. Erosion primarily has been along the leading marsh edge, but also has occurred due to widening of creeks within the main body of marsh, attributable in part to sea-level rise working in combination with biological and mineralogical factors.

Future climate change: this type of coastal morphology is very vulnerable to sea-level rise; under natural conditions it could be possible for the landward margin of the saltmarsh to transgress onto the hinterland behind at a rate relative to the rate of sea-level rise. However, the flood embankments will act to prevent this, thus holding the plan-form position but resulting in coastal squeeze and foreshore narrowing. Flood defences will hold the plan-form position of the shoreline, but the foreshore will narrow due to coastal squeeze. There will be a net loss of surface area of the intertidal flats and marshes, resulting in less attenuation of the wave and tidal energy and increasing vulnerability of the defences to damage. Despite a narrowing of the saltmarsh area, it is possible that they could build vertically as sediment mobilised by wave action is washed up into the saltmarsh, but this is unlikely to occur under the high and medium-high scenarios, as the rate of sea-level rise is likely to be too high to allow natural response, resulting in a submergence of the saltmarsh in front of the embankments.

Under each of the four climate change scenarios there could be increased overtopping of the embankments, resulting in more frequent inundation of the low-lying land behind. This frontage is also highly vulnerable to storm surges; this vulnerability would increase with sea-level rise and increased storm frequency or magnitude. This will mean increased expenditure to maintain defences with an increased risk of failure and breach. Any breach would result in large-scale flooding of the low-lying hinterland.

References

Evans, E., Ashley, R., Hall, J., Penning-Rowsell, E., Saul, A., Sayers, P., Thorne, C. and Watkinson, A., 2004. *Foresight, Future Floating, Scientific Summary: Vol. I – Future risks and their drivers and Vol. II – Managing future risks*, Office of Science and Technology, London.

French, P.W., 1997. *Coastal and Estuarine Management*, Routledge, London.

Halcrow, 2002. *Futurecoast*, Defra, London.

Haslett, S.K., 2000. *Coastal Systems*, Routledge Introductions to Environment Series, Routledge, London.

Jay, H., Burgess, K. and Hosking, A., 2003. 'An awareness of geomorphology for coastal defence planning', *Institution of Civil Engineers, International Conference on Coastal Management*, October.

Komar, P.D., 1976. 'Near-shore currents and sediment transport, and the resulting bed configuration', in *Marine Sediment Transport and Environmental Management*, eds, Stanley, D.J. and Swift, D.J.P., New York, Wiley.

SCOPAC, 2001. *Preparing for the Impacts of Climate Change: a strategy for long term planning and management of the shoreline in the contact of climate change predictions*, Final Report, November.

Stive, M.J.F., Aarninkoff, S.J.C., Hamm, L., Hanson, H., Larson, M., Wijnberg, K., Nicholls, R.J. and Capobianco, M., 2002. 'Variability of shore and shoreline evolution', *Coastal Engineering*, 47, 211–235.

17 Assessment of future coastal erosion risk

Kevin Burgess, Helen Jay, Robert J. Nicholls, Colin Green and Edmund C. Penning-Rowsell

Introduction

Erosion has been a characteristic of the UK's coastlines throughout recorded history, especially in the south of the country where sea levels have historically risen. Over the centuries humans have dealt with this by accepting loss and moving away. However, as human occupancy of coastal areas has increased, alongside greater technical ability to resist natural forces, the societal pressures to continue to protect assets have increased. A consequence of this trend is a greater number and value of assets in potential risk areas than ever before; with accelerated climate change increasing such risks further over the next century.

Chapter 16 describes the influences driving coastal change. This chapter expands on the risks from erosion as a consequence of those drivers at work. There is a strong emphasis on England and Wales, reflecting the available data. In Scotland and Northern Ireland, erosion is less of a problem and it has not been studied as extensively. Nonetheless, erosion is likely to increase as a problem in these areas, as in England and Wales.

Rates of change

Present shoreline changes

Ordnance Survey maps of the coast extend back to the mid-nineteenth century. These enable changes in shoreline position and different coastal features to be determined and provide an understanding of contemporary evolution.

Work undertaken as part of the Futurecoast study (Halcrow, 2002) analysed 1:10 000 scale maps establishing retreat rates at over 1000 locations around England and Wales. A review of this analysis is presented in Fig. 17.1 and Table 17.1; the rates presented relate to the most landward geomorphic feature in each case; either the top of cliff or the back of beach.

The rates presented include the influence of coastal defences; where defences have been built, only the post-defence rates are used. Defended locations represent just over 450 of the locations, of which approximately half fall within the band of

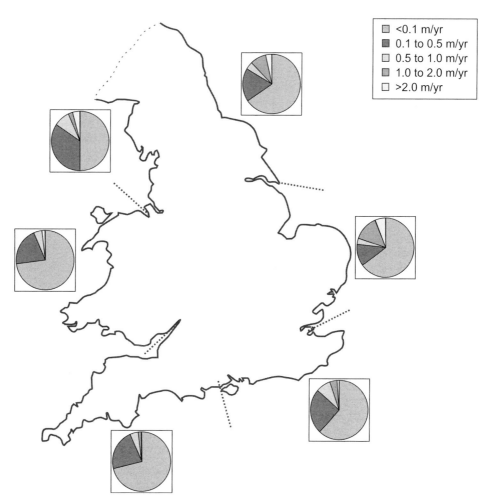

Fig. 17.1. Regional difference in average rates of shoreline movement in England and Wales (data from Table 17.1)

'little change', therefore the other half, where there is some form of defence management, have post-defence rates of change in excess of 0.1 m/yr (some erosion, some accretion).

The largest erosion rates, i.e. greater than 1 m/yr, are seen along the east coast of England, affecting nearly one-fifth of the locations. By comparison, less than one in 20 locations in the other regions have such high rates. This is particularly noticeable in south-west England and Wales, which reflects the nature of the broad geological differences between regions.

These results do necessarily involve some broad-based assumptions in making general conclusions at a national scale, and one should avoid having too narrow a perspective on coastal change and assuming that general conclusions will apply universally. Futurecoast identified that all coastal areas are complex in their response, depending upon the combination of natural features, man-made features, forcing conditions and the state of evolution of that particular system.

Furthermore, while erosion rates are frequently presented as an annual rate, as they are here, it should also be recognised that coastal change is not always a linear or regular process. These annual rates are the average over a long period of time and they may often result from periodic events rather than be a continuous process. For example, in parts of north Norfolk, a section of cliff top may suffer a 40 m failure in a single event, but only once every 40 years.

Table 17.1. Present average rates of shoreline movement for England and Wales (values are number of individual locations where shoreline position has been measured) (Halcrow 2002)

Location	Little change (movement less than ±0.1 m/yr)	Erosion				Accretion (greater than 0.1 m/yr)
		0.1 m to 0.5 m/yr	0.5 m to 1.0 m/yr	1.0 m to 2.0 m/yr	Greater than 2.0 m/yr	
St Abb's Head to Flamborough Head	88	20	1	4	1	8
Flamborough Head to Humber estuary	6	6	4	9	4	0
Humber estuary to Weybourne	15	1	0	2	1	6
Weybourne to Felixstowe	39	9	4	10	3	4
Harwich to Thames estuary	23	4	0	4	3	1
Thames estuary to North Foreland	22	0	4	4	1	0
North Foreland to Beachy Head	24	8	2	0	0	21
Beachy Head to Selsey Bill	16	5	3	0	1	4
Selsey Bill to Hurst Spit, inc. IOW	27	22	3	2	0	5
Hurst Spit to Durlston Head	8	7	2	0	1	4
Durlston Head to Start Point	31	10	3	0	0	28
Start Point to Lizard Point	48	14	0	0	0	6
Lizard Point to Penlee Point	13	2	1	1	0	0
Isles of Scilly	12	5	1	0	0	0
Penlee Point to Hartland Point	44	16	4	1	0	5
Hartland Point to Morte Point	8	2	0	2	0	1
Morte Point to Brean Down	22	3	1	0	0	2
Brean Down to Severn Bridge	5	2	0	0	0	2
Severn Bridge to Penarth	4	0	0	0	0	2
Penarth to Worms Head	23	2	1	0	0	2
Carmarthen Bay	6	1	1	0	0	5
Giltar Point to St David's Head	18	1	1	0	0	3
St David's Head to Bardsey Sound	31	15	4	0	1	7
Bardsey Sound to Great Orme's Head	30	10	1	0	0	11
Great Orme's Head to Welsh border	2	2	1	0	1	3
Welsh border to Fylde	10	2	2	1	1	3
Morecambe Bay	0	2	0	0	0	4
Walney Island to Solway Firth	12	11	2	0	1	18
Totals	587	182	46	40	19	155
Percentage	57	18	4	4	2	15

The present baseline case for coastal erosion

Futurecoast assessed the expected future changes to present erosion patterns as a result of continuing to maintain present defences and management practices. This categorised lengths of shoreline where 'no change' would be expected (defended), or change would be either 'less than', 'similar to', or 'greater than' present rates of change. Details for different coastal behaviour systems are provided in Table 17.2. However, these estimates were made based solely upon natural variability in climatic conditions and did not, therefore, include any quantification of the four future climate change scenarios. Nonetheless, this remains the only piece of work available that has made such a comprehensive assessment of future erosion with defences and as such is a useful indicator of impacts.

A constraint on direct application of this information, however, is that under a scenario of maintaining present defence expenditure, the National Appraisal of Assets from Risk from Flooding and Coastal Erosion (Defra, 2000, 2001) concludes that approximately one-third of present defences could not be replaced. If investment remains at or around present investment levels, then the results imply that effective

Table 17.2. Potential future changes in present rates of shoreline movement in England and Wales as a result of maintaining present defence practices (values are kilometres of shoreline for which estimates have been made)

Location	No change (defended)	Rate of change		
		Less than present	Similar to present	Greater than present
St Abb's Head to Flamborough Head	38	0	252	24
Flamborough Head to Humber estuary	10	0	59	5
Humber estuary to Weybourne	113	46	62	12
Weybourne to Felixstowe	48	3	87	9
Harwich to Thames estuary	107	0	0	0
Thames estuary to North Foreland	66	0	4	0
North Foreland to Beachy Head	93	9	27	12
Beachy Head to Selsey Bill	66	0	14	0
Selsey Bill to Hurst Spit, inc. IOW	63	0	21	79
Hurst Spit to Durlston	34	2	8	3
Durlston Head to Start Point	36	0	178	0
Start Point to Lizard Point	5	0	187	2
Lizard Point to Penlee Point	11	0	33	0
Isles of Scilly	0	0	29	0
Penlee Point to Hartland Point	2	0	212	0
Hartland Point to Morte Point	0	0	48	0
Morte Point to Brean Down	24	0	89	0
Brean Down to Severn Bridge	28	0	25	0
Severn Bridge to Penarth	44	0	1	0
Penarth to Worms Head	31	0	93	0
Carmarthen Bay	7	0	38	28
Giltar Point to St David's Head	4	0	105	0
St David's Head to Bardsey Sound	30	0	218	19
Bardsey Sound to Great Orme's Head	64	0	166	41
Great Orme's Head to Welsh border	56	5	36	7
Welsh border to Fylde	43	50	26	0
Morecambe Bay	63	0	50	6
Walney Island to Solway Firth	38	9	70	32
Totals: km	1124	124	2138	279
Percentage	31	3	58	8

protection can only be provided to selected areas of the country, i.e. a conscious decision might be taken to abandon defences to some less populous areas. This would increase erosion rates, with approximately 10% of areas presently categorised by Futurecoast as expecting 'no change' becoming 'greater than present rates of change'.

The manner in which expenditure would actually be regionally distributed in the future is unknown. However, if it is assumed that the loss of defence would be applied equally to all regions, as summarised in Table 17.3, and, considered in conjunction with the information presented in Table 17.1, a baseline case is produced, against which future scenarios can be compared. This corresponds to the baseline case referred to elsewhere in the book, for present climatic conditions.

Table 17.3 illustrates some particularly interesting regional variations. Those shorelines that are presently most heavily defended, i.e. the east, south-east and north-west of England, are also those that are likely to be subject to rates of change exceeding that previously experienced. This partially reflects the geological differences that exist between the regions, but is largely indicative of the influence of defences and the impacts of maintaining present expenditure levels rather than continuing to provide

Table 17.3. Potential changes in present rates of shoreline movement in England and Wales as a result of maintaining present defence expenditure levels (present baseline)

Location	No change*: %	Rate of change		
		Less than present: %	Similar to present: %	Greater than present: %
North-east England	8	0	80	12
East England	36	10	31	23
South-east England	42	2	14	42
South-west England	10	<1	85	5
Wales	16	<1	66	17
North-west England	25	15	38	22

* This applies to defended coasts, where defences are likely to remain.

existing defence to have the present level of protection. This impact is most noticeable in the east and south-east regions (compare with Table 17.2).

Response to climate change

Simple expressions, e.g. Bruun (1962), are available to assess the influence of sea-level change upon the rate of shoreline erosion. Variations on this have been developed over the years but they all adopt the same basic principles, and all have similar limitations. These expressions provide a relationship between existing erosion rates, a description of the shoreline profile (distance and elevation of the seaward slope) and the relative difference between present and future estimates of relative sea level.

While the rates of erosion and coastal profile do vary considerably around the UK, making the quantified prediction of the actual increase in erosion a site-specific assessment, a relative measure of influence can be obtained simply from comparison of future and existing rates of relative sea-level change. Using modifications on the Bruun Rule (see equation 17.1) to assess the change in erosion rates resulting from these predicted changes in sea-level rise (SLR), the conclusions in Table 17.4 can be drawn regarding the relative influence of the four different UKCIP climate scenarios.

$$R_2 = R_1 + (S_2 - S_1)\frac{L}{h} \quad (17.1)$$

where: R_1 is historical recession, R_2 is future recession, S_1 is historical sea-level rise, S_2 is future sea-level rise, L is the length of the active profile and h is the closure depth.

Table 17.4. Relative differences in natural erosion rate increases between the four UKCIP climate change scenarios

UKCIP02 (SRES)			
Low emissions	Medium-low emissions	Medium-high emissions	High emissions
Present erosion rates would increase, as SLR predicted exceeds present rates, by an amount dependent upon the site-specific characteristics of the coastal profile	The increase in erosion rates would be approximately 20–35% greater than estimated for the low-emissions scenario	The increase in erosion rates would be approximately 40–65% greater than estimated for the low-emissions scenario	The increase in erosion rates would be approximately 70–120% greater than estimated for the low-emissions scenario

Table 17.5. Potential increase in shoreline erosion rates for England and Wales in response to rising sea levels (values are average erosion rates)

Location	Present (baseline) m/year	Low emissions (global sustainability) m/year	Medium-low emissions (local stewardship) m/year	Medium-high emissions (national enterprise) m/year	High emissions (world markets) m/year
St Abb's Head to Flamborough Head	0.13–0.28	0.30–0.46	0.37–0.52	0.42–0.58	0.53–0.69
Flamborough Head to Humber estuary	1.04–2.19	2.02–3.17	2.38–3.53	2.69–3.84	3.29–4.44
Humber estuary to Weybourne	0.25–2.00	2.17–3.92	2.69–4.43	3.12–4.86	3.98–5.72
Weybourne to Felixstowe	0.43–0.69	1.36–1.62	1.61–1.87	1.81–2.08	2.23–2.49
Harwich to Thames estuary	0.46–2.02	2.40–3.95	2.92–4.47	3.35–4.90	4.22–5.77
Thames estuary to North Foreland	0.39–1.74	0.72–2.07	0.82–2.18	0.91–2.27	1.09–2.45
North Foreland to Beachy Head	0.07–0.72	0.61–1.26	0.78–1.43	0.93–1.58	1.22–1.87
Beachy Head to Selsey Bill	0.23–0.82	0.77–1.36	0.94–1.53	1.09–1.68	1.38–1.97
Selsey Bill to Hurst Spit, inc. IOW	0.20–1.38	0.74–1.92	0.91–2.09	1.06–2.24	1.35–2.53
Hurst Spit to Durlston	0.30–0.93	0.70–1.34	0.83–1.47	0.94–1.58	1.16–1.79
Durlston Head to Start Point	0.07–0.38	0.32–0.63	0.37–0.68	0.41–0.72	0.50–0.81
Start Point to Lizard Point	0.03–0.06	0.21–0.24	0.24–0.28	0.28–0.31	0.34–0.37
Lizard Point to Penlee Point	0.17–0.53	0.35–0.71	0.39–0.75	0.42–0.78	0.48–0.84
Penlee Point to Hartland Point	0.03–0.13	0.21–0.31	0.24–0.35	0.28–0.38	0.34–0.44
Hartland Point to Morte Point	0.18–0.28	0.67–0.76	0.77–0.86	0.85–0.95	1.02–1.11
Morte Point to Brean Down	0.06–0.26	0.54–0.74	0.64–0.84	0.73–0.93	0.89–1.09
Brean Down to Severn Bridge	0.07–1.76	1.52–3.21	1.82–3.51	2.07–3.76	2.57–4.26
Severn Bridge to Penarth	0.00–2.90	1.29–4.19	1.59–4.49	1.84–4.74	2.34–5.24
Penarth to Worms Head	0.05–0.16	0.71–0.82	0.86–0.97	0.99–1.10	1.24–1.36
Carmarthen Bay	0.08–0.85	0.74–1.50	0.89–1.66	1.02–1.79	1.28–2.04
Giltar Point to St David's Head	0.02–0.05	0.16–0.19	0.19–0.22	0.22–0.25	0.28–0.31
St David's Head to Bardsey Sound	0.18–0.19	1.11–1.12	1.32–1.33	1.50–1.51	1.86–1.87
Bardsey Sound to Great Orme's Head	0.07–0.34	0.50–0.76	0.60–0.86	0.68–0.94	0.84–1.11
Great Orme's Head to Welsh border	0.48–0.67	1.59–1.78	1.84–2.03	2.06–2.25	2.49–2.67
Welsh border to Fylde	0.35–0.52	1.11–1.28	1.37–1.54	1.58–1.75	2.01–2.18
Morecambe Bay	0.10–0.52	0.87–1.29	1.12–1.54	1.34–1.76	1.76–2.18
Walney Island to Solway Firth	0.18–0.57	0.47–0.87	0.57–0.97	0.66–1.05	0.82–1.22
National (England and Wales)	0.20–0.67	0.82–1.23	0.99–1.38	1.13–1.50	1.41–1.75

This means that at a site where erosion is presently 1 m/yr, if an increase to 1.2 m/yr were calculated under the low-emissions scenario, the increase in erosion for the other three scenarios would be 1.4 to 1.6 m/yr under medium low, 1.7 to 1.9 m/yr under medium high, and 2.0 to 2.6 m/yr under the high emissions scenario.

However, these are broad estimates of *potential* change, which do not take into account local variability, such as the present erosion rate or coastal profile. Therefore, *actual* change, which is location specific, may differ dramatically, with both parameters being variable by an order of magnitude or more.

Although the calculation of erosion rates is dependent upon the specific characteristics of a site, an analysis of regional response to climate change provides some indication of differences in erosion potential around the country. Table 17.5 provides typical changes in the average erosion rate for the various coastal behaviour systems identified by Futurecoast; this sub-division of the coast being adopted for presentation to illustrate the variations that occur within regions. This is also illustrated in Fig. 17.2.

The ranges presented reflect the fact that maintaining present expenditure levels, i.e. the baseline assumption, will produce a reduction in the level or extent of

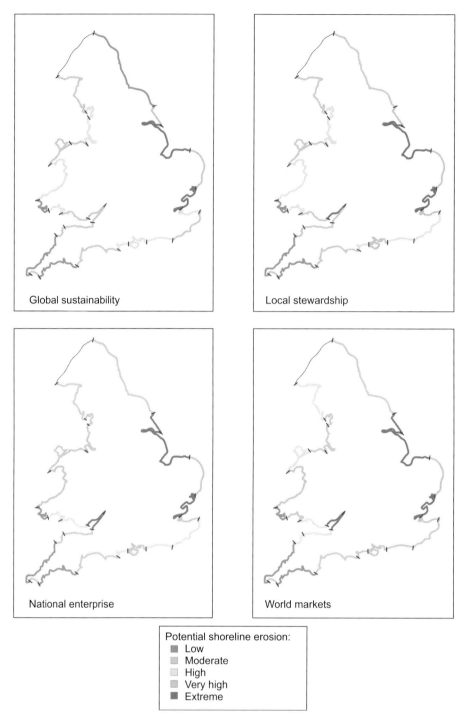

Fig. 17.2. Regional differences in potential shoreline erosion in England and Wales under the four Foresight scenarios

defence provided to the nation rather than simply adopting present erosion rates as the baseline measure of change taking place.

At an England and Wales level, it can be concluded that for all of the four future climate change predictions, a significant increase in the average erosion rates might be expected, with roughly a 0.5 m/yr variation across all four scenarios.

These figures have been calculated for general guidance on relative differences and have to be regarded as indicative only. They are not site-specific and have been derived using the characteristics of only a few typical coastal slopes within each area. Although the differences between the four foresight scenarios will alter the shoreline response at the local scale, it may be concluded that the variations between them is likely to be insufficient to result in a radically different, large-scale coastal response.

Readers can draw their own conclusions from the information presented in Table 17.5 for each coastal behaviour system, although they should note that in addition to the previously described limitations, it is generally believed that the Bruun Rule and other similar 'constant depth profile models' probably over-estimate future erosion. This is because they do not take account of variations in sediment budget, geology or other constraints (e.g. defences), which could limit or even prevent any erosion whatsoever (e.g. Dickson *et al.*, 2005).

It should also be noted that the erosion rates quoted here are those that would be experienced in the future, and there would be an acceleration between the present-day rates and these predictions, following the same trend lines presented for changing sea levels over the next century.

Coastal defence

Associated with increased movement of the shoreline will be greater vulnerability for the coastal defences providing protection against this erosion. Responding to climate change with coastal defences is likely to require a much more significant investment in the future. By the year 2080, the structural improvements needed to maintain defences at their present standards will cost between 1.5 and 4.0 times that of today, depending upon the climate change scenario (Burgess and Townend, 2004).

The effectiveness of defences will be reduced with changes in climatic conditions having an influence upon their integrity and performance, and thus future erosion potential (Burgess and Townend, 2004). This will occur for a variety of reasons, which apply to *all* four of the climate change scenarios:

1. Higher water levels (as a result of sea-level rise) will increase the frequency with which defences are overtopped by waves. The overtopping of defences by waves is clearly important with regard to flood risk, but is also important to all coastal structures as it can increase the erosion of the protected area and indeed lead to failure of the defence itself.
2. An increase in surge heights would produce extreme water levels of even greater elevation, and thus greater water depths at the defence, increasing the magnitude of overtopping under storms and exacerbating the problems stated in point 1 above.
3. Greater water depths, as a result of the factors described in points 1 and 2, will also increase exposure of the defence to larger waves. This will further increase the problems described in point 1, and produce increased forces on structures that reduce their stability and increase their risk of failure.
4. As a result of larger waves (point 3), there is likely to be greater reflection from defence structures and increased scour of the beach, which increases potential for undermining failure of the defence.
5. There will be less potential for beach stability as a result of point 4, plus ongoing coastal 'squeeze', i.e. a landward retreat of the low-water position in response to sea-level rise but the high-water position being constrained. This foreshore steepening will further increase the vulnerability of defences to overtopping and structural failure through the processes described in the above points.

These same points were identified by Townend (1994), which concludes: 'Significant differences between the various parameters studied, leads to the conclusion *that the impact on sea defences will depend upon the particular site conditions*. As such no broad generalisations can be made as to the impact of sea-level rise on sea defence performance'. Townend (1994) also notes: 'If the beach is able to adjust in the manner proposed by Bruun, then the incident wave properties will not be altered. However, where a seawall impedes the landward retreat, this constraint will give rise to an additional setback of the profile', i.e. beach levels in front of a defence will reduce below that which would naturally occur. This means that the position of the defence within the cross-shore zone is also critical to beach response.

A more recent study conducted for Defra by HR Wallingford (2002) further substantiates some of these points. This assessed possible changes in coastal defence vulnerability (to overtopping and erosion) caused by global climate change over the next 75 years, which concluded that:

- There will be considerable increases in the overtopping of defences, caused mainly by sea-level rise rather than changes in other parameters. Based upon an estimate of 0.35 m sea-level rise, overtopping rates could increase by between 50 and 150%.
- If presently observed coastal steepening were to continue, this would serve to increase overtopping rates by an additional 10%.
- Scour of the foreshore in front of seawalls (reported by CIRIA (1986) as the most frequent reason for the failure of such defences) could increase by 16%.

Consequently, it is not possible to provide generic or even regional analysis of how coastal defences will respond to the four scenarios, other than to conclude that problems in maintaining defences against coastal erosion will occur with all of them. However, with each scenario increase in relative sea level, the vulnerability of defences will increase in magnitude, with a greater number of defence failures and reduced standards of protection as a result, leading to further erosion of many areas that are presently protected.

These points all raise an issue with regard to the expenditure required to provide protection in the future. The National Appraisal of Assets from Risk from Flooding and Coastal Erosion (Defra, 2000, 2001) conclude that the investment needed to maintain present standards of coastal defence is approximately £113 million per annum for England alone (£77 million coast protection plus £36 million sea defence – see Table 17.6, appended, for regional division).

Table 17.6. Estimated investment (£ million) needed to maintain present standards of coastal erosion defence for England and Wales (from The National Appraisal of Assets from Risk from Flooding and Coastal Erosion (Defra, 2000, 2001)

	North-east	East Anglia	South	South-west	Wales	North-west	Total
Coast protection: £m							
Replacement	6.67	7.29	24.98	9.22	Figures	7.65	55.82
Maintenance	2.53	2.77	9.49	3.50	not	2.91	21.21
Total CP	9.20	10.06	34.47	12.72	available	10.56	77.03
Sea defence: £m							
Replacement	0.68	7.32	8.61	8.71	Figures	0.61	25.93
Maintenance	0.26	2.78	3.27	3.31	not	0.23	9.85
Total SD	0.94	10.10	11.88	12.02	available	0.84	35.78
Total	10.14	20.16	46.35	24.74	N/A	11.40	112.81

Note: coast protection is the definition for defending against coastal erosion whereas sea defence protects against coastal flooding.

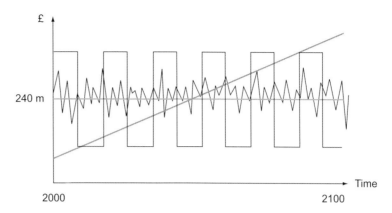

Fig. 17.3. Variation in expenditure profiles that could exist in order to provide coastal protection in the future

This forms part of a requirement for all flood and coastal defence (i.e. including rivers and estuaries) of £361 million per annum to maintain present standards of defence, which compares with the *actual* expenditure (at 2000) of £240 million per annum. Therefore, overall it was estimated that a total increase in expenditure of roughly 50% would be required to maintain present defences. From this it may be concluded that maintaining *present expenditure levels* means that approximately one-third of existing coastal defences could not be maintained, at least not to present standards, unless budgets increase.

A point to note regarding future defence costs is that this expenditure will not be linear and there will be peaks and troughs in expenditure needs. Figure 17.3 gives examples of the various expenditure profiles that could be required. Within the National Appraisal of Assets study, future costs were calculated on the basis that all defences would need to be replaced once every 60 years. Given the variability in the age and residual life of defences, it was assumed that the total costs could be spread evenly over the period. However, the actual expenditure profile is likely to be more erratic than remaining at a constant level or indeed at a constant growth.

Economic expenditure on flood and coastal defence in past decades has often tended to be crisis-driven rather than through damage limitation planning, as a result of significant events, e.g. the 1953 surge on the coast or 1998 and 2000 floods on rivers. As such it might be anticipated that a 'block' profile could result, although much better defence planning, driven by Defra, is now taking place through the development of shoreline management plans and strategy plans, so a tendency of smoothing towards a linear profile might be expected in the future, albeit with some decadal fluctuations. Notwithstanding this potential variability, without an *increase* in the average expenditure, there will be a continual decrease in the effectiveness of defences provided to protect against flooding and coastal erosion and thus a growing risk of loss or damage to those assets currently protected.

The economic impacts of coastal erosion

Table 17.5 indicates that nowhere in England and Wales is unconstrained coastal erosion likely to exceed 5.7 m per year (or 570 m per century) under any of the four future climate change scenarios, and will generally be significantly less than this. Hence, the *economic* impact of this erosion is therefore likely to be a small issue, except perhaps locally, when judged in relation to the national economy or the scale of flood impacts both today and in the future under all four future climate change scenarios.

This is looked at in more detail in three ways:

1. Define the combination of erosion rates and land values that are needed to obtain significant impacts, viewed nationally and over decades.
2. Estimate the increase in the annual average damage from erosion under the future climate change scenarios.
3. Investigate whether serious erosional 'hotspots' exist which are masked by the overall averages.

These are discussed in following sections.

Erosion rates and land values

On the average figures for erosion derived in this Foresight analysis, the economic impacts of coastal erosion are only likely to be significant generally where fixed property values at risk are at least £500 000/h (Fig. 17.4). This would be represented as approximately four houses per hectare at national average values.

So, for example, if the average rate of erosion is 6 m a year (above the maximum of 570 m per century given above) and the fixed property value is £100 000 per hectare, the *capitalised* value of the erosion impacts is £1440 per linear metre or £1.44 million per km. When the assets at risk are worth £500 000, the equivalent figure is £7.2 million per km. These can be regarded as small sums in relation to coastal flooding. That said, within each of the coastal behavioural systems presented in Table 16.5, there would be some areas where erosion could be significant in terms of its impacts. In areas where large landfalls can occur in a single year, or where there are dynamic geomorphological structures that could change drastically, 'overnight' impacts could again be economically significant. Examples include Ventnor on the Isle of Wight (IoW) and breaching of barrier beaches, such as Chesil Bank, although locations where this could produce significant damages in the UK are quite limited.

Erosion impacts with the different climate change scenarios

The increased rates of erosion summarised in Table 17.5 would be expected to lead to increased annual average damages. These will also be influenced by changes in

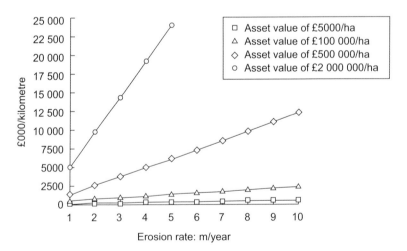

Fig. 17.4. The economic impact of coastal erosion for different asset values, assessed as the annual investment per kilometre of coastline that it is worth spending on to delay the likely impacts

Table 17.7. Average annual damages estimates (for England only) derived from Halcrow et al. (2000) under the four Foresight Futures for the 2080s (£ millions per annum)

	Today	Low emissions	Medium-low emissions	Medium-high emissions	High emissions
North-east	2.6	6	7	10	13
Anglian	1.2	4	5	9	13
Southern	6.4	17	18	36	53
South-west	3.2	15	16	27	38
North-west	1.0	4	4	6	8
Total (England only)	14.4	46	51	87	126

exposure and a reduced length of defended coast under the baseline assumption of maintaining present coast protection and sea defence expenditure. However, only a strip of coast tens to hundreds of metres wide will be impacted over the next century, so relatively precise information on assets at risk is required to make these calculations (e.g. Koukoulas *et al.*, 2005).

However, a surrogate estimate can be made for England using the average annual damages for coastal erosion estimated by Halcrow *et al.* (2000). These values can be adjusted linearly to match the increase in erosion rates given in Table 17.5, and the increase in undefended length. This is presented in Table 17.7 showing that national damages increase three to nine times the present values. Differences in the amount of sea-level rise and the amount of exposed property both influence the magnitude of losses under the four futures. Southern England stands out as the region with the largest potential economic losses (as in today's estimates). However, while these losses appear to be quite large, even under high emissions they are only about half of the losses estimated for tidal flooding at the coast today by Halcrow *et al.* (2000).

'Hotspots': coincidences of high erosion rates and valuable assets at risk

The value of assets at risk at the coast is estimated at just £7 billion (Halcrow *et al.*, 2000). UK GDP in 2001 was £994 billion and investment in fixed capital in that year was £162 billion. Therefore, £7 billion is a comparatively small sum in national terms and averaging that loss over 50 years gives a figure that is insignificant in relation to the error margin in calculating the GDP.

Furthermore, a large part of the erosion-threatened infrastructure, such as ports, gas and oil terminals, piers, and other coastal assets, might not be there in 50 years time if the drive to cut greenhouse gas emissions continues. North Sea oil and gas may, in any case, be nearly exhausted by then but cuts may mean a major shift away from fossil fuels which will eliminate the need for a large part of port capacity and the oil and gas terminals and refineries. Therefore, these infrastructure elements, in the baseline case, will probably not be there in 2050, in which case erosion here may be a somewhat different consideration.

Under the local stewardship scenario, rising agricultural land values could make erosion more important. However, land values would have to rise massively before the economic impact of the loss by erosion of agricultural land became anything other than trivial in relation to total national agricultural output and the national economy.

The major fixed points that will remain at the coast to 2080 are the nuclear power stations. There are several in the coastal zones where erosion rates are moderate to high, for example Sizewell and Dungeness ('very high' under a high-emissions scenario), Hinkley Point ('high' under high emissions), and Bradwell ('extreme' under high emissions).

Detailed cartographic analysis and photographic evidence for these cases indicates, however, that the following situations generally apply for the period of the Foresight timescales:

- *either* there is at least 570 m of land between the high-water mark and the major assets associated with that power station;
- *or* that there are substantial hard defences locally that would be maintained to provide protection for several decades;
- *or* that continued management of the soft coast is capable of providing protection, e.g. shingle recycling.

This analysis therefore suggests that, with some local exceptions, the chances of the predicted rates of erosion up to 2080 having any significant threat to these power stations is minimal; they certainly do not present a major 'unknown'. Indeed, it has always been known that some of these power stations were being built on eroding coasts, and this was considered in their design. The conclusion, therefore, is that there are no major problems expected from an England and Wales perspective due to coastal erosion. While Scotland and Northern Ireland are not considered, erosion is less important than England and Wales, and hence this can be considered a national conclusion. However, locally there may be important issues to address. For example, at Dungeness the costs of sustaining shingle recycling could grow substantially under the Foresight scenarios, while at Bradwell erosion rates may be high enough to be problematic.

Other hotspots are possible, but at a national scale they are likely to average out to the regional values shown previously. Indirect effects, such as the consequence of beach degradation on tourist values, may have impacts but, again, they are likely to be local effects given the relatively low importance of beach-based tourism to the UK economy.

The overall conclusion that has emerged here is that, at a national scale, losses due to coastal erosion on cliffed coasts are not the major concern in comparison to flood risks. It must be remembered that land loss due to erosion is only one aspect of coastal change and erosion will also have a direct influence upon flood risk in coastal lowlands (Hall *et al.*, 2005). When linking to flooding, erosion remains an important issue that will require significant investigation and response over the twenty-first century.

References

Bruun, P., 1962. 'Sea level rise as a cause of shore erosion', *Journal of the Waterways and Harbours Division, Proceedings of the American Society of Civil Engineers*.

Burgess, K.A. and Townend, I.H., 2004. The impact of climate change upon UK coastal defence structures, 39th Defra Conference of River and Coastal Engineers, Defra, London.

CIRIA, 1986. *Sea Walls: Survey of performance and design practice*, Technical Note 125.

Defra, 2000. *National Appraisal of Assets at Risk from Flooding and Coastal Erosion*, Final Report May.

Defra, 2001. *National Appraisal of Assets at Risk from Flooding and Coastal Erosion, Including the Potential Impact of Climate Change*, Final Report July.

Dickson, M.E., Walkden, M.J.A., Hall, J.W., Pearson, S. and Rees, J., 2005. 'Numerical modeling of potential climate change impacts on rates of soft cliff recession, northeast Norfolk, UK', *Proceedings of Coastal Dynamics 2005*, ASCE, New York.

Halcrow, HR Wallingford and Flood Hazard Research Centre, 2000. *National Appraisal of Assets at Risk from Flooding and Coastal Erosion*, Report to MAFF, Defra, London.

Halcrow, 2002. *Futurecoast*, Defra, London.

Hall, J., Dawson, R.J., Walkden, M., Dickson, M., Stansby, P., Zhou, J., Nicholls, R., Brown, I. and Watkinson, A., 2005. 'Broad-scale analysis of morphological and climate impacts on coastal flood risk', *Proceedings of Coastal Dynamics 2005*, ASCE, New York.

HR Wallingford, 2002. *Coastal Defence Vulnerability 2075*, Report SR590, Defra.

Koukoulas, S., Nicholls, R.J., Dickson, M.E., Walkden, M.J.A., Hall, J.W., Pearson, S.G., Mokrech, M. and Richards, J., 2005. 'A GIS tool for analysis and interpretation of coastal erosion model outputs (SCAPEGIS)', *Proceedings of Coastal Dynamics 2005*, ASCE, New York.

Townend, I.H., 1994. 'Variation in design conditions in response to sea-level rise', *Proceedings of the Institution of Civil Engineers, Water, Maritime and Energy 106*, 205–213.

Part 5
Responses to future flood and coastal erosion risks

18 Managing the rural landscape

Stuart N. Lane, Joe Morris, P. Edna O'Connell and Paul F. Quinn

Introduction

Rural land-use management needs to be approached with careful thought as, when compared with other flood risk management measures, its flood risk benefits have yet to be proven as a generic tool for flood risk reduction. Many (but not all) of the measures we discuss below rest upon hypotheses that either: (1) have yet to be tested; or (2) can only be tested meaningfully in relation to specific event magnitudes/frequencies and/or specific geographical locations; or (3) have only been tested and accepted for small catchments (e.g. Boardman, 2003). The difficulties of testing these hypotheses for larger catchments arise primarily because these rural land management measures are 'upstream', and their effects are conditioned by processes that intervene between where they are adopted and their downstream flood risk impacts. We discuss this issue at length at the end of the chapter, but we must emphasise that this uncertainty is both methodological (i.e. it may be addressed through progress in our capacity to scale up land management measures to the catchment scale) and also substantive (i.e. even if a measure can be demonstrated to have a particular benefit for a particular event at a particular location, that benefit may not be realised for all storms at all locations). Indeed, understanding the effects of rural land management is difficult because land management activities that impact upon the flood system are commonly (Lane *et al.*, 2003):

1. diffuse (i.e. low magnitude but spatially distributed, gaining potential severity only when integrated through to the catchment scale);
2. spatially structured (i.e. land management practices vary within (sub-farm scale) and between land (farm) management units;
3. temporally complex (e.g. a change in stocking density within a land management unit over an annual timescale will hide complex patterns of husbandry at the within timescale);
4. context dependent (i.e. dependent upon the soils, geology, relief and climate of the catchment within which they occur); and
5. occurring both above ground and below ground.

Within the broad category of 'rural land management' different functional groups, and subsets of these groups, map onto these properties in different ways. Here, we gather these response measures into three functional groups that might be hypothesised as reducing downstream flood risk: (1) changing the *partitioning* of

Table 18.1. Possible rural land management responses

Response group	Specific measure
Water retention through management of infiltration into the catchment	Arable land-use practices Livestock management Tillage practices Field drainage (to increase storage) Buffer strips and buffering zones Afforestation
Water retention through catchment-storage schemes	Ponds, bunds and ditches Wetlands and washlands (i.e. large-scale floodplain storage) Impoundments
Managing conveyance	Management of hillslope connectivity Channel maintenance Channel realignment

precipitation between overland (fast) and subsurface (slow) flow, under the hypothesis that land management that reduces the generation of fast flow will lead to less downstream flood risk; (2) increasing the *storage* of runoff within the catchment, under the hypothesis that retention of water will lead to reduced downstream flood risk; and (3) reducing the *speed of conveyance* of runoff within the drainage and channel network, under the hypothesis that slower conveyance will lead to greater flow attenuation and hence reduced downstream flood risk. Within these three broad functional groups, Table 18.1 shows the complete list of response measures in this theme. The emphasis here is upon river catchments and does not extend to rural land management at the coast. However, many of the issues associated with rural land management are also relevant to coastal flood defence (e.g. the availability of set-aside land as a solution to coastal zone protection), and these are dealt with in Chapter 20. In an extended conclusion, we draw together some fundamental generic issues that must be considered prior to advocating rural land management as a flood risk response.

Management of infiltration

Overview
Flood risk reduction through the management of infiltration is based upon two hypotheses: (1) that agricultural practices change the partitioning of rainfall between fast routes (e.g. overland flow) and slow routes (e.g. throughflow) to the channel network; and (2) that changing this partitioning can have an impact upon downstream flood risk. Subject to acceptance of these two hypotheses, the aim of measures in this functional group is to increase floodwave attenuation and so produce lower flood peaks by retaining water in the catchment for longer periods. Essentially, this would mean adoption of land-use practices that reduce the generation of rapid overland flow. Assessing the impact of the specific measures detailed under this functional group requires careful attention to be given to three issues. First, water that does not become rapid *surface* runoff may become rapid *subsurface* runoff, notably in well-structured or well-drained soils, requiring careful consideration of the nature of the soil being managed. Second, infiltrated water can itself have a bearing upon the generation of future rapid runoff. While retaining such water within the landscape may increase the probability in the long term that this is lost through evapotranspiration or through baseflow, in the short term it will reduce soil moisture deficits, so

increasing the ease with which rapid runoff may be generated in future rainfall events. Again, the nature of this response will depend upon soil type, drainage and local topography, as well as the sequencing and magnitude of previous rainfall events. Third, the location of the measures within the specific catchment within which they are adopted in relation to the timing of runoff delivery may determine downstream flood impacts. For instance, adopting measures that reduce overland flow generation in downstream parts of catchments may actually reduce attenuation, by causing those parts of the catchment to deliver water to the river system later, possibly at the same time as water delivered from upstream. Similarly, the effects of a measure may depend upon antecedent conditions, including the sequencing of rainfall events. Thus, all of these measures need to be considered in terms of how they upscale to impact upon downstream flood risk locations. There are six specific rural land management measures that could be considered as means of reducing flood risk: (1) changes in arable land-use practices; (2) changes in livestock management; (3) changes in tillage; (4) field drainage to increase storage; (5) use of buffer strips and buffering zones; and (6) afforestation.

Arable land-use practices

The hypothesis here is that flood mitigation can be achieved by adopting land-use types and land-use practices within those land-use types that might lead to increased runoff generation activity. This might include altering tillage regimes (type and timing), adopting spring cropping (versus winter cropping) and use of cover crops. Extensification, set-aside and arable reversion to grassland can lower farming intensity and this may increase infiltration rates and hence delay and reduce the delivery of fast flow to the drainage network. The local scale impacts of these activities are supported by plot-scale experiments: for instance, sizeable reductions (30 to 100%) in runoff have been reported when ploughing is under-taken in spring and autumn instead of winter (e.g. Kwaad and Mulligen, 1991). The main problem is that we have little evidence of how these impacts scale up to downstream locations, how they vary between rainfall events with different return periods, how they are impacted upon by antecedent conditions (e.g. catchment wetness) and their dependence upon local characteristics such as soil type and position within the drainage network.

If they can be demonstrated to reduce downstream flood risk, delivery of these responses will require changes in on-farm management practices. Both extensification and set aside may deliver these sorts of changes, although set aside may require a reasonably long gestation period before any beneficial impacts will be felt. However, many of the measures are contained within Codes of Good Agricultural Practice (COGAP) (Defra, 2004a). These are promoted through voluntary schemes (such as LEAF, 2005) or increasingly required as part of compliance requirements to retain land in good agricultural and environmental condition (GAEC) under the Single Farm Payment Scheme introduced in 2005 (Defra, 2004b). Changes from arable cropping to grassland or woodlands are also promoted by financial incentives provided to land managers by agri-environment schemes such as the Environmental Sensitive Areas Scheme (ESAS), the Country-side Stewardship Scheme (both of these were subsumed in 2005 within a new Environmental Stewardship Scheme (Defra, 2004c)) and the Farm Woodland Grants Scheme. The take up of environmental options under these schemes depends on the motivations of farmers, the suitability of options from a practical farming viewpoint and the financial incentives offered (Lobley and Potter, 1998; Morris et al., 2000). As the rewards to intensive commercial farming decline, the interest in funded environmental options has increased.

Putting the potential for application of these measures aside, two important caveats must be emphasised. First, their impact at the catchment-scale has not been established. Second, their effectiveness during more extreme flood events is also unproven. Indeed, there is only a field scale understanding of the potential benefits of changing the arable cropping regime. However, there may be good reasons for adopting these kinds of measures besides promoting flood mitigation (see 'Conclusions').

Livestock management

Increased stocking rates on grassland areas may result in soil compaction and surface damage ('poaching'), which may increase the generation of rapid runoff. Associated crops such as forage maize may also cause more rapid runoff. Thus, if these activities can be shown to impact upon flood risk, runoff generation may be mitigated by lowering animal stocking densities, improving livestock husbandry practices and choosing forage crops that avoid high-risk runoff generation. It should be emphasised that these types of effects can be complex, not simply because of their location dependence (e.g. soil, vegetation type) but also because husbandry practices are complex (field use, timing, stock migration with seasons into and out of the farm unit) and, as yet, there is no study that has demonstrated that livestock management changes can be used to reduce catchment scale flood risk. Following such a demonstration, the processes that might mitigate against flood risk include: (a) a general reduction in stocking densities; (b) a shift to cattle rather than sheep (for instance, Betteridge *et al.* (1999) demonstrated that different types of livestock had different effects upon the soil surface: cattle caused upward and downward soil movement leading to high levels of soil disturbance; sheep caused more surface compaction); and (c) the improvement of rotation patterns of grazing animals, in order to avoid the over exposure of the soil in one place. It should be noted that livestock practices also interact with other aspects of land management, such as maize production and silage. For instance, a reduction in stocking density might lower the demand for forage crops such as maize which, in turn, might reduce rapid runoff generation.

Tillage regimes

Changing tillage regime to reduce rapid runoff generation may involve:

1. measures to break up the plough layer;
2. altering the tramline direction and angle;
3. reduction in tramline and wheelings depth; and
4. creating intercepting mole drains in the direction of flow.

The beneficial impacts of these in relation to runoff generation have been well-established at the plot and field scale (e.g. Duley and Russell, 1939; Hawkins and Brown, 1963; Davies *et al.*, 1973; Schwab *et al.*, 1993). However, as with livestock management, there has been no unequivocal demonstration of beneficial impacts at the catchment scale. Indeed, results at the plot scale are also variable: for example, reducing plough depth may still break up macropores and causes deeper compaction of the soils below this layer and plough layer runoff and surface saturation may still occur. Conversely, reducing disturbance of the soil in general may allow worms to restore the soil structure more quickly. Generalisation of effects is difficult, due to interdependence between soil type and the constraints imposed on modes of ploughing by field size, field access and local topography (e.g. in upland areas of the UK, where slopes are steep, contour ploughing may be prohibited for safety reasons).

Land drainage

Field drains have contradictory impacts on runoff generation in that they generally increase the potential for on-land storage of water through increasing infiltration and also increase the connectivity of possible source areas to the drainage network, and may remove water quickly from the land if there is a sufficient hydraulic gradient. This second effect is addressed in Chapter 17, 'The economic impacts of coastal erosion'. The contradictory nature of these impacts partly explains why evidence on the effects of field drainage on rapid runoff is equivocal (Robinson and Rycroft, 1999).

By effectively increasing infiltration, drains act to suppress rapid overland flow generation. For instance, Burke (1975) found that drains led to the progressive drying of peat, with water tables 0.20 m below surface in winter and 0.45 m below surface in summer. It was argued that this lowering of the water table would increase water storage and reduce flood peaks. Similarly, although for backfilled rather than open drains, Newson and Robinson (1983) found for peaty gley and podzol soils on Rhiwdefeitty Fawr, Plynlimon, Wales, that drainage lengthened the duration of storm runoff and reduced peak flows due to the lowering of water tables. These field examples lead to the hypothesis that extension of land drainage may serve to reduce flood risk and suppress surface runoff. In the UK, grants for drainage schemes ended in 1983 and since then little or no new field drainage has been installed (Defra, 2002). There is evidence on many farms of localised collapse of field drains, which can create waterlogged areas with reduced production value. Reduced drainage on clay soils systems could cause increased runoff and higher water tables could make the effects of compaction worse. Again, information is lacking on how these impacts might scale up.

Buffer strips and buffering zones

Any zone that is left uncultivated may slow surface runoff, to induce sediment deposition and promote infiltration. Thus, buffer strips and buffering zones may be introduced to reduce runoff generation. Buffer strips are commonly situated in the riparian zone and they are usually of a limited width. A buffering zone can occur anywhere in the catchment and should be sited to intercept pathways of concentrated surface runoff.

The role of buffer strips and zones in nutrient control has now been widely described (e.g. Haycock et al., 1993; Vought et al., 1995), but there has been less research to demonstrate their hydrological function in relation to runoff reduction, both at the plot-scale and the catchment-scale, and it is in this context that any general conclusions regarding the potential benefits of buffer strips and zones must be considered. First, hydrological connectivity varies between catchments with different geologies, soils, hydrologies, vegetation and climates (e.g. Muscutt et al., 1993). Establishing the nature of hydrological connectivity at the catchment scale is a crucial first step in determining its potential as a flood runoff tool. For instance, Blackwell et al. (1999) note that while riparian buffer strips are important in reducing stream bank erosion, they can only be effective controls on rapid runoff generation if the runoff passes through them: much water leaving catchments will do so through drains and watercourses on the surface; or soil pipes and subsurface drains below the surface; that bypass the stream side buffer strip. Burt et al. (1999) reached similar conclusions for a buffer strip alongside the River Thames in Oxfordshire, where much of the agriculturally draining water bypassed the riparian zone, entering the river directly by way of springs or through gravel lenses beneath the floodplain soil. Buttle (2002) argues that much of the controversy in Canada regarding the potential role of buffer zones is related to an incomplete understanding of catchment hydrology including:

1. a failure to consider how particular types of land-use are hydrologically connected to receiving waters;
2. the role of different sources of groundwater (e.g. local, intermediate or regional); and

3. an overly simplistic view that overland flow is the dominant runoff pathway, to the detriment of consideration of channel flow and rapid throughflow, where buffer zones may have little effect. For instance, riparian buffer zones that take the form of narrow strips of land between a hillslope and the river are unlikely to be effective in promoting infiltration as these locations will commonly have lower slope and higher upslope contributing areas and so be wet anyway. Hence, buffer strips will only have an effect upon flood generation if there is the potential for infiltration within them at the start of a flood.

Second, during storm events, a greater buffering capacity is needed in zones of flow convergence and these may extend well away from riparian areas and into topographic hollows. The efficacy of buffer strips during major events needs to be viewed in the context of antecedent conditions: in the same way that they can provide infiltration and temporary storage, this is a finite process and their effectiveness will generally fall as rainfall duration increases.

Third, the presence of riparian buffer strips in the landscape is increasing. The reasons for this are primarily driven by attempts to reduce diffuse pollution and to improve the ecological integrity of river corridors (Lane *et al.*, 2003). Thus, flood risk benefits may be accruing, motivated by other reasons. It would be useful for research to focus upon establishing what impacts these established buffer zones might be having upon catchment flood risk. As yet, we do not have any clear evidence as to their flood risk reduction impact.

Afforestation

Finally, afforestation may be hypothesised as a means of reducing flood risk. The hypothesis is that afforestation should reduce rapid runoff generation due to: (a) increases in evapotranspiration and interception losses; and (b) an increase in throughflow and a reduction in overland flow. These effects will be dependent upon the type of afforestation as a result of differences in the hydrological function of trees planted for commercial logging, new broad leaf forest and energy crops. Research in the UK has focused on afforestation using coniferous woodland in upland areas (O'Connell *et al.*, 2005). This research has shown a substantial reduction in water yield under forest compared with pasture. However, there is a difference between: (1) reductions in yield associated with time-integrating across many rainfall events, the effects of evapotranspiration and interception losses; and (2) the reductions in runoff generation that might occur within individual storm events. At present, evidence for flood impacts is difficult to generalise (e.g. Calder and Aylward, 2006) in that forest effects on peak flows will depend upon storm size, location in the basin, vegetation type, soil type, etc.

Some studies report an increase in peak flow magnitude immediately following planting as a result of land preparation impacts (e.g. Robinson, 1986; Archer, 2003). Hence, land preparation for forestry may *increase* flood risk until the stand is properly developed. Similarly, forest management practices may require clear-felling and this is known to create damaged, bare soil zones that may contribute to rapid runoff generation. Good logging practices and sensible rotation of felled areas might minimise these effects at the catchment scale. This aside, there is now a general consensus that the potential for afforestation to reduce the magnitude of extreme flood events is probably lower than has been widely claimed (O'Connell *et al.*, 2005) and that forestry can probably make only a small contribution as a response to regional or large-scale flood risk (Robinson *et al.*, 2003).

Governance, Foresight scenarios and the management of infiltration

The governance associated with the management of infiltration has two important characteristics: (1) it requires involvement of a large number of land managers or farmers, distributed across the catchment; and (2) there can be a high degree of spatial separation between managers and those responsible for making sure that procedures are implemented effectively. This introduces substantial uncertainty into the land management process (i.e. social uncertainty) in addition to the scientific uncertainty linked to determining the catchment-scale impacts of the measures to be adopted. In the UK, fundamental to all of the measures listed are agri-environment payment systems and their associated implementation: these include rural schemes, such as the Environmentally Sensitive Area Schemes (ESAS), the Woodland Grant Scheme (WGS), the Countryside Stewardship Scheme (CSS) and the new national Entry and Higher Level Schemes (ELS/HLS) (Defra, 2005a, 2005b). Infiltration management may also be delivered through Codes of Good Agricultural Practice.

In some areas, land management activities may be self-governed: in the UK, aside from the activities and impacts of inland drainage boards, drainage management is largely undertaken by land owners and managers. Conversely, in other areas, governance may be more widely established. For instance, the Forestry Commission (FC), that runs the WGSs, has in recent years driven forward the agenda of woodland in the landscape. Even if the scientific question of upscaling plot and field scale analyses to the catchment scale can be resolved, if these kinds of measures are to be successful in reducing flood risk, they are likely to require careful planning at the catchment-scale, and require systems of stakeholder integration and governance that we do not yet have in much of the UK. These governance issues mean that the potential for adoption of the measures in this functional group is significantly affected by the Foresight Future envisaged.

Sustainability

The measures in this functional group score well on some of the sustainability dimensions of flood risk management. For instance, there may be beneficial social justice impacts in that the measures reflect an integrated response, founded in shared knowledge and education among rural communities regarding how upstream management activities act to produce beneficial downstream responses. These measures may provide a route for strengthening the social linkages between rural and urban areas. However, there may be some areas where social justice is reduced. Many of the measures will involve some form of extensification and the rural economy remains a complex environment, with some households (especially non land owners) dependent upon intensive agricultural activity to maintain income. Consequently, under some futures, these measures could be socially divisive, not least because of varying degrees to which individual management units are able to adjust to changes in the agri-environment.

The majority of the response measures score well on environmental sustainability, as they correlate with: (a) general agricultural extensification; (b) the restoration of natural landscape wetness; and (c) activities that may also reduce the impacts of diffuse pollution and lead to the recreation of habitat. Also, as these measures need to be undertaken at the catchment-scale, they promote the restoration of landscape integrity. However, these improvements will not be achieved equally in relation to all specific measures (e.g. intensive coniferous afforestation will lead to a net reduction in environmental quality), and so improved environmental quality will only be realised if the measures described here are undertaken with respect to parameters other than flood mitigation.

In general, environmental schemes are expensive to administer and audit. However, agri-environment schemes are already operational and are likely to be further expanded in future. Hence, adoption and modification of such schemes for flood mitigation may be cost effective. The major challenges are: (a) to factor flood risk reductions into these schemes; and (b) to make sure that they are adopted at locations in the landscape where they are likely to have the most beneficial effects. Administration and auditing, although expensive, could be optimised as part of a more integrated land-use policy. Current environment schemes, European Regional Development Funds and local rural economic initiatives could combine to create a mixed rural economy that suits most stakeholders and that might also promote greater infiltration and a reduction in the rate of rapid runoff generation. Again, it is too early to say whether or not this will lead to benefits in terms of flood risk reduction.

Response interaction and feedback loops

There are strong interaction and feedback loops in relation to the management of infiltration. First, even when their hypothesised role in flood mitigation has been fully tested, they are unlikely to operate in isolation: many of these measures will be required together. Where one measure is not successful, others may be adopted. For instance, if tramline and wheeling exists, then buffer strips can be situated to intercept the flows. Thus tramlines and wheeling could be used advantageously to deliver known surface flows to suitably sized and positioned buffer zones for each field (Quinn and Hewett, 2003). It follows that a crucial requirement is management plans at the scale of individual management units (e.g. farms) in order to identify what measures are required where. Second, there are very strong links with other aspects of environmental management, including nutrient pollution, erosion, pesticide losses and pathogen losses. Third, there is very strong interaction with the core drivers of the agricultural economy and, notably, agricultural subsidies and agri-environment schemes as the prime delivery mechanism. Fourth, there are strong feedbacks from other parts of the agricultural economy. For instance, general agricultural extensification may need to be counter-balanced by the need to maintain agricultural intensity in order to protect high-grade agricultural land, as part of sustaining food supplies (this is especially important under some of the Foresight scenarios).

Case example

There are no case studies at present where rural land management has been successfully used to reduce the magnitude or frequency of flooding in main rivers. There is evidence that beneficial effects may be achieved in relation to flooding away from main rivers, where runoff from fields reaches roads and properties directly. Commonly, these floods have a substantial suspended sediment load and are called 'muddy floods'. Evans and Boardman (2003) report on the case of the 10.6 km² Sompting catchment in the South Downs, where the management of infiltration has been used to deliver protection from muddy floods. Boardman *et al.* (2003) report that the area of all the catchment drilled to winter cereals increased from about 15% in 1975, to c. 35% in 1981 and c. 60% by 1988 and 1991. Boardman and Evans (1991) estimated that this transition from grassland to autumn-sown cereals had lowered the threshold at which flooding took place from one in 100 years to one in three or four years in Sompting. It should be emphasised that these statistics demonstrate that floods will still occur and that these types of floods are not a recent issue. The issue is mitigation of the increase in flood risk that has come from adoption of certain land-use and land management practices. Research showed that the costs of dam building and associated drainage in Sompting were too high and an alternative approach was developed. This recognised the impacts of gross land-use changes, removal of critical field boundaries and certain land management practices. The aim of the alternative approach was to reduce the area in the north of the catchment drilled for winter wheat and to grass-over the valley floors to protect them from erosion. After protracted negotiations, predominantly over the evidence used to link the increased occurrence of floods to the associated land-use change, the period from 1993–1994 saw progressive change of land-use to either set aside or grassland (Boardman *et al.*, 2003). By 2000–2001, it was observed (Evans and Boardman, 2003) that: land under set aside; land that was drilled earlier; and land that was worked along the slope; did not suffer erosion. Spatial organisation of these land use changes was also important (Boardman *et al.*, 2003), especially where it was so as to break up the continuous surface flow that results in the ready export of overland flow from the fields into properties. Boardman *et al.* (2003) found that it was not necessary to change land-use and land management in all fields, only those where connectivity can be broken up (see below). The result was that the housing estate that was being flooded regularly during the 1980s did not flood in October 2000, despite a rainfall event with an estimated return period of greater than 100 years (Evans and Boardman, 2003) and a magnitude larger than that recorded during the 1980 events.

The prime vehicles for delivering these changes were EU funded Common Agricultural Policy-based set aside and re-seeded grazed grassland under the Environmentally Sensitive Area scheme. The major barrier to adoption was persuading the farmers involved (and there were a very small number to persuade) to adopt these measures. However, a very interesting legal situation is reported by Boardman *et al.* (2003), Boardman (2003) and Evans and Boardman (2003). In situations where muddy floods can be linked to farming activities and, crucially, it has been demonstrated before that those activities cause flooding, farmers are being sued for negligence. So far, such cases have been settled out-of-court, precluding the possibility of a formal legal settlement (Boardman *et al.*, 2003). The fact that they have been settled in this way is indicative of the potential role of land management measures in dealing with some aspects of certain types of floods, in this case floods that generate rapid runoff from fields directly into properties.

A cautionary note

We need to emphasise that the key message from the above reviews of each specific measure is that management of infiltration at the farm-scale will impact upon flow partitioning, and this is supported by some plot scale studies. However, we do not believe that the hypothesis that such management can be part of a reliable and effective flood mitigation strategy has yet to be extensively tested in relation to catchment scale flood risks. Further, for higher magnitude flood events with longer return periods, this hypothesis is unlikely to hold.

Catchment-wide storage

Overview

This group of responses hypothesises that, by retaining rainfall and runoff close to source, or within the drainage network, at strategic locations, then it may be possible to increase flood attenuation. This group is distinct from the management of conveyance (where water does not go into store, but its speed of translation through the catchment is reduced). The effectiveness of all response measures in this group is critically dependent upon the location of the measure within the drainage network, and this requires assessment of possible impacts at the catchment-scale. There are three response measures: (1) ponds, bunds and ditches, generally on farm; (2) wetlands and washlands; and (3) impoundments. The latter category involves some overlap with the 'engineered storage' measures described in Chapter 20. However, as such measures involve the transformation of potentially large areas of the landscape, they are implicitly bound up with the practice of rural land management, and the socio-economic environment that influences land management decisions. Indeed, most extant schemes that seek to reduce flood risk through catchment storage have been delivered through negotiated agreements between land owners and stakeholders (Morris *et al.*, 2004a) with the associated engineering design being of secondary importance to negotiation of the rural land management practice that scheme adoption will imply. The key theme in effective operation of this response group is determining the volume and location of flood storage required to produce the risk reduction. Similarly, the location of a storage site is crucial to its ability to deliver flood attenuation.

Ponds, bunds and ditches

In the farming landscape, there are many examples of where surface runoff is deliberately or unintentionally ponded by flow barriers or bunds (such as hedgerows or soil mounds). We can hypothesise that, as part of an integrated, catchment-wide, flood risk reduction plan, all features could be used together, and this may lead to attenuation of flood flows. The kinds of activities that might be adopted include 'off-line' storage ponds, with bunds to direct flows to them; hedgerows that act as both bunds and also create temporary storage ponds; and blocking of ditches to provide on-line storage. As yet, we have no evidence as to the potential impacts of these measures upon catchment scale flood risk reduction.

Wetlands and washlands

Washlands managed specifically for the storage of flood water are currently used as part of some flood defence strategies (e.g. River Aire washlands, North and West Yorkshire). They are distinct from wetlands and washlands used for conveyance management, where water does not go into storage, but rather the flood risk is reduced as the flood wave is delayed and attenuated. Thus, the consideration of wetlands and washlands provided here may not recognise the full range of benefits (especially ecological benefits) that may come from naturally reconnecting a river to its floodplain.

The aim of wetlands and washlands is to store water in areas of floodplain that are isolated from the main river by some form of natural or designed hydraulic control. The storage function below ground will be through infiltration into the root zone and below, although this is commonly not that significant as both wetlands are washlands are typically poorly drained and hence have wetter soils, especially in winter. Wetlands, in that they are commonly associated with surface inundation and high ditch and groundwater levels, intercept, absorb and/or retain potential flood water, as well as moderating its release to the river system. Washlands are areas which are allowed to flood or are deliberately flooded, thus providing natural or artificial storage capacity, sometimes with habitat potential. The contribution of a washland to flood management depends on the storage capacity, the degree of hydraulic control over inflow and outflow, and the washland location within the catchment (Morris *et al.*, 2004b). Washlands can be especially effective in reducing flood impacts, provided they are properly maintained.

Impoundments

Impoundments are a type of flood storage scheme where local terrain dictates that delivering significant flood storage requires the construction of some form of impoundment. Impoundments can be very effective in reducing downstream flood risk, provided they are managed for flood risk. Depending on the frequency and timing of flooding, it may be possible to exploit potential synergy with other objectives such as enhanced biodiversity, landscape and amenity. The Harbitonford scheme in Devon is an example of multi-purpose impoundment, albeit on a small scale. The proposed extension of the Leigh Barrier in Sussex is to incorporate environmental options, such as surface scrapes, in order to integrate flood management and biodiversity objectives (Morris *et al.*, 2004b). Impound-ments involve the clearest overlap with 'engineered-storage' (Chapter 20), but it must be emphasised that they will differ because of the relatively small amount of earthworks and retaining works required. Further, they also involve a major change in land-use and land management, and this places them firmly as an issue that has to be resolved as part of new approaches to managing the agricultural environment that are flood risk reducing.

Governance Foresight scenarios and catchment storage

Ponds, bunds and ditches are relatively diffuse measures that would involve a large number of land managers, with activities located in the correct parts of the landscape. Aside from ongoing uncertainties over their possible impacts at the catchment-scale, to be effective, their potential contribution must be coordinated at the catchment/sub-catchment scale, possibly under the aegis of catchment flood management plans, and promoted to farmers through appropriately designed options within agri-environment schemes. In the UK, the issue of governance in relation to ponds, bunds and ditches is complicated by the fact that responsibility for river and land drainage systems is spread between the Environment Agency, Local Government, Internal Drainage Boards and owner/occupiers. While actions taken on fields and ditches are at the discretion of the land managers and owners, the Environment Agency does have permissive powers. Defra advises codes of good practice for agriculture, and some measures are built into environmental stew-ardship agreements. This is the sense in which administration of agri-environment schemes would need to be coupled to a change in land drainage responsibilities, so that these processes and changes may be delivered. The recent inclusion of an inundation grassland option for floodplains in the new environmental stewardship scheme is a welcome example of how flood risk reduction measures can be encouraged through appropriate development of legislation.

The situation in relation to wetlands, washlands and impoundments is clearer, largely because these measures are less diffuse. In the UK, responsibility for wetland and washland operation normally rests with land managers, but under guidance and supervision from environment protection agencies. The range of land owner categories can be broad: in addition to farmers, English Nature, Countryside Council for Wales, Scottish Heritage, Wildlife Trusts, the National Trust and organisations such as the RSPB own or have management agreements on wetland and washland areas. Impoundments installed specifically for flood storage would normally have a structural responsibility resting with the organisation that commis-sioned the impoundment. However, impoundments may come under the Reservoir Act (1975) (if they impound more than $25\,000\,\mathrm{m}^3$ above the adjacent ground level), which will require additional and much more formal regulation.

Sustainability

Measures to mitigate flood risk by storing water in the upper parts of a catchment or to store flood water in the floodplain have potential to contribute to sustainable solutions to flood management at local and catchment scales. In particular, there may be integration with measures to enhance biodiversity, especially associated with field margins, field ponds and wetlands. As much of our traditional catchment management has involved the loss of wet habitats through disconnection of the river from its floodplain or through land drainage, the recreation of wetter habitat may be an important component of catchment restoration. Such habitat may also contribute to the reduction of pollution loading to the water environment.

In relation to the social justice dimension of sustainability, there may be some beneficial impacts in that these measures require an integrated response, founded in shared knowledge and education among rural communities as to how their upstream management activities may have beneficial downstream responses. These measures are likely to engage and potentially benefit a large number of stakeholders and are entirely compatible with an integrated, people-centred approach to catchment flood management. They may provide a route for strengthening the linkage between rural (upstream) and urban (downstream) areas. However, the upstream emphasis raises interesting issues in relation to the perception of the effectiveness of catchment-wide solutions. They are distanced in space and may not carry the visibility associated with (and in political terms, sometimes required) site-specific flood risk reduction measures.

There is a sliding scale of robustness within this functional response group. The least robust measures are ponds, bunds and ditches, as these depend upon the extent to which administrative influence over land managers is maintained, and this varies with flood Foresight scenario. It is also questionable that this measure can provide significant flood storage during extreme flood events. Wetlands and wash-lands are more robust, as they require less coordinated control or administrative influence across the catchment. However, they still require a willingness to convert potentially productive agricultural land to wetland and washland storage. Impoundments are relatively robust in that they can be relied upon to deliver significant reduction in flood risk without reliance on broadscale cooperation across multiple stakeholders.

The costs of the measures in this functional group include the capital costs of design, supervision, land-take, construction and management, as well as opportunity costs associated with subsequent income loss. Wetland creation usually involves land purchase by a conservation organisation. Where washlands are created for flood storage only, the purchase of easements, equivalent to about 80% of land value, has been used. However, the costs of on-farm and floodplain storage are very site dependent, with significant economies of scale. In the UK, capital works for impoundments or washlands intended for flood storage (but not for biodiversity) currently attract Defra grant aid. Non-government organisations are an important funding source for wetlands. Thus, the major requirement for these specific measures would be augmentation of existing agri-environment schemes to include, for example, the positive nature of ponds and bunds as runoff storage on farms. Additional costs would be associated with maintenance and auditing to check that runoff control structures do indeed provide storage benefits. Compensation for loss of crop or livestock production in ponded areas may be needed. It should be stated that some of these measures perform poorly under the current Defra cost–benefit analyses. If these appraisals were extended to include other benefits (e.g. biodiversity gains, diffuse pollution reduction), then this may make these multi-purpose interventions more attractive.

Case examples of flood risk management through catchment storage

As measures in this functional response group are now widely adopted, there are numerous examples of their use. In relation to ponds, bunds and ditches, there are two recent examples of on-farm, middle catchment detention reservoirs in Somerset (Morris et al., 2002): one involved a 7.4 ha site with a capacity of $15\,000\,\text{m}^3$ (depth 0.2 m) with a design and build cost of £4.60/m^3, £6.5/m^3 including land costs; another involved 24 ha, $100\,000\,\text{m}^3$ (depth 0.4 m) at £2.20/m^3, £3.1/m^3 inclusive of land costs. This is equivalent to between £0.20/m^3 and £0.50/m^3 storage costs per year. On-farm reservoir costs for irrigation in East Anglia provide indicative costs for small-scale storage at an annual cost of about £0.30 to £0.50/m^3 stored (Weatherhead et al., 1997).

In relation to wetlands and washlands, the Beckingham Marshes Scheme, River Trent, was constructed in the 1960s to provide flood protection benefits to 1000 ha of agricultural land and provide $2\,000\,000\,\text{m}^3$ of storage capacity, enough for the

Table 18.2. Results of the River Gaunless flood defence strategy study

Location	Local defences			Storage						Combined storage and defences		
				Spring Gardens			Fylands					
	B/C ratio	Standard of protection	MAFF score	B/C ratio	Standard of protection	MAFF score	B/C ratio	Standard of protection	MAFF score	B/C ratio	Standard of protection	MAFF score
Ramshaw	0.31	N/A	N/A	N/A	N/A	N/A	N/A	N/A	N/A	2.71	100 year	24
West Auckland	2.95	50 year	22	2.52	50 year	22	N/A	N/A	N/A	2.71	100 year	24
South Church Left Bank	3.25	100 year	26	2.52	50 year	22	1.80	25 year	16	2.71	100 year	24
South Church Right Bank	0.83	N/A	N/A	2.52	50 year	22	1.80	25 year	16	2.71	100 year	24

one in ten-year return period event, to help protect Gainsborough. Hydraulic control is by means of a fixed level inflow and flapped outfall supported by pumps as required. Land was purchased from farmers but returned on tenancy. The scheme led to conversion of wet grassland to arable. In recent years, half the area has been returned to grass, and negotiations are underway to create a wetland site, operated under agri-environmental agreements, retaining the flood storage facility (Morris *et al.*, 2004b).

JBA Consulting (2003) provides specific examples of how these sorts of washland and wetland measures can be used to enhance biodiversity. They explored the removal of flood embankments along the Lower River Derwent (Sutton Lock to upstream of Wressle Rail Bridge), in North Yorkshire, but retaining protection adjacent to villages of Bubwith and Breighton. Removal of embankments had no impact upon water levels during flows less than the median flow. Water levels were unaffected during flood flows with a two-year return period or greater. Flood flows between the median flow and the two-year flood had water levels lowered by up to 0.3 m. This resulted in increased inundation of the washland (known locally as 'ings'), but more rapid land drainage at other times. The effects depend on each ing with more frequent inundation but more ready drainage results in drier root zones. For each ing it was possible to identify how the flood storage capacity could lead to enhancement of ecological indicators.

The role of impoundments as part of a flood defence strategy is illustrated by JBA Consulting (2001) who considered alternatives based on local defences, storage schemes, and a combination of the two as a means of achieving cost-effective flood protection on the River Gaunless, County Durham. Table 18.2 shows how it was that a combination of storage and defence offered the required standard of protection at least cost.

Uncertainty

Water retention through catchment storage represents a robust approach to reducing flood risk downstream. The uncertainty associated with these measures is relatively low. Table 18.3 summarises these uncertainties A number of important points emerge. First, within this functional response group, there is substantial variability in uncertainty, largely correlated with the extent to which the recommended measure is diffuse. The more diffuse the measure, the greater the uncertainty. Second, the effectiveness of each of these measures depends upon policies associated with the management of the rural environment in general and farming in particular. Third, there is evidence that much of the uncertainty is

Table 18.3. Uncertainty associated with specific measures in the catchment-wide storage functional response group

Description of source or uncertainty	Quantification of uncertainty	Description of source or uncertainty	Quantification of uncertainty
Ponds, bunds and ditches			
Impact of on-farm retention on sub-catchment and catchment flows	High: high uncertainty at local and catchment scale. Precision of estimates currently vary according to scale, surface and event characteristics, including proportion of catchment that is urban	Uncertainty regarding effectiveness of on farm effective water retention practices. Aggregate catchment scale effects, including contribution relative to urbanization effects, and other forms of regulation	Moderate to high, dependent on funding and research products
Willingness of land managers to adopt water retention measures	High: depends on acceptability and incentives to land managers	Policy framework. Extension services and incentive schemes to promote adoption. Use of regulation or compliance requirements	High: dependent on policy drivers, funding and willingness to adopt, and on use of regulatory methods/compliance requirements
Floodplain storage: wetlands, washlands			
Estimation of flood (and waterlogging) damage costs by frequency, duration, seasonality and depth of inundation (and excessive soil water)	Low to medium: Water regime requirements of commercial crops relatively well known and observable, but knowledge gaps given new technologies, farming practices and systems	Prediction of land use, management practices and farming systems (linked to agriculture as a pathway). Strategic food security issues	Low to Medium: function of agricultural and related policy, markets and prices, including agri-environmental options, land tenure systems, and response/coping strategies of land managers. Potential damage to strategic assets
Feasibility and contribution to flood storage of integrated wetland/washland management options which deliver flood management, bio-diversity and rural livelihood benefits	High: limited empirical or research evidence to support potential opportunities for integrated rural land management	Integration of policy objectives and instruments: agriculture, agri-environment, flood management. Development, testing and guidance on interventions and management practices to achieve potential synergy	Medium to High: need to develop and test new land use and management practices which seek to promote multi-functional floodplain land use. Feasibility of 'joined-up' floodplain management strategies. Willingness of land managers to engage
Impoundments			
Recommendation as a solution within flood defence strategies	Medium: uncertainty as to whether or not consultants consider these options fully	Operation of impoundments	Medium: effectiveness of impoundments depends upon them only being operated for flood storage and that they are operated correctly (e.g. water is released appropriately)
Cost–benefit analyses	High: hard to recommend these as a flood management solution in many cases because of cost–benefit analyses that do not take into account the full potential range of benefits		

conditioned by issues that are not linked properly through to flood risk. For instance, the specification of the form of a cost–benefit analysis will determine whether or not a particular scheme is recommended. Catchment storage is likely to have a much wider range of benefits than flood risk, and many of those benefits may extend beyond the local geographical region (for instance, in terms of maintaining wetter landscapes and a better level of wet connection within the landscape, so facilitating species adaptation to environment change). The nature of future flood risks identified in the Foresight Project, coupled to an ever greater emphasis upon the environmental protection aspects of catchment management, mean that these kinds of upstream storage measures, especially those involving wetlands/ washlands and impoundments, become increasingly attractive as part of an integrated catchment management plan.

Management of hillslope and river conveyance

Overview
This functional response group is concerned with the hypothesis that flood risk reductions can come from managing the pathways by which runoff is conveyed through the hillslope and channel drainage network. It has three broad aspects:

1. The management of hillslope connectivity, by reducing the speed with which generated overland flow is conveyed to the river channel network.
2. The management of river channels and floodplains (e.g. altering flow resistance) in order to increase flood wave attenuation, with a presumption of reducing conveyance in rural areas (i.e. increasing temporary storage).
3. The realignment of river channels in order to increase flood wave attenuation.

These three measures have a fundamental underlying hypothesis: attenuation of the flood wave can be achieved through adopting them in order to produce lower peak flows at critical points in the river system.

Conventional flood alleviation schemes act to increase conveyance, through measures such as channel straightening, vegetation removal and channel resectioning (see Chapter 22). These measures essentially change the way in which a given flow increment is partitioned between changes in width, depth and velocity. If conveyance is greater (e.g. through engineering a lower channel roughness), increments in flow are more associated with increases in velocity than in depth or width. The result is that the flood wave is passed more rapidly downstream but attenuation is reduced leading to the now well-established problems of transferring flood problems through the river network, so impacting upon downstream communities. Increasing conveyance leads to more rapid translation of a flood wave. Increasing attenuation may slow it down, leading to more local storage. Thus, this functional response group involves taking a larger or catchment-scale view of attenuation, such that attenuation is increased upstream of areas that need to be prevented from flooding, under the hypothesis that some rural areas (i.e. those with low-value agricultural land) can be used to increase flood attenuation through water storage.

Rural land management to slow hillslope conveyance
These measures hypothesise that flood wave attenuation can be achieved through reducing the connectivity between source areas of runoff and the drainage network. They have to be adopted through a catchment-scale emphasis: for example, by reversing some conventional land management practices (notably land drainage) that result in the rapid delivery of runoff to the drainage network in headwaters; but maintaining land management practices downstream that remove runoff before

the flood peak from upstream arrives. Specific examples might include removing open drains in upland areas to reduce connectivity and so increase attenuation. This kind of measure suffers from the same kind of scientific uncertainties associated with other diffuse land management measures: specifically, their impacts need to be scaled up through to the catchment scale.

Riparian conveyance

These measures hypothesise that channel and floodplain maintenance regimes can be altered so as to manage conveyance in order to attenuate peak flow. It is based upon the hypothesis that river conveyance is generally greater (per unit width) than floodplain conveyance. Hence, by reducing river conveyance, more water will be transferred on the floodplain, where conveyance is slower. This will lead to greater attenuation. Reduced river conveyance may be delivered by reducing channel maintenance and adopting river restoration schemes in areas where floodplain inundation is acceptable (i.e. low-grade agricultural land) and may be particularly appealing where there is scope for enhanced biodiversity. It may also be achieved in floodplains through increases in surface vegetative roughness, such as through the planting of floodplain forests. Central to these measures is allowing a river to reconnect with its floodplain, and this may have additional environmental benefits besides flood risk reduction.

Rural land management and river realignment

This involves reducing channel conveyance in flood acceptable areas through the reintroduction of more complex channel planforms. We can hypothesise that this may increase flood wave attenuation. Commonly, it will involve reversing historical management activities that resulted in channel straightening. In some cases, it may involve the set-back of flood embankments which gave protection to agricultural land, possibly linked to land-use change promoted by agri-environment schemes. Long Eau in Lincolnshire is an example of this (Morris *et al.*, 2004b).

Governance Foresight scenarios and the management of conveyance

As with the other aspects of rural land management described above, governance is a major issue. In England and Wales, for example, responsibility for conveyance management is shared between: (1) individual land managers on private land; (2) individual land owners, internal drainage boards and local government in relation to maintenance of 'non-main' river; (3) the Environment Agency and individual land owners in relation to maintenance of 'main' river; and (4) the Environment Agency in relation to major channel realignment. However, all of these measures are complicated by the range of institutional influences upon particular decisions, as most of these are not taken simply for flood defence purposes. They are also complicated by: (1) the range of landowners (e.g. NGOs such as the National Trust and Wildlife Trust and landowner attitudes, as illustrated in the variable take-up of agri-environment schemes); (2) the fact that some conveyance decisions are ultimately decided upon by Planning Authorities (as the democratically elected representatives) and as such come under Planning Policy Guidance; and (3) the influence of agri-environment schemes and codes of good agricultural practice.

In relation to the three functional groups, there is some difference between approaches. Management of hillslope connectivity is a diffuse issue: it will require the involvement of a large number of individuals, across the landscape, making governance much more of an issue. Both maintenance and realignment, especially where the result is an increase in flooding of flood acceptable areas will be less diffuse, but will require a close partnership between the land owner, the land manager and the relevant institutions (i.e. the Environment Agency for England and Wales; councils in Scotland).

Sustainability

All three of these functional groups should enhance system sustainability, especially in the context of the Water Framework and Habitats Directives. There is a general presumption that all three measures will reduce the need for ongoing drain and channel maintenance. In a very general sense, all three represent environmental restoration, and as such are respecting one of the government's ten principles of sustainable development (by reducing the environmental limits to achieving sustainability). In relation to social justice, there is a sense in which these measures are fully upstream, addressing the root causes of flood risk: if drainage for agricultural measures and straightening/floodplain disconnection has reduced floodplain storage, then reversing these is akin to addressing the problem closer to source. Thus, there is an element of restoring social justice with this measure. As many of these projects will involve some form of environmental restoration, additional social justice benefits may be delivered. McDonald *et al.* (2004), for example, demonstrate the significant community spirit that can be linked to a river restoration project.

The positive assessment of sustainability issues aside, the main challenge with these measures is their robustness. Effective management of conveyance requires integrated catchment management and planning, with strong geographical control. In turn, this is highly dependent upon the kind of future scenario envisaged for regulation, and the role of planning in environmental decision making.

Potentially, the measures in these response groups have low ongoing maintenance costs, which may make them especially cost effective. Initial costs vary in magnitude. The management of hillslope connectivity can be an especially expensive process unless it is done intelligently (i.e. through identification of exactly where it is needed) or through removing drain management activities altogether, in which case costs are low. Funding for this type of activity may be obtained through agri-environment schemes. Reducing the intensity of channel maintenance may reduce expenditure, although there may be increased frequency of inundation on adjacent farm land and calls for compensation from farmers. Funding schemes are only an issue here if compensation has to be provided. Channel realignment has an initially high level of construction cost plus additional expenditure if the land owner requires some form of compensation. If the design is such that no long-term maintenance is required, the benefits may, in the long term, be high and the costs low. As an example, it cost c. £60 000 (2001 figures) to restore a gravel trap reach in a National Park (c. 200 m length) back to a more normal course. Funding schemes for this type of initiative are more difficult to isolate. In the UK, river restoration schemes, for instance, have traditionally been funded either through specific EU funds (e.g. under Objective Vb) or through the willingness of a particular land owner to invest in such schemes.

Interaction and feedback

There is a strong connection between the management of conveyance and the management of catchment storage: reducing conveyance in a rural area may lead to higher water levels and greater flooding in that area and, hence, catchment-wide storage. The difference is in the *nature of the storage*: we are considering here the storage associated with a connected river-floodplain system, rather than isolated impoundments or ponds that are designed and managed to store water. Similarly, there is an explicit linkage here to management of the urban fabric: if it is necessary to increase conveyance through an urban area, downstream negative impacts may be mitigated through reducing conveyance where suitable rural areas exist. This simple urban-rural division is not necessarily appropriate and a better definition may be between zoned 'flood-acceptable' and 'flood-protected' areas. For instance, some areas of Grade 1 Agricultural Land may be deemed to be of national strategic importance and worthy of protection.

Table 18.4. Impact upon flows at Summerton Bridge, downstream of the study reach

Scenario	Description	Peak flow in 1997–8 event: cumecs	Peak flow in Easter 1998 event: cumecs	Peak flow in October 2000 event: cumecs	Peak flow in scaled October 2000 event: cumecs
Current configuration	Current floodplain and channel	20.7	59.5	25.0	38.0
Restored floodplain	Reduction of instream channel capacity and connection between channel and floodplain	18.8 (−10%)	52.3 (−12%)	20.9 (−16%)	33.0 (−13%)
Embanked floodplain	Embankment of the current channel	32.0 (+54%)	90.5 (+52%)	63.3 (+153%)	92.5 (+143%)

Case example

Acreman (2003) explored the potential role of river restoration in flood attenuation. Computer modelling was used to explore the effects of changes to river channel geometry and construction and removal of embankments upon high flows. This is accompanied by a change in rural land-use, in that it changes the way the river is allowed to behave as well as the magnitude and frequency of flood inundation. The research was undertaken for the River Cherwell, Oxfordshire (Table 18.4). Hypothetical changes to the River Cherwell between Oxford and Banbury suggest further embanking the river increases peak flows by up to 150% over current levels. Restoring the river through the floodplain to pre-engineered dimensions reduces peak flow by c. 10 to 15% with respect to current levels and increases peak water levels within the floodplain by 0.5 to 1.6 m. This demonstrates that where rural land-use permits, river restoration and floodplain management can be part of a sustainable catchment flood management strategy.

Summary: uncertainty and the management of conveyance

The uncertainty associated with this functional group mirrors that associated with the storage functional group. However, two additional and important areas of uncertainty are also present. First, it is clear from the case examples that the management of conveyance can only be considered at the catchment-scale. If the drainage network consisted of a single channel-floodplain system, with all precipitation entering the channel in the headwaters, then attenuation will lead to a progressive reduction in peak flows downstream. As most catchments comprise a series of sub-catchments (and most sub-catchments a series of sub-sub-catchments and so on), the attenuation of flow in any one limb of the drainage network may be countered by addition of flows from other points in the drainage network. This is why peak discharge increases in the downstream direction: the addition of water from sub-catchments counters the attenuation associated with any one catchment. Thus, the management of conveyance can only be considered through an analysis at the scale of the entire catchment. For example, increasing attenuation in one sub-catchment, immediately upstream of a flood-protected area, will delay the flood peak, potentially delivering it to the main river at the same time as the main river peak, resulting in a net *increase* in peak flows in the main river. Further, a problem emerges as it is not only properties of the catchment that influence attenuation, but also the way in which precipitation events travel across the catchment which, itself, is a function of dominant weather types and hence tied to climate change. Thus, and as with the other rural land management measures, producing simple generalisations about land management impacts, without reference to the structure and function of that management, as well as its location, is very difficult. This is a key source of uncertainty in relation to conveyance.

Second, conveyance and its management is a more uncertain science than storage and its management. With storage, there is some form of engineering or hydraulic control that can be used to guarantee the delivery of a particular flood mitigation function. The science of conveyance (e.g. the effects of floodplain structures, of in-channel vegetation and sediment effects) is highly uncertain, and conveyance itself is both spatially (e.g. floodplain blockage effects) and temporally (e.g. vegetation growth and decay) complex. Thus, estimating the impacts of conveyance changes can be uncertain.

Conclusions

Given the five characteristics of rural land management identified at the beginning of this chapter, it is not surprising that establishing a definitive linkage between rural land management practices and the magnitude and frequency of flood events represents a fundamental challenge. O'Connell *et al.* (2005) demonstrate the scientific challenges in this respect. Central to these, and as emphasised above, is determining the catchment-scale impact of a given change in land management practice, as well as the event-specific and location-specific factors that change the nature of any catchment-scale impact. For instance, reversing agricultural under drainage in a lowland area may actually exacerbate flood risk if it delays the delivery of water to the river network such that it arrives coincident with the flood peak from upstream areas. Simple recommendations regarding land-use will need to be properly situated within overall catchment flood management planning. However, this scientific uncertainty is by no means uniform within the rural land management set of responses. Uncertainty is greatest in relation to those responses that are spatially distributed or diffuse (e.g. changing partitioning of runoff between fast flow and slow flow) as scaling up results in magnification of at-a-point uncertainty as well as the introduction of complex timing effects. The effects of more spatially concentrated land management activities, such as a geographically defined washland, may be more readily determined, and this makes the extent to which they can be reliably assessed more straightforward. It is not surprising that flood storage schemes are already commonly factored into options for flood risk reduction.

However, what this chapter has also emphasised is that uncertainty must be more broadly defined than in scientific terms alone. Following the Wynne (1992) categorisation of uncertainty (Table 18.5), all flood management responses will have uncertainties associated with them and these are not just scientific (e.g. over whether or not a particular land management activity reduces flood generation) but also non-scientific (e.g. over whether there is a suitable competent authority to make sure that the land management activity is undertaken as and when it is required). Thus, questions of rural land management are strongly linked to questions of governance and the certainty with which rural land management can be delivered: do our systems of governance provide a sufficient guarantee that a given land management measure will be put into place everywhere that it needs to be and throughout the timescale that this response is required?

Most traditional flood defence schemes have two important characteristics: (1) responsibility for their effective functioning rests with a single competent authority (e.g. long-term maintenance of a flood defence levée); and/or (2) responsibility for action rests with direct flood victims (e.g. installation of boards or sand bags to prevent flood water entering in a house). Rural land management will, to varying degrees, involve many individuals, who have no direct responsibility for preventing downstream flooding (e.g. farmers, at least under conventional flood risk policy

Table 18.5. The Wynne classification of uncertainty

Uncertainty class	Definition	Example
Risk	Quantifiable probabilities	Probability of bund failure within a storm event
True uncertainty	Known uncertainties, unknown probabilities	Effects of land management upon flow partitioning and hence flood flows: i.e. we know that land management will affect partitioning between fast flow and slow flow; we know that this will affect flood flows (making them worse or better according to where the management is situated); but we have yet to develop robust methods to quantify by how much land management will change those flood flows
Ignorance	Things that could be known but that are not yet known (often put as *we don't yet know what we don't know*)	Further scientific research, aided by the development of monitoring technologies, should allow us to understand upland drainage effects upon flood risk at the catchment-scale. However, we cannot yet upscale with any confidence, we do not yet know the effects of this upscaling and there remains the possibility that such an upscaling reveals surprising results
Indeterminacy	Things that could never be known, however much science is undertaken	Actor within a competent authority makes the wrong sequence of decisions in relation to management of an upstream storage scheme

regimes) and who may not themselves have the incentive to act that comes from being the potential victims of flooding.

It follows that this issue of governance will depend quite strongly upon the particular future that is considered. Figure 18.1 conceptualises this issue in terms of two axes: (1) an axis that goes from diffuse, where the policy response relies upon many actors, distributed over a large spatial extent, through to concentrated, where the policy response relies upon a single actor, commonly with responsibility for a single and geographically well-defined location; and (2) an axis that goes from

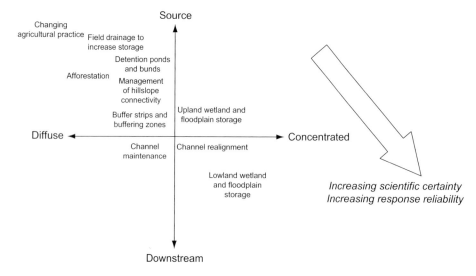

Fig. 18.1. Rural land management options in relation to their governance (from diffuse to concentrated) and location

source, where the policy response is applied some distance from where flood management becomes an issue, through to downstream, where the response measure is close to where flood risk is high. This emphasises the correlation between the scientific uncertainty identified above and the reliability of the response measure identified: some rural land management measures (e.g. wetlands) may have a reliable and predictable effect; others much less so. However, while it appears that these problems relate to establishing effective systems of governance, there are more problematic issues that extend beyond issues of governance. In particular, it may not be possible to ignore the fundamental connections between scientific uncertainty and social uncertainty in relation to flood risk management. The spatial separation of pathway (rural land management) and receptor (downstream flood risk), coupled to the fact that rural land management measures necessarily involve economic impacts, means that the recommendation of rural land management as a flood risk management policy may well entail significant controversy. It may also reduce the extent to which individual actors (in the case of the most diffuse measures) can be relied upon to implement the management measures required of them.

Finally, it is important to recognise that evaluating rural land management as a response to flood risk can become a classic example of a 'wicked' problem. Following Richards (1998), these are problems that fall between policy responsibilities because they are commonly problematic or beneficial across many of the institutions that are responsible for delivering them. As a result of its spatially diffuse nature, land management falls into this class of problem. However, there is a second sense in which rural land management is 'wicked': the benefits of enhanced land stewardship are multi-functional (e.g. flood protection, water quality improvement, biodiversity enhancement). Thus, while some aspects of rural land management, especially the more near-source located, diffuse, may have flood benefits that are difficult to quantify and which are highly uncertain, there may be other (sometimes equally intangible) benefits that can be easily dismissed unless we think outside of the box, across many sectoral interests. Thus, some flood protection benefits may be accrued from other land management policies, by making sure that their linkages to flood protection are clear, even if they cannot be relied upon as flood protection policies *per se*.

References

Acreman, M., 2003. 'The impact of floodplain restoration on flood hydrology', in ed. Defra, *Proceedings of the 38th Defra Flood and Coastal Management Conference 2003*, Keele, Staffordshire, 06.1.1–06.1.12.

Archer, D., 2003. 'Scale effects on the hydrological impact of upland afforestation and drainage using indices of flow variability: the River Irthing, England', *Hydrology and Earth System Sciences*, 7, 325–338.

Betteridge, K., Mackay, A.D., Shepherd, T.G., Barker, D.J., Budding, P.J., Devantier, B.P. and Costall, D.A., 1999. 'Effect of cattle and sheep treading on surface configuration of a sedimentary hill soil', *Australian Journal of Soil Research*, 37, 743–760.

Blackwell, M.S.A., Hogan, D.V. and Maltby, E., 1999. 'The use of conventionally and alternatively located buffer zones for the removal of nitrate from diffuse agricultural run-off', *Water Science and Technology*, 39, 157–164.

Boardman, J., 2003. 'Soil erosion and flooding on the eastern South Downs, southern England, 1976–2001', *Transactions, Institute of British Geographers*, 28, 176–196.

Boardman, J. and Evans, R., 1991. *Flooding at Steepdown*, Report to Adur District Council.

Boardman, J., Evans, R. and Ford, J., 2003. 'Muddy floods on the South Downs, southern England: problems and responses', *Environmental Science and Policy*, 6, 69–83.

Burke, W., 1975. Effect of drainage on the hydrology of blanket bogs, *Irish Journal of Agricultural Research*, 14, 145–162.

Burt, T.P., Matchett, L.S., Goulding, K.W.T., Webster, C.P. and Haycock, N.E., 1999. 'Denitrification in riparian buffer zones: the role of floodplain hydrology', *Hydrological Processes*, 13, 1451–1463.

Buttle, J.M., 2002. 'Rethinking the donut: the case for hydrologically relevant buffer zones', *Hydrological Processes*, 16, 3093–3096.

Calder, I.R. and Aylward, B., 2006. 'Forest and floods: moving to an evidence-based approach to watershed and integrated flood management', *Water International*, 31, 87–99.

Davies, D.B., Finney, J.B. and Richardson, S.J., 1973. 'Relative effects of weight and wheel slip in causing soil compaction', *Journal of Soil Science*, 24, 339–409.

Defra, 2002. *Development of a Database of Agriculture Drainage*, Final Report to Defra Project ESO111, Defra, London.

Defra, 2004a. *Codes of Good Agricultural Practice*, Department for Environment, Food and Rural Affairs, London, available online www.defra.gov.uk/environ/cogap/cogap.htm

Defra, 2004b. *Single Farm Payment Scheme*, Department for Environment, Food and Rural Affairs, London, available online www.defra.gov.uk/farm/capreform/singlepay/overview/

Defra, 2004c. *English Rural Development Plan: Agri-environment schemes*, Department for Environment, Food and Rural Affairs, London, available online www.defra.gov.uk/erdp/schemes/

Defra, 2005a. *Entry Level Stewardship Handbook. Environmental Stewardship*, Rural Development Service, Department for Environment, Food and Rural Affairs, London.

Defra, 2005b. *Higher Level Stewardship Handbook. Environmental Stewardship*, Rural Development Service, Department for Environment, Food and Rural Affairs, London.

Duley, F.L. and Russell, J.C., 1939. 'The use of crop residues for soil moisture conservation', *Journal of American Society of Agronomy*, 31, 703–709.

Evans, R. and Boardman, J., 2003. 'Curtailment of muddy floods in the Sompting catchment, South Downs, West Sussex, southern England', *Soil Use and Management*, 19, 223–231.

Hawkins, J.C. and Brown, N.J., 1963. 'Tillage practices and mechanisation', *Netherland Journal of Agricultural Science*, 11, 140–144.

Haycock, N.E., Pinay, G. and Walker, G., 1993. 'Nitrogen-retention in river corridors – European perspective', *Ambio*, 22, 340–346.

Hickin, A.J., 2002. 'Flood management, communities and the environment: a strategy for the Somerset levels and moors', in *Wetlands and the Community*, ed. CIWEM, Proceedings from a one-day conference.

JBA Consulting, 2001. *River Gaunless Flood Defence Strategy*, Report to Babtie Group.

JBA Consulting, 2003. *Lower Derwent Project Phase 2 (2001–2003): Ings Investigation, Analysis and Conclusions*, July, Report to the Lower Derwent Board.

Kwaad, F.J.P.M. and Mulligen, E.J.V., 1991. 'Cropping system effects of maize on infiltration, runoff and erosion on loess soils in South-Limbourg (the Netherlands): a comparison of two rainfall events', *Soil Technology*, 4, 281–295.

Lane, S.N., Brookes, C.J., Hardy, R.J., Holden, J., James, T.D., Kirkby, M.J., McDonald, A.T., Tayefi, V. and Yu, D., 2003. 'Land management, flooding and environmental risk: new approaches to a very old question', *Proceedings of the Annual CIWEM Conference*, Harrogate, September.

LEAF, 2005. *Linking Environment and Farming*, National Agricultural Centre, Stoneleigh, available online www.leafuk.org/

Lobley, M. and Potter, C., 1998. Environmental stewardship in UK agriculture: a comparison of the environmentally sensitive areas programme and the countryside stewardship scheme in south eastern England, *Geoforum*, 29(4), 413–432.

McDonald, A.T., Lane, S.N., Chalk, E. and Haycock, N., 2004. 'Rivers of dreams: on the gulf between theoretical and practical aspects of river restoration', *Transactions of Institute of British Geographers*, 29, 257–281.

Morris, J., Mills, J. and Crawford, I.M., 2000a. 'Promoting farmer uptake of agri-environmental schemes: the arable options of the Countryside Stewardship Scheme', *Land Use Policy*, 17, 241–254.

Morris, J., Vivash, R., Alsop, D., Lawson, C., Leeds-Harrison, P. and Bailey, A., 2002. *Economic Basis and Practicalities of Washland Creation on the Somerset Moors and Levels*, Report to EU Wise Use of Flood Plains Project, Cranfield University at Silsoe and River Restoration Centre, Silsoe.

Morris, J., Bailey, A.P., Alsop, D., Vivash, R.M., Lawson, C.S. and Leeds-Harrison, P.B., 2004a. 'Integrating flood management and agri-environment through washland creation in the UK', *Journal of Farm Management*, 12, 1–16.

Morris, J., Hess, T.M., Gowing, D.G., Leeds-Harrison, P.B., Bannister, N., Vivash, R.M.N. and Wade, M., 2004b. *Integrated Washland Management for Flood Defence and Biodiversity*, English Nature Research Report, 598, English Nature, Peterborough.

Muscutt, A.D., Harris, G.L., Bailey, S.W. and Davies, D.B., 1993. 'Buffer zones to improve water quality – a review of their potential use in UK agriculture', *Agriculture, Ecosystems and Environment*, 45, 59–77.

Newson, M.D. and Robinson, M., 1983. 'Effects of agricultural drainage on upland stream-flow: case-studies in mid-Wales', *Journal of Environmental Management*, 17, 333–348.

O'Connell, P.E., Beven, K.J., Carney, J.N., Clements, R.O., Ewen, J., Harris, G.L., Hollis, J., Morris, J., O'Donnell, G.M., Packman, J.C., Parkin, A., Quinn, P.F. and Shepherd, M., 2005. 'Impacts of land use management on flood generation: the current state of knowledge', *Proceedings of 40th Defra Flood and Coastal Management Conference*, University of York, July, 04.4.1–04.4.10.

Quinn, P. and Hewett, C., 2003. 'An Earth systems engineering approach to the direct management of runoff flow paths and nutrient remediation at source', 7th International Specialised Conference on Diffuse Pollution and Basin Management, August, Dublin.

Richards, S., 1998. 'Wicked problems and clever solutions', *Aspects of Sustainable Agriculture and Rural Policy*, UK Round Table on Sustainable Development, London, 45–51.

Robinson, M., 1986. 'Changes in catchment runoff following drainage and afforestation', *Journal of Hydrology*, 86, 71–84.

Robinson, M., 1990. *Impact of Improved Land Drainage on River Flows*, Institute of Hydrology Report, 13, Institute of Hydrology, Wallingford.

Robinson, M., Cognard-Plancq, A.-L., Cosandey, C., David, J., Durnard, P., Fuhrer, H.-W., Hall, R., Hendriques, M.O., Mark, V., McCarthy, R., McDonnell, M., Martin, C., Nisbet, T., O'Dea, P., Rodgers, M. and Zollner, A., 2003. 'Studies of the impacts of forest on peak flows and baseflow: a European perspective', *Forest Ecology and Management*, 186, 85–97.

Schwab, G.O., Fangmeier, D.D., Frevert, R.K. and Elliot, W.J., 1993. *Soil and Water Conservation Engineering*, Wiley, New York.

Vought, L.B.M., Pinay, G., Fugslang, A. and Ruffinoni, C., 1995. 'Structure and function of buffer strips from a water quality perspective in agricultural landscapes', *Landscape and Urban Planning*, 31, 323–331.

Weatherhead, E.K., Knox, G., Morris, J., Hess, T.M., Bradley, I. and Saunders, C., 1997. *On Farm Water Conservation*, Research Report to MAFF, Silsoe College, Cranfield University.

Wynne, B., 1992. 'Uncertainty and environmental learning – reconceiving science and policy in the preventative paradigm', *Global Environmental Change – Human and Policy Dimensions*, 2, 111–127.

19 Responses to future intra-urban flood risks

Richard M. Ashley and Adrian J. Saul

Introduction

This chapter provides an overview of the possible responses that could be implemented to manage the increased risks of flooding in the intra-urban area and assesses their relative merits in terms of reducing flood risk in a manner that is both cost-efficient and as sustainable as possible.

The overall effectiveness of the identified available responses in reducing flood risks is assessed and ranked and their performance with respect to sustainability criteria also considered. Attention is also given to the degree of uncertainty associated with different responses and the research necessary to increase confidence in their capability to reduce flood risk sustainably.

The potential responses

In the intra-urban area, spatial scale is of major significance as illustrated in Chapter 10. Here in Chapter 19 the flood risks considered are those arising from the underground 'minor' drainage systems and smaller non-critical watercourses.

Figure 10.1 illustrates the sources and importance of the spatial scales for intra-urban flooding and responses. It is essential to adopt a systems-based approach to these responses, as many of them will be suitable only at different scales. Within the core responses illustrated in Fig. 10.1, are a range of social, environmental and economic factors as well as technical ones. Utilisation of any response will depend upon socio-economic factors as well as technical effectiveness, hence the need to consider the relative sustainability in both implementation of individual responses, and also when used in combination, as is more likely.

The intra-urban flood management system is a combination of above-ground surfaces, with pathways, channels and flow routes (the major system) plus above- and below-ground systems including drains and sewers, comprising and linked to various storage facilities (the minor system). Flooding is a symptom of inadequacy in the system to accommodate different critical storm events, or combinations of these. Urban areas must be considered in terms of existing form, layout and function and also likely future developments. It is probable that existing area drainage

Table 19.1. Response groups for intra-urban area and brief descriptions

Response group	Description	Scale of response
1. Building development, operation and form	Form of roof, building and curtilage drainage. Includes non-main sewer (minor) systems	At the building level to control local risk to the building envelope. The curtilage surrounding the building (overlaps with 3 below)
2. Urban area development, operation and form (including sacrificial areas)	Changes in urban form – building density, layout and other aspects of development, such as greenspace	Street scale up to city scale (overlaps with 3 below)
3. Source control and above-ground pathways	Source control is the management of storm water as close to the point of origin as possible. Above-ground pathways include roads, paths and greenspaces	Local property curtilage, larger developed areas, up to regional scale (overlaps with 1 and 2 above)
4. Groundwater control	Control of groundwater levels	Unlikely to be locally effective – regional scale
5. Storage above and below ground	Ponds, tanks, etc.	Ponds and wetlands may comprise part of 3 above. Tanks, where below ground, are part of the minor drainage system (overlap with 6)
6. Main drainage form, maintenance and operation	Ways in which main drainage systems (minor systems) are managed. Different alternatives	Urban areas in UK have sewerage networks. These convey flows from the local systems (see 1 above)

and urban areas will not change significantly in the near to medium future (2050s) under the scenarios considered, although there are a number of initiatives to utilise water more explicitly in UK urban areas for social, ecological, environmental and aesthetic reasons (e.g. CIRIA, 2003).

In the original Foresight 'future flooding' study (Evans *et al.*, 2004), responses were considered in two distinct ways, in terms of:

1. What happens within the urban area due to floods arriving from outside the area (inundation), due to pluvial causes within the urban area and due to constraints to discharge due to high river or sea levels.
2. Measures implemented in urban areas to alter the volume, spatial distribution and timing of fluvial, coastal and 'muddy floods' in urban areas and the effect on the catchment downstream.

This chapter deals with just the first of these. By expert review, six main response groups were identified, as shown in Table 19.1. Those responses in the urban area that were amenable to some degree to quantification have been considered in detail using hydraulic simulation models.

Response groups and effectiveness

The main aspects of each of the response groups are briefly outlined below. Where feasible, the effectiveness of individual responses is quantified.

Response Group 1: Building development operation and form

This group considered the opportunities to manage flood risk at the building level to control local risk, and also includes the curtilage surrounding the building and

321

floods originating from outside the curtilage as overland flow or from groundwater within the curtilage.

The principal measures considered are:

- Design of building drainage (including green roofs, ponding on roofs, etc.).
- Managing urbanisation at the building and local level (specifically in terms of building development and form).
- Flood proofing individual buildings/parts of buildings including local flood protection (freestanding temporary barriers; removable household products, etc.).
- Rainwater harvesting and local stormwater use, including disconnection of downpipes.
- Changing building and local area drainage standards.
- Road gully inlets control.

The majority of problems relate to existing urban areas, hence responses considered both existing buildings (of a variety of types and in various condition) and new buildings.

Building roof drainage has typically been designed to accommodate storm events with a typical return period of up to 30 years, although more recently extreme value statistical approaches have been recommended in (BS) EN 12056 Part 3: 2000. This includes the use of 'probable maximum rainfall', a dubious concept given the variability in spatial and temporal behaviour of rainfall particularly due to climate change (e.g. Marshall, 2003). Retrofitting of flood risk management systems to existing buildings is likely to be problematic, both technically and economically, whereas it should be feasible to manage new buildings to cope better with flood risk by proofing and altering layouts, with, for example, accommodation planned above ground level.

Imposing a need to respond to increasing flood risk on property owners is unlikely to be feasible, although this could be highlighted in the new 'sellers packs' (Carr, 2004). Securing the building against water ingress could involve the integration of flood barriers, impermeable membranes or self-sealing building components (e.g. ODPM, 2003). Many prestigious new developments seek to remove the rainwater quickly by way of siphonic systems (e.g. Wright *et al.*, 2002). However, the latter may simply lead to other problems downstream where the building drainage interfaces with the curtilage and main drainage systems, particularly as the standards for the design of these systems are still in their infancy (e.g. Bramhall, 2005).

Overall the success of these responses may be good locally (at the building level), but less so for the curtilage and wider catchment when the largest events occur. The most effective responses may be achievable for the larger buildings or groups thereof. Building operation and form is very scenario dependent, as shape, type and use will vary in terms of wealth and lifestyle norms.

In terms of sustainability, a number of recent studies have advocated the use of roof drainage for household water, by way of some form of holding storage tank (e.g. Parkinson, 1999; Dixon, 2000). In the former, this approach was advocated as being more sustainable, although there would be downstream problems in terms of lack of flushing of solids in large existing main drainage systems for the usual once a day peak flow. In each case, a significant amount of stormwater could be collected for on-site use, possibly alleviating to some extent downstream local flood problems.

Response Group 2: Urban area development, operation and form, (including sacrificial areas)

This is the potential to influence the risk of flooding within urban areas through changes in urban form and development. The principal measures considered were:

- promoting green spaces;
- local flood barriers (transferring water);
- controlling new development;
- building regulations for flood risk areas to require flood mitigation strategies;
- abandoning properties most at risk;
- sacrificial local storage areas;
- local and community protection of 'islands' within urbanscapes (temporary).

An understanding of the varying possible functions of land is at the heart of reducing flood risk. As the value of land increases so does the need to consider how different roles can be considered for the space. Green space can, for example, fulfil storage and infiltration roles in addition to leisure and amenity functions. The importance of developing multi-functional greenspace networks in towns and cities is increasingly well recognised, for example by the Commission for Architecture and the Built Environment. However, existing inner cities have little space for storage and infiltration. Preservation of existing greenspace, as well as consequent greening of streets and roofs, can be locally efficient measures to delay runoff. Policies promoting the unsealing of impervious surfaces in commercial zones (e.g. car parks) offer opportunities for increasing infiltration. In low density housing areas, densification needs to be better controlled to avoid further loss of greenspace or private gardens. In addition, urban fringe areas, including green belts, could be assigned a particular role to reduce flood risk, and give them new value (e.g. Forman, 1995).

Even a modest degree of urbanisation will change the hydrological behaviour and runoff characteristics of a catchment. For a typical UK town, with up to 40% impervious surfaces, some 20–50% of the initial rainfall volume appears ultimately as flow in a main drainage network. Strategic management of hard surfaces (and runoff) is therefore likely to be very effective at reducing flood risk. Even where there is control over urbanisation, creep adds hard surfaces in an uncontrolled and unpredictable manner due to domestic activities (Cutting, 2003), hence any control on this is likely to be very effective at reducing local and downstream flood risk. Strategies need to vary at a national level between strongly developing urban areas that will lead to their further compaction and urban areas that are restructuring, often losing population. In the former, the capacity for flood storage may become reduced, and strategies are required on a regional and city level to improve conveyance and storage of floods outside the built areas in functional floodplains and green belt areas (e.g. by creating/restoring wetlands) as is being done in the USA (Pepper *et al.*, 2002). Preservation of greenspace, including 'brownfield sites' or derelict land, is of particular importance and may provide good options for flood storage at a range of scales (Carroll, 2003).

Within urban areas, priority should be given to the creation or restoration of coherent greenspace networks for flood storage and conveyance. In terms of retrospective responses, watercourse 'daylighting' is now becoming more prevalent in the UK, whereby previously culverted watercourses are re-opened (e.g. Pinkham, 2000). On the strategic level, national government is setting the agenda for urban development in the form of Planning Policy Guidance (PPG), being revised into Planning Policy Statements (PPS), and building regulations, in order to enhance adaptation of urban form and reduce flood risks. Various Guidance Notes and Statements (e.g. PPG/S3, PPG/S25) can have different implications for urban flood risks, as the former advocates more compact housing while the latter wishes to limit and control the amount of runoff. There are now signs that developers or residents/business owners will be increasingly required to pay for the costs of extra flood defences associated with new build (e.g. through a Section 106 Agreement) necessitating packages of measures to ensure that new development is 'flood neutral'.

323

Regional Assemblies are required to produce a spatial strategy for their region and this may offer particular opportunities to influence urban form and development, stimulating interventions into the urban fabric to reduce flood risk. Enabling local communities to influence planning and decision making more effectively will be an important step to achieve a more sustainable urban form and development. Local Agenda 21 and Community Strategies are means to achieve this goal, as is the current drive to increase transparency in the planning process and with it more effective stakeholder participation. Although there is an increasing body of evidence on the relationship between urban form and natural processes, this is not yet fully understood and therefore not properly utilised in urban planning in the UK.

Response Group 3: Source control including above-ground pathways

Source control is the management of storm water as close to the point of origin as possible. There is a range of drainage mechanisms, now known as SUDS in the UK, to manage rainfall-runoff in ways other than the use of pipe networks. The principal measures considered here are:

- design of roads and gully pots;
- source control and local 'sustainable' water system management using a variety of techniques;
- water reuse and recycling, etc.;
- reopen culverted watercourses (daylighting) (see also above);
- controlling pathways of runoff;
- pumping off-site;
- multiple drainage systems;
- aesthetic use of water in the urban area;
- detention ponds;
- permeable land cover.

Most of these measures are designed to:

- minimise the amount and rate of runoff;
- minimise runoff volumes using infiltration;
- attenuate peak flows using storage;
- improve the quality of runoff using physical and biological processes.

Source controls comprise a range of possibilities within the concept of a SUDS 'train', i.e. a series of measures in sequence. They can also be 'non-structural' in that they may relate to behavioural changes at the points at which the runoff occurs (CIRIA, 2002).

The hydraulic effectiveness of SUDS for extreme events is a function of their hydraulic design criteria and, where infiltration is used, soil type. Their hydraulic design criteria vary between systems and therefore their ability to cater for extreme rainfall events ranges from very limited to being very effective, as shown in Table 19.2. In general, SUDS systems are more effective to some degree than pipe networks at controlling both quantity and quality of storm water drained; a major consideration for achieving the targets likely under the Water Framework Directive. There are some limitations. Where SUDS and overland flood flow paths are within floodplains, or downstream of a flood source, their effectiveness will be nullified during river flooding. The use of SUDS in these circumstances is likely to be less effective than when using standard pipe systems. Another risk is that the 'creeping urbanisation' problems (Cutting, 2003) that affect current main drainage systems, could be even more risky for SUDS as the SUDS surfaces could themselves become 'urbanised' by careless homeowners.

Most SUDS systems are not designed for large events, and only recently have structures such as ponds been designed to address events of one in 100 years.

Table 19.2. Structural SUDS methods and significance at managing flood flows and volumes (based on recent UK research)

Measure	Peak flow attenuation of extreme events	Volume reduction of extreme events
Green roofs	+ +	+
Water butts	O	O
Domestic soakaway/infiltration trench	+ +	+ +
Filter strips	+	O
Filter trenches	+	+
Swale	+	O
Under-drained swale (trench-trough)	+ + + +	+ +
Pervious pavement	+ + + +	+
Infiltration basin	+ + +	+ +
Detention basin	+ + + +	+
Retention pond	+ + + +	+
Wetland	+ +	+ +

Key: + + + + 80–100%; + + + 60–80%; + + 40–60%; + 20–40%; O 0–20%; NA = not applicable/available – all relative to piped drainage system effectiveness

Where ponds are used and designed to 100-year events, the reduction in peak flow can be of the order of ten times, but requires between 3 and 4% of the contributing catchment land take, which may be expensive. The most effective mechanism for addressing extreme events is by attenuation (ponds, wetlands, etc., Hall *et al.*, 1993) as only relatively limited infiltration can occur during the most extreme events, due to soil saturation and the limited period of flooding.

Overall sustainability in relation to other options, such as piped drainage systems, is still not clear, as balancing the economic, environmental and social aspects is difficult. As a new concept, very few UK studies have been carried out on stakeholder awareness of the existence and purpose of SUDS and also their acceptability to the community (HR Wallingford, 2003). Currently there is significant resistance to their use due to the perception of increased health risk, though this fear reduces once the features become familiar.

Response Group 4: Groundwater control

This is the management of groundwater in urban areas at levels that: allow infiltration during high precipitation, so preventing flooding; prevent groundwater from rising to levels that cause basement flooding and emergence on urban surfaces; avoid aquifers resurfacing in areas where flood risk may be increased either locally or outside of the urban area. The specific measures considered are:

- controlling groundwater levels, e.g. by pumping
- maintaining sewerage capacity by reducing infiltration from groundwater
- permeable land cover maintenance.

In winter 2000/1 many groundwater tables reached surface level for the first time in many years. Much of this led to property flooding lasting for up to 6 months due to groundwater levels not receding. In the future, due to higher temperatures under climate change, there will be more dynamic interactions between the evaporation from the upper layers of the soil and any infiltrating flows. High water-table levels may also compromise infiltration drainage systems which require a minimum of 1 m of clearance above the water table to be reliable (CIRIA, 2002). A review of the issues related to groundwater has recently been completed by Defra (Jacobs, 2004).

The amount of permeable land surface in a catchment will be important for the relative groundwater levels. Within the urban area itself, an increase in paved surfaces may help to reduce the groundwater levels, making it more practicable to use infiltration drainage systems (see also source control).

Solutions to lowering groundwater levels locally involve, e.g., french and other drainage, and, for protection, local flood proofing and pumping. There is typically greater complexity in groundwater based solutions than, e.g., river flooding, which may include diversionary action that may impact downstream (Fleming, 2002). However, groundwater management alone cannot materially influence flood risk. This has to be considered in relation to the inputs and outputs in the catchment flow balance. It is possible that the most useful approach is to consider the conjunctive operation of groundwater for supply purposes together simultaneously with the control of flood risk from rising groundwater, although there are potential quality problems (e.g. UKWIR, 2003).

As regards sustainability, no statutory body is currently responsible for groundwater flooding (Law of the Land Newsletter, Spring, 2002), although this may change under Defra's 'Making Space for Water' initiatives. Nonetheless it is likely that several agencies will be involved in groundwater management. The management of groundwater to control flood risk is a long-term large-scale response, often entailing large volume management with possible high-energy utilisation. It is therefore likely that this type of response may be suitable only in areas where water is normally scarce at certain times of the year. This is not likely to be a feasible response to ensure that local infiltration systems continue to operate and help reduce flood risk.

Response Group 5: Storage above and below ground

This response group consists of additional storage volume provided by physical structures above or below ground to increase the potential of the urban drainage system to act as a flood defence mechanism, and for surface storage this group overlaps with the source control response group. The main focus here is on in-sewer storage (volumetric capacity of sewer network conduits) and tanks/ponds (discrete storage provided by physical structures above and below ground). The specific measures considered are:

- detention ponds;
- mini-storage;
- storage along/adjacent to flood system;
- local ponding in flood retention areas;
- underground storage;
- temporary flood storage (e.g. in parkland).

If additional storage volume is provided in a drainage system, more of the runoff can be temporally stored instead of overflowing, thus reducing the frequency of flooding. Stored water is released back into the network over an extended time period, reducing the peak discharge flow (by more than 80% in some cases) and achieving an attenuation effect. This is potentially the most effective of all the potential response measures in urban areas (e.g. Amandes and Bedient, 1980; WRc, 1997; Lau, 2002; Hall *et al.*, 1993). The main limitation is land-take, even where the storage is below ground.

In practice there are a large number of possible in-sewer tank configurations used, including on- and off-line tanks (in series or in parallel with the sewer line) and tank sewers (as enlarged sections of sewer length). The relative advantages and disadvantages of different kinds of storage on the surface and in-sewer are summarised in Table 19.3.

Below-ground (sewer) storage schemes are designed to achieve standard flood protection levels depending on location, but not traditionally in excess of 30 years.

Table 19.3. Advantages and disadvantages of sewer storage types (Butler and Davies, 2000)

Storage types	Advantages	Disadvantages
Surface ponds	Large capacity	Capital and maintenance costs
Detention ponds	Runoff reduction of major storms Aesthetics Multi-purpose use Pollution reduction	Large footprint Pollution and eutrophication Pest breeding potential Aesthetics Safety hazards
Underground tanks	Runoff reduction of storms Pollution reduction No visual intrusion Capital cost	Maintenance costs Access difficulties
Tank sewers	Runoff reduction of storms Pollution reduction No visual intrusion Capital cost	Maintenance costs Access difficulties

The design life is 25–50 years, but many existing below-ground structures are considerably older.

Above-ground storage (in ponds and other attenuation systems) is now being designed for 100-year storm events and PPG25 requires consideration of down-stream flood risk when these can no longer contain the flows. Balancing ponds are used extensively by the Highways Agency and others to control runoff from road systems. One problem with these ponds is their propensity to accumulate sediments and lose capacity with time. Even where there are on-stream balancing ponds, there may be downstream flood risk problems necessitating management by way of, e.g., storage systems. Above-ground storage has a proportionately large land take. Temporary local storage is also advocated as an option when dealing with extreme events and the 'failure' of the system (CIRIA, 2005).

There is clear interaction between the storage responses and the source control responses, as some of the measures can be categorised as being relevant in both groups. Wide adoption of source control type responses (i.e. more distributed storage and retention) could lead to reduction in volumes needed to be accommodated by centralised storage and alter its main function from a stormwater flood control strategy into a water quality control strategy as well as a back-up strategy for extreme events. This may be a useful win–win situation and lead to long-term sustainability, although there is some resistance to new ponds in the UK due to the perception that these are a health hazard (HR Wallingford, 2003).

As regards sustainability there are difficulties with the ownership and operation of above-ground storage systems due to maintenance and responsibility being vested in the land owner. Centralised storage is an engineering solution, which is effective in combating flooding, immediate in its effectiveness (i.e. starts to contribute at maximum capacity immediately after work completion), but expensive in terms of capital costs and also material energy use. This may be a poor solution in sustainability terms (Gouda *et al.*, 2003), although it has a sound track record and effectiveness is well established. If the system is coupled with real-time control (RTC) strategies it could lead to simultaneous improvement in both flooding and river water quality (from overflows, e.g. Zawliski and Sakson, 2005). Even existing sewerage could be made more effective by using RTC to maximise the use of the estimated typical 50% spare capacity of existing sewerage under extreme events.

Response Group 6: Main drainage form, maintenance and operation

This response group consists of the physical form of the urban drainage system and operation with respect to the impact on flood control. It can comprise both pipes and other (surface) conveyance systems. It has been considered in terms of three response sub-groups:

1. System form:
   - sewer separation;
   - managing wrong connections;
   - limiting inflows by constricting inlets or surface disconnections;
   - limiting groundwater infiltration into sewers by rehabilitation;
   - localised non-return valves;
   - pump stations.
2. System operation:
   - real-time control;
   - pumping.
3. System maintenance:
   - planned;
   - integrated.

The UK has more than 96% coverage of sewerage connected to properties, of which some 70% is combined (Butler and Davies, 2000). This existing asset base puts a huge inertia on any potential major innovations that require a different approach or usage of these systems. The relative merits of combined or separate systems of sewer in relation to flood risk are summarised in Table 19.4.

There are a number of possibilities for preventing sewer flooding that are low cost (May *et al.*, 1998). The case for bypass sewers is also presented. Such measures will be effective at the individual property level or for a few local properties. In local terms, their implementation may be very effective, although service levels would typically be based on the 100-year return period for internal flooding and lower levels for external flooding.

Limiting inflows of stormwater by constricting inlets or disconnecting roofs and paved areas is considered in more detail in the source control response group.

Table 19.4. Relative merits of combined or separate sewer systems in relation to flood risk

Separate systems	Combined systems
Advantages	**Disadvantages**
No CSOs hence less spills and downstream watercourse overloading risk. Also less pollution from extreme storm events	CSO necessary: downstream watercourse overloading risk, also more pollution
Flooding occurs only with storm-water system (fewer health risk implications)	If surcharge of manholes occurs and surface flooding, foul sewage will escape and increase health risks
Sewers can follow own optimum line and depth, which improves capacity and operation	Lines and depths are a compromise, which limits effective operation
	Most UK systems are combined and new systems mainly connect into these, often leading to downstream overloading
Disadvantages	**Advantages**
Extra capital cost (possibly lower operating cost)	Lower construction costs (but higher operational costs)
High risk of wrong connections potentially overloading storm or foul sewer	House drainage simpler as no risk of wrong connection
Storm-water outfall may lead to high downstream flows and flood risks	

Limiting groundwater infiltration by sealing cracks, fissures and joints in sewers will increase capacity available for storm flows (Weiß *et al.*, 2002), as in some areas, such as Thames Tideway, this is some 50% of the dry weather flow (Thames Water, 2005) and is implicated in excessive CSO discharges.

Dynamic management of sewer system operation, by way of RTC, (e.g. CIRIA, 1996), is seen as a cost-effective way of gaining additional flow and storage capacity in existing systems in many countries (e.g. Duong *et al.*, 2005), but is not utilised in the UK due to perceptions of risk.

Proactive or planned drainage system maintenance is an area of current interest in the UK water industry in terms of the new serviceability approach being taken under the current Asset Management Planning five-year plan in England and Wales. The main link to flooding is by way of sewers in poor condition or sediment and fat which, if allowed to accumulate, can significantly reduce the capacity of the sewer system and hence reduce flood protection (Ashley *et al.*, 2004). Flood protection can potentially be improved by establishing better-organised, prioritised and integrated maintenance. The adoption of a 'common framework' approach to this in England and Wales should help in the future (Heywood *et al.*, 2002).

In terms of sustainability, it has been argued (Veldkamp *et al.*, 1997 and others) that the most sustainable solutions are those promoting exclusion, local use of storm water, followed by those promoting infiltration of part of it into the aquifer, followed by separate systems, and finally by combined systems (due to the environmental and health implications of CSO and combined sewer flooding). This would imply that reducing the inputs of storm water into the system is potentially more sustainable than building more separate sewer systems or separating existing systems. Dealing with a problem locally (low impact development) is normally considered to be the more sustainable approach (e.g. Walesh and Carr, 1998), although not the approach being proposed to solve the Thames Tideway problems (Thames Water, 2005), despite evidence of effectiveness from elsewhere in the world.

Quantification of responses

The responses were those considered by the expert group as amenable to modelling and representing typical responses that could readily be effected. These are:

1. storage – either above or below ground;
2. sewer upsizing;
3. disconnecting impervious areas (assuming new infiltration or equivalent facilities);
4. the potential for flood management by directed overland flow flood pathways.

These were considered for the three pilot catchments described in Chapter 10. In each case, the outline sizes and scale required for the response were determined for the specified return period (of storm input). These were then related by unit costs to direct capital costs. Finally, the link was made from numbers of properties originally flooded and subsequently protected for the whole of each catchment to frequency – providing an estimate of the equivalent expected annual damage (EAD) in terms of costs for response implementation.

This provided the EAD and response costs for the medium-high climate change scenario for each individual response in each area. As this covered only the main drainage network, additional costs had to be estimated for the local drainage and property flood risk reduction. These were based on published information and assumptions were made about the scale-up for local risk based on recently published information on the extent of local drainage systems in the UK (Atkins,

Table 19.5. Unit cost of option per property at risk of internal flooding (main drainage only) – as addressed by sewerage undertakers

Catchment	Unit cost per at risk property	FEH			2080 (UKCIP98)		
		10: £	30: £	100: £	10: £	30: £	100: £
1 (pluvial only)	Storage	146 578	194 683	209 815	68 369	98 067	77 492
	Conveyance	79 825	76 221	57 026	28 178	27 134	17 740
2 (major drainage system interactions)	Storage	75 144	112 266	137 189	114 764	141 195	174 637
	Conveyance	258 847	238 499	222 147	191 617	145 787	149 795
3 (coastal and tidal interactions)	Storage	896 833	789 033	696 059	771 320	702 148	660 507
	Conveyance	1 678 833	829 833	435 735	930 520	514 648	238 507

2003). Ideally, recorded property flooding information should be used but, after consultation with ABI, it was apparent that this was not available. Also, such information is typically under-reported due to the perception that it will damage property values.

The EAD and cost curves were then assumed to be applicable across the UK. Hence the cost-effectiveness of the individual responses was determined by scale-up in terms of population.

The modelling considering responses showed that results for the national enterprise scenario were dependent largely on changes in rainfall rather than catchment characteristics or any other variable, although changes in urban paved surfaces (disconnection) would have as significant an effect as rainfall.

It was shown that the extent of flooding and the potential scale of remedial works correlated well with rainfall. This meant that the effects of other scenarios could be evaluated with reasonable confidence by scaling from projected rainfall change, rather than having to repeat the whole modelling impact assessment for each case (Ashley et al., 2005). This enabled national enterprise to be used as the baseline and the other three economic scenarios to be evaluated using the scaling factors outlined in Chapter 10.

The below-ground storage and conveyance options are those used typically by the sewerage undertakers in alleviating property flood risk in terms of the OFWAT DG5 register. Table 19.5 shows the option cost per property within the three test catchments as determined by modelling results. The costs may be compared with the values of the average cost per property of increasing capacity to solve sewer flooding for groups of more than ten properties of around £37 000, ranging from a minimum of £5000 to £90 000 identified by OFWAT in 2002, and a range of £17 000–£150 000 reported by water companies in their response at the time the Foresight report was produced (OFWAT, 2002a, 2002b).

Following a further report on the benefits of sewer flooding control (Pearce, 2003), OFWAT now allow a cost per DG5 incident remediation of £120 000 for the period 2005–2010. Table 19.5 shows that costs increase with return period of the rainfall, but that they are also dependent on site-specific circumstances. In catchment 1, the proximity of watercourses capable of accepting discharges from the urban area makes the conveyance option more cost efficient. However, the interaction between the urban catchment and local watercourses in catchment 2 and the tidal interactions in catchment 3 has a profound effect on costs in these areas. In both these cases, the length of pipe required to deliver flows to a suitable discharge point makes the conveyance option inappropriate for less severe rainfall. However, under more onerous conditions, the increase in storage requirement makes the conveyance option more cost effective. This demonstrates the potential difficulties

Table 19.6. Summary of model results from main drainage modelling and interpretation for typical current responses

Catchment	Responses: £/yr capital costs							
	Storage below ground[a]		Storage in SUDS[a]		Upsized sewer (conveyance)		Disconnection[b]	
	FEH	2080	FEH	2080	FEH	2080	FEH	2080
1	956 322	1 367 982	29 770	44 458	387 729	413 203	555 554	777 776
£ per capita	11.2	16.0	0.35	0.52	4.5	4.8	6.5	9.1
2	1 624 786	4 230 143	59 034	153 701	3 688 551	4 787 062	–	–
£ per capita	6.2	16.1	0.22	0.58	14.0	18.2	–	–
3	1 970 029	3 506 780	71 580	127 410	2 135 911	2 461 815	–	–
£ per capita	16.2	28.9	0.59	1.05	25.0	28.8	–	–

[a] One-third of the area only assumed amenable to this response.
[b] Does not include cost of land.

in the selection of appropriate options and the importance of choice of levels of service in both short-term and long-term planning.

It may be inferred from the table, that coincident fluvial and pluvial flooding is likely to result in a significant cost increase over and above the cost for pluvial flooding alone and that coincident coastal and pluvial flooding has an even greater effect. This means that special attention should be paid to areas where coincident flooding may occur.

The analysis for the catchment-wide storage solutions, including surface and/or SUDS options, are shown in Table 19.6. This shows that both the inland and coastal catchments (catchment 2 and 3 respectively in Table 19.6) will require large storage volumes to resolve all the predicted flooding. However, the ratio of required storage against increase in rainfall is higher for the storage solutions than for the pipe upsizing (conveyance). The ratio of storage required is significantly larger for the inland catchment, which would suggest that the increase in water levels in the water-courses could be having an impact on the outflows from the overflows in the catchment. Although the ratio between storage requirements and rainfall is significantly higher than for the pipe upsizing solutions the cost is significantly less, even though the latter does not include disruption costs during construction – likely to be spread out over much larger (linear) areas than the local storage solutions. Therefore, storage would appear to be the most cost-effective solution.

Catchment 1 flooding was in a residential area and was investigated to assess the possibility of using the highways and open areas to route any excess flow ejected from the sewer network. Catchment 2 was away from the residential area and therefore such flooding would not affect properties directly. The third catchment was close to only a few properties and the gradient of the land would tend to move surface flooding into a recreation ground away from the properties.

Any flow from the major flooding area in catchment 1 would take the water along the highway and will try to return it back into the sewer network further downstream. Any flow would need to exceed kerb level to route through a property into a drain to the south. The potential for managing this flow by diverting along the highway and between properties into an adjacent watercourse was shown to be viable by investigating the pathways using GIS (Ashley *et al.*, 2005). Guidance to using such approaches has now been provided in a recent report (CIRIA, 2005).

Following the quantification of the engineering solutions above, the overall response costs were scaled up to national level under perceived current conditions (FEH rainfall and current investments). For this and the future National Enterprise scenario, an evaluation of the costs of the responses within the different drainage

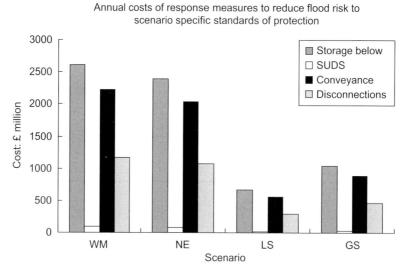

Annual costs of response measures to reduce flood risk to
scenario specific standards of protection

Fig. 19.1. Annual costs of the response measures to be introduced in each scenario

sectors: (public sewers; private sewers; overland flow control) was used to determine a total response cost of some £5 million for the current projections and of £22 million for the 2080 national enterprise scenario.

These figures may be compared with the equivalent flood risk EAD estimates of £270 million and £5055 million respectively. Differing levels of flood risk protection were selected for each of the scenarios by expert workshops and then the response costs evaluated to deliver these. The annual costs of the response measures to be introduced in each scenario are illustrated in Fig. 19.1. The SUDS or storage solutions do not include land costs as this is more highly site specific than for the other responses.

Even if these responses were to be implemented, the residual EAD under each scenario was estimated as shown in Table 19.7, from expert workshop assessment of the likely effectiveness of each response. The table also shows the original risk multiplier from the 2080s drivers, compared with how these might change following implementation of the responses.

Uncertainty in the assessments has been considered largely by expert judgement. The quantification using hydraulic computational models is of more limited uncertainty in terms of the performance of the minor systems, expected to be within some 20% of the true flows, although the key drivers are not likely to be that precise. However, once ejected from the minor drainage system, the relative accuracy of

Table 19.7. Annual cost of most likely responses and subsequent residual flood risk costs and multipliers

Scenario	World markets	National enterprise	Local stewardship	Global sustainability
Cost of responses likely under the scenario (£M per annum)	540	260	400	110
Residual expected annual damages (£M per annum) following responses	4200	2400	490	720
Original risk multiplier, year 2080 (without responses)	29	7	19	3
Residual risk multiplier following implementation of most likely responses	17	4	13	1

Table 19.8. Scores for responses to reduce flood risk (S = multiplier on baseline risk)

No.	Response group	World markets	Global responsibility	National enterprise	Local stewardship
1	Building development operation and form	1.0	0.5	1.0	0.8
2	Urban area development, operation and form (including sacrificial areas)	0.8	0.5	1.0	0.8
3	Source control (+ above ground pathways)	0.8	0.5	1.0	0.7
4	Groundwater control	1.0	1.0	1.0	1.0
5	Storage above and below ground	0.8	0.5	1.0	0.8
6	Main drainage form, maintenance and operation	0.9	0.8	0.7	1.0

modelling the movement of floods across the urban landscape is poor; expected to be within some -50% and $+100\%$ of the results given here. Compounded uncertainties occur due to the climatic and socio-economic scenarios, and the need to use expert judgements, leading overall to response performance and economic uncertainties of the order of at least -50% to $+100\%$ of the values given here.

The above were used to inform the expert assessment of the results of the scoring and ranking exercise for the degree of reduction in flood risk that each response group could achieve under each scenario, as listed in Tables 19.8 and 19.9.

Table 19.9. Response groups ranked by potential for flood risk reduction

Rank	World markets	Global responsibility	National enterprise	Local stewardship
1	Storage above and below ground	Storage above and below ground	Main drainage form, maintenance and operation	Source control (+ above-ground pathways)
2	Source control (+ above-ground pathways)	Source control (+ above-ground pathways)	Storage above and below ground	Storage above and below ground
3	Urban area development, operation and form	Urban area development, operation and form	Groundwater control	Urban area development, operation and form
4	Main drainage form, maintenance and operation	Building development operation and form	Source control (+ above-ground pathways)	Building development operation and form
5	Groundwater control	Main drainage form, maintenance and operation	Urban area development, operation and form	Main drainage form, maintenance and operation
6	Building development operation and form	Groundwater control	Building development operation and form	Groundwater control

Legend

Shade	Interpretation
	Major reduction in flood risk (S < 0.7)
	Marked reduction in flood risk (0.7 < S < 0.9)
	Minor reduction in flood risk (0.9 < S < 1.0)
	No impact (S ~ 1)

Sustainability assessment

An introduction to the sustainability issues in each of the response categories is given above. Here the formal sustainability assessment for the intra-urban responses is summarised from the Foresight report.

Only one of the responses, urban area development, operation and form, failed significantly on the sustainability criteria of: cost-effectiveness; environmental quality and social justice and then only under the world markets scenario. In two of the scenarios – urban area development, and operation and form were deemed to be effective and could be beneficial in sustainability terms. Those that performed reasonably well across at least three scenarios in terms of their impact on flood risk and had no negative impacts in terms of cost effectiveness, environmental quality and social justice are highlighted in Table 19.10. These include: main drainage form, maintenance and operation; storage above and below ground; and, to a lesser extent, source control. However, performance would depend on how these are implemented.

Three responses – storage above and below ground (cost-effective); urban area development, operation and form (environmental quality); and source control (environmental quality) – were found to reduce flood risk under at least three scenarios and provide benefits, but none of the responses is likely to produce win–win situations across the three main criteria of sustainability. The two responses that provide cause for concern in their ability to reduce flood risk under more than one scenario, while also incurring sustainability penalties under environmental

Table 19.10. The flood response measures in the urban zone that produce a reduction in flood risk across at least three scenarios and which have no sustainability penalties

Sustainability criteria			
a. Cost effectiveness	**b. Environmental quality**	**c. Social justice**	**d. Overall**
Building development, operation and form	Building development, operation and form	Building development, operation and form	Building development, operation and form
Urban area development, operation and form	Urban area development operation and form	Urban area development operation and form	Urban area development operation and form
Source control	Source control	Source control	Source control
Groundwater control	Groundwater control	Groundwater control	Groundwater control
Storage above and below ground	Storage above and below ground	Storage above and below ground	Storage above and below ground
Main drainage form maintenance and operation	Main drainage form maintenance and operation	Main drainage form maintenance and operation	Main drainage form maintenance and operation

Legend	
Shade	**Interpretation**
	Social justice failure in one scenario
	Have no sustainability penalties
	Response fails in one or more respects

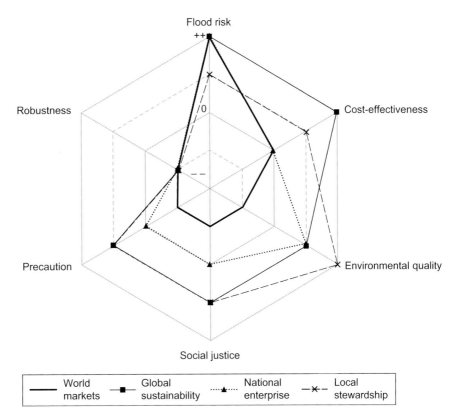

Fig. 19.2. Building development operation and form

quality, are building development, operation and form (which also failed under social justice) and groundwater control.

The sustainability 'spider diagrams' for the intra-urban area response groups are given in Figs 19.2–19.7.

Portfolios of responses were also considered, and in the intra-urban area the responses in the national enterprise and global sustainability scenarios were found to be more cost effective than in the world markets scenario. Building development, operation and form and groundwater control were seen as being relatively ineffective responses in terms of reducing flood risk and are also judged to produce environmental disbenefits although the former could be effective under two of the scenarios.

In contrast, urban development, operation and form and source control are seen to be potentially effective in reducing flood risk in the urban area and providing environmental benefits. This comes from controlling new development and the promotion of coherent green spaces to increase flood storage and conveyance and from the reopening of culverted water courses, the creation of detention ponds and the aesthetic use of water in the urban area through SUDS. The way in which these responses are implemented will be critical in determining the extent of the environmental benefits. Inevitably there will be problems in retro-fitting a range of these measures within established urban areas. However, flood risk management indicates that a priority consideration in urban development should be the preservation of greenspace, including brownfield sites where these may provide good options for flood storage and conveyance and also to provide biodiversity sites.

Only two of the measures that were effective in reducing flood risk (urban development, operation and form, and source control) failed on the grounds of social justice but only in the world markets scenario.

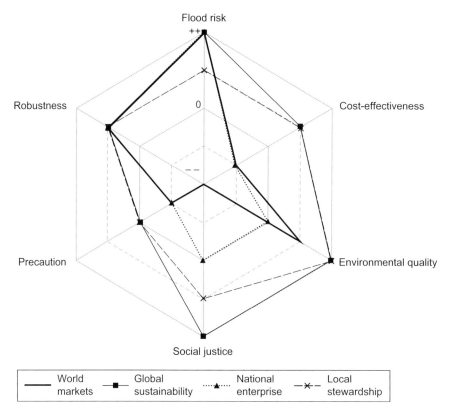

Fig. 19.3. Urban area development operation and form

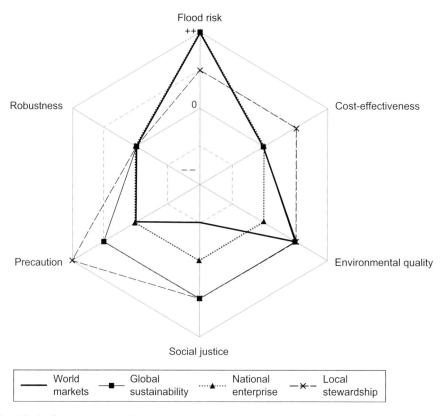

Fig. 19.4. Source control

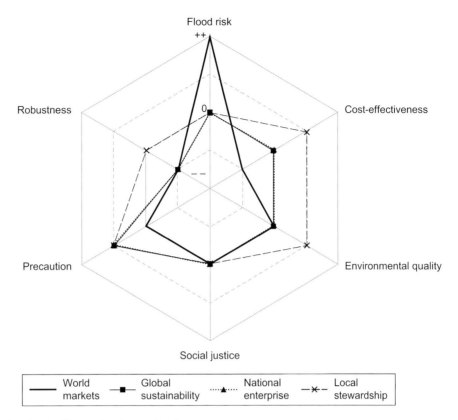

Fig. 19.5. Groundwater control

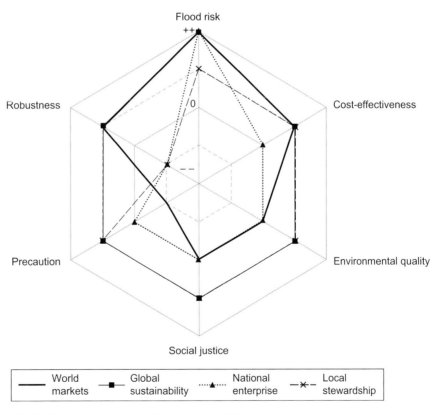

Fig. 19.6. Storage above and below ground

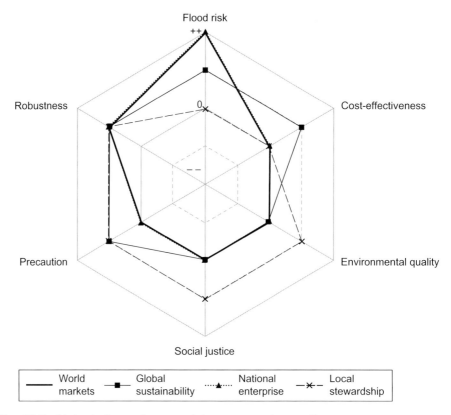

Fig. 19.7. Main drainage form, maintenance and operations

References

Amendes, C. and Bedient, P.B., 1980. 'Storm water detention in developing watersheds', *J. Env. Eng. Div.*, 106, 403–415.

Ashley, R.M., Bertrand-Krajewski, J.-L., Hvitved-Jacobsen, T. and Verbanck, M. (eds), 2004. *Sewer Solids – State of the Art*, International Water Association Scientific and Technical Report No. 14, IWA Publishing.

Ashley, R.M., Balmforth, D.J., Saul, A.J. and Blanskby, J.D., 2005. 'Flooding in the future – predicting climate change, risks and responses in urban areas', *Wat. Sci. Tech.*, 52(5), 265–274.

Atkins, W.S., 2003. *Review of Existing Private Sewers and Drains in England and Wales*, July.

Bramhall, M., 2005. The performance of syphonic rainwater outlets with gutters, PhD thesis, University of Sheffield.

BS EN 12056-1:2000. *Gravity Drainage Systems Inside Buildings*. Parts 1–5, BSI, London.

Butler, D. and Davies, J., 2000. *Urban Drainage*, E&F Spon, London.

Carr, H., 2004. *Housing Act 2004 – A Practical Guide*, Jordan Publishing Limited, Bristol.

Carroll, B.A., 2003. 'Strategic water planning for south east England: preparing for proposed development', *Wat. Sci. Tech.*, 48(10), 9–16.

CIRIA, 1996. RP543 *Risk Management for Real Time Control in Urban Drainage Systems*, CIRIA, London.

CIRIA, 2002. *Sustainable Urban Drainage Systems – design manuals for England and Wales and for Scotland and Northern Ireland*.

CIRIA, 2003. *Sustainable Water Management in Land Use Planning*, Funders Report RP627.

CIRIA, 2005. *Design for Exceedence*. Funders Report RP699.

Cutting, J., 2003. 'Property creep', Wastewater Planners Users' Group annual conference, Blackpool, November (published on WaPUG website).

Dixon, A.M., 2000. Simulation of domestic water re-use systems: greywater and rainwater in combination, PhD thesis, Imperial College.

Duong, D.D.T., Charron, A., Colas, H. and Lamarre, J., 2005. Optimising the operation of large interceptor systems. *Proceedings 10th International Conference, Urban Drainage*, Copenhagen, August.

Evans, E.P., Ashley, R.M., Hall, J., Penning-Rowsell, E., Sayers, P., Thorne, C. and Watkinson, A., 2004. *Foresight. Future Flooding Vol. II – Managing future risks*, Office of Science and Technology, London.

Fleming, G. (ed.), 2002. *Flood Risk Management*, Thomas Telford, London.

Forman, R.T.T., 1995. *Land Mosaics. The ecology of landscapes and regions*, Cambridge University Press, Cambridge.

Gouda, H., Ashley, R.M., Gilmour, D. and Smith, H., 2003. 'Life cycle analysis and sewer solids', *Water Sci. Tech.*, 47(4), 185–192.

Hall, M.J., Hockin, D.L. and Ellis, J.B., 1993. *Design of Flood Storage Reservoirs*, CIRIA/Butterworths, London.

Heywood, G., Lumbers, J., Reid, S., Balance, T., Chalmers, L. and Haywood-Smith, B., 2002. *Capital Maintenance Planning: A common framework*, Vol. 1, UKWIR Report Ref. 02/RG/05/3.

HR Wallingford, 2003. *An Assessment of the Social Impacts of Sustainable Drainage Systems in the UK*, Report SR622, December.

Jacobs, J.E., 2004. *Strategy for Flood and Coastal Erosion Risk Management – Groundwater flooding scoping study*, Project Specification Reference (LDS 23), Defra, London, available online www.defra.gov.uk/environ/fcd/policy/strategy/gwl.pdf

Lau, K.T., 2002. Optimising storage within the integrated urban wastewater system, PhD thesis, Imperial College London, University of London.

Marshall, R., 2003. *Taking a Calculated Risk*, Wastewater Planning Users' Group (WaPUG), Spring meeting (www.wapug.org).

May, R.W.P., Martin, P. and Price, N.J., 1998. *Low-cost options for prevention of flooding from sewers*, CIRIA Report C506.

OFWAT, 2002a. *Flooding from Sewers – a way forward*, OFWAT, Birmingham.

OFWAT, 2002b. *Flooding from Sewers, Response to Consultation*, OFWAT September, OFWAT, Birmingham.

ODPM, 2003. *Preparing for floods* (Interim guidance for improving the flood resistance of domestic and small business properties), October, The Stationery Office, Norwich.

Parkinson, J.N., 1999. Modelling strategies for sustainable domestic wastewater management in a domestic catchment, PhD thesis, Imperial College, London.

Pearce, D., 2003. *Estimating the Benefits of Sewer Flooding Control*. Report for the National Audit Office, July.

Pepper, A., Stonecipher, C. and Vein, K.A., 2002. 'Flood management: lessons from a US city', *Municipal Engineer*, 151(4), 295–304.

Pinkham, R., 2000. *Daylighting: New life for buried streams*, Rocky Mountain Institute, Colorado.

Thames Water, 2005. *Thames Tideway Strategic Study*, Steering Group Report, February.

UKWIR, 2003. *Implications of Changing Groundwater Quality for Water Resources and the UK Water Industry*, Report No. 03/WR/09/5.

Veldkamp, R.G., Hermann, T. *et al.*, 1997. 'A decision network for urban water management', *Water Science and Technology*, 36(8–9), 111–115.

Walesh, S.G. and Carr, R.W., 1998. *Controlling stormwater close to source: an implementation case study*, American Public Works Congress, Las Vegas, September.

Weiß, G., Brombach, H. and Haller, B., 2002 'Infiltration and inflow in combined sewer systems: long-term analysis', *Wat. Sci. Tech.*, 45(7), 11–19.

WRc, 1997. *Sewerage Detention Tanks – A design guide*, WRc, Swindon.

Wright, G.B, Swaffield, J.A. and Arthur, S., 2002. 'Investigation into the performance characteristics of multi-outlet siphonic roof drainage systems', *9th International Conference on Urban Drainage*, Portland, MI.

Zawliski, M. and Sakson, G., 2005. 'Optimal control strategies for stormwater detention tanks', *Proceedings 10th International Conference Urban Drainage*, Copenhagen, August.

20 Flood event management

Sue M. Tapsell and David J. Ball

Introduction

Until recently, flood defence policy was dominated by a technical world view. Much flood risk management has been aimed at stopping or alleviating damage occurring through structural means (i.e. defence schemes). In addition, the response to hazards has taken a rather 'command and control' approach that focused on clean-up and the rescue of survivors. However, in recent years the socio-economic aspects of flood risk management have gained in importance (Mileti, 1999). There is now a realisation that true flood prevention and mitigation will need to address not only the hydrological factors but also the economic, social and political factors influencing wider society and underpinning the impact of damaging floods (White and Howe, 2002).

Flood defence is now evolving into flood risk management and the notion of sustainable floodplain development which focuses on the use of an integrated approach to flood hazard mitigation and prevention (Mileti *et al.*, 1995; Defra, 2004). Non-structural measures of providing protection from flooding are now being encouraged, such as flood forecasting, warning and response systems; land-use planning; flood insurance; and self-help strategies, such as flood protection products. Response to flooding has also changed to an emphasis on the reduction in loss of life and property through mitigation, preparedness, response and recovery (Cutter *et al.*, 2000).

This chapter outlines a number of these response measures that can be taken to avoid or reduce flood damages and losses prior to and during a flood event. These measures were organised into five response categories:

- pre-event measures;
- real-time flood forecasting and warning dissemination;
- flood fighting actions to manage flood waters and defences;
- collective-scale damage-avoidance action;
- individual-scale damage-avoidance action.

This chapter begins with a brief explanation of how the data were collected. Each of the five response measures is then outlined, followed by their potential for application within the four Foresight future scenarios. The issues of sustainability and uncertainty are highlighted and finally some conclusions are drawn.

Data collection

The first stage of the research reported here involved the gathering of data from a range of sources. Initially, existing data known to the authors were consulted. This was followed by a search for additional secondary source literature from academic and professional sources, through libraries and the Internet. Leaflets, brochures and marketing materials from various organisations and businesses were also collected.

A key aspect of the data collection took the form of consultations with key informants and experts in the relevant fields. Informants were drawn from academia, engineers and consultants specialising in aspects of flood risk management, the emergency services, local authority emergency planners, voluntary and non-profit organisations, and businesses supplying flood protection products, see Table 20.1.

Table 20.1. Sources consulted for the analysis of flood event management measures

Organisations consulted	Measures
Environment Agency (Regional and Area Flood Risk Managers and engineering staff)	Pre-event measures, real-time forecasting and warning dissemination, flood fighting: actions to manage flood waters and defences during the event
Police (New Scotland Yard Emergency Procedures Section)	Pre-event measures, collective-scale damage-avoidance action
London Fire Brigade (Assistant Divisional Officer)	Pre-event measures, collective-scale damage-avoidance action
County and Borough Councils (Emergency Planning Officers)	Pre-event measures, flood fighting: actions to manage flood waters and defences during the event, collective-scale damage-avoidance action, individual-scale damage-avoidance action
National Flood Forum	Flood fighting: actions to manage flood waters and defences during the event, collective-scale damage-avoidance action, individual-scale damage-avoidance action
Women's Royal Voluntary Service	Pre-event measures, collective-scale damage-avoidance action
Aqua Barrier International Ltd	Flood fighting: actions to manage flood waters and defences during the event
Geodesign Barriers Ltd/Pallet Barrier	Flood fighting: actions to manage flood waters and defences during the event
Individuals consulted	**Measures**
Professor Ian Cluckie, Director of Water and Environmental Management Research Centre, University of Bristol	Real-time forecasting and warning dissemination, flood fighting: actions to manage flood waters and defences during the event
Professor Dennis Parker, Flood Hazard Research Centre, Middlesex University	Real-time forecasting and warning dissemination
David Crichton, Visiting Professor, Flood Hazard Research Centre, Middlesex University	Flood fighting: actions to manage flood waters and defences during the event
Dr Dawei Han, University of Bristol	Real-time forecasting and warning dissemination
Russell Burton, Flood and Emergency Management Consultant	Pre-event measures, flood fighting: actions to manage flood waters and defences during the event
Literature from other sources	**Measures**
CIRIA website various advice sheets: www.ciria.org/flooding	Individual-scale damage-avoidance action
Flood proofing literature from: Floodguards International Ltd Floodgate Ltd FloodProtector Flood Pro-Tech Systems Ltd	Individual-scale damage-avoidance action

341

Response measures for managing flood events

Pre-event measures

Pre-event measures are those actions of preparedness, that can be undertaken prior to a flood event occurring, to ensure that people and responding agencies are prepared for flooding, to mitigate any negative impacts, and to ensure the smooth management of the event. Key pre-event measures addressed here are:

- flood preparedness planning, e.g. emergency or major incident plans for flooding;
- education, communication and awareness-raising;
- the utilisation of flood risk maps;
- family and community flood plans;
- flood risk logbooks.

These measures are crucial for many aspects of managing flood events. They are necessary for successful warning dissemination, and both collective and individual-scale damage avoidance activities, including those aimed at reducing flood losses covered in Chapter 21.

Flood preparedness planning

Successful emergency response through emergency planning, communications and major incident plans can significantly reduce the impact of flooding on lives and property. Recent years have seen an increase in emergency planning for flooding, particularly following the 1998 and 2000 floods, and the resulting reviews and criticisms (e.g. Bye, 1998), and Defra's (formerly MAFF's) *High Level Targets for Flood and Coastal Defence* (MAFF, 1999).

It is essential that robust emergency preparedness plans exist for all flood risk areas and that these are regularly exercised. Preparedness planning involves close liaison and effective communications within and between professional partners and all those organisations responding to flood events, including voluntary organisations, community groups and the communications media.

Those organisations responsible for responding to a major flood event in England and Wales include the Environment Agency, emergency services, local authorities, utility companies, and British Waterways. The Civil Contingencies Act now places a legal duty on local authorities to take actions to prevent flood events; they became Category 1 responders along with the emergency services, the Environment Agency and the National Health Service. However, major flood events, and preparing for them, can exact a heavy toll on responding agencies and each agency has its own budget for emergency preparedness planning and response. Local councils and police authorities may also apply for financial assistance for certain purposes in emergency situations through the government's Bellwin scheme (Penning-Rowsell and Wilson, 2006).

The autumn 2000 flooding was geographically dispersed and saw the vast majority of flood incidents involving less than half a dozen properties. Therefore, pre-planning of emergency response could yield significant dividends at the local level (Penning-Rowsell *et al.*, 2002).

Education and awareness raising

An effective response to flood risk can be achieved by a change of attitude and expectation among the general public. If people who live in a flood risk area are aware of the risk, they are much more likely to be receptive to flood warnings and more inclined to protect themselves and their property. Education and awareness raising on flood issues is needed to mobilise the cooperation of a prepared and responsive public in the process of flood risk management and to minimise the total damages. Legislation such as the European Water Framework Directive should help to encourage increased levels of public participation in future environmental decision making and hence awareness of such issues.

Public awareness campaigns are, since 1999, an integral part of the Environment Agency's overall strategy for flood risk management. Money allocated to the campaigns is currently around 0.5% of the total flood risk management expenditure, a cost equivalent to around £1 for every property at risk from flooding, per year. The campaigns use a mix of media to get their messages across and there is some evidence that these campaigns are effective, although there is room for improvement. In the 2004 'At risk' survey (BMRB, 2004), 64% of respondents were aware that their address was in an at-risk area, an increase of 13% since 2001. However, only around one person in ten actually said they would take any steps to prepare.

Flood risk maps

Flood maps help to raise awareness of areas in the natural floodplain and aid in preparedness planning. The Indicative Floodplain Maps (IFM) for England and Wales, provided by the Environment Agency following the 1998 floods, aimed at raising such awareness and in guiding local planning authorities on development control. The Agency's *Flood Mapping Strategy* (2003a) initiated a five-year programme of further mapping to improve and increase information on flood risk over time. In 2004 a new Flood Map for England and Wales replaced the IFM. The map also indicates likelihood of flooding ('significant', 'moderate' or 'low') based on the presence and effect of all flood defences, predicted flood levels and ground levels.

Family and community flood plans and flood risk logbooks

The production of family and community flood plans can be effective response measures in the preparation for flooding and reducing flood impacts. Family plans have long been used in the USA in the preparation for hurricanes and earthquakes, and can include plans for evacuation, how to contact other family members, and a list of what actions need to be taken. Businesses can develop plans relevant to their particular circumstances and some community flood plans are also being developed (Hampshire Flood Steering Group, 2002).

Flood 'log books', although potentially effective in informing new residents in areas at risk, have implications for the saleability of properties and for insurance cover. One suggestion is for a Community Log Book to keep a record of local flood events rather than identifying individual properties (National Flood Forum, personal communication, 2003).

Real-time flood forecasting and warning dissemination

Real-time flood forecasting plays a key role in the management and reduction of residual flood risk (Khatibi and Haywood, 2002). Along with flood warning dissemination, the measure aims to provide flood warnings in sufficient time for people or organisations to take effective mitigating actions to reduce flood risk and impacts. Real-time flood forecasting and warning involves the detection, forecast generation, uncertainty propagation, warning, dissemination and response to flood incidents. The forecasting and warnings only apply to river, tidal and coastal flooding, and not to flooding from other causes such as surface water or drains.

This response measure is crucial for a number of other measures that are dependent on an accurate flood forecast and effective dissemination of flood warnings. These measures include the operation of water-level control structures, temporary flood defences, moving assets at risk and evacuation. There are also links with other measures, discussed in Chapter 21, on improving people's ability to recover from flooding.

Flood forecasting

The principal aim of a forecasting system is to reduce and manage the risk associated with the occurrence of flooding (Khatibi and Haywood, 2002). The identification of the source of the risk is generally concerned with the meteorological origin of a potential event. The forecasting process then follows with its inherent uncertainty being cascaded through the hydrological, hydraulic, estuarial and coastal process models in order to generate a warning that must be disseminated (Cluckie and Han, 2002). Flood forecasting requires the real-time modelling of complex non-linear systems for which often only limited measurements are available. In most cases this involves the development of models on the basis of incomplete and often imprecise information.

Although there are current limitations in sensing, the exploitation of weather radar and satellite-based remote sensing will have a large influence on the development of flood forecasting capabilities in the future and will particularly enhance flood forecasting capabilities in the UK, where the lead times of most British catchments are relatively short. However, it should be noted that certain physical limitations will always impose limits on precipitation measurement capability. At the present time, the lack of real-time updating capability in most current models and systems is also a severe impediment.

Flood warning dissemination

The function of warning dissemination systems is to alert people to the possibility of flood risk in order that they can take appropriate mitigating actions. The receipt of a flood warning can lead to reductions in the amount of losses resulting from flooding, and can be particularly effective in reducing the distress from loss of personal items.

There are many types of methods that are used for disseminating warnings. Some are simple alert systems such as a siren, while others include information on the likelihood or severity of flooding and what actions need to be taken. Each system has its advantages and disadvantages. The main dissemination methods currently in use in England and Wales are: automatic voice messaging (AVM) using land-line and mobile telephones, faxes, pagers, sirens, loudspeakers, face-to-face door knocking, written communication, flood wardens, TV weather reports, teletex and radio. Other methods of dissemination currently being explored in the UK and overseas include e-mail, text messaging to mobile telephones, digital radio, public address systems, centrally activated in-home alert systems, and flashing road signs (Tapsell *et al.*, 2004).

The communication of risk and the recipient response are key challenges in flood warning dissemination (Drabek, 2000), and the effective dissemination of warnings is dependent upon a number of conditions being met by the receivers (Parker, 1991). For example:

- people need to be aware of the existence of the warning system(s) available;
- people need to be receptive to adopting the particular system(s);
- people need to have access to the system(s), which may have cost implications;
- people need to be available to receive the warning (now made easier with the wide use of mobile telephones);
- people need to be physically and mentally able to respond to the warning;
- people need to understand the message (i.e. perceive it as a warning) and take action upon its receipt;
- any actions taken need to be effective.

The effectiveness of different methods of dissemination therefore requires careful scrutiny of the user interface and different users will have different requirements. Warnings therefore need to be responsive to local needs. Warning lead time is also often crucial. Commercial and retail organisations receive the same flood warning information as household residents. This is not thought to be accurate enough for many large-scale operations to take decisions which may result in extreme business implications by suspending trade, services, or manufacturing (Penning-Rowsell *et al.*, 2005).

Governance and funding issues

The Environment Agency has the lead responsibility for issuing warnings in England and Wales, and aims to provide these in sufficient time for people to take effective actions. Since 1998 the Agency has revised flood warning codes and made a number of significant other improvements to the system. Some of these improvements were tested in the autumn 2000 floods and generally worked very well. The floods also saw a significant increase in the use of the Agency's live website. However, engagement with new flood warning dissemination technologies to date has been slow and the exclusion rate of older cohorts from access to new technology is still of concern (NSO, 2003).

In Scotland, responsibility for warnings lies with the Scottish Environmental Protection Agency, while in Northern Ireland it is the Rivers Agency. The biggest contrast is that England and Wales have a proactive flood forecasting warning and response service, whereas Scotland and Northern Ireland have 'passive' ones, and do not actively alert the populations at risk.

The costs of developing flood forecasting systems are met by those public organisations responsible for their operation. These are supported by additional funds from central government and from levies on local drainage boards where these exist, thus introducing severe complexity into the funding regime. This has had the effect of working against the development of national systems and has generally inhibited the application and exploitation of the latest scientific knowledge. In recent years the Environment Agency's budget has been increased in England and Wales and the Agency's *Flood Warning Investment Strategy* (2003) recommends a total investment of £247 million in the period 2003/4 to 2012/13 for flood warnings and forecasting generally. This sum is said to result in around £1041 million net present value of flood damage avoided over the 10 years, out of a cumulated annual average damage estimate of £11 760 million over the same period.

Flood fighting: actions to manage flood waters and defences during the event

This response cluster involves measures and actions to manage floodwaters and peak flows during flood events to reduce flood impacts. For example, these measures include water level control structures, demountable flood defences, emergency repair of failing defences and emergency diversions of flood waters.

There are a number of different types of water level control structures, both fixed and moveable (see Table 20.2). The structures can be effective in controlling and regulating water levels and in reducing flood impacts. However, these structures and demountable flood defences are dependent upon preparedness plans being in place and the effectiveness of these measures relies upon receiving sufficient, reliable and trusted forecasting and warning, and upon the availability of a trained workforce to construct, operate, maintain and repair them. Water level control structures can be the responsibility of the Environment Agency, local authorities, Internal Drainage Boards or riparian land owners, which can have implications for

Table 20.2. Water-level control structures and measures

Structure or measure	Function and efficacy
Radial gates	Among the most common form of control structure. They are either automated by employing a drive actuator or wire rope mechanism and level sensors, or by means of a float system that raises the gate when the river levels rise and lowers the gate when levels fall again
Lock gates	Used when navigational requirements dictate that the gates are able to be rotated clear of the navigable river channel. The gates can either be locked shut ahead of a flood event to prevent tidal flow upstream or locked open to maximise flood flow discharge
Sluices and vertical gates	Typically operated by a vertical riser, and either a hand wound mechanism, or electrically driven actuator. This operation can be automated using ultrasonic level sensors to detect increases in water levels upstream during flood flows. Vertical gates are usually restrained in side channels and lifted using wire ropes. Both sluices and vertical gates are also used at coastal locations to prevent back-flow over the high tide
Flap gates/valves	These gates are essentially non-return valves, and are typically used at the point of river discharge to the sea. Discharge will occur by gravity over the period of low water, and the rising tide will then cause the flap gate to swing closed to prevent back-flow into the river system over high tide
Flood gates	Normally openned to allow access through defences when river flows or tide cycles permit. They are closed when forecasts indicate that the opening should be blocked to prevent a breach of the defence
Weirs/stop logs	Structures provided generally to maintain water levels in times of low flow for environmental, agricultural and amenity (e.g. navigation) reasons. Weirs also provide a means of flow measurement at gauging stations. Most are fixed structures and become 'drowned out' during high flow/flood conditions. There are tilting and adjustable weirs, which can be operated to increase conveyance during periods of high flow. Stop logs are generally used to retain water levels during the summer and are removed ahead of the anticipated 'flood season'
Pumping stations	A variety of types of pumping station are used to pump water from low-lying rivers, either into other river systems, storage areas, or to the sea. Most stations are automated, and are powered by electric motors, controlled by level sensors. Pumps can be axial, submersible, or Archimedean screw, depending upon flow volumes and height differentials. The importance of trash screens/grills with regular means of clearing cannot be overstated, as blockages can very quickly result in flooding
Flood storage areas/ reservoirs	These structures typically attenuate flows by storing water behind an embankment or dam, so that the peak flood flow is reduced. Water is released either over spillways, gates or by hydro-brake, a device that produces constant output flows regardless of retained water height
Tidal barriers or barrages	The most impressive structure built to date of this type is the Thames Barrier, which has been designed to prevent extreme tidal surges from passing the barrier upstream
Demountable barriers and temporary defences	Demountable and temporary flood defences are portable free-standing barriers located (normally along river banks) at a distance from the group of properties to be protected. Their function is to hold back or deflect floodwater from reaching groups of properties or roads in order to reduce the damage and disruption from flooding. There are two types of barrier available: flexible and rigid. Flexible barriers can include water- or air-filled tubes. Rigid barriers are often fully engineered, can be of lightweight plastic that fill with water to stabilise them, or of aluminium and wooden construction, with waterproof covers and separate steel base-plates for support

Table 20.2. Continued

Structure or measure	Function and efficacy
Demountable barriers and temporary defences – *Continued*	Demountable barriers can be very effective in reducing flood risk and impacts on the lower reaches of large river catchments where there is sufficient warning. They can be rapidly erected by only a few people and no permanent planning permission is required. They cannot prevent seepage of groundwater through subsoils below properties, nor can they prevent flooding as a result of backflow from an overloaded drainage or sewer system. The barriers are still relatively new to the market and there are a growing number of private companies providing these products, both in the UK and overseas. There is now a certification scheme in England and Wales for temporary freestanding and demountable barriers managed by the British Standards Institution that approves products awarding them a BSI Kitemark or symbol of quality
Emergency repairs and shoring up of failing defences	Flood events can occur with very short warning periods (say 2–12 hours). Structures generally fail under load, and so conditions prevailing at the time of failure or impending failure, generally preclude any immediate attempt at repair. Possible exceptions to this are where there is tidal influence, and repairs can be undertaken over the low-water period (e.g. to release a jammed tidal flap gate). The ageing nature of the vast majority of the water level structures owned and/or operated by the Environment Agency, means that failure upon demand will become increasingly likely
Emergency diversions: cut through channels or breaking of dikes	This involves the process of cutting or breaking through flood defences to remove or reduce pressure of flood water behind defences in the flooded area, either by breaching the existing defences or by partially diverting the water elsewhere. Some of these structures are designed to self-breach in extreme conditions. Flood defence structures generally fail under load, and so conditions prevailing at the time of failure or impending failure generally preclude any immediate attempt at repair, except in the case of some coastal structures. In practice these diversions of floodwaters are extremely rare and would not be considered by the Environment Agency except in extreme circumstances. Should the situation arise, Environment Agency staff would carry out the procedure, as it might mean 'sacrificing' one area to 'save' another. These measures can be effective in extreme conditions but would be likely to be used only as a last resort. Planned diversion channels are having wider take up; these usually have just a 'sweetening' flow during normal operations, but in extreme events take overflow from the main channel. Examples of this include Chichester Flood Alleviation Scheme and the Jubilee River in Maidenhead

their maintenance and operation. Additionally, where structures are also used for navigation purposes and for water abstraction, there may be a potential conflict of interest.

The costs of these measures vary enormously depending upon their size, the type of materials used, the costs of construction and maintenance. Although demountable defences have lower up-front costs than permanent schemes, they do have higher operational costs (e.g. for removal, transportation and storage). These costs need to be weighed against the potential savings that they could provide, e.g. from restoration of buildings, replacement of belongings, temporary accommodation, loss of earnings and business losses.

Collective-scale damage-avoidance actions: evacuation of floodplains and coastal areas at risk

This response measure involves collective action, in this case through a publicly organised or spontaneous evacuation of people, pets or livestock from properties and areas at risk from flooding to a safe location. Demountable flood defences can also be categorised as collective-scale actions but these are covered in 'Flood fighting', above. The function of evacuation is to save lives and reduce the danger to people and animals during a flood event. Evacuation measures are only normally taken during serious floods when it is not safe or practicable for people to remain in their properties, or for those living in basement or ground-floor accommodation, or mobile homes.

Evacuation can be effective. However, there is evidence that the evacuation process itself is extremely distressing and worrying for people, particularly where family or social structures are disrupted (FHRC, 1996). Most people do not want to leave their homes. This raises an issue relating to evacuation in that frequently people will not be prepared to evacuate unless flooding is likely to result in risk to life, unless it is certain and imminent, or until it has been confirmed by another trusted source. All of this makes the process more difficult for responding agencies. Many of those flooded and evacuated during the autumn 2000 floods commented that they would not do so in the event of future flooding. The situation could change if there were more faith in the system and those managing it, as well as better coordination between emergency services, local authorities and the public.

In England and Wales, the police take the final decision on whether to initiate any official structured evacuation, although they have no powers to enforce this. Fire-fighters and local authorities also assist, and voluntary sector workers may be called upon to help at rest centres and provide feeding for emergency responders. Local authorities have a legal duty to house those made homeless from a flood event and are also obligated to their own council tenants. The costs of evacuation and providing rest centres are met by those agencies responsible, i.e. emergency services and local authorities, while the costs of temporary accommodation are met by local authorities, by the flooded themselves or their insurers.

The decision to evacuate is influenced by public perception of flood risk, accuracy and public trust in flood forecasting, effective flood-warning dissemination, information received about the flood (i.e. likely depth and duration), and pre-flood education and preparedness plans (official and unofficial). Warning lead time is crucial in allowing an effective and orderly evacuation. Evacuation plans need to be in place prior to flooding to enable emergency services and local authorities to provide support for the evacuation of vulnerable groups, e.g. residential homes and the disabled. Moreover, evacuation is a process and not necessarily a short-term response and it is not complete until those who have had to leave their homes have returned (FHRC, 1996).

Individual-scale damage-avoidance actions: temporary flood proofing and moving of assets at risk to safety

Temporary flood proofing can be achieved by the fitting of removable products or devices that seal or delay potential flood routes into buildings. Along with the removal of belongings and assets to safety out of the reach of flood waters, these measures help mitigate flood damage and losses, both tangible and intangible.

Temporary flood proofing

The function of temporary flood-proofing measures is to reduce the amount of ingress of flood waters into properties, or at least to hold back flood waters long enough to enable homeowners to move belongings and pets to a safe place. Measures include plastic, wooden or metal products that are temporarily fitted to the building, such as flood gates on external doors, windows and patio doors, covers on airbricks, flexible plastic 'skirting' systems, and non-return valves. These measures can be very effective for short duration shallow floods and may mean the difference between minimal flood damage or a large-scale clean up and restoration. The measures have many benefits including being able to be fitted in minutes and being easy to store and maintain (Crichton, 2003).

However, these products are not usually suitable for floods deeper than 1 m above ground-floor level. Moreover, they cannot prevent seepage of groundwater through subsoil into properties in areas where this is likely due to geological characteristics, nor can they prevent flooding as a result of backflow from an overloaded drainage or sewer system (unless a non-return valve is fitted), or penetration of flood water through a party wall of an adjacent property. Therefore, a pump and, preferably, also a sump should ideally be installed to remove such leakage. There is now a certification scheme for removable products, such as flood gates, managed by the British Standards Institution, awarding them a BSI Kitemark or symbol of quality. There is, however, an allowed leakage on these products of 1 litre of water per metre of panel per hour.

One drawback with flood-proofing products is their cost, which puts them out of reach for those on a low income. Costs for an average home are around £2000. Possible flood losses need to be weighed up when considering the cost of fitting these products. However, it is possible for householders to make their own gates more cheaply. Community flood action groups have called for a grant system to be available from local authorities for these products, and this is currently being considered by governments in England and Wales.

Sandbags are another response measure, although, flood gates and airbrick covers offer much better protection and are easier to use than traditional sandbags. Different variations on sandbags include earth-filled bags and synthetic absorbent cushions. The latter, unlike sandbags, are lightweight when dry, can be cleaned, are easy to store, and do not need to be filled. Each local authority has their own policy on the provision of sandbags. This is very confusing for the public and can be a contentious subject for local authorities and emergency responders.

Moving assets at risk to safety

Moving assets at risk to safety, either to a higher location, to upper floors or to another location, can be extremely effective in reducing flood losses and the distress caused due to lost or damaged sentimental possessions (Tapsell *et al.*, 1999; Tapsell and Tunstall, 2001). For homeowners this could mean moving personal belongings and papers, items of sentimental value and cars. For farmers it could mean moving machinery and livestock, while for businesses it could involve moving stock, equipment, raw materials, documents or vehicles.

Both temporary flood proofing of properties and moving assets at risk depend upon accurate and respected flood forecasting and early receipt of a flood warning (where feasible). More awareness of flooding issues and increased confidence in the forecasting and warning system might lead to earlier and more effective response in the future. The measures also depend upon people knowing what actions to take upon receipt of such a warning and upon people's ability to take such actions. Therefore, prior awareness of flood risk is essential, along with pre-existing preparedness plans.

Potential application of measures to future scenarios

The potential for the application of each group of response measures under the four future Foresight scenarios varies greatly, depending upon the characteristics of the scenario and of the individual measures. Each scenario is considered below.

World markets

There is clear potential for the application of pre-event measures under this scenario due to relaxed planning controls and building restrictions exacerbating flood risk. The wide use of information and communications technologies, coupled with high income levels will aid in awareness raising and preparedness for those with access to these technologies and information, or who are able to pay for it. However, those on lower incomes are likely to remain uninformed and unprepared, leading to increased inequalities and risk, especially in those communities with no front-line defence measures. An ageing population may mean that older cohorts are excluded from accessing information by way of newer technologies.

The minimalist approach to government will mean that preparedness and education initiatives may be coordinated but poorly resourced. The privatisation of services, including the emergency services, may mean that these will be concentrated in wealthier areas. It will largely be those who can afford to pay who benefit from these services, including businesses. The emphasis on self-reliance will result in households and communities formulating their own preparedness plans and proactively seeking out flood risk information, and may also lead to family or community flood plans that require little resources being developed among lower-income groups. The high numbers of immigrants will raise problems of effective communication with regard to awareness raising of flood risk. Large-scale awareness campaigns and preparedness planning seem unlikely, and the lack of public resources, inferior community organisation and increased inequalities may limit the application, particularly at the local level where detailed information is necessary.

There is high potential for application of flood forecasting and warning dissemination measures under this scenario, in that high rates of technological innovation will provide benefits in improved forecasting and warning lead times (where feasible), and in warning dissemination technologies. High income levels will allow those who can afford them to avail themselves of these measures. Where this requires access to new technology, the gap between the 'haves' and 'have nots' increases. Services such as AVM and Floodline may be privatised and require subscription, thereby excluding large sections of the population.

Successful dissemination of warnings could be limited by inequalities in income and education levels and other socio-economic factors. Moreover, an ageing population may result in limited take-up of certain newer dissemination methods. The opportunities for informal warning systems increase, particularly among the more disadvantaged groups such as those on low incomes and immigrants. However, ethnic minority groups, such as immigrants, may not benefit from some of these measures due to poor language skills. It is possible that high levels of innovation may lead to the cheaper production of warning technologies, such as in-home alert systems, making them affordable to those on low incomes.

Although there is clear potential for application of flood-fighting measures, privatisation of services and inferior community organisation and training may act as a deterrent. Flood-fighting measures are very likely to be required under this scenario by those communities that have been otherwise neglected in alternative strategies or that face residual risks. However, the most 'at-risk' communities are likely to be those with least resources and they may also be ill-equipped to implement flood-fighting measures through lower social cohesion.

The prospects for evacuation under this scenario appear meagre since it requires regional or community-wide preparation and planning, which will not be forthcoming unless other options are seen as less desirable on cost–benefit grounds. Moreover, the likely provision of large-scale flood defence schemes under this scenario may reduce the perceived need for this measure. Evacuation is generally reserved only for the more serious threats, thus it is more of a last resort than an opportunity to manage risk, particularly under this scenario. At-risk populations might be reluctant to evacuate in a situation in which faith in the system is consequently lacking.

There is clearly a potential application for temporary flood-proofing measures and moving of assets at risk if at-risk groups are willing to do so. In this scenario the challenge is for the private sector to produce competitively priced and effective products, including DIY kits for the less well off, and for the central flood agencies to build a reputation for, and provide, reliable forecasting. Constraints on implementation relate largely to the perception by at-risk groups of the threat posed by the hazard, and whether they think the measures are cost-effective according to their own value systems, i.e. not standard cost–benefit tests.

National enterprise

There is less general potential for application of pre-event measures under the national enterprise scenario. Take up of the measures may be reduced by under investment in public services, weak community structures, and by the ability to pay for information and services, but could be effective for those on higher incomes. Although these measures would be organised at the national level, there are fewer opportunities for the measures, due to reduced incomes and innovation, poor public services, privatisation of services, rising inequalities and institutional rigidity.

Coordination of preparedness plans among those responding to flood events is likely to be weak. However, these factors increase the importance of these measures for reducing flood risk and impacts, and it is possible that the more stable economy and the importance of small and medium enterprises (SMEs) may help to stimulate local provision of information for those who can afford to pay for it. Increased self-reliance and independence will lead to people making their own preparedness plans that could be effective in reducing risk. There is potential for self-help in the way of family flood plans for lower income groups.

The potential for the application of real-time forecasting and warning dissemination measures under this scenario is more limited than under other scenarios. Although there would be national provision of flood warnings, lower GDP, low levels of technological innovation and socio-economic inequalities would limit forecasting capability and equal access to warning dissemination. Increased self-reliance and independence will lead those with access to resources, i.e. wealth, to take up these measures; however, the potential for social unrest is high. This could lead to internal political pressures to provide these services, at least for the more vulnerable and disadvantaged groups within society. Informal warning systems may flourish as low innovation may limit development of hi-tech forecasting and warning dissemination technologies. Failure to invest in infrastructure in other areas of flood risk management might mean that this measure moves closer to the front line of options.

There will certainly be the potential and a need for the application of flood-fighting measures under the national enterprise scenario, but their uptake may be reduced by ability to pay, problems of coordination and lack of community cohesion. The measures will be needed by local communities, particularly those that have not been protected in other ways. However, the measures are only suited to certain types of flood events and this affects their overall utility.

Although there would be national provision for evacuation under this scenario, social tensions and fear of property looting and crime are potential threats to the successful implementation of this measure. At best the measure is designed to deal only with the more extreme events and its effectiveness may be limited by social factors, under-investment and poor public services. Failure to provide sufficient back-up to displaced populations could predispose against willing cooperation; however, failure to invest in other areas of flood defence might give these measures more potential.

While a clear need exists for self-help measures, such as temporary flood proofing and moving of assets at risk in this scenario, implementation will be hampered by the ability to pay, competing priorities for available income, an ageing population with reduced immigrant labour, and a service-provider sector driven by its own self-interests. Although there will be an 'opportunity' in the sense of a need for implementation of individual-scale damage-avoidance measures, low incomes will undermine the uptake of some of these measures. The slowed spread of technology implies perhaps a reduced likelihood of appropriate warnings being transmitted and/or received. Moreover, the consequences of longer duration or deep flood events, and flash floods, will not be mitigated by these interventions.

Global sustainability

The potential for the application of pre-event measures and real-time forecasting and warning dissemination measures would be high under this scenario. A strong and coordinated government that aspires to social and environmental goals and a search for sustainable solutions will provide a good opportunity for placing preparedness measures and educational awareness raising high on the political agenda. A strong economy and high levels of innovation are likely to provide opportunities for good provision and application of flood forecasting measures aimed at the public good because of its fundamental interests in public education, information and health. The search for sustainable solutions will provide further opportunities for warning dissemination. All of these will be facilitated by fast-growing education and training systems and low unemployment, thereby alleviating any potential for social unrest.

Medium to high economic growth and innovation in technological systems and information services will prove instrumental in facilitating communications. However, strict development controls may reduce flood risk in certain locations, thereby reducing perception of the need for preparedness planning and awareness raising. Large systems engineering may provide other flood defence measures that would result in less emphasis on providing warnings, although these seem unlikely on environmental grounds.

The potential for the application of flood-fighting measures is high given the likely need and availability of resources for these measures and local support. The prospect of communities, government and high-tech industries working together points to an opportunity for the effective application of flood defence measures. The comparative prosperity under the scenario suggests that funding will be less problematical. Also beneficial is the high growth in services and innovation. There will be a long-term move towards sustainable development and the measures have a low environmental impact that should add to the likelihood of uptake that can be effective at the local level. Government plays a positive role in providing workable and effective forecasting systems because of its fundamental interests in public education, information and health. Constraints relate to the fact that some of the measures are only applicable during certain types of flood events.

The willingness of communities, government and high-tech industries to work together bodes well for the good provision and effective application of evacuation. The potential for application is also good for temporary flood proofing and moving of assets at risk, given the likely availability of resources for these measures and government support. This scenario presents good opportunities for uptake of these measures because of the availability of reasonable income and grants, and the willingness of communities, including their high-tech industries, to work together. Also beneficial is the high growth in services. The measures have a low environmental impact that is also consistent with the aspirations of the scenario, adding to the likelihood of uptake. The main limitation for evacuation is that it does not reduce damages to property and belongings. Constraints on flood proofing and moving assets relate to the perceived risk, and its comparison with other currently perceived risks and valued items competing for the same budget. Moreover, these latter measures are only effective for certain types of flooding.

Local stewardship

There is high potential for the application of all five groups of response measures under this scenario. For pre-event measures this is due to the community-orientated nature of society and the fact that the measures are environmentally and socially sustainable. Given the self-help nature of communities, it is to be expected that there will be a greater coordination of activities and improved sharing of knowledge. Strong community support will result in increased potential for the provision of preparedness measures and awareness raising at the local level, where it has the most potential to reduce flood losses. Larger household sizes and more family support would help facilitate the development of family and community flood plans. The measures are particularly successful if implemented at the local level due to the importance of the local context in flood risk management.

Despite the low levels of GDP, the community-orientated nature of this scenario also suggests that there is a good opportunity for the uptake of all of the other groups of response measures, or at least certain types of them. There is less potential for sophisticated forecasting systems but high potential for successful warning dissemination due to strong community participation. Under this scenario there would be localised provision of flood forecasting and warning, where it could be most effective. A fast-growing small-scale manufacturing sector could provide forecasting and warning dissemination technology at lower costs and on a larger scale.

Moderate levels of unemployment, a larger voluntary sector, and strong community support could also see an increase in unofficial warning systems. However, lower economic growth, lower levels of technological innovation and under-investment could place constraints on both these measures and pre-event measures under this scenario. Tight planning controls may also remove the risk of flooding in certain areas, thereby reducing the perceived need for both these groups of measures.

Sluices, weirs and emergency repair provision can all contribute significantly to local flood avoidance and within this scenario should find widespread application, partly because of the relatively low cost, environmental friendliness, and the local nature of the control measures. Demountable defences require a good flood warning system, but this may not be in place in this scenario as it requires significant national investment. Other constraints on the use of demountable defences would also apply but it can be envisaged that emergency repair services would be well coordinated.

There is likely to be local provision for evacuation, and local communities are more likely to be able to 'pull together' so managing the process effectively and minimising the downside. The utility of evacuation is nonetheless restricted, being generally a measure of last resort because of the disruption and distress that it entrains; it may be restricted to the more serious flood events. Even under this scenario it is not likely to offer a first order solution except in the event that major flood occurrences become common.

With individual-scale actions, low income and the affordability of temporary flood-proofing products are counter-balanced to some extent by community-wide interest in fairness and self-help. Grants may be available, although perhaps not as much as under the global sustainability scenario due to lower GDP. Cheap DIY versions of flood-proofing products may also be encouraged. Additional constraints depend upon the competing priorities for available resources and the perceived risk posed by flooding.

Sustainability issues

A crucial question regarding the response measures discussed here is: 'Are they sustainable?' Each measure was considered against the Government's Guiding Principles for Sustainable Development in relation to each of the four scenarios.

The results are outlined below and illustrated with the use of a series of 'spider diagrams' (Figs 20.1 to 20.5).

Pre-event measures, where they are effective, are sustainable in that they help to raise awareness of flood risk and provide information to help people (including professional partners) make preparations to take effective actions for reducing future risk and damages. These measures are compatible with the government principles for sustainable development of: putting people at the centre, taking a long-term perspective, combating social exclusion and encouraging participation, using scientific knowledge, and providing information and transparency (Fig. 20.1).

Flood forecasting and warning dissemination places people at the centre of the function and recognises the government's guiding principles on sustainable development by furthering the use of scientific knowledge to follow a precautionary principle in relation to managing residual flood risk (Fig. 20.2). However, not all potential recipients of warnings will have access to the same types of technology in order to receive the warning. This has the potential to lead to social exclusion and a divide between 'haves' and 'have-nots'. There are clear possibilities for regional and social-demographic inequalities in access to new technology that would have implications for future expansion of new dissemination systems, such as e-mail.

Automatic water control structures are sustainable both in terms of energy and cost, as they require little maintenance and no manual input to operate. There are potential environmental impacts from using water-level control structures and emergency diversions, both negative and positive. For the latter, there is also the moral issue of who/what to save and who/what to flood. Demountable barriers are environmentally friendly and are potentially cost-effective. The barriers could be used in areas that traditional analysis has concluded would not be cost-beneficial to protect under the current priority scoring systems for flood defence schemes (Fig. 20.3).

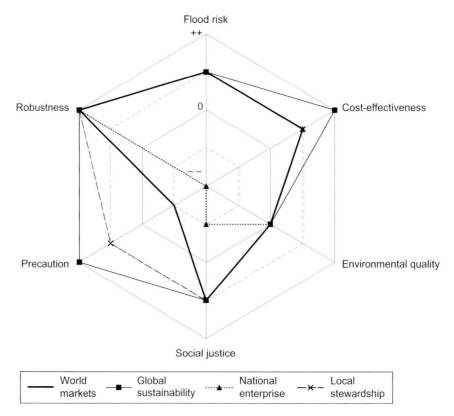

Fig. 20.1. Pre-event measures (Evans et al., 2004)

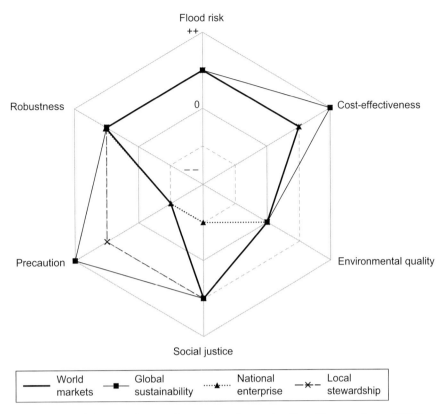

Fig. 20.2. Flood forecasting and warning dissemination (Evans et al*., 2004)*

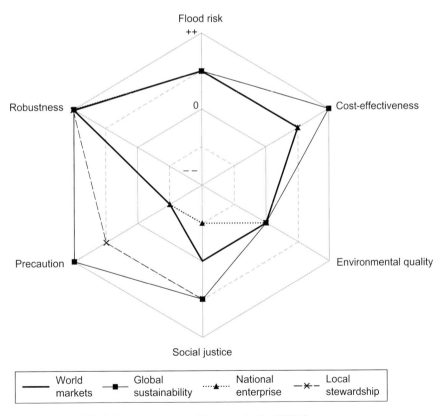

Fig. 20.3. Flood-fighting measures (Evans et al*., 2004)*

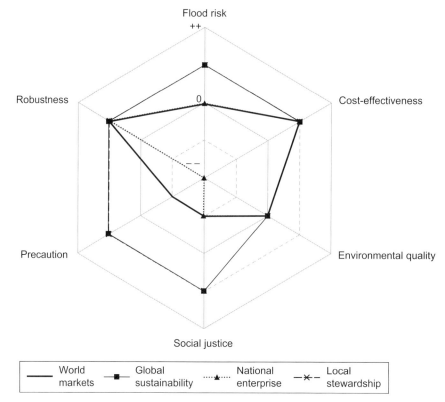

Fig. 20.4. Collective-scale action: evacuation (Evans et al., 2004)

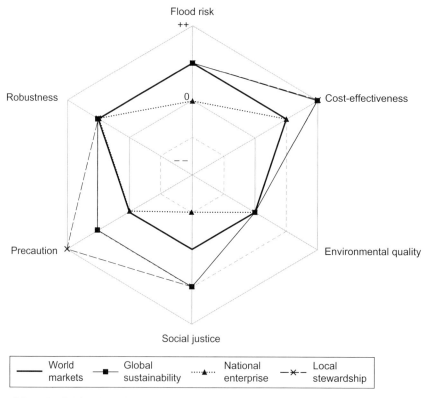

Fig. 20.5. Individual-scale actions: temporary flood proofing and moving of assets at risk (Evans et al., 2004)

Evacuation of floodplains and coastal areas at risk is compatible with three government principles for sustainable development: it is a measure that puts people at the centre, it is environmentally friendly or neutral, and it maintains the precautionary principle (Fig. 20.4). Temporary flood proofing and moving of assets at risk to safety measures are also sustainable in that they are environmentally friendly and encourage people to think about the longer-term perspective of helping themselves and creating more resilient communities (Fig. 20.5). Moving assets is relatively easy to implement and can be very cost-effective. However, in households comprising the very elderly, disabled, or those living alone, support may be necessary.

Future uncertainty

Much that will influence the effectiveness of the various response measures is uncertain. Factors influencing uncertainty include: the frequency of flooding and associated perception of risk, the availability of funding and resourcing, income levels, government policies and political stability, the degree of technological innovation, changing population demography and social and cultural values, the extent of public participation, and the existence of community-focused groups. Each of the five sets of response measures is likely to be affected in different ways. Many conditions need to be right for the various measures to be implemented. Having 'right' conditions does not depend just on hardware, education, and accurate information, but also on considerations of trust, equity and the general state of the world, which are not amenable to forecasting.

Most of these uncertainties will apply to pre-event measures. Although considerable uncertainty exists over almost all aspects of extreme flood-producing storm behaviour over the next 30 to 100 years, the degree of uncertainty in relation to the technical aspects of likely future flood forecasting system development is relatively low. This is because flood forecasting system design is specifically focused on managing extreme behaviour. There is uncertainty of how recipients will respond to warnings and whether public awareness campaigns will continue to be influential.

There are not likely to be any great changes in the use of water-level control structures, emergency repairs and diversions in the foreseeable future. A mixture of permanent and temporary defences is likely to be the way forward in the UK in the longer term, particularly in locations where cost–benefit analysis would not justify a permanent scheme, and also in the context that in the autumn 2000 floods the vast majority of flood incidents involved less than half a dozen properties.

Evacuation is always likely to be a common response measure where there is a risk of properties and people being affected by flooding. However, uncertainty over whether people will evacuate (for a number of different reasons) could be a problem. The wider adoption of individual flood-proofing measures is currently uncertain, although it is highly likely that take-up will increase. Many of these products are recently developed and there is still widespread ignorance concerning them. It is more likely that people will continue moving assets at risk to a place of safety in the future. There is uncertainty over flood forecasting and warning and people being alerted to the possibility of flooding in order to move their assets. However, awareness of the possibility of flooding and basic preparedness plans could make a difference to saving assets.

Conclusions

There are a number of response measures that can be taken to avoid or reduce flood damages and losses prior to and during a flood event.

As outlined above, the robustness of the various response measures will vary according to the characteristics of the measures themselves and those of the four scenarios. Pre-event response measures are likely to be needed and could be instituted across all scenarios. This makes the measures robust; however, certain measures might be more applicable under different scenarios. Flood forecasting and warning dissemination systems have the potential to be fairly robust across all scenarios, with perhaps less application under national enterprise and a more even social distribution under global responsibility and local stewardship.

Flood-fighting measures are likely to be needed and could be instituted across all scenarios. In that sense the measures are robust. Collective-scale damage-avoidance action is feasible under all scenarios but more likely to occur and be effectively implemented under the global responsibility and local stewardship scenarios. Individual-scale damage-avoidance actions could also take place across all scenarios and in that sense are robust. However, the degree of take up, and hence effectiveness, is predicated upon scenario characteristics and a wide range of other factors.

Based upon the inter-dependence in terms of deployment and use of the various groups of measures outlined above, it can be suggested that to be effective certain measures would need to be combined with, or applied alongside, other measures. Thus, both evacuation (collective action) and flood fighting are more or less dependent upon a flood forecast and effective warning dissemination and therefore upon the time available in which to act. Without this forecast there can be very little effective response.

Some of the individual-scale damage avoidance actions are also dependent upon some warning, but damage can be averted even as flood water enters a property. These measures can therefore be left separate, not least because the collective actions are undertaken by agencies of the state, whereas most individual-scale actions are not.

In combining groups of measures we are therefore left with only three groups:

- pre-event measures;
- real-time event management (including flood forecasting, warning and response, flood fighting and evacuation);
- individual-scale damage avoidance.

In the final assessment of the effect of all responses considered in the Foresight Project, the rank order of importance of measures was determined by scoring all response groups.

Overall, the above three measures were shown to have varying levels of significance in their potential for flood risk reduction, depending upon the scenario in question. Conditions under the local stewardship scenario would lead to the greatest flood-risk reduction potential for these measures, with individual damage avoidance being ranked third after land-use planning and management and flood proofing of buildings, followed by pre-event measures at rank 6 and real-time event management at rank 7.

Under the national enterprise scenario the measures would have the least potential in reducing risk, being located 12th, 13th and 16th in the rankings, although they could still make a valuable contribution.

References

BMRB International, 2004. *At Risk 2004 Report*, BMRB, London.

Bye, P. and Horner, M., 1998. *Easter 1998 floods, Vol. I. Report by the Independent Review Team to the Board of the Environment Agency*, Environment Agency, Bristol.

Cluckie, I.D. and Han, D., 2002. 'Fluvial Flood Forecasting', *Water and Environmental Management*, 14(4), 270–276.

Crichton, D., 2004. 'Temporary local flood protection in the United Kingdom – An independent assessment', *Post Magazine*, 29 January.

Cutter, S.L. *et al.*, 2000. 'Revealing the vulnerability of people and places: a case study of Georgetown County, South Carolina', *Annals of the Association of American Geographers*, 90(4), 713–737.

Defra, 2004. *Making Space for Water: Developing a new government strategy for flood and coastal erosion risk management in England*, Consultation document, Defra, London.

Drabek, T.E., 2000. 'The social factors that constrain human responses to flood warnings', in *Floods*, ed. Parker, D.J., Routledge, London, 361–376.

Environment Agency, 2003a. *Flood Mapping Strategy – July 2003*, Environment Agency, Bristol.

Environment Agency, 2003b. *Flood Warning Investment Strategy Appraisal Report 2003/4 to 2012/13*, Environment Agency, Bristol.

Evans, E., Ashley, R., Hall, J., Penning-Rowsell, E., Sayers, P., Thorne, C. and Watkinson, A., 2004. *Foresight, Future Flooding. Scientific Summary: Vol. II – Managing future risks*, Office of Science and Technology, London.

FHRC Technical Annex 14, 1996. *Evacuation, EUROflood Project*, Middlesex University Flood Hazard Research Centre, London.

Hampshire Flood Steering Group, 2002. *Managing Flood Risks in Parishes: A best practice guide*, 2nd edn, Environment Agency, Bristol.

Khatibi, R. and Haywood, J., 2002. 'The role of flood forecasting and warning in sustainability of flood defence', *Proceedings of the Institution of Civil Engineers – Municipal Engineer*, 151(4), 313–320.

MAFF, 1999. *High Level Targets for Flood and Coastal Defence and Elaboration of the Environment Agency's Flood Defence Supervisory Duty*, MAFF, London.

Mileti, D.S., 1999. *Designing Future Disasters: An assessment and bolder course for the nation*, Joseph Henry Press, Washington, DC.

Mileti, D.S. *et al.*, 1995. 'Toward an integration of natural hazards and sustainability', *The Environmental Professional*, 18, 117–126.

National Statistics Office, 2003. *Individuals Accessing the Internet: national statistics omnibus survey*, National Statistics Office, London.

Parker, D.J., 1991. *The Damage Reducing Effects of Flood Warnings*, Report prepared for Halcrow/National Rivers Authority (Anglian Region) Regional Telemetry Scheme Appraisal, Flood Hazard Research Centre, London.

Penning-Rowsell, E.C. *et al.*, 2002. *Autumn 2000 Floods in England and Wales: Assessment of National Economic and Financial Losses*, Report to the Environment Agency, Flood Hazard Research Centre, London.

Penning-Rowsell, E.C. *et al.*, 2005. *The Benefits of Flood and Coastal Risk Management: A manual of assessment techniques*, Flood Hazard Research Centre, London.

Penning-Rowsell, E.C. and Wilson, T., 2006. 'Gauging the impact of natural hazards: the pattern and cost of emergency response during flood events', *Transactions, Institute of British Geographers*, 31(2), 9–15.

Tapsell, S.M. *et al.*, 2004. *The Social Performance of Flood Warning Communications Technologies*, Draft Technical Report to the Environment Agency, Middlesex University Flood Hazard Research Centre, London.

Tapsell, S.M. and Tunstall, S.M., 2001. *The Health and Social Effects of the June 2000 Flooding in the North East Region*, Report to the Environment Agency, Middlesex University Flood Hazard Research Centre, London.

Tapsell, S.M. *et al.*, 1999. *The Health Effects of the 1998 Easter Flooding in Banbury and Kidlington*, Report to the Environment Agency, Thames Region, Middlesex University Flood Hazard Research Centre, London.

White, I. and Howe, J., 2002. 'Policy and practice – flooding and the role of planning in England and Wales: a critical review', *Journal of Environmental Planning and Management*, 45(5), 735–745.

21 Reducing flood losses

Nigel W. Arnell and John B. Chatterton

Introduction: A classification of approaches

This set of measures reduces flood losses by reducing the exposure of property, infrastructure and people to the damaging effects of flood water. A broad distinction is drawn here between *spatial planning measures*, which influence the location of existing and new development, and *flood-proofing measures*, which affect the ability of existing and new structures to resist damage due to flood water.

Many factors influence the adoption and effectiveness of such measures, including technical feasibility, financial feasibility, social and political acceptability, and legislative support (as outlined in more detail below). Particularly important are the mechanisms in place to facilitate recovery from flood loss, such as insurance and charitable or state aid. The measures do not in themselves reduce flood damages, although they can be used to encourage the adoption of damage-reducing measures and may, if inappropriately implemented, encourage continued unwise use of flood-prone areas. Unusually, insurance against the flood risk is widely available in the UK, and has a major influence on the adoption and future effectiveness of measures to reduce loss.

Facilitating recovery from loss: insurance and public relief

Several measures exist to allow flood victims to recover from the financial and economic impacts of flooding. These measures include:

- insurance;
- state aid or compensation;
- tax credits for economic losses;
- public charitable relief;
- self-insurance.

Flood insurance
Flood insurance basically involves the purchase of a policy for an annual premium which provides for reimbursement of defined losses after a flood (Arnell, 2000; Crichton, 2002; Clark *et al.*, 2002). Insurance can, in principle, be bought to cover not only tangible financial losses but also indirect losses, such as loss of production or business due to disruption. For the individual floodplain occupant, insurance,

therefore, spreads the cost of loss over time. Flood insurance is currently provided in different ways in different countries (and is not available at all in many), with varying degrees of government involvement and linkages with other flood management responses. In the most general terms, there are four key issues for insurance as a response to flooding, as discussed below.

1. Who is able to buy insurance, and what happens to those who do not? Flood insurance can be provided as part of a comprehensive insurance policy (as currently applies in the UK and France for domestic household insurance) or as a separate policy which needs to be actively purchased (as currently in the USA). In principle it is possible to make purchase mandatory for all property owners (as proposed in the new German flood insurance programme), or just for those seeking further loans. Restricting flood insurance only to those in identified flood-prone areas excludes cover for 'disconnected flooding' and narrows the customer base very significantly, while allowing all to purchase flood cover spreads the risk very widely at the expense of those who are not exposed to flood risk at all. Where insurance is not mandatory, experience in many countries shows that those most vulnerable to loss are least likely to purchase insurance (Arnell, 2000). From a private sector insurance company perspective this is not necessarily a problem, but from a public flood risk management perspective is important (Priest *et al.*, 2005). Either the purchase of insurance can be encouraged through the benefits system or alternative means of reimbursing flood losses (see below) can be found.

2. How can the availability and price of insurance influence the adoption of measures to reduce losses? Traditionally, private-sector insurance companies have assumed that policyholders take all reasonable steps to reduce losses (Arnell, 1987) but increasingly, in many areas of insurance, are either making insurance conditional on loss reduction measures or offering incentives to adopt loss reduction measures (see below).

3. How are insurance premiums calculated? In principle, for a scheme to be financially viable premiums should be at least equal to the long-term average annual flood damages. While it is feasible to calculate this on a case-by-case basis for high-value properties, such as industrial sites, some generalised method is necessary to estimate rates rapidly for domestic and smaller commercial and industrial properties. One way, as used in the US National Flood Insurance Program, is to construct standard tables presenting rates as a function of flood properties at a site (effectively the slope of the flood frequency curve) and location of the at-risk property (expressed, e.g., as the frequency with which flooding affects the property or elevation relative to a defined frequency event).

4. How can the insurance scheme pay for claims that occur? Flood insurance is similar to other types of insurance related to environmental hazards in that claims tend to occur rarely, but occur in large numbers when they do. Claims payouts therefore vary significantly from year to year, and the potential for catastrophic loss may be very high. These fluctuations can be managed through private-sector or government re-insurance.

The provision of flood insurance is influenced not just by the characteristics of the flood hazard, but also by the characteristics of the insurance industry, including specifically the nature of competition (intense competition can make it difficult to charge variable rates) and the way insurance is sold (direct insurers are more able to 'cherry-pick' than traditional insurers).

Flood insurance in the UK is provided by the private-sector insurance industry, and flood cover is generally included as standard in comprehensive household structure and contents policies. This developed following an agreement with government in 1961 (Arnell, 2000), and persisted unchanged until the floods of 2000 and 2002. Following these large flood losses, the insurance industry began to withdraw cover from high-risk areas (or to charge very high premiums) and threatened to withdraw from the 1961 agreement to provide cover to all.

From 2004, the insurance industry has agreed to provide cover at standard rates where property is protected to at least the 75-year return period, or where protection is planned for the next few years (ABI, 2002). In other circumstances, insurance is available at considerably higher rates or with conditions attached. The insurance industry has invested in the development of methods to estimate exposure to flood loss, in order both to support decisions on new policies and to estimate total exposure and hence re-insurance needs.

One of the reasons behind the insurance industry's rising concern over the provision of flood cover is the fear of continually increasing claims, due not only to increasing development in flood-prone areas and higher exposed property values, but also possible increases in the frequency of flooding due to climate change.

State aid or compensation

State aid or compensation involves payments from local or national (or in Europe, international) governments for flood losses. State aid schemes can take the form of grants or cheap loans, and can be individually tailored (i.e. depending on amount of loss) or allocated equally between victims. The relationship between state aid and private-sector insurance can be problematic and could become more so in the future set against a back drop of increasing flood risk. In general, private-sector insurers see state aid to flood victims as discouraging the purchase of flood insurance.

The approach is used on the European continent and in the USA, but has not been used to provide support directly to flood victims in the UK. However, local councils are eligible for flood relief from the national government under the Bellwin scheme to cover their additional expenditure after a flood. Bellwin claims totalled over £26 million for county, district and unitary authorities following the autumn 2000 floods (Penning-Rowsell et al., 2002).

Another form of state aid, widely used in Europe, is to award tax credits for economic losses caused by flooding. This differs from compensation in that the state does not actually pay the money to the victim, but rather charges lower taxes in subsequent years. This is likely to be most effective for businesses and other tax payers accustomed to personalised tax returns: it will be of limited or no help at all to victims who pay little or no tax.

Public charitable relief

Public charitable relief, in the form of money, labour or goods, plays a large part in response to major international flood events (particularly in less economically developed countries). Some charitable organisations, such as the International Committee of the Red Cross and various religious groups, are poised to act when and wherever a flood occurs, but other funds are established in response to specific events. Charitable relief usually takes the form of emergency aid, and has not played a major role in the longer-term recovery from flooding in Britain for decades. The last national appeal in the UK followed the 1953 floods: the widespread flooding in 1998, 2000 and 2002 did not trigger major charitable appeals, although local relief through 'mayoral' fund raising initiatives played a significant part in the restitution of flood damages in the largely uninsured community housing estates in North Muirton following the Perth floods in Scotland of 1993.

Self-insurance

Self-insurance is where a property owner puts aside money to pay for loss or damage: it is not the same as simply paying for losses once they have been incurred. In practice, self-insurance is only available to organisations with surplus income and a large number of at-risk sites (in order to spread the risk).

Spatial planning for reducing flood losses

The context

Spatial planning seeks to determine where development should, or should not, take place, and operates at a range of different scales. Strategic spatial planning is concerned with the broad picture, and the identification of areas within a region suitable for development. The primary driver behind strategic spatial planning historically has been economic development, although the Planning and Compulsory Purchase Act 2004 placed sustainable development at the heart of the planning system. Environmental conditions have so far rarely determined strategic spatial plans, although may pose some regional developmental constraints, but this is likely to change as the Planning and Compulsory Purchase Act 2004 becomes implemented: Defra's consultation document *Making Space for Water* (Defra, 2004) states that 'flood risk is a key environmental factor of physical sustainability'.

The government's review of future housing requirements (ODPM, 2003) estimates that an additional 200 000 homes would be needed by 2016, with much of the growth contained in identified growth areas in south-east England, including the Thames Gateway, Milton Keynes/South Midlands, London-Stansted-Cambridge-Peterborough, and Ashford. A study for the insurance industry (Entec *et al.*, 2005) shows very clearly that the new developments in Thames Gateway, Ashford, the South Midlands and M11 corridor could increase the costs of flooding by more than £50 million per year if steps to manage potential losses are not taken.

Local spatial planning is concerned with the zoning of development within a local area, and environmental considerations – such as exposure to flood risk – are much more important at this scale.

A broad distinction can be drawn between spatial planning measures which affect existing development (primarily local spatial plans) and measures which seek to influence the location of new development (which can be strategic or local).

Reducing exposure to flood loss of existing developments

This group of measures seeks to reduce the effect of flooding on existing property and infrastructure simply by relocating it away from flood-prone areas. There are essentially three variants:

1. Voluntary relocation: individual property owners decide of their own volition, either to move away from a flood-prone area or not to rebuild after suffering damage. This is not really a formal planning measure.
2. Encouraged relocation: individual property owners are encouraged to move away from flood-prone areas through, for example, grants to relocate, public purchase of flood-prone property, or high insurance premiums for continued occupation (as is currently encouraged, for example, following flood loss under the US National Flood Insurance Program).
3. Compulsory relocation: planning policies prevent reconstruction in a flood-prone area after loss, or condemn exposed property. This could be a component of a local regeneration plan. Wholesale redevelopment and regeneration of the floodplain is one option for reducing flood risk, where structural improvements would be expensive and potentially uneconomic.

Two factors influence the effectiveness and feasibility of measures to reduce exposure by relocating existing development.

First, removal of property and infrastructure from flood-prone areas requires the definition of areas exposed to flood risk. Such information has only been available in a consistent and reasonably robust manner since 2000, when the Environment Agency's Indicative Flood Plain maps showing the estimated 100-year fluvial and 200-year coastal floodplain were published and made available across the Internet. While these maps represented a major advance on information previously available to planners (and, far less easily, the public) several weaknesses became apparent.

The maps were deliberately portrayed as being indicative, rather than locally specific, but were widely misinterpreted and given a spurious degree of precision (Brown and Damery, 2002). They did not distinguish between defended and undefended floodplains, or between different degrees of hazard. They did not show areas at risk from localised or disconnected flooding: around 40% of the losses in the autumn 2000 floods occurred outside the indicative floodplain (Crichton, 2001).

Updated maps were published in 2004 incorporating flood defences and considering risk from many smaller rivers. These new 'flood zone' maps also describe the likelihood of flooding as 'significant', i.e. more frequently than an average of 1.3% per year (one in 75 years); 'moderate', i.e. the chance of flooding in any year is 1.3% (one in 75) or less, but greater than 0.5% (one in 200); or 'low', i.e. the chance of flooding in any year is 0.5% (one in 200) or less. The maps, however, still present an impression of precision.

Second, there may be sound reasons for property and infrastructure being located in flood-prone areas. Location in these areas may add significant economic or competitive advantage, or prevent social and economic stagnation, even after the costs of flooding to the property and indeed downstream are considered. Alternative locations simply may not be available. Rivers have been the lifeline for communities and commerce since the dawn of civilisation. Wholesale movement to allow managed realignment would in many cases be contrary to articles 1 and 8 of Human Rights legislation and the 'Right to peaceful enjoyment'.[1] As a result, the deliberate flooding of land without compensation may be challenged, and the decision not to maintain existing defences to a sufficient standard leading to flooding and damage to property may also be challenged. There must also be safeguards against arbitrary decisions by authorities affecting these rights, under the right to a fair and public trial within reasonable time.

However, there is obviously a clearer case for certain critical facilities – emergency services, hospitals etc. – to be relocated away from risk areas.

Controlling future development

Measures to limit future exposure to flood risk include:

- public planning policies which prevent future development in flood-prone areas;
- policies to discourage future development in flood-prone areas through, e.g., charging or other incentivising measures;
- policies by individual developers, utilities or other investors not to develop in flood-prone areas.

Implementation of any of these measures depends critically on the identification of flood-prone areas. As noted above, the indicative floodplain and more recent flood zone maps are – intentionally – only indicative, and it is, in fact, technically very difficult precisely to identify flood-prone areas. Measures to estimate flood magnitudes and translate these into flood extent are uncertain, and a changing

---

[1] The right to peaceful enjoyment of possessions and protection of property (Article 1); and the right to respect for private and family life, home and correspondence (Article 8).

Table 21.1. National planning guidance on development and flooding

UK country	National guidance on development and flooding	Nomenclature for flood risk zones
England	PPG25: Development and Flood Risk	Zone 1: Little or no risk Zone 2: Low to medium risk Zone 3a: High risk, developed area Zone 3b: High risk, undeveloped and sparsely-developed areas Zone 3c: Functional floodplain
Scotland	SPP7: Planning and Flooding	Zone 1: Little or no risk Zone 2: Low to medium risk Zone 3a: High risk, within areas already built up Zone 3b: High risk, undeveloped and sparsely developed areas, including functional floodplains
Wales	TAN15: Development and Flood Risk	Zone A: Little or no risk Zone B: Low to medium risk Zone C1: High risk – defended Zone C2: High risk – undefended

(Adapted from CIRIA, 2003)

climate makes the identification of the boundaries of flood-prone areas more difficult.

Also as noted above, there may be very good reasons why property and infrastructure is located in flood-prone areas: they may be the only areas that are technically suitable, or they may offer economic or indeed cultural advantages. The goal of land-use planning should not, therefore, necessarily be to prevent all new development in the floodplain.

Planning policies and procedures across the UK are the mechanism by which property development and land-use is regulated, with the aim of promoting sustainable development. Flood risk is an important factor to be considered by Local Planning Authorities (LPAs) when preparing development plans and, when appropriate, it is a 'material consideration' to be taken into account by LPAs when determining planning applications.

Separate planning policy guidance documents relating to flood risk have been issued for England, Scotland, Northern Ireland and Wales (Table 21.1). In each case, a sequential approach is recommended, with actions dependent on degree of risk. The aim of these guidance notes is to strengthen the coordination between land-use and development and improve the operational delivery of flood defence strategy. When following guidance, local authorities should:

- apply the precautionary principle using a risk-based approach;
- ensure that development plans outline the consideration given to flood issues;
- implement flood management policies on a catchment-wide basis;
- seek advice from the EA/SEPA/NI Rivers Agency on flood issues;
- ensure that developers provide the cost of any flood defences required as part of their development proposal.

Virtually all LPA Development Plans include flood risk statements and/or policies, but relatively few reflect the new guidance in PPG25, SPP7 and TAN15 (in England, Scotland and Wales respectively). LPAs are advised to submit applications in flood zones to the Environment Agency (England and Wales), SEPA (Scotland) or NI Rivers Agency (Northern Ireland) for comment, although there is evidence that only just over 50% of relevant applications are in fact submitted (Environment Agency, 2004).

In 2003/4 22.5% of applications advised against by the Environment Agency were permitted by LPAs (Environment Agency, 2004), largely because local economic or social benefits were perceived to outweigh the risk of flood loss. However, the insurance industry is increasingly refusing to provide insurance (and hence mortgage cover) for development that takes place against advice (Defra, 2004).

The planning guidance, and LPA practice, allows development in flood-prone areas if that development is protected against the 1% (river) or 0.5% (coastal) flood, with the developer paying for flood defence costs. This reinforces current unsustainable practices (Parker, 1995; Howe and White, 2001; White and Howe, 2002), and leads to several problems. The overall storage capacity of the floodplain may be reduced, and this is exacerbated by the case-by-case treatment of applications. The new development would still be flooded by floods larger than the design standard, with the protection works perhaps exacerbating damages by, e.g., preventing drainage or discouraging mitigating actions (see next below). Finally, flood defences need to be maintained, and it is highly likely that responsibility for this would pass, by default, to the public purse.

A protectionist policy also creates a cycle of vulnerability. Building on floodplains creates a demand for defences, which in turn increases the attractiveness and safety of floodplain occupancy, encouraging further development. A focus on defences may also lead to a false sense of security and a decrease in individual preparation, raising the potential damage when defences are breached.

Public policy in the UK on development in flood-prone areas has so far focused on the planning permission process: development proposals are either approved, approved with conditions, or rejected. Another way of managing land-use is through financial measures.

Oxera concluded, in their flood and coastal defence funding review (Oxera, 2001), that a beneficiary levy on properties on the floodplain is feasible, especially if introduced gradually over a period of time, and would permit substantial devolution of decision making to the local level. It presents some challenges, such as the definition of the floodplain boundary, and the level of risk (as discussed in the preceding section, 'Reducing exposure'), but at the same time would raise awareness of flood risk among property owners. A charge on developers would probably have little influence on the location decisions of developers, but might make a substantial contribution towards the financing of defences for areas that are currently undefended. It would be straightforward to introduce and could operate as a standard set of charges under the planning gain provisions.

One of the problems with this tax would be to achieve a sufficiently well-defined boundary between payers and non-payers, or between tiers of payers. While flood zone maps have been published, their resolution is quite coarse (as discussed above), and likely to be open to challenge. However, boundary problems have not prevented the introduction of charging and communal insurance schemes in the USA. Also, in order to minimise the number of disputes over the location of the boundary:

1. the charge could be introduced initially at a low level and gradually increased;
2. the quality of floodplain mapping could be improved; and,
3. the status of households could be switched from charged to uncharged, but not the other way around.

In summary, a tiered charge, reflecting standards of defence (and risk) sets the best incentives for authorities. It may, however, be administratively more complex, and the charging boundaries may be open to challenge. The risk of challenge can be minimised by the introduction of the charges at a low level, and the careful refinement of the charged areas.

Flood proofing and building standards

Spatial planning determines where development should take place; flood proofing and building standard determine the exposure to loss of individual properties.

'Retro-fitting'

This group of measures seeks to reduce the effect of flooding on established property and infrastructure by changing the characteristics of the exposed structures ('retro-fitting'). Measures within this group fall into two types: permanent changes to structures or their occupancy, and temporary measures which are installed following a warning ('removable flood products'). Permanent measures include actions such as raising electrical sockets or vulnerable equipment above an expected flood height or sealing floors to stop water entering from below. These measures are often implemented when renovating after flooding. Temporary measures include a wide variety of door and window shields, covers for air-bricks, temporary sealants and temporary free-standing barriers (Bramley and Bowker, 2002).

There are two broad factors influencing the efficacy of retro-fitted flood proofing in reducing aggregate flood damages.

The first is the rate of uptake of flood-proofing measures. Only those who believe they are exposed to flooding will consider implementing flood proofing, and only those who believe that flood proofing will be effective and can afford it will actually install it. Take-up is therefore likely to be highest immediately after a flood, and the role of financial incentives and conditions imposed by insurance companies is crucial. Barriers for domestic doors typically currently cost between £300 and £700, and a typical house could probably be protected to 1 m and against short-duration flooding for less than £2500. More comprehensive flood proofing, involving demountable barriers, can cost ten times as much. At present, funding must be provided by individual occupiers. However, it is conceivable that funding for property-scale flood proofing could be provided through public grants (akin to energy efficiency grants) or loans.

The second factor is the effectiveness of the measures in actually reducing flood losses. The effectiveness of removable flood products depends rather obviously on whether a warning is received, the lead time of that warning, and whether people are available to install the products: removable flood products are therefore least effective where warning times are short or when flooding occurs during the night. Given that a measure is actually fitted, there are many technical limitations to retro-fitted flood proofing (US ACE, 1998).

Effectiveness varies with the type and characteristics of flooding. For example, measures to prevent the entry of water through windows and doors are ineffective where water enters the property through the floor, and flood proofing is unlikely to provide significant protection where velocities are high or flood water contains damaging debris. Walls of typical British houses can withstand up to around 1 m of flooding, but floods above that depth would probably result in structural damage (Environment Agency, 2003). Retro-fitted flood proofing is therefore unlikely to eliminate damages completely. Modelling simulations by Kelman (2002) indicate that retro-fitted flood proofing can reduce damages to a house following infiltration through walls by 80% and following penetration through doors by 67%, but has little effect where water enters through other openings or causes structural failure.

Flood depths in fluvial flood-prone areas in Britain, however, are relatively low – the median depth in a 100-year flood within lowland river floodplains, such as the Severn and Thames, is less than 1.2 m (Penning-Rowsell and Chatterton, 2000) – and velocities are low, so flood proofing is generally likely to be effective. This contrasts with, e.g., the USA or central Europe where, with flood depths regularly in excess of 4 m (River Odra floods, Poland in 1997), flood proofing is largely ineffectual.

There is, however, considerable scope for technical innovation, and over the last few years the flood product industry has expanded considerably (see www.floodprotectionassociation.org and Environment Agency (2002, 2003)). The DTLR's (2002) report, *Preparing for Floods*, provides numerous examples of measures that individual property owners have implemented following flood damage to reduce further losses. These include replacement of electrical sockets and wiring at higher levels, and installation of food fryers on hydraulic jacks. CIRIA has produced a list of fact sheets for property owners wishing to implement flood proofing.

Building codes and construction practices

This group of measures seeks to reduce flood losses by ensuring that new buildings and infrastructure are designed to be resilient to damage. These measures include building codes applied to all new structures (or perhaps just to flood-prone structures), and the design of individual buildings. They include both development control (i.e. control through regulations and the planning process) and voluntary actions by developers in flood-prone areas.

In principle, it is possible to design building codes and new buildings to reduce losses significantly during flooding and exposure to risk. In practice, measures implemented will be determined by the balance between cost and benefits in terms of reduced losses. There are two broad groups of measures. One operates at the property scale, and seeks to reduce the level of loss when a building is flooding. The other operates at the scale of the development unit, and seeks to reduce runoff, and hence risk of flooding, from local source areas (see also Chapter 10). There are therefore significant linkages between flood damage limitation and source control, particularly in urbanised environments.

The role of local authorities is crucial (1) in implementing and monitoring development (and being able to cope with appeals), (2) in being flexible in assessing potentially innovative solutions, and (3) in ensuring that measures to reduce exposure to flood loss do not increase exposure to other types of loss. The construction industry and organisations such as CIRIA can also play a significant role in influencing and changing developer behaviour and providing a lead in the education of new planning processes and design practices (e.g. CIRIA, 2003). Any changes to runoff practices will also have to include the water and sewerage undertakers and other potential stakeholders, such as local authorities. The insurance industry could also play a key role in influencing public (and developer) behaviour with regard to building design/materials/practices (Treby *et al.*, in press).

It is important to note that all major stakeholders should be involved in any tightening or changing of building codes, construction practices and building design as the key factor will not be the identification of possible changes, but an effective translation of these into standard practice.

While it may be unclear as to whether the implementation of improved building codes, construction practices and building design will be more expensive, an awareness of the current costs of the present policies suggests that there may be scope to tap into new funding mechanisms. The insurance industry could be a driver in this area as in recent years they have suffered heavily through expensive flood claims. Reduced flood insurance rates for certain designs or a stipulation that any building once flooded would have to incorporate new design practices when retrofitted are two examples. The costs in these instances would be borne by the developer or homeowner.

The developer could also be encouraged to fund these new methods by a strict planning process. In this case they would normally simply pass on any extra costs to the end user; in practice this would be the simplest option.

Implications for future national flood losses

Reducing flood losses during the twenty-first century

Measures to reduce flood losses by spatial planning, flood proofing and building standards are heavily influenced by economic and political conditions, and their implementation and manifestation can be expected to vary between the four Foresight socio-economic scenarios. Table 21.2 outlines how these measures *might* evolve under the four future worlds. A key point to note is that the two market-orientated worlds do not necessarily lead to uncontrolled floodplain development, because the market generally and insurance companies in particular may act as significant constraints on development in high-risk areas.

Table 21.2. Measures to reduce flood losses under different socio-economic worlds

	World markets	National enterprise	Global sustainability	Local stewardship
Land-use planning and management	Government support for 'enterprise zones', but little formal detailed land-use planning. Businesses and those able to choose may avoid flood-prone areas for economic reasons; floodplains likely to be occupied by lower income groups. Insurance industry may require planning in high-risk areas	Central and local support for 'enterprise zones'. Little formal detailed land-use planning (in case development goes 'elsewhere'). Businesses and those able to choose may avoid flood-prone areas for economic reasons; floodplains likely to be occupied by lower-income groups	Strong land-use planning, with specific policies affecting existing development. Strategic planning takes flood risk into account	Strong land-use planning, with specific policies affecting existing development. No strategic planning
Flood proofing	Strong incentives from risk-avoiding insurance industry. Technological innovation	Strong incentives from risk-avoiding insurance industry. Little innovation. Strict design and development control measures to maximise freedom in competition	Incentives from insurance industry. Relatively weak building regulations because it is assumed that all development is located away from risk areas. National state support for implementation	Incentives from insurance industry. Strong building controls/regulations. Local state support for implementation
Availability of insurance	Private sector, with international reinsurance. Risk-focused, with incentives for adoption of risk reduction measures. Risk-based premiums	Private sector, with government reinsurance. Risk-focused, with incentives for adoption of risk reduction measures. Risk-based premiums	Public–private partnership. Incentives for adoption of risk reduction measures. Premiums do not vary much with risk	Public–private partnership. Incentives for adoption of risk reduction measures. Premiums vary with risk
Other financial assistance measures	No support for those who cannot afford insurance	No support for those who cannot afford insurance	Public support for recovery through public/private partnership	Public support for recovery through public/private partnership

Sensitivity to changing physical conditions

Each potential response to flooding is sensitive in a different way to changes in the future flood risk.

The financial feasibility of flood insurance, and other measures to reduce financial consequences of flooding, is very sensitive to the future frequency of flooding, but this sensitivity can be substantially reduced through the implementation of development control and flood-proofing measures.

Local spatial planning is, in contrast, likely to be relatively unaffected by changing physical flood hazard. It is based on the identification of flood-prone areas (e.g. the 100-year floodplain), and at the scales relevant for planning, these areas are unlikely to change significantly. Many – but not all – floodplains are topographically defined, and changes in the flood hazard in these floodplains are likely to be manifest in changes in depth rather than the extent of flooding. However, there are two large exceptions: areas where topography is gentle and floodplains are poorly defined, and areas where changing physical flood hazard results in changes in structural defences. For example, a policy of coastal realignment and the abandonment of coastal defences would alter the inland floodplain.

Flood-proofing and building control measures are robust to changes in the physical flood hazard. Most measures are sized according to technical feasibility rather than anticipated flood magnitudes, and changes in the frequency of flooding would not affect design. The financial benefits of flood proofing and building controls depend on the frequency of flooding but, because costs are substantially less than the damages incurred during a single flood, changes in flood frequency would not affect the economic case for implementation. Perceived changes in frequency would, however, alter the likelihood of flood proofing and building control measures being installed.

Effect on future national flood losses

The effect on national flood risk (average annual flood damages) of spatial planning, flood proofing and building control measures depend not only on their effectiveness *per se*, but also on (1) the future mix of 'old' and 'new' development in the floodplain and (2) the degree to which the measures are implemented as a package.

Table 21.3 shows the assumed effectiveness *per se* of spatial planning and flood proofing on existing and new developments within flood-prone areas, with effectiveness expressed as a factor change to average annual flood damages to existing or new development. For example, measures to manage existing floodplain land-use would have a minimal effect under the national enterprise world (only reducing damages to 90% of existing values) but a rather larger effect under the global responsibility world (reducing damages to half their current values).

Measures to control future floodplain land-use would reduce damages to new development under the national enterprise world to 75% of the damages that would have occurred in the absence of any flood policy; similar measures would reduce damages under the global responsibility world to 25%. The figures for the effectiveness of flood proofing existing structures take into account not only physical effectiveness at reducing losses but also assumed uptake of measures. It is assumed that retro-fitted flood proofing reduces losses by 50% where installed, but take-up varies between 50 and 75%. It is important to note that there is virtually *no* empirical evidence on which to base these estimates of inherent effectiveness, so the uncertainty ranges are very wide.

The effect of these measures on *total* future flood losses depends on the mix in flood-prone areas of existing and new development. The proportion of future floodplain development which is 'new', however, is not equal simply to the net rate of development growth. Much of the existing development in the floodplain will be rebuilt over the next few decades, so the total amount of 'new' development is equal to growth plus rebuild and replacement. Table 21.4 shows the assumed

Table 21.3. Inherent effectiveness of measures in reducing losses to existing or future floodplain development

	World markets	National enterprise	Local stewardship	Global sustainability
Managing existing floodplain land-use	1.00 (0.80–1.10)	0.90 (0.80–1.00)	0.50 (0.25–1.00)	0.50 (0.25–1.00)
Controlling future land-use	0.90 (0.60–1.00)	0.75 (0.50–1.00)	0.25 (0.00–0.75)	0.25 (0.00–0.75)
Floodproofing existing structures	0.63 (0.50–0.90)	0.63 (0.50–0.90)	0.63 (0.50–0.90)	0.75 (0.50–0.90)
Building controls for new structures	0.75 (0.50–1.00)	0.75 (0.50–1.00)	0.50 (0.25–1.00)	0.50 (0.25–1.00)

The table shows the factor effect of the measure on average annual flood damages to existing or new development. The figures in parentheses represent an estimated uncertainty range.

Table 21.4. Assumed proportion of future flood-prone areas made up of new development

	World markets	National enterprise	Local stewardship	Global sustainability
Percentage of development which is 'brand new' – i.e. growth	35	29	0	3
Assumed rate of rebuild and replacement (not compound): %	0.5	0.5	0.25	0.25
Proportion of 2080 properties developed since 2000: %	61	57	20	22

proportion of 2080 floodplain development which is 'new' (growth plus rebuild and replacement) under the four worlds, assuming rebuild rates of 0.25% per year (not compound) for the global sustainability and local stewardship worlds and 0.5% per year for the world markets and national enterprise worlds.

Table 21.5 shows the effect of the four measures on reducing *national* future flood risk. It was effectively constructed by weighting Table 21.3 by Table 21.4. In

Table 21.5. Effect of each measure on national *future flood risk if used alone*

	World markets	National enterprise	Local stewardship	Global sustainability
Effectiveness in reducing national flood risk *on their own*				
Managing existing floodplain land-use	1.00 (0.8–1.0)	0.96 (0.8–1.0)	0.60 (0.4–1.0)	0.61 (0.4–1.0)
Controlling future land-use	0.94 (0.7–1.0)	0.86 (0.7–1.0)	0.85 (0.7–1.0)	0.83 (0.7–1.0)
Floodproofing existing structures	0.86 (0.7–1.0)	0.84 (0.7–1.0)	0.70 (0.5–1.0)	0.81 (0.5–1.0)
Building controls for new structures	0.85 (0.7–1.0)	0.86 (0.7–1.0)	0.90 (0.8–1.0)	0.89 (0.8–1.0)
Effectiveness in reducing national flood risk *if used together*				
Just spatial planning	0.94 (0.8–1.0)	0.81 (0.7–1.0)	0.45 (0.3–0.7)	0.44 (0.3–0.7)
Just flood proofing	0.70 (0.5–0.9)	0.70 (0.5–0.9)	0.60 (0.4–0.8)	0.69 (0.4–0.8)
All measures implemented together	0.66 (0.5–0.9)	0.56 (0.4–0.8)	0.28 (0.15–0.5)	0.32 (0.15–0.5)

practice, it is highly unlikely that the measures would be implemented individually. Table 21.5 also shows the effects of spatial planning measures and flood-proofing measures on national flood risk, together with the effects of implementing all the measures. These latter three sets of values are relatively insensitive to assumed rates of development in the floodplain.

Sustainability appraisal of measures to reduce flood losses

Figure 21.1 summarises the sustainability performance estimated for measures to reduce flood losses, against the six measures of performance, under the four worlds. The 'reducing flood risk' measure refers to losses to either existing (left two panels) or future (right two panels) developments, not to total national flood loss. The figures are based on those in Table 21.3 and as discussed in the previous section, with the maximum effect corresponding to reducing losses to zero.

All the four measures are assessed to be cost-effective, under all four worlds: implementation costs are generally low relative to damage costs. The two spatial planning measures are assessed to have positive effects on environmental quality under each world – primarily through providing opportunities for increased 'green spaces' within urban environments – although the two flood-proofing measures have no clear environmental effect on their own. Measures affecting future developments are assessed to have no clear effect on social justice issues or equity (even where land-use planning in general is designed to reduce future inequities, the

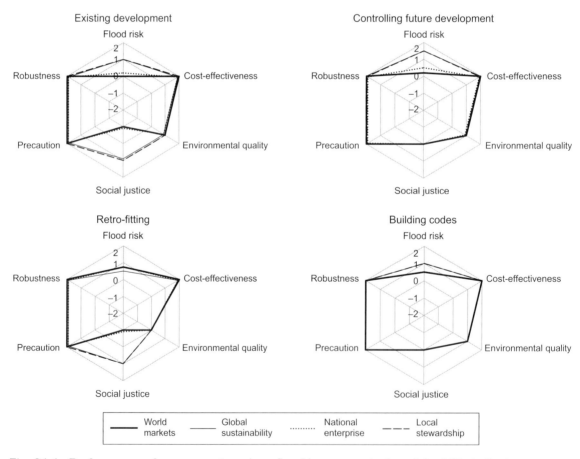

Fig. 21.1. Performance of measures to reduce flood losses against sustainability indicators

marginal effect on social justice of accounting for flood risk would be small), but measures affecting existing developments do have social justice implications.

Under the two economically orientated worlds (world markets and national enterprise) it is likely that such measures would be most widely adopted by wealthier floodplain occupants, so the burden of flood losses would fall increasingly on poorer occupants; under the other two worlds, however, it is likely that measures would be implemented in a way that reduced, rather than enhanced, inequities. Finally, all four measures score highly on the 'precautionary' and 'robustness' measures. They can be seen as no-regrets measures, necessary to reduce losses even without changing physical or economic conditions, and as shown in the preceding section detailed designs are not significantly affected by hydrological uncertainties.

Conclusions

This chapter has described measures to reduce flood losses through control of developments in flood-prone areas and alterations to existing or new developments to reduce susceptibility to flood damage. The effectiveness of these measures depends not just on technical design, but largely on the economic and political conditions under which they are applied. Attitudes towards land-use planning and building controls, for example, are important, and the actions of the insurance industry in encouraging the adoption of measures to reduce risk are particularly significant.

Table 21.5 implies that implementing spatial planning, flood-proofing and building control measures would have the effect of reducing average annual flood losses by around 70% under the local stewardship and global sustainability worlds, but only by between 35 and 45% under the world markets and national enterprise worlds. Clearly, the measures have the potential to reduce future flood losses substantially. However, the figures presented in these tables are extremely uncertain, largely because there has been very little research into the effectiveness and uptake of measures to reduce flood losses through building works and spatial planning.

References

ABI, 2002. *Renewing the Partnership: How the insurance industry will work with others to improve protection against floods*, ABI, London.

Arnell, N.W., 1987. 'Flood insurance and floodplain management', in *Flood Hazard Management: British and international perspectives*, ed. Handmer, J.W., GeoBooks, Norwich, 117–133.

Arnell, N.W., 2000. 'Flood insurance', Vol. 1, in *Floods*, ed. Parker, D.J., Routledge, London, 412–424.

Bramley, M. and Bowker, P., 2002. 'Improving local flood protection to property', *Proceedings of the Institution of Civil Engineers – Civil Engineering*, 150 (special issue 1), 49–54.

Brown, J.D. and Damery, S.I., 2002. 'Managing flood risk in the UK: towards an integration of social and technical perspectives', *Transactions of the Institute of British Geographers*, NS 27, 412–426.

CIRIA, 2003. *Development and Flood Risk: Guidance for the Construction industry – draft report*, December 2003-12-06, London, CIRIA.

Clark, M.J., Priest, S.J., Treby, E.J. and Crichton, D., 2002. *Insurance and UK Floods: A strategic re-assessment*, University of Southampton, Report to TSUNAMI Project.

Crichton, D., 2001. 'Flood news from the insurance front line', *Town and Country Planning*, 70(7), 183–185.

Crichton, D., 2002. 'UK and global insurance responses to flood hazard', *Water International*, 27, 119–131.

Defra, 2004. *Making Space for Water*, Consultation Document, Defra, London.

DTLR, 2002. *Preparing for Floods*, Department for Transport, Local Government and the Regions, London.

Entec, HR Wallingford, John Chatterton Associates, 2005. *Making Communities Sustainable: Managing flood risks in the government's sustainable growth area*, Report to Association of British Insurers, Entec, London.

Environment Agency, 2002. *Damage Limitation. How to make your home flood resistant*, Environment Agency and CIRIA, Bristol.

Environment Agency, 2003. *Flood Products. Using Flood Protection Products: A guide for householders*, Environment Agency and CIRIA, Bristol.

Environment Agency, 2004. *High Level Target 12: Development and flood risk 2003/4*, Report to Defra and ODPM, November, EA, Bristol.

Howe, J. and White, I., 2001. 'Flooding: are we ignoring the real problem and solution?' *Regional Studies*, 35, 368–370.

Kelman, I., 2002. *Physical Flood Vulnerability of Residential Properties in Coastal, Eastern England*, PhD dissertation, University of Cambridge.

ODPM, 2003. *Sustainable Communities: Building for the future*, ODPM, London.

Oxera, 2001. *Flood and Coastal Defence Funding Review*, Report to Ministry of Agriculture, Fisheries and Food, Oxera, Oxford.

Parker, D., 1995. 'Floodplain development policy in England and Wales', *Applied Geography*, 15(4), 341–365.

Penning-Rowsell, E.C. and Chatterton, J.B., 2000. *Flood Depth Model: Development and specification*, Middlesex University Flood Hazard Research Centre, London, unpublished Report for Experian.

Penning-Rowsell, E.C., Chatterton, J.B., Wilson, T. and Potter, E., 2002. *Autumn 2000 Floods in England and Wales: Assessment of national economic and financial losses*, Flood Hazard Research Centre, Middlesex University, London.

Priest, S.J., Clark, M.J. and Treby, E.J., 2005. 'UK Flood Insurance: The challenge of the uninsured', *Area*, 37(3), 295–302.

Treby, E.J., Clark, M.J. and Priest, S.J., (in press). 'Confronting flood risk: insurance as a barrier to risk transfer', *Journal of Environmental Management*.

US Army Corps of Engineers, 1998. *Flood Proofing Performance: Successes and Failures*, USACE National Flood Proofing Committee, Washington, DC, December.

White, I. and Howe, J., 2002. 'Flooding and the role of planning in England and Wales: a critical review', *Journal of Environmental Planning and Management*, 45(5), 735–745.

22 River engineering responses

Peter H. von Lany and John Palmer

Introduction

This chapter identifies, describes and assesses river engineering measures that have the potential to manage flood risk at a catchment scale, as defined in earlier chapters. Practical experience identified a broad range of possible engineered measures capable of reducing the risks from fluvial flooding. Descriptions of each measure were then developed through consultation with a range of experts and stakeholders, supplemented by a literature review (ICE, 2001; Ward *et al.*, 1994; Parker, 2000; World Commission on Dams, 2001).

River engineering measures are wide-ranging in scope. They include measures that reduce river flood water levels in areas exposed to flooding by altering river conveyance and/or increasing flood storage, measures that transfer flood water away from flood-prone areas, and flood defences to limit the spread of flood water. Engineering measures that share a common purpose in terms of flood risk reduction were placed in four functional response groups:

- altering river conveyance;
- creating flood storage;
- transferring flood water;
- flood defences.

River engineering measures within each of the above response groups are summarised in Table 22.1. Descriptions of the four response groups and the range of measures within each group are given in the next section. These cover:

- definitions of each response group and examples of the types of measure included within each group;
- descriptions of the efficacy of each group in managing flood risk;
- an assessment of the ways in which the responses interact with the river system and stakeholder attitudes to flood risk management;
- a case example to illustrate each response group.

Consideration was given to more general issues of governance, costs and standards of service. The potential sustainability of each response group was assessed by considering what factors in each of the four Foresight future scenarios would encourage or restrict the implementation of river engineering measures within each response group.

Table 22.1. Summary of river engineering response groups and measures

Response group	Possible measures or interventions
River conveyance can be altered to increase the hydraulic capacity of river channels and of flood flow paths on floodplains in order to reduce flood water levels locally	Altering the cross-section and reducing the hydraulic roughness of river channels at specific locations Canalisation of river reaches – sometimes creating multi-stage channels Forming flood bypass channels
Flood storage increases the capacity of fluvial systems to store flood water temporarily thus attenuating the flood hydrograph and reducing flood water levels downstream	Creating 'on-line' flood storage through the construction of a dam across a river to create a reservoir Creating washlands on floodplains Enhancing natural storage provided by the floodplain Developing artificial 'off-line' storage adjacent to the river system
Flood water transfer involves engineered measures that convey excess water from one river system to another water system that is better able to deal with the flood water and the associated flood risk	Engineering works to allow pumped or gravity transfer of flood water to a receiving water system 'Compensatory' works in the recipient water system to control the resulting flood risk
Flood defences are engineered structures, sometimes combined with natural formations, whose main purpose is to control the spread of flood water	Flood embankments and walls along river channels, sometimes with associated river bank protection measures Ring dikes around vulnerable areas Specialist structures, such as demountable defences and flood gates, which prevent flood water entering specific areas

Assessment of each response group under the Foresight scenarios

The assessment of each river engineering response group began with an overview of each Foresight future scenario to draw out those responses that are most consistent with the societal values and wealth of each scenario. Table 22.2 provides details of the engineering measures for flood defence that might be envisaged under each of the four scenarios.

The long-term perspective adopted for the Foresight Project (30 to 100 years) means that it is not possible to make judgements about the specific flood management infrastructure that may be implemented. Recognising this, the analysis of river engineering response groups has necessarily been performed at a high level. It deals with broad approaches that can in future be adapted to suit policies that will evolve in response to the relevant socio-political circumstances and take advantage of technological advances. In all cases we assume that the engineering measures will sit within portfolios of structural and non-structural responses.

Engineering responses nest not only in such portfolios but within local and national policies that will dictate the scale of the engineering approach – that is one, or a combination of: a system of large-scale structures forming the defence system; a series of linked, smaller-scale structures; or dispersed, localised structures.

Response group descriptions

This section describes each river engineering response group in turn. In particular it outlines the function and efficacy in reducing the flood risk of each group of measures. It considers the possible interactions of the measures within the group with other aspects of the river system and flood risk generation. A case example is included to illustrate each response group.

Table 22.2. Foresight scenarios interpreted in terms of engineering measures for flood defence

	World markets	**National enterprise**	**Local stewardship**	**Global sustainability**
Summary	Reliance on modern engineering to protect high-value land and property from flood damage. Increasingly efficient provision of hard-engineering measures	Locally planned flood and coastal defence schemes. Piece-meal and diverse approaches. Technologically stagnant	Soft defences to protect metropolitan areas and key infrastructures. Widespread abandonment and re-instatement of floodplains and coasts	Strategic modern engineering with an emphasis on a portfolio approach combining engineering with non-structural measures to ensure sustainability. Strategic provision of hard defences in metropolitan areas. Some managed re-alignment
Flood/coastal defence embankments	Reliance on hard defences to protect areas of high economic value	Reliance on hard defences to protect areas of high economic value	Retreat and abandonment. Defences to protect urban areas	Sustainable design of defences. High-tech monitoring and control of soft systems
Storage or rural detention	Major strategic storage systems and flood-relief channels. High-technology control	Some storage schemes	Major retreat from floodplains sees restoration of natural floodplain functions. Limited engineering control of these systems	Major strategic storage systems and flood relief channels. High-tech control
Urban drainage	Cost-cutting reduces investment in maintenance and renewal. High technology control and other technologies to maximise the performance of existing systems	Cost-cutting reduces investment in maintenance and renewal. Increasingly challenged urban drainage system	Emphasis on reducing urban runoff and reconfiguration of the urban environment to accommodate flooding. Limited new investment in conventional drainage infrastructure	Increased investment in repair/renewal. High-tech control and other technologies. Urban storage (above and below ground). Design of cities for surface flows
River management	River management to maximise conveyance, protecting environments with high-value amenity	River management to maximise conveyance	Widespread restoration of natural river systems	Multi-use river management for conveyance and environment

Altering river conveyance

River conveyance is usually altered to increase the hydraulic capacity of river channels and flood flow paths on floodplains in order to reduce flood water levels. Specific measures in this response group include:

- improving the hydraulic capacity of channels by altering their cross-section and reducing their hydraulic roughness by removing excess vegetation;
- canalisation of rivers, sometimes creating multi-stage channels;
- forming flood-bypass channels that follow natural or artificial flood flow paths on the floodplain.

In some cases the conveyance of floodplains is decreased as a consequence of river restoration and the establishment of natural floodplain vegetation. This has the effect of increasing storage on the floodplain, thus attenuating the flood hydrograph and reducing flood levels further downstream. This aspect of altering conveyance is included with measures to increase flood storage, and is described in the next section.

Function and efficacy

The objective of increasing conveyance is to improve the ability of the river reach to carry flood water through and away from a flood-prone area. Improved conveyance lowers flood-water levels locally, thereby also reducing the frequency, extent and duration of flooding along improved river reaches.

The efficacy of measures to alter channel conveyance is limited by what is feasible and morphologically stable. Improved conveyance can reduce the attenuation of the flood wave in the altered reach thereby increasing flood-water levels downstream of the reach.

Interactions

Measures to alter conveyance can be implemented individually or as part of an integrated set of measures from different response groups. Altering conveyance can create a set of potentially complex interactions. For example:

- Changes in river-channel conveyance can influence the dynamics of sediment erosion and deposition, leading to changes in the geomorphological characteristics of the river channel over the long term.
- An increase in flood risk downstream of a reach with improved conveyance can reduce public acceptance of such measures.

In cases of river and floodplain restoration, where river channels become more varied and floodplain conveyance is reduced, natural instream, channel edge and floodplain habitats can develop, thereby enhancing biodiversity (Hughes, 2003).

Case example

The recently completed Maidenhead, Windsor and Eton scheme (Petts *et al.*, 2002) is a good example of increased conveyance for flood alleviation. The man-made Jubilee River is a major flood diversion channel that takes excess flood flow out of the River Thames upstream of Maidenhead and discharges it back into the Thames downstream of Windsor. Over the length of the Thames bypassed by the Jubilee River, the flow in the Thames is controlled to a level that is below its flood risk threshold. There will still be some risk of flooding in the event of a flood above the design standard. The Jubilee River has been designed and constructed to mimic a natural river with much attention to habitat creation and environmental enhancement. Issues relating to the performance of the scheme during a flood event in 2003 highlighted the importance of integrating hydraulic and morphological parameters into the design.

Flood storage

Flood storage measures increase the capacity of fluvial systems to store flood water temporarily, thus attenuating the flood hydrograph and reducing flood-water levels downstream. Flood storage can be created through a variety of engineered measures, combined, where appropriate, with natural features of the river system and its floodplain. Specific measures covered by this response group include:

- creating 'on-line' flood storage through the construction of a dam across a river;
- creating washlands on floodplain land;

- enhancing natural storage provided by the floodplain topography through river restoration;
- developing artificial (off-line) storage adjacent to the river system.

Function and efficacy

The primary function of flood storage is to temporarily retain flood water, thereby reducing the immediate threat of flooding downstream. The stored flood water is then released at a controlled rate within the flow-carrying capacity of the river system.

While offering the potential significantly to reduce flood risk over large areas downstream, flood storage alone may not provide complete and cost-effective flood protection. The available flood-storage capacity at a site can vary with the time of year and the antecedent conditions at the storage site. Storage capacity can reduce over time, through deposition of sediment.

Construction of reservoirs for flood storage is difficult to justify in economic terms alone (Freer, 2001). Under many circumstances, flood storage in a reservoir is combined with other purposes, such as hydroelectric power generation, water-resources management, and maintaining river levels for navigation. Alternative reservoir functions at times have to take precedence over providing flood storage leading to conflicting priorities in the operation of the reservoir.

Interactions

Flood storage is usually combined with other engineering measures, such as linear flood defences, and improved channel conveyance. Measures to improve storage can initiate feedback within the dynamics of fluvial systems. For example:

- In the case of on-line storage, the increase in flood risk upstream of the storage site as well as the flooding of the site itself can have negative social and environmental implications; and by influencing the sediment transport regime, can encourage deposition (upstream of the dam) and erosion (downstream of the dam) in the medium to long term.
- Unless carefully managed, the above interactions can change the character of the river and its floodplain, especially downstream of the storage site.
- In the case of washlands, designated land-uses may need to be changed.
- Increasing floodplain storage can enhance the character of the floodplain and its ecology, providing an opportunity for environmental gain through the restoration of forest and wetland habitats.

Case example

The Leigh Barrier in Kent is a good example of a reservoir with a primary purpose of flood control. The barrier on the River Medway creates the largest on-line flood-control reservoir in Europe at 278 ha and, together with existing flood walls, improves the level of protection against floods in Tonbridge from a ten-year event to approximately a 150-year event. The barrier was operated several times during the autumn 2000 floods, but with some conflict of interest between protection of Tonbridge and alleviating flooding at Yalding, some distance downstream on the lower reaches of a tributary of the Medway.

Flood-water transfer

Flood-water transfer covers engineered measures that convey excess water from one river system to another that is better able to deal with the flood water and the associated flood risk. Measures included in this response group include:

- engineering works to allow pumped or gravity transfer of flood water by way of natural or artificial channels to a receiving water system;

- 'compensatory' works in the recipient system to control the resulting flood risk – these works could include increasing conveyance, flood embankments and the provision of flood storage.

Function and efficacy

The primary function of flood-water transfer is to convey excess flood water from one system to another. Transfer of flood water is not a common means of alleviating flooding because of the practical difficulties and cost implications of meeting all the potential hydraulic, social, economic and environmental requirements in the receiving system.

While able to reduce the level of flood risk in the source system, flood-water transfer in itself is unlikely to provide complete flood protection. The efficacy of flood-water transfer is limited by the capacity of the transfer infrastructure. This could reduce with time if the physical condition and/or capacity of the transfer system deteriorate; or if the ability of the receiving system to accept the flood water (at an acceptable level of risk of flooding and to the environment) reduces with time.

Interactions

Flood-water transfer schemes can involve a range of integrated hydraulic and flood-control measures which can create interactions within both the source system and the receiving system. For example:

- Transferring flood water can influence the dynamics of sediment transport in the source and receiving systems, creating the potential for unwanted erosion and deposition in both systems in the medium to long term.
- The removal of water from the source system and the mixing with water in the receiving system can alter the ecology of both river systems.
- Flood-water transfer moves the flood risk from one system to another, and an unacceptable increase in flood risk in the receiving system could lead to opposition to the measure from local stakeholders.

Case example

As already noted, flood-water transfer is not a common means of flood control, and there are few examples in the UK. The Manchester Ship Canal carries excess flood flows from the River Mersey, but the operation of both systems needs to be integrated to maintain satisfactory water levels in the Ship Canal (Tonks et al., 2002). The use of the Fossdyke Canal to convey flood flows from the River Till system, north-west of Lincoln, to the River Trent was considered as an alternative to the provision of a washland (Wakelin et al., 1987). This option proved uneconomic due to the need for pumping, the cost of compensatory works on the Trent, and major improvements to the Fossdyke Canal itself.

River defences

River defences are engineered structures, sometimes combined with natural formations, the main purpose of which is to control the spread of flood water. The measures included in this response group are:

- flood embankments and walls along river channels, sometimes with associated riverbank protection measures to reduce erosion that might threaten the flood embankments;
- ring dikes around vulnerable areas;
- specialist structures such as demountable defences and flood gates, which prevent flood water entering specific areas where permanent structures would be visually intrusive and disrupt access across the riverbank.

In some cases transportation infrastructure, such as road and rail embankments, form part of flood-defence systems.

Function and efficacy

The primary function of flood defences is to reduce the frequency and extent of flooding, thereby reducing flood risk. Flood defences can rarely remove the risk of flooding entirely. There always remains a chance of overtopping of the defences by an extreme flood event, and the likelihood of consequential structural or operational failure.

The efficacy of flood defences can decline if river flood flows become larger and more frequent or if their physical condition deteriorates. Flood defences along a reach of river can raise flood-water levels upstream of the reach, and pass higher peak flows downstream, potentially increasing flood risk in both these areas.

Interactions

Flood defences can be used alone, but it is increasingly common to combine them with other forms of flood risk management. Flood defence measures can initiate changes within the dynamics of river systems. For example:

- The presence of barriers on the floodplain can impede the transfer of fish to natural lakes on the floodplain, as well as the deposition of sediments and nutrients carried by the flood water on the floodplain soils.
- By confining transported sediment to the river-channel flood defences can influence broader sediment erosion and deposition patterns along the river, which can raise its channel above the floodplain in the long term.
- Flood defences that cut across natural drainage lines need to incorporate gravity or pumped drainage structures to avoid impeding drainage.

A broad feedback loop can be created. The presence of flood defences can encourage increased occupancy of the floodplain by creating a perception that the flood defences have removed the flood risk almost entirely, thus leading to further development. This increase in development behind the flood defences can, in turn, be used to justify even higher flood defences, and so on. This has been described as the 'escalator' effect (Burby *et al.*, 1988). The false sense of security from flooding may leave those living behind flood defences ill-prepared for extreme flood events that could overtop and/or breach the defences.

Case example

Flood defence engineering is as old as the history of urban civilisation and flood embankments have changed little in concept and application over the centuries (ICE, 2001). Raised flood defences are a key response to flood control along British rivers and some, such as the Barrier Banks that contain the Ouse Washes flood storage area, are now over 400 years old (ICE, 2001). Flood walls are widely used where rivers pass through towns and cities. There are also flood embankments along many rivers that pass through valuable agricultural areas. One of the most widespread applications of flood embankments is in Hungary, where over 4000 km of primary flood embankments and flood walls, some up to 6 m high, are the principal measure for flood risk management along its major rivers (Johnson *et al.*, 2000).

Governance, costs and standards of service

An overarching feature of flood risk management is the extent to which society, through a combination of collective and individual actions, protects itself from flood hazards. These actions include measures to reduce the probability of flooding, to reduce vulnerability to flood hazards and to minimise the impacts of flooding.

Issues of what are acceptable and affordable levels of flood risk determine standards of service relating to flood control. These issues are central to the development and implementation of flood risk management solutions, and have a strong influence on the nature of governance required to deliver these solutions.

The latter part of the twentieth century saw a move towards integrated river basin planning and flood risk management and away from a series of reactive responses to flooding issues (HM Treasury *et al.*, 2005). This proactive approach is now established and accepted in an effort to control future flood risk at acceptable levels. At a strategic level it is currently practiced in England and Wales through the programme of catchment flood management plans, which in turn identify the need for flood management strategies and solutions. A strong governance dimension is implicit in this approach from the fact that it is not possible to separate engineering from land-use planning and flood risk management policy. This comes to the fore in cases of retreat and realignment of defences, and restoration of rivers and their floodplains.

Governance

Current governance within the UK is established around the basis that there is no public right to flood protection. In England and Wales, Defra sets policy for flood management and the Environment Agency has permissive powers to undertake flood defence work on main rivers. In Wales, the Environment Agency shares responsibilities for flood defence with the National Assembly of Wales. In Scotland, duties and responsibilities for flood defence are distributed between riparian owners, central government, local authorities and the Scottish Environmental Protection Agency. The statutory flood defence authority for Northern Ireland is the Rivers Agency, within the Department of Agriculture and Rural Development.

Measures to alter river conveyance need to be approved by public authorities and riparian owners. Measures to engineer flood storage are usually implemented by a public authority, although there is in principle no restriction on the potential ownership of a scheme. Creation of flood storage establishes a change in land-use, which may affect access rights and land values, and requires planning permission. It can create the need for special land-owner responsibilities to ensure effective flood control. Flood-water transfer schemes need to be coordinated by public authorities, and require planning permission. Since flood-water transfer changes the spatial distribution of flood risk, this may affect land values and create the need for restrictions and new stakeholder responsibilities to ensure effective flood control. Flood defences can be privately or publicly implemented and owned and also require planning permission.

Costs

The costs of measures to alter conveyance depend on the type and scale of the works. Costs generally increase with the scale of the work but are at the same time influenced by many other factors, including the type of material removed from the river channel, how and where it is disposed of, the numbers of structures affected, and any land compensation costs. Capital costs range from tens to hundreds of thousands of pounds per kilometre of river; this may need subsequent periodic interventions to maintain conveyance, at an annual cost of 1% to 5% of the initial capital cost.

The capital cost of dams, reservoirs and embankments can vary significantly, depending on the topography of the storage site and the type of construction. The capital cost of a dam, reservoir or engineered storage may be several millions of pounds, compared with hundreds of thousands of pounds for the creation of a washland. Annual operation and maintenance costs can range from 1% to 5% of the capital cost, and may be proportionately higher for a washland than for a dam.

There is a threshold cost to establish infrastructure below which flood-water transfer is not cost effective. Costs then rise non-linearly with the size of the transfer scheme. The capital cost of transfer works and compensatory measures could range from a few to many millions of pounds. Annual operation and maintenance costs could range from 1% of the capital cost, increasing to up to 10% if significant pumping is involved and maintaining enhanced conveyance in the receiving system forms a principal compensatory measure.

While the costs of flood defences vary linearly with the length of works, they rise non-linearly with the scale of the works. Capital costs per kilometre of defence vary from a few hundreds of thousands of pounds for low, earth embankments, to a few million pounds for high embankments, and tens of millions of pounds if river training works are also required to protect the flood defences for river bank erosion. Annual operation and maintenance costs range from 1% to 5% of the capital cost, depending on the form of construction of the works and the inclusion of river training works.

Issues influencing standards of flood protection

The government has an interest in any commitment it makes, actual or implied, to reduce risk through the provision of flood defences and other schemes that are funded through taxation, levies, subscriptions and so on. We think of an actual or implied commitment to reduce the probability of flooding to a given limit as a standard of flood protection. This is expressed in terms of the severity of the flood that the flood defence system is designed to resist. There are important limitations in this approach:

- It focuses on flood defence systems and does not clearly account for the effects of many other measures of flood risk management.
- It does not account for the performance when floods are more severe than the design range of the defences.

Despite these limitations, the terminology of standard of flood protection provides a broad impression of the standard of flood risk reduction that a society, present or future, aims to achieve.

The standard of flood protection will evolve through a political process that makes trade-offs between society's expectations for flood risk reduction, its cost, and society's willingness to pay. Expectations for risk reduction will, in turn, depend on the perception of risk and society's attitude to different types of risk.

Societies, on the whole, show greater tolerance for the risk of natural hazards than for man-made hazards and hazards where the risk is poorly understood. Nonetheless, in general, and in more consumerist societies in particular, we can expect reducing tolerance of flood risk in future.

The insurance industry has some influence when standards of flood protection are being considered. The cost to the insurance industry following the widespread flooding in the UK in 2000 was very high and resulted in some rethinking of attitudes to flood damage insurance, particularly with respect to new development.

Measures to reduce risk should be *proportionate* in that the resource invested in risk reduction should roughly reflect the magnitude of the risk. In flood management terms, this is reflected in the fact that densely populated areas are afforded a greater standard of flood protection than sparsely populated rural areas. This principle is applied in most countries where there is a concerted effort to manage flood risk. However, it does depend on how society values different types of land-use.

If risk to people is the focus of risk management, then population density will be the main determinant of the standard of flood protection. On the other hand, an emphasis on the protection of key industries, perhaps including agriculture, will lead to a different set of standards of flood protection related to land-use. Coastal and fluvial floodplains are treated differently because flooding by the sea is more hazardous to people and causes more economic damage to houses, agriculture and industry.

The costs of achieving a particular standard of flood protection include direct costs, such as implementing works on the ground and providing flood warning, together with indirect costs, such as the development opportunities foregone and increased regulation of land-use. The costs also have an environmental dimension, e.g. costs associated with the impact of flood defences on habitats or use of natural resources.

The wealth of future societies will influence their willingness to pay for flood management. Their orientation – consumerist versus community – influences their willingness to transfer resources to particular sectors of society, such as people living on floodplains and, in particular, disadvantaged sectors of the population that may be at risk and unable to fend for themselves.

Attitudes to flood risk management under the Foresight scenarios

Government will continue to adapt to changing flood risk and public expectations for flood risk management, as well as to the broader societal and environmental changes that set the context for flood management.

Under the world markets scenario there will be reliance on modern engineering to protect high-value land and property from flood damage, with relative neglect of environmental considerations. There will be increasingly efficient provision of hard engineering measures.

The national enterprise scenario is less wealthy than the world markets scenario and more inward looking. Flood defences will be locally planned with economic development rated as more important than the environmental quality of rivers and coasts. The emphasis will be on protection of strategic industries, including agriculture, with the response characterised by piecemeal and diverse approaches, demonstrating technologically stagnant engineering measures.

The local stewardship scenario is characterised by approaches to flood management that are regionally devolved and environmentally conscious. There will be an emphasis on soft defences to protect metropolitan areas and key infrastructure, including some agricultural land. Widespread abandonment of floodplains and reinstatement of natural systems will be evident.

In the global sustainability scenario, government continues to be the major institution for delivery of society's expectations for effective risk management and environmental responsibility. Flood defence engineering is employed, particularly in dense urban areas, but there is an emphasis on soft engineering to work with and, where possible, restore natural processes. Strategic modern engineering is evident with the implementation of sustainable measures that are resilient to future uncertainties.

Assumed standards of flood protection under the Foresight scenarios

As outline above, target standards of flood protection emerge from a combination of social and political processes. These vary between the different Foresight scenarios.

The baseline analysis indicated the extent to which flood risk will increase if there are no further measures to reduce risk. It showed that economic damage under this baseline assumption is likely to be greatest in the world markets and national enterprise scenarios because of the increased probability of flooding, the growth in value of areas at risk and because of the more flood-vulnerable nature of development. There could be higher social and individual expectations for risk reduction in these consumerist-orientated scenarios, although balanced against this is the question of affordability. For instance, under the national enterprise scenario, the resources available for flood protection could be smaller due to lower economic growth. This will feed through into lower standards of flood protection. Resources for flood management will be further stretched in the national enterprise scenario by the need to protect strategic industries, including agriculture.

In the global sustainability scenario and, in particular, the local stewardship scenario, flood risk is likely to increase slowly. There will be less expectation for risk reduction. On the other hand, the global sustainability scenario will be characterised by government efforts to manage risks to people and the environment in a concerted and pre-emptive way. Standards of flood protection in the local stewardship scenario may show a great deal of national variation, reflecting local decision making.

In the globally orientated scenarios, world markets and global sustainability, there will be less emphasis on agriculture than in the national enterprise and local stewardship scenarios. This is reflected in a withdrawal of flood protection from agricultural land other than land of high grade.

Flood risk multipliers under the Foresight scenarios

For each Foresight scenario, the effect on flood risk of the measures in each response group was considered. This assumed that the groups were implemented in isolation and in a manner consistent with the opportunities and constraints identified for each scenario and the assumed target standards of flood protection. In particular, for each response group, the possible reduction in the flood risk was assessed by considering the effects of the measures on the possible risk increases for each of the flood-risk drivers.

The scaled impacts of each response group were then expressed as a multiplier of the level of risk that was predicted under the baseline assumption. These multipliers are given in Table 22.3 for each response group. The results indicated that river defences would have most impact by a significant margin and flood-water transfer the least under all scenarios. Under the world markets and national enterprise scenarios,

Table 22.3. Effectiveness for each response group expressed as a multiplier on the baseline level of flood risk under each Foresight scenario, indicating uncertainty

Response group	World markets	National enterprise	Local stewardship	Global sustainability
River conveyance	0.83	0.78	0.89	0.89
Flood storage	0.89	0.83	0.83	0.78
Flood-water transfer	0.99	0.99	1.00	0.99
Flood defences	0.55	0.55	0.78	0.62

1. The score in each cell is the multiplier by which the baseline level of flood risk under each scenario could be reduced by the set of river engineering measures within each the response group if applied on its own.
2. The shading each cell denotes the *level of uncertainty* associated with the multiplier, expressed as an *uncertainty band-width* (B), where B is the ratio of the upper and lower bound estimates of the flood risk reduction multiplier. A black cell denotes high uncertainty (B ≥ 1.5); a light grey cell denotes medium uncertainty (1.5 > B ≥ 1.1); and a white cell denotes low uncertainty (B < 1.1).

altering river conveyance would have more impact than flood storage, whereas this is reversed for the local stewardship and global sustainability scenarios.

Throughout the Foresight Project it has been recognised that considerable uncertainty exists regarding practically all aspects of flood risk change in the next 30 to 100 years. An important aspect of the work has therefore been to understand the nature and extent of the various uncertainties. To account for uncertainty in assessing the impact of responses, expert teams were requested to add upper- and lower-bound estimates to their best estimate of the flood risk multiplier. The upper-bound estimate for each scenario was then divided by the lower-bound estimate to define a geometric band of uncertainty for each response group under each scenario. The results of the uncertainty assessment are indicated in Table 22.3.

Sustainability

The groups of river engineering responses were evaluated against a range of sustainability metrics related to the three pillars of sustainability (environmental, social and economic), drawing on UK government guidance on sustainable development. The six sustainability metrics (see Chapter 26) are: environmental quality; social justice; robustness; precaution; flood risk reduction; and cost-effectiveness.

The evaluation recognised that it is how and in what form you apply the response rather than the response itself that determines sustainability. For instance, widening and deepening (and possibly straightening) a channel and a geomorphologically designed multi-stage channel are two approaches to increasing river conveyance that are very different in sustainability terms (Brookes, 1988).

Sustainability assessment

The scores achieved by each response group against each of the six metrics are presented (Figs 22.1–22.4) as 'spider diagrams'. In each spider diagram, the score for each metric is represented on a scale from '– –' to '+ +' running radially outwards from the centre of the web. The scores for each metric are joined to create a 'polygon' that represents the overall sustainability performance of that response group. On the diagrams, four separate polygons are plotted – these represent the scores for each future scenario. When interpreting the polygon, a key factor is whether the perimeter falls inside or outside the neutral line that represents a set of zero scores and indicates the threshold of acceptability in sustainability terms.

The sustainability of altering conveyance under the Foresight scenarios is illustrated in Fig. 22.1. Sustainability is potentially highest in the community-orientated scenarios, global sustainability and local stewardship, but with some relative reduction in efficacy and precaution under the local stewardship future. Sustainability is threatened by issues of social justice and environmental quality under the consumer-orientated scenarios world markets and national enterprise, but improving conveyance may nevertheless be an effective option in urban areas where available land is limited and potential damages are high.

Although measures that increase conveyance are generally robust and positive in reducing flood risk, and potentially cost-effective, there is uncertainty over the morphological and environmental change that such measures could induce. Maintenance costs associated with large-scale works of the type that might be implemented within the world markets and national enterprise scenarios could be high. Issues of cost and the environment may be easier to deal with on smaller-scale works such as those that might be implemented within the local stewardship scenario, where environmental criteria will carry more weight in decision making.

Various types of flood storage allow different forms to be adopted to suit the values and governance under each Foresight scenario. The effectiveness of storage

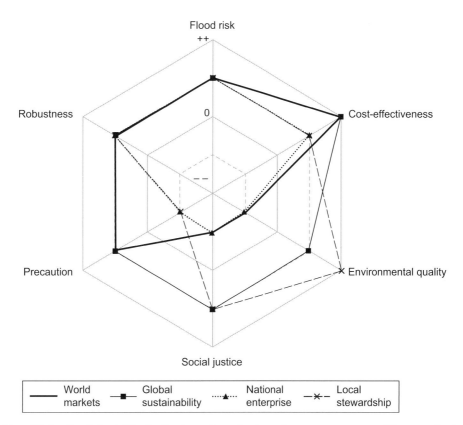

Fig. 22.1. Sustainability indicators for altering river conveyance (Evans et al., 2004)

in reducing flood risk is therefore 'reasonable' to 'good' under all the scenarios (see Fig. 22.2). Under the more consumer orientated scenarios, national enterprise and world markets, there may be a stronger preference for dams and off-line storage than for washlands and river restoration. The latter measures might be favoured in the more community focused scenarios, global sustainability and local stewardship. The overall sustainability of engineered-storage measures looks most promising under the global sustainability and local stewardship futures.

Flood storage in principle offers many opportunities for sustainable flood alleviation. These include restoring natural floodplain storage through the process of river restoration, and the use of distributed forms of temporary storage through the development of washlands, where floodplain land is available.

However, certain forms of flood storage, such as that provided by dams, are potentially un-sustainable. As in the case of flood defences, it may be technically feasible and cost-effective to respond to increased flood risk by simply raising the height of storage structures, but it may not be desirable or sensible to do so. Social concerns over relocation of people from the sites of large reservoirs together with the effect of changes in river flow regime on the riverine environment can limit the sustainability of large dams.

The potential for flood-water transfer in the UK is limited by topographical and hydraulic factors as well as environmental concerns. As indicated in Fig. 22.3, the sustainability of flood-water transfer is not high under any of the Foresight scenarios. This is due to concerns over the robustness of this form of intervention, the environmental implications of transfer between river basins, and social concerns over the equitable redistribution of flood risk. The broad regional scale of works would make them particularly unattractive in the local stewardship scenario.

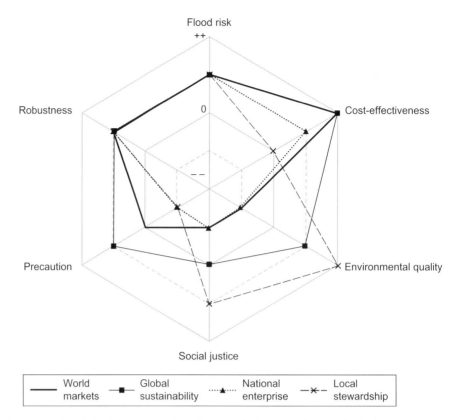

Fig. 22.2. Sustainability indicators for flood storage (Evans et al., *2004)*

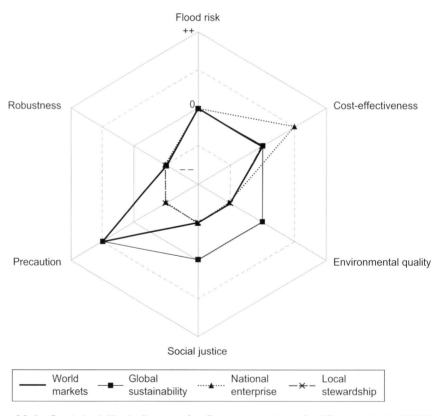

Fig. 22.3. Sustainability indicators for flood-water transfer (Evans et al., *2004)*

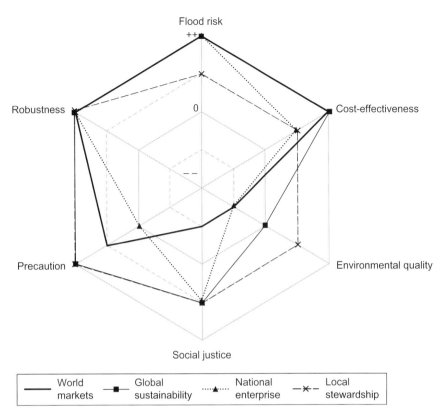

Fig. 22.4. Sustainability indicators for river flood defences (Evans et al., 2004)

The fact that some flood defences in Britain are over 400 years old indicates historical but not necessarily inherent sustainability. While it is technically possible and potentially cost-effective to respond to the predicted increases in inland flood risk by simply raising the height of defences, as has historically been the case, this may not always be sustainable to do so. Factors such as cost-effectiveness, the 'escalator effect', stakeholder attitudes, and long-term morphological change within the river channel tend to limit the sustainability of flood defences.

The effectiveness of flood defences is potentially high under all the Foresight scenarios (see Fig. 22.4). The reduced value placed on the environment and social justice under the more consumer-orientated world markets and national enterprise scenarios, could threaten their sustainability without specific safeguards in place. Sustainability looks more promising under the community-based scenarios of global sustainability and local stewardship, but with some concerns over cost-effectiveness, stakeholder attitudes and morphological change. Sustainable approaches may involve relocation of flood defences to allow river and floodplain restoration in certain areas, and the integration of flood defence measures with complementary structural and non-structural measures.

Summary

River engineering responses have been the traditional solution to flood defence problems for many generations. The Foresight study has concluded that river engineering remains an integral part of current and likely future approaches to flood risk management.

Some significant points have emerged from this review:

a. River engineering measures are wide-ranging in scope and include measures that reduce river flood-water levels in areas exposed to flooding by altering river conveyance and/or increasing flood storage; measures that transfer flood water away from flood-prone areas; and flood defences to limit the spread of flood water.

b. Flood defences are generally the most effective group of engineering measures at reducing flood risk; increasing flood storage is typically less effective than flood defences but performs well across all four Foresight scenarios; altering river conveyance is usually less effective and less flexible than flood storage; and flood-water transfer is generally the least effective and flexible of all the river engineering response groups – these observations represent broad patterns in relative effectiveness, and individual measures within each group may perform better than the group as a whole.

c. Current approaches favour proactive and integrated flood risk management rather than reactive responses to a flood defence problem. They often include river engineering components as part of an integrated package or portfolio of measures, and this looks set to continue – integrating responses also presents the opportunity for medium- to long-term retreat from the riverbank and restoration of lost floodplain where appropriate.

d. The implications on governance of integrated approaches are that they require stakeholder consultation and multi-agency cooperation, which takes note of influential voices, such as those of environmental and social stakeholder groups, including, the insurance industry.

While the implementation of a portfolio of structural and non-structural responses has the potential to decrease the cost of and reliance on engineering, there will remain a need for engineering responses to meet the likely increase in flood risk envisaged under the Foresight scenarios. The key message that emerges from the assessment of sustainability is that while individual groups of response measures may raise concerns in relation to their impacts on the environment, and to a lesser extent on aspects of social justice, it is **how individual measures within each response group are implemented**, rather than the responses themselves that is the key to developing sustainable solutions to flood risk management.

References

Brookes, A., 1988. *Channelised Rivers: Perspectives for environmental management*, John Wiley, Chichester.

Burby, R.J., Bollens, S.A., Holloway, J.M., Kaiser, E.J., Mullan, D. and Sheaffer, J.R., 1988. *Cities Under Water: A comparative evaluation of ten cities' efforts to manage flood plain land use*, Institute of Behavioural Science, University of Colorado, Boulder, CO.

Defra, 2005. *Making Space for Water – Taking forward a new government strategy for flood and coastal erosion risk management in England – First government response*, Defra, London.

Evans, E., Ashley, R., Hall, J., Penning-Rowsell, E., Saul, A., Sayers, P., Thorne, C. and Watkinson, A., 2004. *Foresight Future Flooding, Scientific Summary, Vol. II – Managing future risks*, Office of Science and Technology, London.

Freer, R., 2001. 'The Three Gorges Project on the Yangtze River in China', *Proceedings Institution of Civil Engineers*, 144, February, 20–28.

Heathcote, J., Martin, D. and Petts, G., 2002. *Urban Rivers – Our Inheritance and Future*, International Water Association Publishing, London.

Hughes, F.M.R. (ed.), 2003. *The Flooded Forest: Guidance for policy makers and river managers in Europe on the restoration of floodplain forests*, FLOBAR2, Department of Geography, University of Cambridge, Cambridge.

ICE, 2001. *Learning to Live with Rivers*, Report of the President of the Institution of Civil Engineers' Review Commission, Thomas Telford, London.

Johnson, G.P.G., Von Lany, P.H., Evans, E.P. and Varsa, E., 2000. 'A strategic approach to flood risk management in Hungary', *Proceedings Flooding – Risks and Reactions*, Conference by CIWEM and ICE, London, October, 73–83.

Parker, D.J. (ed.), 2000. *Floods – Vols I and II*, Routledge, London.

Tonks, D.M., Howells, R., Bettess, R. and Morris, M.W., 2002. 'Woolston New Weir and River Mersey diversion', *Proceedings Institution of Civil Engineers*, Water and Maritime Engineering, 154(1), 51–61.

Wakelin, M.J., Walker, T.G. and Wilson D., 1987. 'Lincoln flood alleviation scheme', *Proceedings Institution of Civil Engineers*, 82, Part 1, August, 755–776.

Ward, D., Holmes, N. and Jose, P. (eds), 1994. *The New Rivers and Wildlife Handbook*, The Royal Society for the Protection of Birds, Sandy.

World Commission On Dams, 2001. *Dams and Development: A new framework for decision making*, Report by the World Commission on Dams.

23 The management of coastal flooding and erosion

Robert J. Nicholls, Nicholas J. Cooper and Ian H. Townend

Introduction

Coastal erosion and tidal flooding are often interlinked hazards in areas where natural shoreline features, such as gravel barriers or sand dunes, front low-lying flood-prone hinterland – even coastal defences are usually designed assuming some natural toe protection and energy dissipation. Therefore, erosion management is often a fundamental element in schemes that are primarily a response to tidal flood risk, such as the well-known recent schemes at Hurst Spit (Bradbury and Kidd, 1998) and Hayling Island (Whitcombe, 1996), both in Hampshire, Pevensey in East Sussex (Hardacre, 2001), Sea Palling in Norfolk (Thomalla, 2001) and Skegness and its environs in Lincolnshire (Thomas, 1992). In contrast, in areas where the topography of the hinterland is elevated and characterised by sea cliffs, it is coastal erosion or cliff instability that poses the principal hazard. There is a large legacy of defences designed to limit cliff recession and instability. Recent examples include Robin Hood's Bay in Yorkshire, Lyme Regis in Dorset and Castlehaven on the Isle of Wight.

A wide variety of options exist for responding to coastal hazards, including erosion and tidal flood risk (e.g. Nicholls and Klein, 2005). For the purposes of the Foresight analysis, four generic response groups relevant to flood and coastal defence are defined in Table 23.1. This paper describes the options in each response group in more detail, including case studies. The application and effectiveness of each of these response groups are then considered for each Foresight future scenario (see Chapter 2), including issues of sustainability.

Coastal defences

Coastal defences are artificial structures that prevent water from entering a defined area or limit the magnitude of coastal erosion. To do this they must be high enough to prevent water flowing over their crest and of a design that limits the amount of wave overtopping. Examples include tidal barriers, such as the Thames and Eastern Scheldt Barriers, longitudinal dikes, embankments, sea walls, revetments and temporary barriers, such as demountable flood walls.

Table 23.1. Generic response groups for coastal management and engineering

Generic response groups	Response measure, policy or intervention (with length of UK experience)
1. Coastal defences: construct or raise physical barriers to flooding and coastal erosion	• Tidal flood barriers (25 years) • Permanent dikes, embankments and seawalls (>100 years) • Temporary flood walls (<10 years)
2. Coastal energy reduction measures: morphological features, structures or devices to reduce the energy of near-shore waves and currents	• Soft engineering/nourishment on beaches (50 years) • Soft engineering on muddy coasts (10 years) • Offshore barriers (15 years) • Energy converters (research and development phase)
3. Realignment of defence infrastructure: landward relocation of coastal defences, managed or unmanaged abandonment of defences	• Change configuration of coastline (<15 years for managed realignment) (>100 years for unmanaged realignment)
4. Morphological protection: allow or engineer desirable changes in the coastal morphology to develop self-sustaining forms which provide flood and coastal defence functions	• Promote broad-scale formation of natural landforms to provide protection, including the above measures (research and development phase)

Coastal defences operate by reducing the probability of flooding or erosion, usually to some specified 'standard of service'. This standard varies according to the assets being protected, but needs to be provided in a uniform manner to an individual flood compartment, so as to avoid the overall defence system failing at 'weak points'. All coastal defences have a finite design life, typically in the range of 20 to 50 years for structural solutions. Coastal defences can fail by excess water overflowing or overtopping (Fig. 23.1), breaching, or undermining of the toe, including through loss of the foreshore/beach sediment, linking the performance of coastal defences to energy reduction (Fig. 23.2) (see the following section). The risk of toe failure can be exacerbated by high beach volatility, and becomes increasingly

Fig. 23.1. Flooding at Tywyn, Gwynedd due to extensive overtopping of coastal defences during a storm

Fig. 23.2. Flooding at Hayling Island, Hampshire on 3 November 2005 due to overtopping of the coastal defences (and nourished shingle beach) by unusual 18-second period waves. (Photograph by Clive Moon, Havant Borough Council)

likely on coasts that are eroding or steepening: a situation that is already widespread in the UK (Chapter 16).

Responsibilities for flood and coastal defence vary within the United Kingdom. In England and Wales, the Environment Agency is responsible for managing the risk of tidal flooding on estuarine and low-lying coasts. Maritime local authorities have responsibility for the provision of protection works against coastal erosion on higher open coasts and cliffs, and regulation of schemes proposed by other operators (e.g. Network Rail, British Energy) or private owners through the land-use planning and development control system. In Scotland, flood and coastal defence are the discretionary responsibility of maritime local authorities. Northern Ireland has a statutory regime of sea defences for the protection of land against flooding, but no legislation specifically dedicated to coastal erosion. Essential works within the spheres of interest of various Northern Ireland government departments are dealt with under existing legislation, according to an inter-departmental agreement.

The costs of coastal defences depend on their type, design and location. For 'conventional' seawalls, revetments and embankments, costs can generally be reasonably well predicted in terms of costs per metre run. While structure costs vary approximately with the square of their height, the exposure of the structure can have a dramatic effect on costs. Hence an embankment behind saltmarshes will typically cost an order of magnitude less per unit length than a structure on the open coast.

Most funding presently comes from the central government and covers a large percentage of the capital costs, with the balance being met by local contributions. Central government grants are awarded only to those schemes that meet the necessary technical feasibility, economic viability and environmental acceptability criteria in accordance with pre-established Project Appraisal Guidance and, in recent years, also need to exceed a threshold priority score that is based on economic, social and environmental factors. Other operators, developers or private owners can fully fund defences that obtain the necessary planning consents and approvals in line with existing planning guidance and legislation.

Coastal defences require periodic maintenance and repair to keep them operating as designed. This typically costs about 3% of the capital cost per annum. Maintenance costs for movable barriers are greater than those for fixed structures, at around 5–10%. However, Burgess and Townend (2004) estimate that by the 2080s the annual cost of maintaining coastal defences will be between 150% and 400% of the current levels (depending on the amount of climate change). The costs were predicted to increase because structures were found to be very vulnerable to increases in water depth. This is because the wave conditions for the majority of the UK are depth limited. Raised water levels, or steeper foreshores, will therefore result in an immediate increase in the forces impacting the structures.

Coastal defences are likely to interact with the prevailing coast/estuary processes with the potential to alter the morphology not only in the immediate vicinity of the scheme but also further afield. Some morphological adjustments, such as beach/foreshore lowering in front of a seawall (Kraus, 1988) or coastal squeeze of salt-marsh between eroding coasts (due to sea-level rise or other causes) and static flood embankments (Brampton, 1992; French, 2001) can tend to reduce the efficacy and design life of coastal defences. Other responses, such as the reduction or cessation of sediment input from a newly defended sea cliff, can lead to the loss of earth science heritage resources, such as geological exposures (Lee and Marker, 1995), or create adverse effects elsewhere due to reduced sediment supply to down-drift frontages (Dickson *et al.*, 2005), with potential biodiversity impacts (Cooper *et al.*, 2001). The main technical challenge in the next 30 to 100 years is to develop designs and structures that provide adequate flood and coastal defence while avoiding (or at least minimising) adverse morphological and ecological interactions. In addition, the provision of this type of protection tends to attract development behind it so exacerbating the risks posed by flooding and coastal erosion for future generations and further compounding the need for such defences.

There are many examples of coastal defences in the UK, such as the embankments around many estuaries, groynes and sea walls along many developed sections of coast, and rock headlands. The Thames Barrier, which protects London from flooding, provides a useful case study (Fig. 23.3). Construction of the barrier commenced in 1974 and it became operational in 1982. It is designed to block extremely large surge events (up to a one in 1000 year return period in 2030) that build up in the North Sea and propagate up the Thames, threatening London (Lavery and Donovan, 2005). However, this type of structure has a finite life and planning is already underway to establish how best to meet future needs through the twenty-first century given rising sea levels and other changes.

Fig. 23.3. Thames Barrier. (Photograph courtesy of the Environment Agency)

Coastal energy reduction measures

This approach purposely extracts wave or tidal energy so that it is reduced at the shoreline. There are three different means of achieving this goal:

1. through the dissipating effects of sub-tidal and intertidal coastal morphology;
2. through dissipation effects caused by physically blocking or modifying the incoming energy at some distance seaward of the shoreline; and
3. by extracting and harnessing energy from waves and tides.

Enhanced energy dissipation across the intertidal surface can be achieved through changing the surface roughness, reflection or percolation properties of the intertidal zone, or increasing its size. This may utilize natural (or quasi-natural) means, such as beach nourishment using sand or shingle, or through the introduction or restoration of saltmarsh vegetation, to increase surface roughness and promote accretion. Artificial means can also be used, including the laying of mats with baffles in the intertidal or nearshore subtidal zone to promote sedimentation.

Physically blocking or modifying the incoming wave energy can be achieved through the use of offshore breakwaters (wave energy reduction due to reflection, percolation and diffraction through the gaps) (Fig. 23.4), offshore tables mounted on piles or submerged offshore reefs (both to induce wave breaking further offshore), or fishtail groynes to divert tidal flows away from the shoreline.

Existing renewable energy production techniques include wind and tidal turbines, wave devices, tidal impoundment schemes and tidal barrages that harness the energy to generate power and, in so doing, reduce the amount of tidal or wave energy on their shoreward side. Such devices and structures are presently being developed primarily for the purpose of generating renewable energy, but an opportunity also exists to explore combining their use with flood and coastal defence schemes.

Fig. 23.4. Offshore breakwaters and the resulting development of beach salients at Sea Palling, Norfolk, which are designed to prevent flooding of the northern Norfolk Broads. (Photograph courtesy of the Environment Agency)

For schemes that dissipate wave and tidal energy for coastal defence, government agencies and authorities have principal interest, although some private owners are able to implement their own schemes if appropriate planning consents are obtained. For energy extraction schemes, private utilities and entrepreneurial developers are likely to be the lead organisations. The Crown Estate has interests in the seabed below mean low water and many energy modulation schemes will necessarily involve seaward consideration to beyond this limit.

Public bodies already fund beach nourishment, saltmarsh regeneration schemes and offshore breakwaters for improved energy dissipation. The cost of these schemes can range from the order of £100 ks to £10 ms. The opportunity for using energy extraction devices to both reduce flood and erosion risk and generate renewable energy could be promoted by a public–private partnership sharing of funding between flood and coastal defence authorities and renewable energy developers. Costs are high due to the developing nature of the technology, requiring extensive public- and private-sector backing of research and development, trial application and ultimately full-scale use. However, under some future scenarios, technological advances coupled with an emphasis on renewable sources of energy may bring down investment costs to the point that local and commercial funding of shared-use schemes becomes viable.

There are locations where this response group could be implemented alone, but more often it would be implemented in conjunction with some form of coastal defence (i.e. seawall along the shoreline). For example, an offshore reef might be used to reduce the intensity of wave attack on a coastal embankment. It could also potentially be implemented alongside managed re-alignment (see next section), and/or in conjunction with more extensive morphological engineering ('Morphological protection' later in this chapter). For example, energy dissipation might be used to steer morphological evolution of coastal features to generate a more favourable coastal configuration with respect to fixed infrastructure.

Reducing the incoming energy will influence local sediment transport processes and morphodynamics, possibly leading to increased deposition and/or a change in sediment character in the areas where the energy has been reduced. There could be positive or negative environmental and social consequences of these changes, depending on their magnitude and location. Hence, the ability to predict accurately the impact of such schemes on the wider environment is important.

A series of eight offshore breakwaters was constructed at Elmer in West Sussex in 1993 with the intention of reducing incoming wave energy and, hence, reducing the risk of flooding due to overtopping for properties located in the hinterland (Holland and Coughlan, 1994). To date, the scheme has proved effective in achieving this aim. In the French Riviera, offshore breakwaters are used to achieve the dual aims of reducing wave energy and creating amenity beaches in their lee in the more sheltered areas of beach (Anthony, 1994).

Beach nourishment is widespread throughout the UK (see review in Hanson et al., 2002), especially along the south coast, with one of the earliest and longest running programmes being on the Bournemouth frontage of Poole Bay, Dorset (Harlow and Cooper, 1996). This scheme commenced in 1970, with a major fill in 1974/1975 and has required major re-nourishments in 1989/1990 and 2005/2006 (Fig. 23.5). The nourished beach functions in conjunction with a coastal defence (seawall and wooden groynes to trap sediment) and acts first to reduce the intensity of wave attack on the defence and second to prevent foreshore steepening that might otherwise undermine its foundations. The scheme also has wider amenity benefits to the tourist resort of Bournemouth. Shingle nourishment is also widespread in the UK (e.g. Fig. 23.6).

The wave and tidal energy dissipation properties of salt marshes has long been recognised in the UK (Owen, 1984; Brampton, 1992). In several estuarine locations

Fig. 23.5. Sand beach nourishment at Bournemouth in Feburary 2006, showing pre- and post-nourished sections, and sand being pumped onshore from a dredger. (Photograph by David Harlow, Bournemouth Borough Council)

in Essex, efforts have been made to regenerate salt marshes to provide an improved naturally dissipative buffer against wave and tidal energy. Such approaches have included attempts to enhance natural rates of sedimentation on salt marshes through the construction of polders or brushwood fencing (French, 2001), or the placement of energy dissipaters, such as biodegradable straw bales or sunk barges (Thames lighters). More recently, salt marsh regeneration processes have also included recharge of muddy intertidal foreshores with dredged material, to raise the elevation to levels conducive to vegetation growth (English Nature, 2001). These techniques can be combined with re-alignment of defence infrastructure (see the next section).

Historically, tidal mills formed an early example of power generation coupled with some form of local water management. More recently, attention has returned to the possibility of combining flood and coastal defence with renewable energy production (e.g. Henderson *et al.*, 1979), although there are no known schemes in

Fig. 23.6. Shingle beach nourishment at Pevensey, East Sussex: (a) shingle being delivered by dredger at high tide; (b) forming the design profile at low tide. (Photograph by Ian Thomas, Pevensey Coastal Defence Ltd)

the UK. However, prototype tidal turbines (e.g. Lomax and Olliver, 2003) and wave energy extractors (e.g. Whittaker, 2003) are in development. Much work has also previously been undertaken to investigate the possibility of harnessing the energy of the tides in the Severn Estuary. It has the second largest tidal range in the world and could produce 6% of the total electricity demand in England and Wales (17 000 million kilowatt-hours/year). Ongoing feasibility studies are investigating the potential for a range of renewable approaches, such as wave, tidal current and wind energy devices and tidal impoundment schemes, to aid coastal protection in Bridgwater Bay, Somerset (Foresight Marine Panel, 2003). Present findings from this study suggest tidal impoundment as the only (presently) viable option.

For schemes aimed at reducing the incoming wave and tidal energy, some technical uncertainty exists in selecting an appropriate design capable of reducing the energy to sufficiently low levels to be effective. Some offshore breakwater schemes and fishtail groynes can have detrimental effects on wider coastal processes, in particular reducing or preventing downdrift sediment supply, such as at Sea Palling (Thomalla, 2001) (see Fig. 23.4). Clearly, for the scheme to be effective it must cause some reduction in incoming energy but it is not easy at present to predict the downdrift impacts with confidence. Furthermore, design needs to consider the effects of climate change on key design parameters: mean and extreme sea levels and waves, including the very large uncertainties (Chapter 9). There is also uncertainty relating to whether wave and tidal energy generators can coincidentally be used as effective means of reducing flood and coastal risk. Testing the feasibility of dual use schemes requires a major research effort to establish whether such approaches can be designed to be operationally effective.

Re-alignment of defence infrastructure

This can occur by planned abandonment or relocation of defences (widely termed managed re-alignment), or unplanned abandonment of defences if, for example, the financial resources to maintain defences are not available. Here the focus is on managed re-alignment.

Managed re-alignment is a new approach that has evolved from the shoreline management planning process over the last ten to 15 years (Leafe et al., 1998; Cooper et al., 2002; Defra, 2006). The basis of managed re-alignment is to consider re-aligning existing defences landward, to provide a more resilient and dynamic foreshore. (In contrast, under regulated tidal exchange the defence line is maintained (see Rupp-Armstrong and Nicholls, in press).) By re-establishing natural shoreline process-response mechanisms, managed re-alignment potentially reduces the cost of providing a given standard of protection, most especially if the defence line can be abandoned to rising ground, or greatly reduced in length. There are however important environmental implications for coastal habitats, especially coastal grazing marsh (see Chapter 3). To date, managed re-alignment has been targeted at areas with limited development, and many suitable sites have been identified. To apply managed re-alignment more widely, the considerable amounts of existing infrastructure that are driving the need for protection of long lengths of coast would have to be relocated inland. Given the great length of retreating coastline around the UK (see Chapter 16), widespread implementation of this response has the potential to radically alter economic and social activity in the coastal zone.

The potential for cost-effective reduction of flood and coastal erosion risk by removing existing defences and returning low-lying land to inter- and supra-tidal habitats has been increasingly explored in recent years. To date, implementation of re-alignment projects has been tentative, with most schemes limited to breaching

existing embankments, or making a conscious management decision not to intervene should a natural breach occur (i.e. abandonment of defences). This creates
new habitat but does little to restore the dynamics of the coastal or estuarial
system. As a result, there is great potential for wholesale removal of embankments
and other defences, particularly around estuaries. On the open coast, allowing saltmarshes and gravel barriers to migrate landward would increase their resilience
and energy-dissipating function, so increasing the level of protection afforded to
the immediate hinterland. If a new line of defences is required, re-alignment will
usually substantially reduce the cost of engineering works and, where defences are
no longer required (i.e. flooding can occur back to naturally rising ground), engineering problems may be eliminated.

Along extensive lengths of the UK coast, major infrastructure (e.g. roads and
railways) is found at, or close to, the shoreline. The existence of this infrastructure
often constrains engineering solutions and distorts the cost–benefit analysis in favour
of holding the coast in its existing position simply to protect inappropriately located,
linear infrastructure. Relocating such infrastructure inland opens up the potential for
re-alignment or removal of coastal defences as a way of eliminating the problem. As
discussed in 'Coastal defences', in a future with sea-level rise, increased wave height
and more frequent and severe storm surges (Chapter 9), the cost of holding the line
will rise dramatically, making re-alignment an increasingly attractive option.

A further opportunity for re-alignment arises within coastal towns at risk of
erosion, where over the long term (30–100 years) it may be appropriate to acquire
and remove the front line of property so that coastal defences (especially seawalls)
can be adapted or re-aligned (Leafe *et al.*, 1998). This represents a potentially
viable alternative to holding the line through heavy investment in raising defences,
probably coupled with an open-ended commitment to foreshore management and
beach nourishment. The amount of set-back required to provide sufficient backshore to accommodate several decades of allowed coastal retreat is often relatively
modest.

At present, re-alignment schemes are predominantly located in southern and
eastern England and concern creation of inter- and supra-tidal habitat in formerly
flood-prone areas (see Rupp-Armstrong and Nicholls, in press). The relevant
authorities can consider this option within coastal towns, but the current planning
horizons are too short for the economic and environmental benefits to balance the
costs. Some coastal landowners, such as the Highways Agency and Network Rail,
may have major roles to play in implementing responses that involve managed
re-alignment, as re-locating linear infrastructure could only occur within the
long-term cycle of expenditure planning and infrastructure renewal. This implies
much stronger links between shoreline management plans and other coastal
planning and the need for better modelling tools to predict future coastal erosion.

A wide range of bodies, from both the public and private sector, are already
funding managed re-alignment. For the re-alignment of infrastructure, there may be
scope for use of public–private partnership, but much of the funding is likely to
remain public. There is a need for a long-term and broad spatial scale perspective
when assessing costs in order to demonstrate how the large short-term costs associated with moving infrastructure, for example, can be offset by the longer-term cost
savings associated with removing the need for defences or structural modifications.

This response interacts with land-use behind the defences. If agricultural demand
were to change, the importance of these currently protected areas may also change.
Conversely, more extensive intertidal habitats will increase the benthic fauna, bird
feeding and nursery areas for fish. In the extreme, some elements of the national
transport network would have to be abandoned or relocated, with particular implications for some local communities, which may become more isolated, and in some
cases regionally (e.g. the Dawlish to Teignmouth railway line).

Fig. 23.7. Beneficial use of mud to create intertidal mudflat habitat as part of the Defra Wallasea re-alignment scheme on the Crouch Estuary, Essex. This project provides compensatory habitat, and improved flood defences. (Photograph by Mark Dixon, Environment Agency)

The railway line between Aberdyfi and Barmouth on the coast of Cardigan Bay, Wales, frequently runs close to the shore, sometimes being precariously perched at the top of the beach or immediately behind the shingle ridge. Much of this coast is eroding so that local 'pinch points' are developing, where the railway is increasingly overtopped during storms, and protecting the railway in situ is progressively forcing the coast away from its natural alignment (Gwynedd Council, 1998). This situation is likely to deteriorate as sea levels rise and the exposure to storms and surges increases (Chapter 9). There is considerable political and social pressure to maintain the railway line, although the economic viability is much more questionable and consequently it is unlikely that the operators will consider relocating the line landward simply to restore natural processes on the coast. This is only likely to be considered if adequate protection cannot be secured along the existing alignment.

An experimental managed re-alignment was implemented at Tollesbury over ten years ago. This has provided valuable information to allow the science and engineering of such schemes to be advanced. Since then, there have been at least 17 schemes in England with a concentration on the east coast, comprising a total area of about 420 ha (Rupp-Armstrong and Nicholls, in press). There appears to be a large potential for future re-alignment based on existing coastal land-uses (agricultural and other low-grade uses) (Nicholls and Wilson, 2001; Halcrow *et al.*, 2002). One of the most recent schemes is on the Humber at Paul Holme Strays, where some 70 ha of intertidal habitat has been created to offset the losses being caused as a result of coastal squeeze. A new embankment has been built landward and the original defences have recently been breached. This scheme is the first stage of a longer-term plan, being promoted as part of the Humber Estuary Shoreline Management Plan, where it is hoped to restore in the range of 200–600 ha over the next 50 years, depending on the rate of sea-level rise (Edwards and Winn, 2003; Townend and Pethick, 2002). Another large scheme is on the Crouch Estuary where 110 to 120 ha of intertidal habitat are presently being created (Fig. 23.7).

Managed re-alignment is in the process of moving from novel to established practice for agricultural and other low-grade land-uses. Large-scale adjustment of national infrastructure and properties in built-up areas is much more uncertain. It is unclear how this could be funded and whether it will be acceptable to local communities.

Morphological protection

A more radical approach is to take a broad-scale perspective of an entire geomorphological unit, such as a coastal cell, sub-cell or estuary, and consider how the morphology can be 'engineered' to a form that requires the minimum maintenance to sustain its flood and coastal defence (and other) functions. This can include the creation or management of morphological features, such as ebb tidal deltas and spits, near the mouths of tidal inlets, and working with natural processes to optimise the configuration of the coastal and estuarine morphology. All of these features buffer the shoreline from incident wave and tidal energy and are large reservoirs of sediment, providing a more self-sustaining solution that can readily accommodate dynamic changes that occur in forcing conditions and sediment supply over the long term. Hence, this response group occurs at a higher scale than the other response groups already considered, and may utilise elements of some, or all, of these other response groups in order to create a new morphological form.

Morphological features provide an effective form of natural protection to the coast. Coastal features develop and evolve continually in response to changes in the coastal system (particularly relating to forcing conditions and sediment supply) so that while the standard of protection provided by morphological features will vary in the short term, the longer-term resilience of the coastal system is maintained. The challenge is to understand the evolution of the coastal system across a range of scales, to the extent that we can understand when intervention is prudent (Stive *et al.*, 2002). Implicit in the use of morphological protection is recognition of the need for the natural buffer zones to be maintained and allowed to respond dynamically to changing conditions (see Rochelle-Newall *et al.*, 2005).

This form of response does not deliver the full benefits immediately. While engineering measures may be used to prompt or trigger morphological change in a favourable direction, the timescale for change depends on the morphological response times of the component features, which may in turn depend on the occurrence of suitable forcing events. Hence, there may be a considerable delay between the initiation of a flood and coastal defence scheme based on morphological protection and achievement of the intended standard of protection. The implications of this transition will also need to be considered.

Specific responses in this group range from managing and enhancing existing features, such as coastal dunes or gravel ridges, to creating new features or re-creating lost ones, such as saltmarshes. More radical approaches can include the 'geomorphological engineering' of the coast or estuary at the scale of the coastal or estuarine system, to enable a more sustainable form and function to evolve (Pethick, 1998). This could involve the creation of a new inlet along an open coast section so that increased protection is provided to the adjacent coast due to the newly created ebb tide delta and/or spit(s). This option has been considered at Brancaster in north Norfolk (Pethick, 2001). Similarly, the shape of the open coast could be manipulated by creating a hard point at a strategic location so that an embayment can develop adjacent to it and, ultimately, become stabilised as gradients of net longshore transport tend to a minimum (ideally zero) (Silvester and Hsu, 1994). Inadvertent bay formation of undefended coast between defences is common around the UK coast, including the Naish Farm and Becton Bunny sites in Christchurch Bay, Hampshire. Lastly, erosion and flood risk could be considered together at the scale of the sub-cell, as cliff protection usually degrades beaches and enhances flood risk in neighbouring coastal lowlands. For example, a preliminary analysis of sub-cell 3b in Norfolk, suggests that abandoning cliff defences could have significant benefits in terms of reducing downdrift flood risk within the sub-cell (Hall *et al.*, 2005a). Realising such benefits remains a political challenge.

The management of morphological features for flood and coastal defence is principally governed by the relevant government agencies and authorities, although both statutory (e.g. English Nature, CCW, SNH) and non-statutory conservation bodies (e.g. RSPB, National Trust) have advocated such approaches. These organisations manage some features specifically for nature conservation and earth science heritage purposes. The shared interests of multiple stakeholders in governance of coastal morphology provide both an opportunity and a difficulty. The potential exists for 'win–win' situations where engineered morphology can achieve flood and coastal defence goals while also promoting sustainability and increased biodiversity and geodiversity. However, there may be difficulties in persuading conservation-orientated bodies that the science-base exists from which to design and implement engineering intervention in the operation of natural processes at the system scale with an acceptable level of certainty regarding the outcome.

At present, the relevant government agencies and authorities have principal responsibility for these responses, as nature conservation bodies provide management purely for nature conservation and earth science heritage reasons. Morphological protection schemes that have flood and coastal defence benefits should be eligible for central government grant funding to cover certain percentages of their costs. Potentially, capital costs can range from minimal amounts (e.g. the creation of a new tidal inlet by excavation of a breach and channel in an existing sea defence) to larger sums where greater structural intervention is required (e.g. the construction of hard points to engineer an, ultimately, stable embayment downdrift). Equally, the benefits of such a response can vary from local through to much larger scales.

The intention of measures in this response group is to interact with the wider coastal/estuarine processes to drive morphological responses. For example, the creation of a new tidal inlet would be designed to lead to the formation of ebb and flood tide deltas, which would, in turn, shelter the shoreline along the neighbouring open coast and in the estuary mouth. However, these features would store sediment that would otherwise accumulate elsewhere in the natural system and the implications of these changes need to be considered. The flow created through the inlet could also intercept littoral sediment drift, potentially flushing shoreline sediments offshore. Clearly, while interaction is the aim of geomorphological engineering, a thorough and complete knowledge of the interaction and feedback loops generated is an essential prerequisite to implementation.

Presently, large-scale engineered morphological protection in the UK is at the research and development stage, so it is necessary to consider natural analogues. In 1996 a natural breach occurred in a gravel barrier at Porlock, Somerset. This resulted in flooding of the backing land to rising ground and the creation of a new tidal inlet through the ridge (Orford and Jennings, 1996). Although this caused a large section of hinterland to revert to intertidal habitat, the breach relieved pressure on the ridge and the newly created spits and deltas now afford protection to the shoreline close to the breach. A conscious decision was made by the Environment Agency not to repair the breach, but instead to allow the geomorphological features to evolve and develop. Managed US east coast inlets, such as Ocean City, Maryland, show that ebb tidal shoals and natural sediment bypassing may take many decades to become effective, but these changes are predictable (Kraus, 2000).

Great uncertainty exists in predicting the response of natural systems to radical engineered morphological interventions. The principal uncertainties lay in the quantitative prediction of coastal evolution with and without the scheme and in identifying the wider impacts on related morphological and ecological systems. Also, the extent to which diverse stakeholders concerned with providing flood and coastal defence, promoting nature conservation and protecting national heritage must cooperate in order to achieve the ambitious goals of morphological protection is unprecedented. There are major uncertainties concerning whether the degree of cooperation can be achieved given current institutional and governance arrangements in the UK.

Use of the coastal response groups

Current policies are pushing coastal management and engineering away from coastal defences towards the other three response groups, as some of the earlier discussion has shown. National assessments of flood and erosion risk (Halcrow *et al.*, 2001), as well as shoreline management planning (Leafe *et al.*, 1998; Cooper *et al.*, 2002) combined with more rigorous project appraisal methods (e.g. Penning-Rowsell *et al.*, 2003) are making cliff protection schemes more difficult to justify, and many existing cliff defences may be abandoned over the coming decades. The abandonment of cliff defences at Happisburgh, Norfolk could be the beginning of this process. The new 'Making space for water' policy for England (Defra, 2004) also has profound implications and will clearly favour widespread managed re-alignment and, possibly, morphological protection approaches.

However, looking to the 2080s, the UK could develop in quite different and distinct ways irrespective of current trends in coastal management and engineering. The four Foresight futures capture a range of these different directions, which in turn present different opportunities and constraints to application of the various responses to coastal flooding and erosion. The implications of these four futures for coastal management and engineering are now considered.

Application of the response groups in the four futures

When considering the four Foresight futures, the authors considered the likely take-up of the different response groups as outlined in Table 23.2 based on expert judgement.

World markets

Under world markets, protection of coastal land and assets will be driven primarily by economic analyses of the alternatives. The extent and intensity of increases in the forcing drivers under this high-emissions scenario will increase erosion and flood risk at many locations, and erosion and flooding will continue to be prevented only where the economic case is clear. Hence, renewal of existing coastal defences in front of developments and urban areas is expected and land with particular value for tourism and recreation may be protected, for example, high cliffs with coastal vistas. Given weak controls on land-use, new developments in coastal areas are likely to be built in areas at risk from erosion and flooding, leading to demands for increased coastal protection. Due to these growing demands, high economic growth and societal values, this future scenario would protect against erosion and flooding more than the other scenarios. Therefore, the coast would probably experience much greater sediment starvation than today. If beaches are to be maintained, this would require extensive beach recharge and recycling, mainly from external sources, offshore, for example, with high costs and uncertain consequences for seabed environments. Tourism and recreation benefits

Table 23.2. A summary of the coastal management and engineering responses under each future scenario (see also Hall et al., 2005b)

		World markets	Global sustainability	National enterprise	Local stewardship
Overall summary		Free market provision of measures to reduce impacts of flooding and erosion. Major engineering measures to keep pace with increasing risk	Strategic regulation of development, management and reduction of impacts. Strategic soft coastal engineering. Universal protection through public–private schemes	Limited regulation and limited emphasis on the environment. Piecemeal engineering measures to reduce risk	National wealth does not keep pace with increasing risk. Abandonment of coastal floodplains and re-instatement of natural systems. Natural coastal processes re-instated
Coastal defences	Tidal flood barriers	Barrage construction as flood protection and possibly for renewable energy, if economic (see energy converters)	Thames barrier upgrade on present alignment. No new barrages	Barrage construction as flood protection and possibly for renewable energy, driven by national security considerations	Thames barrier upgrade on present alignment. No new barrages
	Permanent dikes and embankments	Widely applied where economically justified	Strategically important defences are maintained	Widely applied, but in a piecemeal fashion	Limited defences due to economic constraints
	Temporary flood walls	High interest for desirable flood-prone areas	Limited interest, as the overall goal is to avoid hazardous locations with planning	High interest for desirable flood-prone areas	Limited interest, as hazardous areas are abandoned
Coastal energy reduction measures	Soft engineering (beaches)	Widespread where economically justified including amenity benefits	Widespread application, with an emphasis on sediment recycling	Applied especially where there are additional benefits (e.g. amenity)	Less interest with an emphasis on re-alignment of defences (below)
	Soft engineering (estuaries)	Less interest	Widespread application	Less interest	Less interest with an emphasis on re-alignment of defences (below)
	Offshore barriers	Widespread, including minimising soft engineering costs on beaches	More limited due to environmental impacts	Widespread, including minimising soft engineering costs on beaches	More limited due to environmental impacts
	Energy converters	Where economically justified, possibly using tidal flood barriers	Strong interest	Where economic and national security concerns can justify, possibly using tidal flood barriers	Strong interest, but tension with environmental impacts and limited resources for investment
Realignment of defence infrastructure	Planned (managed re-alignment)	In areas of abandoned agricultural production. This could be a planned or unplanned process	Strategic managed retreat in rural and some isolated urban areas	Limited by parochial pressures	Widespread retreat, some planned and some unplanned causing migration away from the coast
	Unplanned		Not applicable	Some unplanned abandonment where defence costs cannot be justified	
Morphological protection		Limited interest	Strong interest, linked to strategic re-alignment and soft engineering measures (above)	Limited interest	The scale of re-alignment of defences presents important opportunities, but the ability to exploit is limited and some morphological protection may be inadvertent rather than planned

will probably justify such investment, but on a piecemeal basis with the promoters of such schemes using breakwaters and large groynes to retain the sediment in specific locations.

National enterprise

Under national enterprise there will also be urban development in coastal areas, together with marked expansion of tourism and recreation pressures due to reduced access to overseas coastal destinations, especially in North America, the Caribbean, the Far East and others. Under this medium-high emissions scenario, erosion and flooding would be both more intense and extensive than today. The result would be to favour local solutions aimed at reducing erosion and flood risk at key sites. Given a chronic shortage of land for food production and urban expansion, there would be strong resistance to the loss of 'valuable' land to the sea in any form of managed re-alignment. However, relatively low economic growth and harsh economic realities might lead to unmanaged abandonment of defences in poorer areas, with little regard to social equity.

Local stewardship

Under local stewardship, approaches based on anything but local solutions would be hampered by lack of strong regional planning and governance. This would make it difficult to implement integrated shoreline management responses based on cells and sub-cells. At the same time, weak economic growth and lack of inward investment may make all but the major coastal settlements vulnerable to increased flooding and erosion risks due to abandonment of defences. A shift to managing erosion in remaining settlements, particularly tourist resorts such as Bournemouth, is most likely under this future, as their economic base would significantly decline. If technically and economically feasible, erosion and flood management responses based on extraction of wind and wave energy are likely to develop under this scenario, given the strong market for local development of renewable sources of energy. While philosophically favouring managed re-alignment, there is a potential conflict between giving space to nature and agricultural self-sufficiency. Forced abandonment of some coastal defences appears likely, possibly resulting in migration away from coastal areas.

Global sustainability

Under global sustainability, erosion and flood problems could still be significantly higher than today. However, the response to this problem would place great emphasis on sustainability of coastal management, favouring approaches based on a strategic policy of managed re-alignment, which in turn promotes morphological protection approaches. National and local governance would promote land-use planning to avoid placing new coastal developments at risk of future erosion and flooding, and also to progressively relocate existing infrastructure, assets and even whole settlements along eroding coasts to safer inland locations. Stakeholders would proactively plan these changes using improving knowledge and models of coastal evolution from local to broad estuary/cell scales. However, it is likely that important seaside resorts, such as Bournemouth, Brighton and Blackpool, would have sufficient socio-economic significance to continue to receive protection through a combination of defences and beach nourishment to stop erosion and maintain tourist beaches. Beach recycling within sub-cells and cells (as opposed to seabed mining of new sediment sources) would be particularly favoured where it is technically feasible. Exploitation of renewable energy sources may have some benefits in reducing erosion and flood risk as part of multi-purpose schemes, but the economic viability of such schemes, as well as their environmental impacts, are likely to limit opportunities in a global sustainability future.

Summary across the Foresight futures

The widest distinctions in responses between the four Foresight futures are likely to centre on issues of governance and sustainability with an emphasis on piecemeal flood and coastal defences under world markets and national enterprise, and an emphasis on managed re-alignment and morphological engineering under global sustainability. There are contradictions within the local stewardship scenario that make the response less clear: the desire for self-sufficiency in food versus allowing natural processes by way of defence re-alignment. A mixture of planned and forced abandonment of some coastal defences appears likely due to economic constraints. Similar issues are apparent under national enterprise. Some beach nourishment is likely to feature in all cases, but with important differences in the balance between external sources of new sediment and recycling within natural sediment systems.

Effectiveness and sustainability of the response groups

This is explored in more detail in Chapters 22, 23 and 25, and only summary details specific to the coastal response groups are provided here. Each response group was scored on its potential for flood risk reduction under each of the four Foresight futures by the 2080s (Table 23.3). It should be noted that, in some instances, one response group may rely upon another for successful implementation. Under all futures, with the exception of local stewardship, the coastal responses are likely to result in major or marked reductions in flood risk, although the mix of uptake is likely to differ substantially between futures, as already discussed in the previous subsection.

While the potential abilities of these response groups to reduce flood risk are important, there is also a need to consider the wider implications of the responses under each scenario. Therefore, each response group was considered in terms of five sustainability metrics:

- environmental quality;
- cost-effectiveness;
- social justice;
- robustness; and
- precaution.

It is observed that while, for example, coastal defences provide the potential for a major reduction for flood risk under all scenarios, this response group does not satisfy the metric for environmental quality. A detailed discussion of the sustainability issues across the four response groups is provided in Table 23.4. It is apparent that to develop the full potential across the response groups and remove

Table 23.3. Summary scoring for coastal response groups on the potential for flood risk reduction in the 2080s for all futures. The ranking is relative to all 26 response groups considered in the overall Foresight study (Chapter 22)

Response group		World markets		National enterprise		Local stewardship		Global sustainability	
		Impact	Rank	Impact	Rank	Impact	Rank	Impact	Rank
Coastal defences		Ma	2	Ma	2	I	14	Ma	4
Re-alignment	Relocate	Mi	6	Ma	4	I	15	Mi	7
	Abandon	N	–	Ma	6	I	18	N	–
Reduce coastal energy		Mi	4	Ma	3	I	17	Mi	8
Morphological protection		Mi	5	Ma	5	I	16	Mi	9

Ma = major reduction; Mi = minor reduction; I = liable to increased flood risk; N = not applicable to the scenario

Table 23.4. *Generic response groups versus sustainability issues, following the nomenclature of the book*

Sustainability issue		Generic response groups			
		Coastal defences	Coastal energy reduction measures	Realignment of defences	Morphological protection
'Flood Risk', including scientific knowledge		Effective for most futures. Knowledge has improved rapidly over the last 30 years and it is now possible to predict impacts reasonably well both locally and to some extent at the scale of the coastal sub-cell or estuary system within which the defence is located. Need better long-term morphological and ecological predictions associated with the use of defences (~50 years)	Effective for most futures. A reasonable body of knowledge already exists on the performance of beach nourishment, saltmarsh generation and offshore breakwaters in the UK coastal environment. However, there is no experience of offshore tables and offshore (submerged) reefs in the UK. Renewable energy extraction is an area of increasing development	Effective for most futures – unplanned realignment is possible. An area of rapid scientific and engineering development as monitoring of early schemes provides information to improve design process. Long-term evolution (~50 years) requires more research	Highly effective, but present knowledge is focused on management of inter-tidal and supra-tidal areas such as saltmarshes and sand dunes, with the creation of new tidal inlets and associated protective tidal deltas and spits limited to empirical evidence from natural or inadvertent engineering analogues
'Robustness'		Reasonably robust against unexpected futures, but large changes could overwhelm defences	Reasonably robust against unexpected futures, but large changes could overwhelm these measures, or make less effective	Highly robust against unexpected futures, and generally enhances the capacity to respond to unexpected changes	Reasonably robust against unexpected futures, but due to relatively limited knowledge there is some uncertainty
'Precaution'	Precautionary principle	Well established and reversible approach, but removal can be both costly and politically controversial as defences often encourage coastal development (see Realignment of Defences)	Soft approaches, especially beach nourishment are, or are becoming, well-established techniques in the UK. Structural approaches, such as offshore breakwaters and fishtail groynes are less established in the UK, hindering application	Realignment is becoming an established technique. Empirical evidence of existing schemes can be used to overcome some of the caution that is associated with 'giving up land to the sea'	Considerable uncertainties in quantitatively predicting the long-term morphological response and variability, and hence wider consequences often preclude consideration of engineered morphological responses
	Putting people at the centre	Often the preferred response locally, with the wider (often adverse) consequences being less apparent	Breakwaters and sediment management are often attractive options, especially if the beach is enhanced for recreational purposes. Renewable energy approaches would appeal to 'green' perspectives	Achievable in the long-term, but making the change is likely to be disruptive and often resisted locally	Whilst aiming to reduce the risks from flooding and erosion, there is often a perception that this is being undertaken for the benefit of the natural environment or Westminster rather than the affected people. Limited experience
	Taking a long-term perspective	Defences have a finite life and provide an immediate solution that may or may not be sustainable over the longer term, especially considering changing drivers (sea level, etc.)	Hard measures (e.g. breakwaters) raise the same issues as artificial coastal barriers. Soft measures work with nature, but may require regular re-nourishment. Renewable energy approaches are untested, but will contribute to reducing climate change	Widespread application of this response could significantly reduce reliance on coastal defences	Allowing short-term natural dynamism to occur unimpeded enhances the longer-term resilience of the coast

'Cost Effective' Taking account of direct costs and benefits	Built into existing 'Project Appraisal Guidance' funding procedures	Conventional flood and coastal defence analyses for this approach. New methods are required to assess renewable energy generation combined with flood and coastal defence	Existing funding procedures address realignment of defences. Relocating infrastructure may be much more difficult and requires more strategic coastal planning	Costs may be relatively small, with significant and far-reaching benefits in terms of self-sustaining natural protection. Requires more strategic coastal planning
Wider economic effects	Secondary benefits such as tourism and leisure functions	Beaches and other intertidal habitats promote recreation and other benefits (e.g. fishery nurseries). Renewable energy development could also promote development	Realignment can be used to promote recreation and ecotourism. But relocated infrastructure may be crucial to local and regional transport networks	Secondary benefits such as the creation or enhancement of educational and recreational resources
'Environmental Quality' – Respecting environmental limits	Can cause problems locally and more widely within coastal cells or estuaries, as defences constrain the natural functioning of ecological and morphological systems. Historically, the largest effects have been the loss of intertidal areas due to land claim around estuaries	Soft engineering encourages flexibility, although need to consider impacts on sediment sources. Renewable energy production is consistent with an environmentally sensitive approach. However, artificial structures and devices could have adverse impacts on nearshore habitats and ecosystems	Maintains or restores natural dynamics. Current focus on inter-tidal habitats does not adequately acknowledge the importance of sub- and supra-tidal habitats	Recognises that coastal systems are dynamic environments that function and evolve in a self-regulating manner with significant environmental and other benefits
'Social Justice' Transparency, information, participation and access to justice	Decision making rests with local and national government. Advice is sought from statutory advisors (e.g. English Nature, Countryside Council for Wales) and professional consultants. Decisions are often challenged by local stakeholders and single-issue pressure groups through the planning system and public inquiries. This can slow implementation of schemes, sometimes for decades. Open to all	Land owners, developers and public bodies can all promote managed realignment through the existing planning process. The scale of realignment of major infrastructure means that this is more likely to be a public endeavour	No experience to draw upon. Hence, the transparency of the design process is less clear than other response groups, with much reliance on expert assessment and application of theoretical principles. Addressing these issues requires improved scientific knowledge, and consideration of the widespread implications of this response group	
Poverty/social exclusion	Cost–benefit criteria can discourage protection of poorer areas. But defences promote investment	Cost–benefit criteria can discourage protection of poorer areas. But defences promote investment and renewable energy generation may offer local development opportunities	If infrastructure is abandoned this could isolate some areas and increase poverty. But if strategically planned, realignment could provide improved opportunities	Could open-up eco-tourism opportunities, leading to jobs. Newly created inlets could cut off communities/limit access to beaches

an over-reliance on coastal defences, better long-term system-based coastal morphological models are required that allow the inclusion of coastal management and engineering interventions. Further, shoreline management needs to be integrated much more closely with wider coastal planning to exploit opportunities for re-alignment of defences and the development of morphological protection.

These analyses were taken further and combined with other response groups to produce 'response portfolios' for each future scenario. These were then used in combination with analysis of changing flood risks to quantify the future risks of flooding on a national scale, as discussed Chapter 25. Nationally, erosion risk is estimated to be two orders of magnitude smaller than flood risk (Halcrow *et al.*, 2001) and hence, it would not make a significant contribution to national risk estimates. When using the response groups outlined here in realistic combinations for each future, the probability of flooding and the associated flood risk is substantially reduced, suggesting that these are appropriate methods to deal with the flood and erosion risk management challenges of the twenty-first century.

Conclusions and emerging issues

This chapter has shown that there are a wide range of coastal management and engineering methods available to respond to the challenges of flood and erosion risk in coastal areas. The UK experience of these methods varies substantially, from over 100 years with coastal defences, to methods which are still at the research and development stage, such as combining renewable energy generation with flood and coastal defence, or morphological protection. Hence, to make the full portfolio of methods described here available for shoreline management purposes, more science and engineering research is required. A fundamental gap in our knowledge is long-term morphological prediction over decades of natural coastal units such as coastal cells or estuaries. While system-based models are beginning to emerge, they require substantial further development. Fully exploiting these response options will also require more strategic planning and a clear vision of the desired coastal future. This will allow opportunities for re-alignment of defences and adoption of morphological protection to be exploited as they emerge, while new coastal development can be planned with erosion and flood risks as an explicit consideration. The issues raised by each of the response groups are now considered in turn.

The use of coastal defences is likely to play a part in reducing flooding and coastal erosion risks under all four future scenarios. It is certainly the case that, if no other response was adopted, then continuing to provide defences is likely to remain feasible from both an engineering and cost perspective. The indicative costs of simply raising the defences everywhere on the coast are of the order of £8–9 billion and do not appear to be overly sensitive to any given scenario. The other issue that emerges is the extent of defences that exist to protect linear infrastructure along the coast, such as roads, railways, pipelines, etc. If these could be relocated landward, it would significantly reduce the lengths of required defence, showing how different response groups can work together.

The incorporation of renewable energy opportunities within coastal defence schemes is beginning to be evaluated, but this is targeted at wholesale replacement rather than a partial contribution to overall defence. As the market for renewable energy matures, there may be more scope for partial combinations, where the energy device reduces the exposure of the coast but does not eliminate the need for defences.

There is a conflict between the potential need to retain agricultural land – or use the land to meet local needs – and the potential to implement managed re-alignment. The need to limit the extent of coastal squeeze by moving some of the defences landward is becoming acute, particularly around our estuaries. The desire to maintain intertidal habitats is likely to continue to be one of the key drivers behind the policy of managed re-alignment. As already noted, re-alignment of infrastructure, such as roads and railways, could substantially reduce the need for coastal defences, but funding mechanisms are currently difficult to envisage, except possibly under the global sustainability scenario. This is because this response is desirable for sustainability and environmental reasons, but is unlikely to be economical unless the particular infrastructure is due to be replaced in any event. More integrated planning may facilitate this goal.

Morphological protection has the merit of delivering a high degree of long-term sustainability, but it can conflict with other interests and drivers in most scenarios. While this response is seen as highly desirable from many perspectives, it often requires a cross-sectoral or cross-agency effort to promote such a scheme. Consequently, most efforts to date have been relatively small scale. For this approach to make a significant contribution to the overall management of the coast and reduce the need to provide hard defences, some larger-scale initiatives will need to be promoted.

Acknowledgements

The authors thank Ms Susanne Rupp-Armstrong, University of Southampton and Dr Loraine McFadden, Middlesex University for comments on an earlier version of this manuscript.

References

Anthony, E.J., 1994. 'Natural and artificial shores of the French Riviera: An analysis of their interrelationship', *J. Coastal Research*, 1994, 10(1), 48–58.

Bradbury, A. and Kidd, R., 1998. 'Hurst Spit stabilisation scheme – design and construction of beach recharge', *Proceedings 33rd MAFF Conference of River and Coastal Engineers*.

Brampton, A.H., 1992. 'Engineering significance of British salt marshes', in *Saltmarshes: Morphodynamics, conservation and engineering significance*, eds Allen, J.R.L. and Pye, K., Cambridge University Press, Cambridge, 115–122.

Burgess, K. and Townend, I., 2004. 'The impact of climate change upon coastal defence structures', *Proceedings 39th Defra Flood and Coastal Management Conference*.

Cooper, N.J., Hooke, J.M. and Bray, M.J., 2001. 'Predicting coastal evolution using a sediment budget approach: a case study from southern England', *Ocean and Coastal Management*, 44, 711–728.

Cooper, N.J., Barber, P.C., Bray, M.C. and Carter, D.J., 2002. 'Shoreline management plans: a national review and an engineering perspective', *Proceedings of the Institution of Civil Engineers, Water and Maritime Engineering*, 154, 221–228.

Defra, 2004. *Making Space for Water – Developing a new government strategy for flood and coastal erosion risk management in England – A consultation exercise*, Defra, London.

Defra, 2006. *Shoreline Management Plan Guidance. Volume 1: Aims and requirements*, Defra, London, available online www.defra.gov.uk/environ/fcd/policy/smpgvol1.pdf

Dickson, M.E., Walkden, M.J.A., Hall, J.W., Pearson, S.G. and Rees, J.G., 2005. Numerical modelling of potential climate-change impacts on rates of soft-cliff recession, northeast Norfolk, UK, *Proceedings of Coastal Dynamics 2005*, ASCE, New York.

Edwards, A.M.C. and Winn, P.J.S., 2003. 'The sustainable management of the Humber Estuary', *Coastal Management*, Thomas Telford, London, 127–140.

English Nature, 2001. *The Success of Creation and Restoration Schemes in Producing Intertidal Habitat Suitable for Water Birds*, English Nature Research Reports, No. 425.

Foresight Marine Panel, 2003. *The Potential for 'Wet' Renewables to Aid Coast Protection: A report based on the Bridgwater Bay situation*, Department of Trade and Industry, London.

French, P.W., 2001. *Coastal Defences*, Routledge, London.

Gwynedd Council, 1998. *North Cardigan Bay Shoreline Management Plan Stage 1 Consultation Document*, February.

Halcrow, HR Wallingford and John Chatterton Associates, 2001. *National Appraisal of Assets at Risk from Flooding and Coastal Erosion, Including the Potential Impact of Climate Change*, Defra, London.

Halcrow, Centre for Social and Economic Research on the Global Environment (CSERGE) and Cambridge Coastal Research Unit (CRU), 2002. *Managed Realignment Review*, Project Report, Defra, London.

Hall, J.W., Dawson, R.J., Walkden, M.J.A., Nicholls, R.J., Brown, I. and Watkinson, A., 2005. 'Broad-scale analysis of morphological and climate impacts on coastal flood risk', *Proceedings of Coastal Dynamics 2005*, ASCE, New York.

Hall, J.W., Sayers, P., Walkden, M. and Panzeri, M., 2005. 'Impacts of climate change on the coast of England and Wales: 2030–2100, *Phil. Trans. of the Royal Society A*, 364, 1027–1049.

Hanson, H., Brampton, A., Capobianco, M., Dette, H.H., Hamm, L., Laustrup, C., Lechuga, A. and Spanhoff, R., 2002. 'Beach nourishment projects, practices, and objectives – European overview', *Coastal Engineering*, 47(2), 81–111.

Hardacre, G., 2001. 'Pevensey Coastal Defences PPP: The contractor's perspective', *Proceedings 36th MAFF Conference of River and Coastal Engineers*.

Harlow, D.A. and Cooper, N.J., 1996. 'Bournemouth beach monitoring: the first twenty years', in *Coastal Management: Putting policy into practice*, ed. Fleming, C.A., Thomas Telford, London, 248–259.

Henderson, G, Donald, K.J. and Webber, N.B., 1979. 'Utilization of wave power at a coastal site', *ICE Proceedings, Part 2*, 67, 1–11.

Holland, B. and Coughlan, P., 1994. 'The Elmer coastal defence scheme', *Proceedings 29th MAFF Conference of River and Coastal Engineers*.

Kraus, N.C., 1988. 'The effects of seawalls on the beach: an extended literature review', *J. Coastal Research*, SI4, 1–28.

Kraus, N.C., 2000. 'Reservoir model of ebb-tidal shoal evolution and sand bypassing', *J. Waterway, Port, Coastal, and Ocean Engineering*, 126(3), 305–313.

Lavery, S. and Donovan, B., 2005. 'Flood risk management in the Thames Estuary: Looking 100 years ahead', *Phil. Trans. of the Royal Society A*, 363, 1455–1474.

Leafe, R., Pethick, J. and Townend, I., 1998. 'Realising the benefits of shoreline management', *Geographical Journal*, 164, 282–290.

Lee, E.M. and Marker, B., 1995. 'Earth science information in coastal planning', *Proceedings 30th MAFF Conference of River and Coastal Engineers*.

Lomax, C. and Olliver, G., 2003. 'Development and testing of the Stingray tidal power system', *Proceedings of the Institution of Civil Engineers Annual Conference*, Belfast.

Nicholls, R.J. and Klein, R.J.T., 2005. 'Climate change and coastal management on Europe's coast', in *Managing European Coasts: Past, present and future*, eds Vermaat, J.E., Ledoux, L., Turner, K. and Salomons, W., Springer (Environmental Science Monograph Series), Berlin, 199–225.

Nicholls, R.J. and Wilson, T., 2001. 'Integrated impacts on coastal areas and river flooding', in *Regional Climate Change Impact and Response Studies in East Anglia and North West England (RegIS). Final Report of MAFF project no. CC0337*, eds Holman, I.P. and Loveland, P.J., 54–101.

Orford, J. and Jennings, S., 1996. 'The importance of different time-scale controls on coastal management strategy: the problem of Porlock gravel barrier, Somerset, UK', in *Coastal Defence and Earth Science Conservation*, ed. Hooke, J.M., Geographical Society, London.

Owen, M., 1984. 'Effectiveness of saltings in coastal defence', *Proceedings of MAFF Conference of River and Coastal Engineers*.

Penning-Rowsell, E.C., Johnson, C., Tunstall, S.M., Tapsell, S.M., Morris, J., Chatterton, J.B., Coker, A. and Green, C., 2003. *The Benefits of Flood and Coastal Defence: Techniques and data for 2003*, Flood Hazard Research Centre, Middlesex University, London.

Pethick, J.S., 1998. 'Coastal management and sea level rise: a morphological approach', in *Landform Monitoring, Modelling and Analysis*, eds Lane, S. *et al.*, Wiley, London.

Pethick, J.S., 2001. 'Coastal management and sea level rise', *Catena*, 42, 307–322.

Rochelle-Newall, E. *et al.*, 2005. 'Group report: Global change and the European coast: Climate change and economic development', in *Managing European Coasts: Past, present and future*, eds Vermaat, J.E., Ledoux, L., Turner, K. and Salomons, W., Springer, Environmental Science Monograph Series, 239–254.

Rupp-Armstrong, S. and Nicholls, R.J. (in press) 'Coastal and estuarine retreat: a comparison of the application of managed realignment in England and Germany', *Journal of Coastal Research*.

Silvester, R. and Hsu, J.C.R., 1994. 'Coastal stabilization: innovative concepts', Prentice Hall Inc., Englewood Cliffs, NJ.

Stive, M.J.F., Aarninkoff, S.J.C., Hamm, L., Hanson, H., Larson, M., Wijnberg, K., Nicholls, R.J. and Capobianco, M., 2002. 'Variability of shore and shoreline evolution', *Coastal Engineering*, 47, 211–235.

Thomalla, F., 2001. 'The effects of the segmented shore – parallel breakwaters at sea palling on the longshore transport of sand', *Proceedings 36th MAFF Conference of River and Coastal Engineers*.

Thomas, R.S., 1992. 'The defences for Lincolnshire', in *Coastal Zone Planning and Management*, ed. Barrett, M.C., Thomas Telford, London, 269–281.

Townend, I.H. and Pethick, J., 2002. 'Estuarine flooding and managed retreat', *Philosphical Transactions of the Royal Society London A*, 360, 1477–1495.

Whitcombe, L.J., 1996. 'Behaviour of an artificially replenished shingle beach at Hayling Island, UK', *Quarterly Journal of Engineering Geology*, 29, 265–271.

Whittaker, T., 2003. 'Wave power Islay 2 and further developments', *Proceedings of the Institution of Civil Engineers Annual Conference*, Belfast.

24 Response scoring, ranking, uncertainty and sustainability

Jonathan D. Simm and Colin R. Thorne

Introduction

The response scoring and ranking exercise was designed to provide a consistent and concise means of reporting expert judgement of the potential effectiveness and sustainability of the responses to flood risk described in detail in Chapters 18 to 23.

The process employed to estimate the reductions in future flood risk that could be delivered by the responses was essentially similar to that adopted in scoring and ranking the drivers of increased flood risk (see Chapter 12). Deep descriptions of

Table 24.1. Governance under the four Foresight scenarios (Evans et al., 2004)

World markets	National enterprise	Local stewardship	Global sustainability
Customer-orientated governance in a rights-based culture	Customer-orientated governance with a 'statist' approach	Heavy regulation of markets	Fairly heavy regulation of markets
Limited public involvement at the local level	Very little involvement at local level	Citizen-orientated governance with participatory approach	Citizen-orientated governance with consultation approach
Preference for instruments based on self-regulation, transparency, public–private partnerships and economic incentives	Preference for instruments based on economic incentives and self-regulation	Very strong local participation	Strong public involvement at the local level
	Pressure to reduce taxes	Decision making is devolved, with strong emphasis on local level	Policy mix of negotiated agreements, market instruments and traditional regulation
Pressure to reduce taxes	Relative decline of public expenditure	Preference for traditional regulation, planning instruments	Relatively high levels of taxation
Relative decline of public expenditure (but high GDP growth)		Local implementation varies	Relative increase of public expenditure
		High levels of taxation	
		Relative increase of public expenditure (but low GDP growth)	

414

responses were prepared and the performance of each group of responses was eval-uated both in terms of its potential impact in reducing future flood risk and its performance against a range of sustainability metrics.

The potential for a given measure or intervention to deliver a reduction in flood risk is strongly scenario dependent, as its performance varies as a function of the wider conditions under which it is implemented. For example, regulatory or funding constraints specific to a scenario may hinder (or favour) the implementa-tion of a particular response. The responses were, therefore, scored within the context of each of the four Foresight future scenarios. Detailed scenario contexts were provided as part of the research performed by the experts studying govern-ance and these are reported in Chapter 27, but they are also summarised briefly here for ready reference (Tables 24.1 and Table 24.2). However, scoring of

Table 24.2. Governance and policy response themes under the four Foresight scenarios (Evans et al., 2004)

Response theme	World markets	National enterprise	Local stewardship	Global sustainability
Managing the rural landscape	Limited other than in intensively managed agricultural areas	Limited other than in intensively managed agricultural areas; spatial coordination also problematic	Potentially strong but spatial coordination may be problematic	Potentially very strong as part of shift to less intensive agricultural support systems
Managing the urban fabric	Generally only where it is cost-effective	Generally only where it is cost-effective locally	Commitments to local SUDS schemes, but spatial coordination may be poor	Commitments to local SUDS schemes
Managing flood events	Effective forecasting but strong reliance then placed on local/individual flood proofing and temporary defences in the most economically important areas	Less coordinated forecasting; local/individual flood proofing and temporary defences in the most economically important areas	Possibility of asset removal and effective evacuation programmes in certain localities	Central government planning and awareness schemes linked to evacuation programmes and flood fighting
Managing flood losses	Mainly property-level actions; self-insurance supplemented by charitable donations	Mainly property-level actions; self-insurance supplemented by charitable donations	Potentially strong local support networks; pooled insurance to share costs in flood-prone areas; possibility of local floodplain charging schemes	State compensation for losses; tax credits and strong land-use planning to steer development away from flood-prone areas; possibility of national floodplain charging schemes
River and coastal engineering	Strong preference for large-scale schemes to protect nationally important economic areas	Strong preference for large-scale schemes to protect nationally important economic areas	Strong local opposition to large-scale schemes; limited government investment may curtail other large-scale schemes, e.g. re-alignment	Shift to softer approaches such as re-alignment, energy generation and, where necessary, surrender of the most flood-prone areas

415

responses was based on current societal values and preferences, with no attempt being made to judge how future societal values and preferences might differ. This decision was taken to avoid the scoring exercise becoming over-complicated, and because it was argued that changes in societal values and preferences are already implicit in the socio-economic scenarios and that to take them into account again explicitly would over-represent their influence.

To support uncertainty analysis, the deep response descriptions were also used to make upper- and lower-bound estimates for each response impact score. The ratio between the upper and lower bounds defined a band that represented uncertainty in the estimate of the potential for each response to reduce flood risk under the scenario specified. Uncertainty bands for all responses were tabulated to highlight those responses that have both a high potential to reduce flood risk and a great deal of uncertainty.

Expert scoring of potential flood risk reductions

The specialist team for each response theme (Table 24.3) considered, for each scenario, what the effect would be on the level of future flood risk if the measures in each response group were implemented in a manner consistent with the opportunities and constraints identified for that scenario. To assess the reduction in the future flood risk for each response group, experts carefully considered the effect of the measures in that group could have in two stages.

Table 24.3. Topic specialists responsible for scoring response impacts in each response theme

Response theme	Topic specialists	
	Name	**Affiliation**
Managing the rural landscape	Stuart Lane	Durham University
	Joe Morris	Cranfield University
	Enda O'Connell	Newcastle University
	Paul Quinn	Newcastle University
Managing the urban fabric	Richard Ashley	Sheffield University
	Adrian Saul	Sheffield University
	John Handley	Manchester University
	Joe Howe	Queens University
Managing flood events	Sue Tapsell	Middlesex University
	David Ball	Middlesex University
	Ian Cluckie	Bristol University
Managing flood losses	Nigel Arnell	Southampton University
	John Chatterton	Chatterton Associates
	Robert Nicholls	Middlesex University
River and coastal engineering	John Palmer	Halcrow
	Peter von Lany	Halcrow
	Ian Townend	ABP Marine Environmental Research
	Nick Cooper	ABP Marine Environmental Research

First, experts addressed the question of the degree to which the measures in each response group could offset the estimated risk increases associated with the relevant flood risk drivers, as set out in Chapter 12 of this volume. However, experts were mindful that, as explained in Chapter 12, the *overall* increase in flood risk for a given scenario is neither a simple multiple of the component effects of the various drivers (fully independent case) nor is it the maximum value (fully dependent case). Thus, the potential flood risk reductions associated with the impacts of a response group on individual flood risk drivers gave only a general guide to the overall reduction in flood risk that might be delivered by that response group.

Second, experts deliberated on the estimates of overall flood risk increase associated with each scenario under the baseline assumption (see Table 12.11). As that assumption held flood management policies, technologies and investment levels constant, those estimates provide the projected levels of increases in overall risk that the responses would seek to reduce.

Process support using electronic spreadsheets

A series of linked electronic spreadsheets was used to facilitate the compilation and ranking of response risk reduction scores. The master spreadsheet listed all the response groups discussed in Chapters 18 to 23, with a linked sub-spreadsheet created for each of the five response themes. Topic specialists for each response theme were provided with the sub-spreadsheet corresponding to the theme for which they were responsible. This sub-spreadsheet contained a list of the response groups in the theme, with blank cells into which could be added the upper, best estimate and lower-bound scores (that is flood risk reduction factors) for each response group. The score cells were contained in an array (page) that was repeated for each scenario. When the sub-spreadsheet entries had been agreed, they were saved and submitted to the core team for compilation in the master spreadsheet.

The approach for generating response reduction scores was as follows. The spreadsheet already contained the estimates of future flood risk for each scenario based on the driver descriptions and quantitative analysis presented in Parts 2 and 3 of this volume. The first step for the experts was to revise the flood risk multiplier for each scenario to reflect their best estimate of the effect that each response group in their theme would have if the measures in it were implemented in a manner consistent with the opportunities and constraints identified for that scenario (see Tables 24.1 and 24.2). This revised risk multiplier was entered into the relevant cell of the Responses Ranking Spreadsheet. On entry, the ratio of this revised multiplier for future flood risk to the baseline value was calculated automatically by the spreadsheet.

In deriving their reduced flood risk multipliers, experts were instructed that revisions could not simply be envisaged in terms of either a constant percentage or a constant absolute reduction in the future flood risks envisaged for the baseline case. This was the case because, under the baseline assumption, the world markets and national enterprise scenarios had very large increases in overall future risk (multipliers of 21 and 15.7, respectively), while increases under local stewardship and global sustainability scenarios were more modest (multipliers of 1.6 and 4.9, respectively).

It follows that, if their flood risk multiplier reductions were simply expressed as a *constant percentage* of the baseline increases across all scenarios, that would imply much larger *absolute* reductions in risk under, say, world markets, than would be possible under global sustainability. Conversely, if the flood risk multiplier reductions were expressed as a constant *absolute* amount across all scenarios, that would imply a much larger *percentage* reduction in the risk associated with the

417

global sustainability or local stewardship scenarios compared to anything possible under world markets and national enterprise scenarios.

Experts were therefore careful to take full account of the factors affecting both the flood risk multiplier for the baseline case for each scenario *and* the degree to which each measure could be implemented effectively to reduce future flood risk under that scenario. The results were, consequently, best estimates of the potential for the measures in each response group to affect future flood risk that were scenario specific in the fullest possible sense.

Response group scoring

Draft response scores were subject to wide peer review obtained through specialised workshops, open meetings, independent refereeing of draft documents and electronic publication of draft results. The response scores were modified and mediated in light of feedback and critical reviews in two specific ways.

First, it was recognised that, where a response theme affected pathway drivers, care was required to ensure that the flood risk reduction score for the response reflected its impact nationally rather than within the area of the UK actually at risk of flooding by way of any particular pathway. This was necessary as, in the analysis of driver impacts, the baseline multipliers for local flood risk (Table 12.3) had been reduced to reflect increases in nationally averaged flood risk (Table 12.4). Accepting the need for this 'area correction', responses in two themes were adjusted to account for the difference between the area affected by the response groups in that theme and the overall area of the UK at risk of flooding. The two response themes affected were:

Managing the urban fabric: the flood risk reduction scores for response groups in this theme (Chapter 19) were reduced to take account of the urban area of the UK at risk of river and/or coastal flooding as a proportion of the overall area of the UK at risk of flooding.

River and coastal engineering: the response groups in this theme were split into fluvial defences (Chapter 22) and coastal and estuarial defences (Chapter 23). When calculating the impact of response measures and groups on national flood risk, the scores were reduced to take account of the fact that fluvial interventions only reduce the risk of river flooding and coastal and estuarial interventions only protect the coastal floodplain. To account for this, a correction was applied to the initial scores on the basis of the proportion of annual economic damages associated with the two types of floodplain in the 2080s (45% coastal and 55% fluvial).

Second, it emerged that a correction was required when considering the impacts of scores for responses in the managing flood losses response theme. The responses in this theme were assessed for their effectiveness in reducing exposure to flood loss. This included assessing the effect of land-use management and flood-proofing measures applied to existing building stock, and the effect of land-use planning, changing building codes and altered construction practices applied to new building stock. Clearly, to properly represent the overall effect of these measures in reducing national flood risk, these assessments must account for the proportion of new and existing buildings that would have been located in the floodplain under the scenario in question had the planning response not been implemented. In light of this finding, the corrections applied to the draft response impact scores are as follows:

- As figures for the proportion of new build varied only slightly from one scenario to another, it could be assumed, for simplicity, that in all scenarios 45% of the properties in 2080 would be new.

Table 24.4. Flood risk reduction multiplier scores for individual response groups

Response group	World markets	National enterprise	Local stewardship	Global sustainability
1. Rural infiltration	1.00	0.90	0.90	0.90
2. Catchment-wide storage	1.00	0.80	0.80	0.60
3. Rural conveyance	1.00	0.90	0.85	0.70
4. Urban storage	0.97	0.95	0.94	0.94
5. Urban infiltration	1.00	1.00	1.00	0.95
6. Urban conveyance	1.00	1.00	0.97	0.95
7. Pre-event measures	0.86	0.89	0.81	0.80
8. Forecasting and warning	0.81	0.88	0.81	0.76
9. Flood fighting	0.81	0.86	0.81	0.80
10. Collective damage avoidance	0.95	0.93	0.88	0.86
11. Individual damage avoidance	0.86	0.92	0.75	0.80
12. Land-use management	1.00	0.96	0.60	0.61
13. Flood proofing	0.86	0.84	0.70	0.81
14. Land-use planning	0.94	0.86	0.85	0.83
15. Building codes	0.85	0.86	0.90	0.89
16. Insurance, shared risk and compensation 17. Health and social measures and policies	Note: these responses act to reduce flood risk indirectly by way of response groups 12, 13 and 15 and their impacts are included in the risk reduction multipliers for those groups			
18. River conveyance	0.83	0.78	0.89	0.89
19. Engineered flood storage	0.89	0.83	0.83	0.78
20. Flood water transfer	0.99	0.99	1.00	0.99
21. River defences	0.55	0.55	0.78	0.62
22. Coastal defences	0.64	0.63	1.17	0.68
23/ Coastal defences re-alignment: split	0.71	0.68	1.30	0.71
24. scores are for re-alignment (upper) and abandonment (lower) under NE and LS		0.69	1.53	
25. Reduce coastal energy	0.71	0.67	1.37	0.72
26. Morphological coastal protection	0.71	0.68	1.36	0.74

NE = National enterprise; LS = Local stewardship

- It was estimated that, of the remaining 55%, only a small proportion of properties would have been rebuilt each year since 2002:
  - under the world markets and national enterprise scenarios the proportion of housing stock replaced each year was estimated to be 0.5% of the existing stock per annum;
  - under the local stewardship and global sustainability scenarios this figure was reduced to 0.25% per annum.

The results of the initial scoring exercise for the reduction in flood risk that each response group could achieve under each scenario are listed in Table 24.4.

Combining interdependent response groups

The aim of the scoring exercise is to allow the response groups to be ranked in terms of their potential to reduce flood risk in the 2080s under each Foresight future. However, it emerged during consultation and debate of the scores for the individual response groups, listed in Table 24.4, that treating some groups in isolation was so unrealistic that the resulting scores misrepresented their potential effectiveness in reducing future flood risk. This is the case because the efficacy of some response groups is strongly dependent on their being implemented as part of an integrated approach involving other, functionally related responses. It was concluded that the only way to represent the potential of these responses properly was to score them in association with the related responses to which they were inextricably linked. Consequently, specialists working on three response themes chose to pool some of the groups in their response themes to produce fewer but more realistic, combined response groups. The themes that took this step were managing the urban fabric, managing flood events and managing flood losses.

In the theme concerned with managing the urban fabric, specialists argued convincingly that to increase urban flood storage would necessarily involve modification of the pathways conveying flood water through built-up areas, while also seeking to improve the performance of pervious areas in absorbing surface water by increasing infiltration. It was concluded that the potential for an integrated flood management scheme (employing increases in urban flood storage in concert with changes to conveyance and enhanced infiltration) to reduce future pluvial flood risk was much greater than the sum of the potentials for these response groups acting alone. Hence, when considering flood risk reduction scores, the three groups in this theme were combined to produce a combined response group termed managing urban runoff.

Effective flood event management depends on timely and efficient actions to reduce the extent and impacts of flooding on people, property and infrastructure. For example, flood fighting and collective-scale damage avoidance (through evacuating people and/or moving their possessions to places of safety) depend on accurate forecasting and timely flood warning. Based on this practical interdependence, these three response groups in the managing flood events response theme were pooled to produce a combined group termed real-time event management.

In the theme concerning managing flood losses, measures involving land-use planning and land-use management are closely related in terms of governance and their potential for reducing flood risk is maximised when they are invoked in combination. Also, treating them in combination when assessing their potential to reduce future flood risk reduces uncertainty because it negates the requirement to estimate the proportions of new build and rebuild likely to occur in flood risk areas under different scenarios. Consequently, these groups were combined as land-use planning and management. Also, flood proofing and building codes both relate to the fabric of structures in the floodplain and they work better (to produce a much larger reduction in flood risk) when undertaken within a coordinated policy framework designed to make buildings at risk more resilient to flooding. Hence, they were pooled to produce a combined response group termed 'flood-proofing buildings'.

Table 24.5. Scores for combined response groups

Response theme	Associated groups	Combined response group	WM	NE	LS	GS
2. Managing the urban fabric	4. Urban storage 5. Urban conveyance 6. Urban infiltration	Managing urban runoff	0.99	0.98	0.97	0.95
3. Managing flood events	8. Forecasting and warning 9. Flood fighting 10. Collective damage avoidance	Real-time event management	0.83	0.89	0.82	0.79
4. Managing flood losses	12. Land-use management 14. Land-use planning	Land-use planning and management	0.83	0.89	0.82	0.79
	13. Flood proofing 15. Building codes	Flood-proofing buildings	0.71	0.70	0.60	0.69

WM = world markets; NE = national enterprise; LS = local stewardship; GS = global sustainability

The scores for the combined response groups that resulted from pooling interdependent responses are listed in Table 24.5.

Ranking responses to future flood risk

The purpose of the scoring exercise was to support ranking of the responses in terms of their potential for reducing future increases in flood risk, so that experts could assess their potential for contributing to future flood risk management as part of an integrated portfolio of responses. Given the high degree of uncertainty associated with many of the responses (see the following section) it was decided to group them in the ranking table (Table 24.6) according to the scores assessed for the flood risk reduction multiplier (S) using the following tiers:

- Major reduction in flood risk $S < 0.7$
- Marked reduction in flood risk $0.7 < S < 0.9$
- Moderate reduction in flood risk $0.9 < S < 1.0$
- Ineffective $S \sim 1$
- Liable to increase flood risk $S > 1.0$

Commentary

Under the world markets scenario, responses stem primarily from the river and coastal engineering theme, with direct intervention in the physical flooding system being the preferred approach to reducing flood risk. Of the 14 response groups with potential to reduce flood risk effectively, river and coastal defences are the only ones to produce major risk reductions and so occupy the top two ranks, with other direct interventions, such as reducing coastal energy, increasing river conveyance and engineered flood storage expected to deliver marked flood risk reductions. However, the market-led approach to flood management limits the deployment of structural defences to only those areas where the economic justification is clear. Consequently, a policy of allowing the coast to adjust morphologically to rapidly rising sea levels and increased storm surge and wave heights, unless major infrastructure or urban areas are at risk, results in high rankings for morphological coastal protection and re-alignment of coastal defences. Responses designed to reduce flood losses reflect the individualistic nature of the world markets scenario, with property owners expected to manage down their own risk through flood proofing buildings and taking the steps necessary to achieve individual damage avoidance. The *laissez-faire* approach to regulation limits the government's contribution to damage reduction to assisting individuals to reduce their personal losses through pre-event measures and real-time event management. Conversely, dominance of the free-market limits the effectiveness of land-use planning and management and managing urban runoff, and it prevents effective implementation of measures to reduce catchment runoff through catchment-wide storage, managing rural conveyance and increasing rural infiltration.

Direct interventions in the physical flooding system also dominate the national enterprise scenario, but with some notable differences to world markets that reflect the desire of the state to defend the land and other national assets at risk, particularly at the coast. A strong sense of national identity fosters an environment in which all 18 flood response groups can be implemented effectively to deliver flood risk reductions. Engineering-led response groups involving structural defences, energy reduction and re-alignment are expected to produce major flood risk reductions, with increased river conveyance and engineered flood storage also delivering

Table 24.6. Response groups ranked by potential for flood risk reduction in the 2080s (Evans et al., 2004)

Rank	World markets	National enterprise	Local stewardship	Global sustainability
1	River defences	River defences	Land-use planning and management	Land-use planning and management
2	Coastal defences	Coastal defences	Flood proofing buildings	Catchment-wide storage
3	Flood proofing buildings	Reduce coastal energy	Individual damage avoidance	River defences
4	Reduce coastal energy	Re-align coastal defences	River defences	Coastal defences
5	Morphological coastal protection	Morphological coastal protection	Catchment-wide storage	Flood proofing buildings
6	Re-align coastal defences	Coastal defence abandonment	Pre-event measures	Rural conveyance
7	Real-time event management	Flood proofing buildings	Real-time event management	Re-align coastal defences
8	River conveyance	River conveyance	Engineered flood storage	Reduce coastal energy
9	Individual damage avoidance	Catchment-wide storage	Rural conveyance	Morphological coastal protection
10	Pre-event measures	Land-use planning and management	River conveyance	Engineered flood storage
11	Engineered flood storage	Engineered flood storage	Rural infiltration	Real-time event management
12	Land-use planning and management	Real-time event management	Manage urban runoff	Pre-event measures
13	Manage urban runoff	Pre-event measures	Flood water transfer	Individual damage avoidance
14	Flood water transfer	Rural conveyance	Coastal defences	River conveyance
15	Catchment-wide storage	Rural infiltration	Re-align coastal defences	Rural infiltration
16	River conveyance	Individual damage avoidance	Morphological coastal protection	Manage urban runoff
17	Rural infiltration	Manage urban runoff	Reduce coastal energy	Flood water transfer
18		Flood water transfer	Coastal defence abandonment	

Legend

Interpretation	Tint code
Major reduction in flood risk (S < 0.7)	
Marked reduction in flood risk ($0.7 \leq S < 0.9$)	
Moderate reduction in flood risk ($0.9 \leq S < 1.0$)	
Ineffective (S = 1.0)	
Liable to increase in flood risk (S > 1.0)	

marked reductions. However, the high cost of coastal defences in this economically weaker scenario means that it is not possible to hold the line everywhere, making it necessary for coastal defences to be re-aligned in some places and abandoned in others, allowing morphological adjustments to provide coastal defence in the longer term. This scenario is less technologically advanced than either world markets or global sustainability, limiting the contributions of pre-event measures and real-time event management. Conversely, the stronger agricultural base, freedom to incentivise rural stakeholders without being bounded by international agreements on farming subsidies and willingness to control development in the national interest, allow catchment-wide storage and land-use planning and management responses to deliver marked flood risk reductions.

Local stewardship is a low-growth, low-technology future under which only 12 response groups are capable of delivering reductions in flood risk. A strong commitment to schemes that are locally planned, inexpensive and environmentally aligned, characterises flood risk management in this scenario. This reduces the scope for direct interventions involving river defences and river conveyance, while boosting the potential for more diffuse catchment-based measures, involving flood storage, and rural conveyance, to be effective. Conversely, the inability to design, finance and implement coastal schemes at anything but the local scale entirely negates their effectiveness in reducing risk nationally. In fact, the major reductions in flood risk that can be achieved under this scenario stem from rigid application of land-use planning and management to prevent new building in flood-prone areas and relocate existing settlements and infrastructure away from river and coastal floodplains. Properties remaining at risk benefit substantially from community led schemes for flood proofing buildings. In this community-centred society, raised public awareness of flood risk means that individual damage avoidance, pre-event measures and real-time event management are also capable of delivering marked risk reductions.

Under the global sustainability scenario, 14 responses are capable of producing major or marked reductions in flood risk – more than under any other scenario. The integrated approach to flood risk management that characterises this scenario is illustrated in the outcome of the ranking exercise, which places three pairs of responses in the top six places. Coordinated management delivers major decreases in risk through reduced losses (land-use planning and management and flood proofing buildings), managed runoff (catchment-wide storage and rural conveyance) and reduction of residual risks to acceptable levels using structural measures (river and coastal defences). Application of the other responses in a flood-aware society generates the capability for marked risk reductions, with the exception of rural infiltration, managing urban runoff and flood water transfer. The moderate risk reductions that can be delivered by these groups more reflect physical and technical constraints on their effectiveness in the UK than any difficulty related to governance or socio-economics.

Uncertainty assessment

Uncertainty in operation of the responses

Considerable uncertainty exists regarding practically all aspects of future flood risk change and this includes the flood risk reductions that might be delivered by the responses considered in this chapter.

Scientific uncertainty concerns our lack of understanding of hydrological processes and imperfect ability to describe the physics of flooding mathematically. However, uncertainty does not stem only from limited scientific knowledge and must be more broadly defined. Following the Wynne (1992) categorisation of

Table 24.7. The Wynne classification of uncertainty (modified from Wynne, 1992)

Uncertainty class	Definition	Example
Risk	Quantifiable probabilities	Probability of embankment failure under load during a storm event
True uncertainty	Known uncertainties, unknown probabilities	Effects of land management on flow partitioning and hence flood flows: i.e. we know that land management will affect partitioning between rapid and delayed runoff routes; we know that this will affect flood flows (making them worse or better according to where the management is located within the catchment), but we have yet to develop robust methods to quantify the degree to which land management will change those flood flows
Ignorance	Things that could be known but that are not yet known	Essentially: *we don't yet know what we don't know*
Indeterminacy	Things that could never be known, however much science is undertaken	Actor within a competent authority makes the wrong sequence of decisions in relation to management of an upstream storage scheme

uncertainty (Table 24.7), all the possible flood management responses will have uncertainties associated with them and these are not just scientific, but also non-scientific. For example, there will be uncertainty regarding whether, under a given scenario, there is likely to be a suitable competent authority to ensure that appropriate activities are undertaken when and where they are required for responses in a theme or group to be effective in reducing flood risk. Thus, questions of uncertainty are strongly linked to questions of governance, which are explored further in Chapter 27 of this volume.

In performing their tasks, specialists were instructed to be entirely frank concerning the degree of uncertainty concerning each response group and a section of the response description was earmarked for identification of those aspects of each response group that are most uncertain and, where scientific or governance-related uncertainty is great, for recommendations of what research should be undertaken to improve the situation.

Uncertainty was further considered in assessing the flood risk reductions that might be achieved by each response group under each of the Future scenarios. Experts expressed uncertainty by making upper- and lower-bound assessments of the effect on flood risk of the response group and entered these scores into the Responses Ranking Spreadsheet, alongside the best estimates.

Uncertainty in responses was then expressed using the same approach as that applied for driver impacts, with the upper-bound estimate being divided by the lower-bound score to define a geometric band of uncertainty for each response group under each scenario. The band widths were then grouped using the following tiers:

- high level of uncertainty – band width >1.5.
- medium level of uncertainty – band width between 1.1 and 1.5.
- low level of uncertainty – band width <1.1.

The results are shown in Table 24.8. For ease of comparison with the ranking results, the responses are listed in the same order as they appear in Table 24.6, so that the responses with the greatest potential to reduce flood risk are at the top.

While the levels of uncertainty associated with flood risk responses are generally lower than those identified in the driver analysis, there are a number of potentially

Table 24.8. Uncertainty associated with response groups (note: the order of response groups in this table reflects their flood risk ranks, as listed in Table 24.6) (Evans et al., 2004)

Rank	World markets	National enterprise	Local stewardship	Global sustainability
1	River defences	River defences	Land-use planning and management	Land-use planning and management
2	Coastal defences	Coastal defences	Flood proofing buildings	Catchment-wide storage
3	Flood proofing buildings	Reduce coastal energy	Individual damage avoidance	River defences
4	Reduce coastal energy	Re-align coastal defences	River defences	Coastal defences
5	Morphological coastal protection	Morphological coastal protection	Catchment-wide storage	Flood proofing buildings
6	Re-align coastal defences	Coastal defence abandonment	Pre-event measures	Rural conveyance
7	Real-time event management	Flood proofing buildings	Real-time event management	Re-align coastal defences
8	River conveyance	River conveyance	Engineered flood storage	Reduce coastal energy
9	Individual damage avoidance	Catchment-wide storage	Rural conveyance	Morphological coastal protection
10	Pre-event measures	Land-use planning and management	River conveyance	Engineered flood storage
11	Engineered flood storage	Engineered flood storage	Rural infiltration	Real-time event management
12	Land-use planning and management	Real-time event management	Manage urban runoff	Pre-event measures
13	Manage urban runoff	Pre-event measures	Flood water transfer	Individual damage avoidance
14	Flood water transfer	Rural conveyance	Coastal defences	River conveyance
15	Catchment-wide storage	Rural infiltration	Re-align coastal defences	Rural infiltration
16	River conveyance	Individual damage avoidance	Morphological coastal protection	Manage urban runoff
17	Rural infiltration	Manage urban runoff	Reduce coastal energy	Flood water transfer
18		Flood water transfer	Coastal defence abandonment	

Legend

Uncertainty band width: B (B = ratio of upper- to lower-bound estimates of flood risk impact multiplier)	Tint code
B ≥ 1.5	
1.5 > B ≥ 1.1	
B < 1.1	

effective responses for which uncertainty is high. Notable examples, which merit a high priority for research to reduce uncertainty, include:

- land-use planning and management;
- flood proofing buildings;
- catchment-wide storage;
- rural conveyance.

Sustainability analysis

Sustainability metrics

While the effectiveness of each response group in reducing flood risk is vital, their performance in terms of sustainability is just as important. In assessing sustainability the approach adopted drew on the government's guidance on sustainability (www.sustainable-development.gov.uk/indicators/index.htm) to support analysis of environmental and social impacts in addition to the economic ones addressed by strategic risk modelling in the Foresight Project. For this exercise, sustainability and uncertainty were disaggregated into a series of *metrics*, as detailed below:

Environmental quality: the impact on biodiversity, and the area and quality of habitats (cf. the UK Government's Sustainable Development Strategy Indicators R3, *Biodiversity in coastal/marine areas*; H12, *Rivers of good or fair quality*; H13, *Populations of wild birds*).

Cost effectiveness: the value for money of implementing the response option. This appraisal was, for most responses, based on expert judgement, with specialist teams making an overall judgement of economic cost-effectiveness relative to a benchmark response such as raising the height of flood embankments, for which cost data are available.

Social justice: the impact of action on different types of household, in particular the differential impact of the response on households with a relatively low income (E2, *Index of local deprivation*; H4, *Indicators of success in tackling poverty and social exclusion*; SDS indicators relating to social cohesion: T7, *Public understanding and awareness*; L1, *Number of local authorities with Local Agenda 21 strategies*; L3, *Community spirit*).

Robustness: the ability of the response actions to cope with uncertainty relating to scenario differences in socio-economic factors and climatic change. In addition to uncertainty concerning the potential for each response to deliver risk reductions in all four futures, there is additional uncertainty relating to unanticipated factors, including extreme events. While an option robust enough to be effective under all four socio-economic and climatic futures should also be able to accommodate some unanticipated factors, appraisal of a response group's capacity to cope with unforeseen or catastrophic events adds further confidence that it is likely to be worthwhile irrespective of what the future may hold.

Precaution: in addition to the environmental and socio-economic uncertainties already identified, this criterion relates also to the possibility of extreme events and to operational uncertainty in implementing the themes. Key factors in compliance with the precautionary principle are:

- support of science relating to the monitoring and early detection of hazards;
- identification of the capacity for environmental reversibility; and
- participatory involvement in policy making, that includes lay or local knowledge as well as input from specialists, and that considers the different values and priorities of different social groups.

426

Scoring sustainability metrics

Unlike other indicators provided in the scenario matrix (e.g. GDP, technological turnover times, etc.), issues related to sustainability embody important *value differences*. For example, sustainability in a local stewardship future would be conceived very differently from that in a world markets future. For this reason, the metrics were not defined in quantitative terms, but were scored on a positive/neutral/ negative scale of measurement. This still allows comparisons to be made across the responses and scenarios, and can also permit evaluations of some absolute degree to be made (i.e. a benchmark or threshold can be defined, not just relative or comparative measures). The scoring scale is summarised in Table 24.9 and described in detail in Table 24.10.

In the multi-criteria assessment of sustainability, the key question addressed by the specialist teams was,

'What would be the impact on each metric if the measures in the flood response group were implemented in a manner consistent with the opportunities and constraints appropriate to that scenario?'

In scoring the flood-risk impacts of those sustainability metrics that related to flood risk, the sequence of tasks completed by each specialist team was:

1. Score the proposed response group against all metrics, except cost-effectiveness.
2. Consider the likely feasibility and maximum spatial extent of the proposed response in relation to:
   • the current level of response including its spatial extent that may be included in the scenario;
   • public and private expectations under the given scenario;
   • the funding that might be available in the scenario to implement the proposed response group.
3. Given the expected reduction in flood risk and likely costs of achieving it, score the proposed response group for cost-effectiveness and modify other non-flood risk sustainability metrics if necessary.

Experts scored the metric impacts of response groups according to the $++$ to $--$ scale in Table 24.9 using descriptions in Table 24.10. The results were entered into the Response Ranking Spreadsheet using pull-down menus provided for the relevant cells. The spreadsheet automatically converted the numerical flood risk reduction scores entered in the previous part of this analysis into a $++$ to $--$ score, using the conversion scheme set out in Table 24.11. A facility was included in the Response Ranking Spreadsheet to display the results of the sustainability investigation as a series of radar diagrams or spider diagrams (see Fig. 24.1 for an example), which some response themes found particularly useful in their analysis.

The sustainability analysis was applied to response groups individually, rather than in the combined response groups given in Table 24.5. This was done so that information on the sustainability performance of individual response groups was retained and could be dealt with in detail in the qualitative analysis of the

Table 24.9. Scale of measurement for sustainability metrics

$++$	Very positive
$+$	Positive
0	Neutral/mixed
$-$	Negative
$--$	Very negative

Table 24.10. Descriptors for scoring sustainability metrics

Score	Robustness	Precaution	Social justice	Cost-effectiveness	Environmental quality
++	The action can be implemented in all four socio-economic/climate scenarios, and successfully addresses flood risk	Justifications for pursuing the response action (and alternatives), as well as its potential risks, are systematically and openly scrutinised. Although some risks associated with action are unknown, expert and local knowledge is sought to address ignorance in ongoing regulatory appraisal, including the strategic anticipation of serious events. Monitoring and hazard warning systems are in place for timely responses when concerns are identified. Values and concerns of different social groups are taken into full consideration	Action increases the capacity to deliver improved standards of social justice (fairness in distribution of benefits and costs, and in engagement), promptly, and with associated progressive re-evaluation	The action is highly cost-effective, with substantial net benefits	Action strongly enhances biodiversity, improves environmental quality (habitats, water quality)
+	The action can be implemented in all four scenarios	Risk assessments for the action and some ongoing monitoring activities are carried out; regulatory appraisal is timely	The action provides some capacity to deliver improved standards of social justice	The action is cost-effective, with some net benefits	Action has a positive effect on biodiversity and environmental quality
0	The effect of implementing the action is scenario independent	Existing precautionary approaches are adopted unchanged. No effect on society's ability to cope with uncertainties, including those relating to climate change	No deterioration of social justice	The action is marginally cost-effective	No effect on biodiversity indices or environmental quality measures
−	The action cannot adequately be implemented under one or more scenarios; or implementing the action has a mixed effect (social, economic or environmental) depending on the scenario	Implementation of response action is not accompanied by ongoing technological and regulatory appraisal of risks and benefits. Inadequate research into early warnings and a non-inclusive approach to information gathering restricts timely responsiveness to emerging concerns	The action reduces capacity to deliver minimum standards of social justice	The action is costly and benefits are very limited	Action causes some loss of biodiversity
− −	The action is impossible to implement under one or more scenarios; implementing the action has a strongly adverse effect under one or more scenarios	Implementation of response action has inadequate technological and regulatory appraisal of risks and benefits. Inadequate research into early warnings, limited information gathering, and failures in institutional communication means that risks are not understood until the costs and impacts are very severe	Action strongly reduces capacity to deliver minimum standards of social justice, causes measures of social justice to worsen	The action is costly, and benefits are unlikely to be realised	Action causes severe loss of biodiversity and negative impacts on habitats and water quality

Table 24.11. Conversion scheme for translating numerical flood risk reduction scores into ++ to -- scores

Flood risk reduction score: S	Equivalent metric impact score
S < 0.7	++
0.7 < S < 0.9	+
0.9 < S < 1.1	0
1.1 < S < 1.3	−
S > 1.3	−−

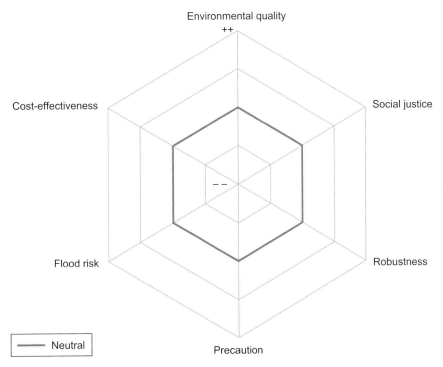

Figure 24.1. Sample radar plot or spider diagram used to present the results of scoring response groups according to selected sustainability metrics

responses (already presented in Chapters 18 to 23) as well as forming the basis for the broader treatment of sustainability presented in Chapter 26 of this volume.

Reference

Evans, E., Ashley, R., Hall, J., Penning-Rowsell, E., Saul, A., Sayers, P., Thorne, C. and Watkinson, A., 2004. *Foresight Future Flooding. Scientific Summary: Vol. II – Managing future risks*, Office of Science and Technology, London.

Wynne, B., 1992. 'Uncertainty and environmental learning: reconceiving science and policy in the preventive paradigm', *Global Environmental Change*, 2, 111–127.

Part 6
Assessment of flood risk responses

25 Quantitative assessment of future flood risk management portfolios in England and Wales

Paul B. Sayers, Jim W. Hall, Mike Panzeri and Robert Deakin

Introduction

The development of a risk assessment model capable of quantifying flood risk at national level is described in Chapter 13. The model, based on the most abstract of the RASP methods, the so-called RASP high-level method (HR Wallingford, 2004, Hall *et al*, 2003a), provides an ability to explore, at a national scale, future changes in flood risk. This represents a significant advance over earlier national scale methods (HR Wallingford, 2000).

Following the quantification of possible future changes in flood risk, assuming present-day flood management approaches remain unaltered in Chapter 13 (the so-called baseline case), this chapter considers how this might be changed through modified management practice and policy. Four portfolios of integrated flood risk management responses are considered (one associated uniquely with each Foresight future) and compared with the performance of a single-response approach based on an engineering-led solution.

Overview of the methodology

Standards of protection under the four Foresight futures

For each of the four future scenarios different target standards of flood protection and defence condition grade are defined (see Tables 25.1a and b). The standard of flood protection is to represent the total expectation of flood protection to be afforded by a combination of structural and non-structural responses.

The target standards of flood protection and condition grades reflect the different aspirations under each future scenario. Under world markets, for example, the level of protection afforded to an urban area is assumed higher than present-day, whereas the protection afforded to a rural area is assumed to reduce. The associated favoured management approach is to promote structural solutions (such as defence raising) to achieve these standards of protection. In contrast, a greater reliance is placed upon non-structural measures in Global Sustainability (such as

433

Table 25.1a. *Target standards of protection under the four future scenarios*

Land-use band	Comment	Present-day		World markets		National enterprise		Global sustainability		Local stewardship	
		Target SoP (fluvial)	Target SoP (coastal)	Target SoP (fluvial)	Target SoP (coastal)	Target SoP (fluvial)	Target SoP (coastal)	Target SoP (fluvial)	Target SoP (coastal)	Target SoP (fluvial)	Target SoP (coastal)
				Above present in urban areas. No new protection for agricultural areas		Above present in urban areas. Improved standard for agricultural areas		As present, apart from highest value urban areas. No new protection in low-grade agricultural areas		General reduction in standard, apart from highest value urban areas, where standard is maintained	
A*	Where legislation takes precedence over SoP, the current legislation will be assumed under the future scenarios	200	1000	1000	10 000	200	1000	1000	10 000	100	500
A	Typically large urban areas at risk from flooding	50–200	100–300	200	500	200	500	100	200	50	100
B	Typically less extensive urban areas with some high grade agricultural land	25–100	50–200	100	200	100	200	50	100	25	50
C	Typically large areas of high grade agricultural land at risk from flooding and impeded drainage with some properties also at risk from flooding	5–50	10–100	10	25	25	50	10	25	10	25
D	Typically mixed agricultural land with occasional, often agricultural related, properties at risk from flooding. Agricultural land may be prone to flooding or waterlogging	1.25–10	2.5–20	No new protection	No new protection	5	10	No new protection	No new protection	5	10
E	Typically low grade agricultural land, often grass, at risk from flooding or impeded land drainage, with isolated agricultural properties at risk from flooding	1–2.5	1–5	No new protection	No new protection	3	5	No new protection	No new protection	No new protection	No new protection

Standard of Protection (SoP) is defined as the return period (in years) of the storm event that is likely to overtop a given defence.

Table 25.1b. Target defence condition grades under the four future scenarios

Land-use band	Comment	All Scenarios
		Target condition grade (Cg) (fluvial and coastal)
		% distribution of Cg in urban areas (protection in agricultural areas remains in present-day conditions)
A*	Where legislation takes precedence over SoP, the current legislation will be assumed under the future scenarios	Cg 1 = 30% Cg 2 = 50% Cg 3 = 20% Cg 4 = 0% Cg 5 = 0%
A	Typically large urban areas at risk from flooding	Cg 1 = 10% Cg 2 = 30% Cg 3 = 45% Cg 4 = 15% Cg 5 = 0%
B	Typically less extensive urban areas with some high-grade agricultural land	Cg 1 = 10% Cg 2 = 30% Cg 3 = 45% Cg 4 = 15% Cg 5 = 0%
C	Typically large areas of high-grade agricultural land at risk from flooding and impeded drainage with some properties also at risk from flooding	Cg 1 = 0% Cg 2 = 20% Cg 3 = 55% Cg 4 = 25% Cg 5 = 0%
D	Typically mixed agricultural land with occasional, often agricultural related, properties at risk from flooding. Agricultural land may be prone to flooding or waterlogging	No change from present-day (2002)
E	Typically low-grade agricultural land, often grass, at risk from flooding or impeded land drainage, with isolated agricultural properties at risk from flooding	No change from present-day (2002)

Condition grade describes the structural condition of a defence ranging from Cg = 1 (as-built condition) to Cg = 5 (near collapse).

435

improved flood warning and evacuation procedures) but with the aim of providing similar overall standards of protection.

Quantifying the change in flood risk associated with each portfolio of responses

Each response either influences the probability of flooding or the associated consequences. It has therefore been possible to group the wide range of possible responses based on the way they influence flood risk. Their collective influence has then been characterised through a change in one of the primary input parameters to the RASP HLM risk analysis model as shown in Table 25.2.

Estimating the cost of implementing each portfolio of responses

Each response portfolio seeks to reduce risk through a combination of both structural and non-structural measures. It has not been possible to estimate the *true* costs of implementing the combination of measures proposed within each scenario (the costing of the non-structural measures at a high level is particularly problematic). The costs have, therefore, been based on the investment required to implement the engineering component of the portfolio (as described in Box 25.1).

The cost assigned to each portfolio therefore reflects the reliance placed on structural responses to address the residual risk not addressed by the non-structural measures[*].

The degree to which structural solutions feature within each scenario reflects three issues:

- The reduction in the defence standard and condition observed under the baseline assumption for each scenario.
- The degree of urbanisation of floodplain under each scenario (as structural solutions are typically associated with urban areas).
- The emphasis placed upon structural flood risk mitigation measures within each scenario.

Given knowledge of these, the relative investment requirements have been established based on a number of assumptions concerning the cost of modifying the defence infrastructure, namely:

- The defence infrastructure is upgraded on its present alignment.
- Improvements in defence standards are achieved through raising them (rather than construction of major infrastructure, such as barriers, barrages or offline storage).
- Within any flooding system (defined as a self-contained floodplain and associated defences) *all* defences are raised to the same target standard of protection.
- The cost of maintaining the defences over time (and in some cases rebuilding due to failure in structural condition) is not considered.
- The costs are assumed to be the one-off capital costs of raising the defence to the required standard.
- All costs are considered as present-day costs and both inflation and discounting are excluded.

---

[*] When reviewing the results presented, it is important to note that implementation costs associated with the non-structural solutions, although extremely difficult to estimate and not included here, would be significant and not come free.

Table 25.2. Translating flood risk management responses to parameters used by the RASP HLM national-scale modelling tool

Response theme	Responses group		RASP parameter	Impact in world markets	Impact in national enterprise	Impact in global sustainability	Impact in local stewardship
Managing the rural landscape	Water retention and management of infiltration into the catchment	1	Standard of protection (SoP)	No change	No change	SoP increased by 5% of difference between present-day and GS scenario in the baseline case	No change
	Water retention through catchment-storage schemes	2	Standard of protection (SoP)	No change	SoP increased by 20% of difference between present-day and NE scenario in the baseline case	SoP increased by 40% of difference between present-day and GS scenario in the baseline case	SoP increased by 20% of difference between present-day and LS scenario in the baseline case
	Managing conveyance	3	Standard of protection (SoP)	No change	No change	SoP increased by 30% of difference between present-day and GS scenario in the baseline case	No change
Managing the urban fabric	Increase storage in urban areas	4	Standard of protection (SoP)	SoP increased by 5% of difference between present-day and WM scenario in the baseline case	SoP increased by 9% of difference between present-day and NE scenario in the baseline case	SoP increased by 12% of difference between present-day and GS scenario in the baseline case	SoP increased by 13% of difference between present-day and LS scenario in the baseline case
	Increase infiltration in urban areas	5	Standard of protection (SoP)	No change	No change	SoP increased by 25% of difference between present-day and GS scenario in the baseline case	No change
	Manage conveyance of land surface	6	Reduced expected annual damage (EAD)	No change	No change	EAD reduced by 9%	EAD reduced by 4%
Managing flood events	Pre-event measures	7	Reduced damages and fewer people at risk	EAD (residential and commercial) reduced by 9% in all areas. 5% reduction in people at high risk	EAD (residential and commercial) reduced by 6%	EAD (residential and commercial) reduced by 12%	EAD (residential and commercial) reduced by 9%
	Real-time forecasting and warning	8	Reduced damages and fewer people at risk	EAD (residential and commercial) reduced by 10% in all areas. 5% reduction in people at high risk	EAD (residential and commercial) reduced by 6%	EAD (residential and commercial) reduced by 12%	EAD (residential and commercial) reduced by 10%

Table 25.2. Continued

Response theme	Reponses group	RASP parameter	Impact in world markets	Impact in national enterprise	Impact in global sustainability	Impact in local stewardship
Managing flood events – continued	9 Flood fighting: actions to manage flood waters and defences during the event	Standard of protection (SoP)	SoP increased by 19% of difference between present-day and WM scenario in the baseline case	SoP increased by 14% of difference between present-day and NE scenario in the baseline case	SoP increased by 20% of difference between present-day and GS scenario in the baseline case	SoP increased by 19% of difference between present-day and LS scenario in the baseline case
	10 Collective-scale damage-avoidance actions	Number of people at risk and EAD	Reduce the number of people at high risk of flooding by 5% in all areas. No change in EAD	Reduce the number of people at high risk of flooding by 7%	Reduce the number of people at high risk of flooding by 14% in all areas. No change in EAD	Reduce the number of people at high risk of flooding by 13%
	11 Individual-scale damage-avoidance actions	Reduced damages	14% of uptake of measures which reduce the damages by 80% during events of less than 0.5 m	EAD (residential and commercial) reduced by 8%	20% of uptake of measures which reduce the damages by 80% during events of less than 0.5 m	EAD (residential and commercial) reduced by 25%
Managing flood losses	12 Reduce current exposure to flood loss through land-use management	Changed property distribution	No change	No change	5% decrease in existing properties within the IFM	5% decrease in existing properties within the IFM
	13 Reduce current exposure to flood loss through flood proofing	Reduced damages to existing properties	10% take up of flood proofing (by property no.) and is 70% effective in reducing damages for inundation to depths up to 0.5 m	5% take up of flood proofing is 50% effective in reducing damages for inundation to depths up to 0.5 m	30% take up of flood proofing is 70% effective in reducing damages for inundation to depths up to 0.5 m	20% take up of flood proofing is 50% effective in reducing damages for inundation to depths up to 0.5 m
	14 Limit increase in exposure to flood loss through land-use planning	Changed property distribution	10% reduction in new properties built within the IFM above those assumed in baseline case	25% reduction in new properties within the IFM	75% reduction in new properties within the IFM	75% reduction in new properties within the IFM
	15 Limit increase in exposure to flood loss through changing building codes and construction practices	Reduced damages to new properties	20% take up of improved building codes which are 70% effective in reducing damages for inundation at depths up to 1 m	20% take up of improved building codes which are 50% effective in reducing damages for inundation at depths up to 1 m	90% take up of improved building codes which are 70% effective in reducing damages for inundation at depths up to 1 m	20% take up of improved building codes which are 50% effective in reducing damages for inundation at depths up to 1 m
	16. Blank					
	17. Facilitate economic and financial recovery from flood loss					

18.	Engineering and other large-scale interventions (fluvial)	Lessen the health, social and practical impacts of flooding (excluded from the quantified analysis)					
19		Increase conveyance or flow passed downstream	Standard of protection (SoP)	Major engineering schemes undertaken to meet new SoP targets through increased conveyance accounting for 33% of the overall defence length	Major engineering schemes undertaken to meet new SoP targets through increased conveyance accounting for 26% of the overall defence length	Major engineering schemes undertaken to meet new SoP targets through increased conveyance accounting for 26% of the overall defence length	Major engineering schemes undertaken to meet new SoP targets through increased conveyance accounting for 12% of the overall defence length
20		Increase storage	Standard of protection (SoP)	Engineering schemes undertaken to meet new SoP targets through provision of increased storage account for 19% of the overall defence length	Engineering schemes undertaken to meet new SoP targets through provision of increased storage account for 18% of the overall defence length	Engineering schemes undertaken to meet new SoP targets through provision of increased storage account for 26% of the overall defence length	Engineering schemes undertaken to meet new SoP targets through provision of increased storage account for 29% of the overall defence length
21		Flood-water transfer	Standard of protection (SoP)	Flood-water transfer schemes undertaken to meet new SoP targets account for 6% of the overall defence length	Flood-water transfer schemes undertaken to meet new SoP targets account for 5% of the overall defence length	Flood-water transfer schemes undertaken to meet new SoP targets account for 2% of the overall defence length	No change
22a		Physical barriers	Standard of protection (SoP)	37% of defences raised to meet new SoP targets	34% of defences raised to meet new SoP targets	26% of defences raised to meet new SoP targets	24% of defences raised to meet new SoP targets
22b		Re-alignment	Standard of protection (SoP) and reduced damages	5% of defences re-aligned (40% of which is within land-use band D and 60% within band E)	7% of defences re-aligned (67% of which is within land-use band D and 33% within band E)	20% of defences re-aligned (4% of which is within land-use band A, 7% within band B, 15% within band C, 30% within band D and 44% within band E)	15% of defences re-aligned (distributed equally across bands A to E, i.e. 20% per band)
22c		Abandonment	Standard of protection (SoP) and reduced damages	No defences abandoned	10% of defences abandoned (67% of which is within land-use band D and 33% within band E)	No defences abandoned	20% of defences abandoned (3% of which is within land-use band B, 14% within band C, 28% within band D and 55% within band E)

439

Table 25.2. Continued

Response theme	Responses group		RASP parameter	Impact in world markets	Impact in national enterprise	Impact in global sustainability	Impact in local stewardship
Engineering and other large-scale interventions (coastal and estuarial)	23	Physical barriers	Standard of protection (SoP)	75% of defences raised to meet new SoP targets	65% of defences raised to meet new SoP targets	50% of defences raised to meet new SoP targets	50% of defences raised to meet new SoP targets
Engineering and other large-scale interventions (coastal and estuarial) – continued	24	Re-alignment of flood defence infrastructure	Standard of protection (SoP) and reduced EAD	5% of defences re-aligned (40% of which are in land-use band D and 60% within band E)	7% of defences re-aligned (67% of which are in land-use band D and 33% within band E)	20% of defences re-aligned (4% of which are in land-use band A, 7% within band B, 15% within band C, 30% within band D and 44% within band E)	15% of defences re-aligned (distributed equally across bands A to E, i.e. 20% per band)
	25	Reduce energy	Standard of protection (SoP)	15% of coastal defences improved to SoP targets	15% of coastal defences improved to SoP targets by energy modulation	20% of coastal defences improved to SoP targets by energy modulation	5% of coastal defences improved to SoP targets by energy modulation
	26	Morphological protection	Standard of protection (SoP)	5% of coastal defences improved to SoP targets by morphological protection	3% of coastal defences improved to SoP targets by morphological protection	10% of coastal defences improved to SoP targets by morphological protection	5% of coastal defences improved to SoP targets by morphological protection
	27	Abandonment	Standard of protection (SoP) and reduced EAD	No defences abandoned	10% of defences abandoned (67% of which is within land-use band D and 33% within band E)	No defences abandoned	20% of defences abandoned (distributed equally across bands A to E, i.e. 20% per band)

EAD = expected annual damage: £

Box 25.1 Estimating the cost of structural responses

The cost associated with defence raising has been based on the Environment Agency's Unit Cost Database and information held by Defra. These were used to provide a total cost of construction for the key defence types described in the RASP HLM risk model. The cost estimates are shown in the table below and represent the typical total cost of constructing a new flood defence (including design and supervision costs but excluding any costs associated with land purchase or significant environmental mitigation measures).

Indicative cost of construction per kilometre of defence[1]

RASP HLM defence type	Comments	Average total cost/kilometre: £
Earth embankment	Typical cost	550 000
Culverts	Typical cost	2 000 000
Protected embankments and sea walls	Typical cost	2 700 000
Dunes	Management activities of planting/ fencing only, *not* replenishment	53 000
Shingle beaches	Includes the typical costs of associated structures such as groynes, breakwaters, etc., where part of scheme	5 100 000

Defences were raised, and costs incurred, where their future SoP (taking account of the projected climate change) and/or condition fell below the target standard appropriate for the Foresight future and land-use in the lee of the defence. The costs associated with raising the defences reflected the magnitude of the increase in the SoP required, as follows:

If SoP $\Leftarrow 0.2 \times$ Target SoP_{mid} then 100% base costs[2] applied.
If SoP is between 0.21 and 0.5 $\times$ Target SoP_{mid} then 40% base costs applied.
If SoP is between 0.51 and 0.75 $\times$ Target SoP_{mid} then 20% base costs applied.
If SoP is between 0.76 and 0.9 $\times$ Target SoP_{mid} then 10% base costs applied.
If SoP is between 0.91 and 1 $\times$ Target SoP_{mid} then 5% base costs applied.

In areas where there are currently no raised defences, the present-day ground level was used to assign an equivalent SoP. New raised defences, where required, were then constructed to achieve the future levels of protection and a cost, equivalent to 100% of the estimated rebuild cost for embankments, incurred.

The cost estimates reflect the capital expenditure required to raise current defences to meet the target SoP in each of the Foresight futures and exclude maintenance and non-structural costs. In particular, there is no attempt to construct a time series of costs and damages avoided and further work would be needed to perform a cost–benefit analysis or to compare with present-day expenditure levels.

1 Experience from previous studies indicates that the estimates of costs are likely to contain significant uncertainties and would not be appropriate for detailed local comparisons without significant data improvement.
2 Base cost is the regionalised and factored (for new build or rebuild) cost of constructing a particular type of defence from the Unit Cost Database.

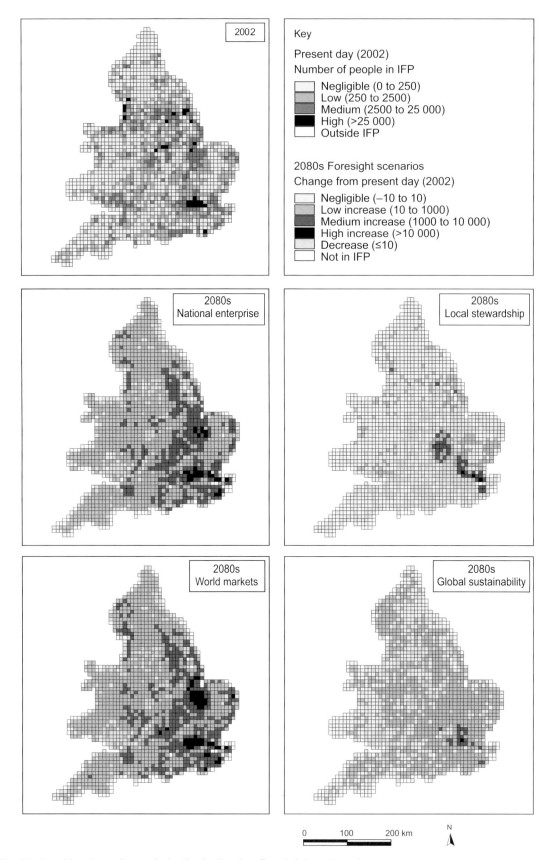

Fig. 25.1a. Number of people in the indicative floodplain – baseline case

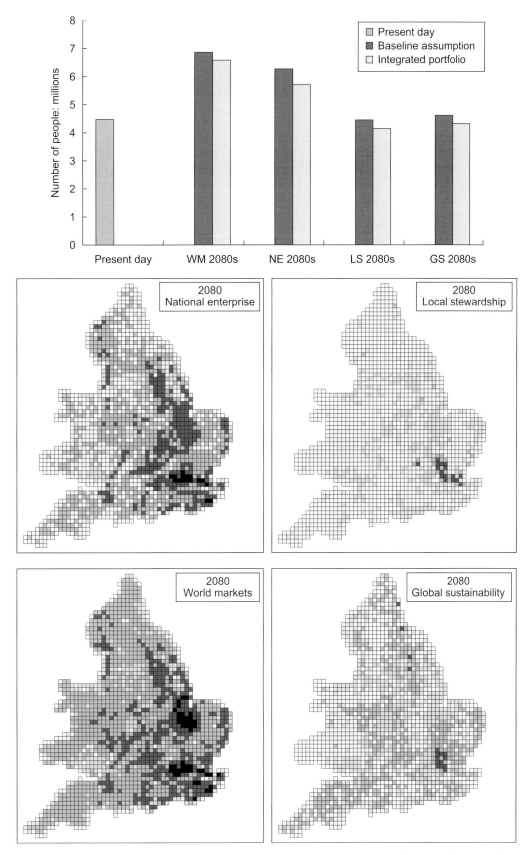

Fig. 25.1b. Number of people in the indicative floodplain – response portfolios implemented

Future fluvial and coastal flood risk

How the results are presented

The future change in flood risk is presented in terms of the following measures:

- Annual probability of flooding.
- Number of people living within the floodplain (based on the underlying scenario assumptions).
- Number of people at high risk of flooding.
- Expected annual damage (residential and commercial properties).
- Expected annual damage (agricultural).
- Social flood vulnerability.

The geographical distribution of the risks, and their relative magnitudes, are displayed through two distinct types of map which are colour coded as follows:

- Maps primarily using shades of blue represent total values of risk as estimated in 2002.
- Maps using a grey scale to represent changes in risk compared with present-day (2002). Progressively deeper shades of grey indicate progressively increased risk when compared to the 2002 risk assessment results. Light grey indicates reduced risk.

Two sets of maps are presented for each risk measure: one showing the baseline management case and the other showing the change assuming implementation of the portfolio of responses established for each Foresight future.

Changes in the number of people living within the floodplain

The total number of people living within the indicative floodplain (IFP) has been modified to take account of the influences of regulation and land-use planning proposed under each response portfolio (Fig. 25.1). Perhaps most striking is our inability to reduce occupancy of the floodplain, with a maximum of a 10% reduction observed in the global sustainability and local stewardship futures. This reflects the inertia within the system and difficulty in reducing floodplain occupancy below present-day levels. The findings of the analysis are discussed in Table 25.3.

Expected annual probability of inundation

The expected annual probability of inundation from flooding estimated under the baseline case (Fig. 25.2a) has varied, reflecting the effectiveness of the integrated portfolios of responses as outlined in Tables 25.1 and 25.2 (Fig. 25.2b). The findings of the analysis are discussed in Table 25.4.

Number of people exposed to 'frequent flooding' flood risk

This provides a count of the total number of people exposed to a probability of flooding greater than one in 75 in any one year. The results are reproduced in Figs 25.3a (baseline case), and 25.3b (for the integrated portfolio of responses). The findings of the analysis are discussed in Table 25.5.

Expected annual damage: residential and commercial properties

The expected annual damage estimated under the baseline scenarios has been modified to take account of the protection against flooding and the management of

Table 25.3. Discussion of plots – number of people within the indicative flood plain (Fig. 25.1)

Scenario	Interpreting the effectiveness of an integrated portfolio of responses
Present-day	The number of people within the IFP is indicative of the degree of urbanisation. As such we see significant numbers in Greater London, a corridor stretching from the Lancashire coast across to the Humber, areas along the Severn Estuary as well as smaller concentrations along the south-east coast and in the Midlands. The sparsely populated areas of the fenlands also stand out as having a significant number of people living in the IFP. This reflects the extensive nature of the IFP in East Anglia rather than the density of urbanisation
World markets 2080s	The limited regulation and unstructured land-use planning makes little impact on the number of people living within the IFP with the continued concentration of populations within large urban areas
National enterprise 2080s	Similar to world markets, regulation and land-use planning play a limited role within the context of an integrated management response. Hence, limited difference is observed between the baseline and integrated response scenarios
Local stewardship 2080s	The improved land-use planning – albeit largely *ad hoc* – reflects in a 10% decrease in the number of people within the IFP compared to the baseline case
Global sustainability 2080s	The more structured and integrated land-use planning and regulatory instruments are seen to achieve a 10% decrease in the number of people within the IFP compared to the baseline case

its impacts proposed under each integrated portfolio of responses (Figs 25.4a and b). The findings of the analysis are discussed in Table 25.6.

Expected annual damage: agriculture

The expected annual damage to agricultural land, estimated for the baseline case, has been re-assessed to take account of the revised flood management responses in each of the Foresight futures. The findings of the analysis are discussed in Table 25.7.

Social vulnerability to flooding

Social vulnerability is the most difficult risk metric to estimate and interpret. It combines both a notion of a community's social vulnerability – in terms of wealth, health and age – with their ability to respond and recover from flooding. A spatial representation of the effectiveness of different approaches using current techniques to characterise social vulnerability (based on the Social Flood Vulnerability Index derived by the Flood Hazard Research Centre, Middlesex University) reveals little due to the local complexity and therefore has not been included here. The interested reader is referred to Tapsell *et al.* (2002) for further discussion of the social vulnerability to flooding.

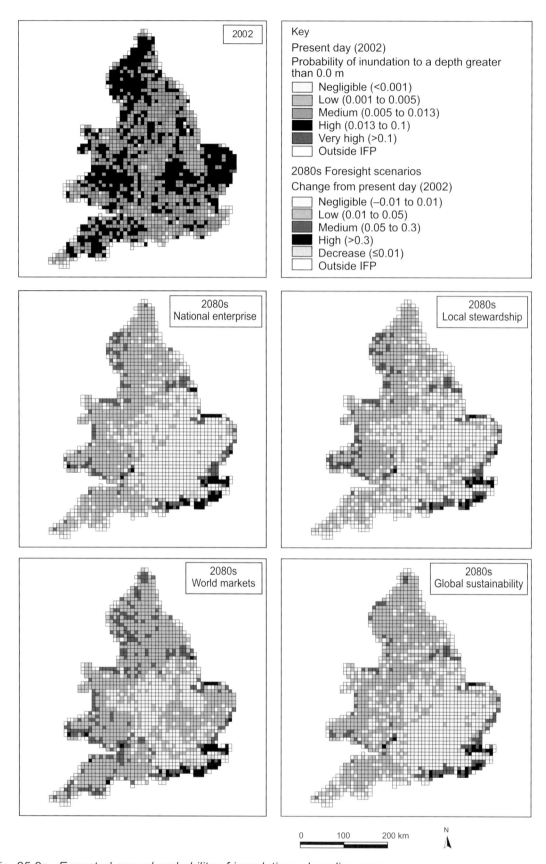

Fig. 25.2a. Expected annual probability of inundation – baseline case

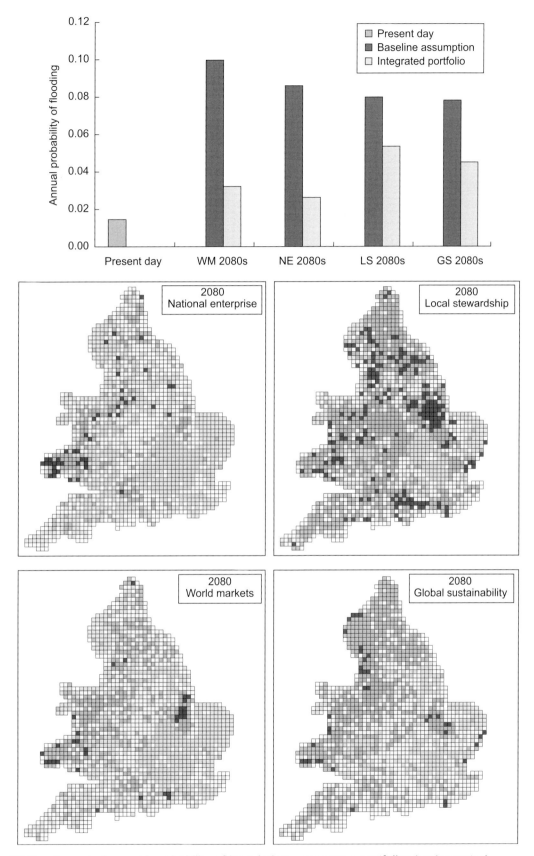

Fig. 25.2b. Expected annual probability of inundation – response portfolios implemented

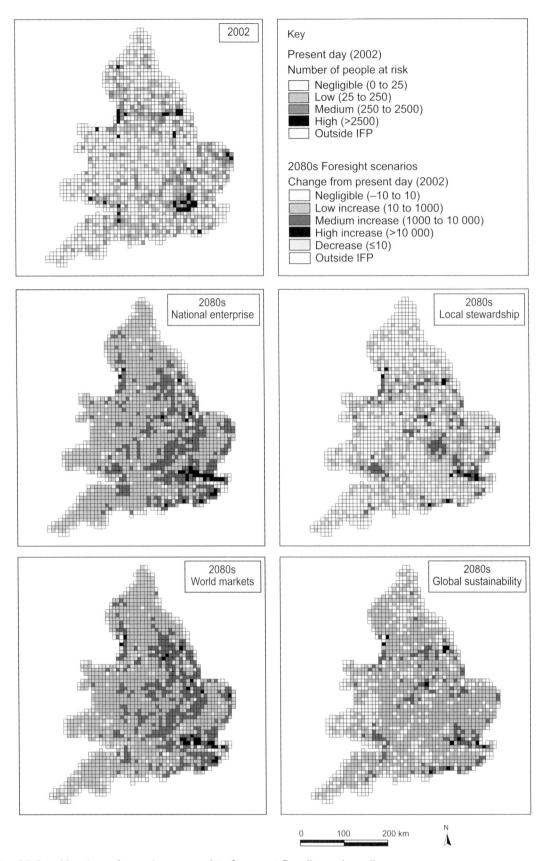

Fig. 25.3a. Number of people exposed to frequent flooding – baseline case

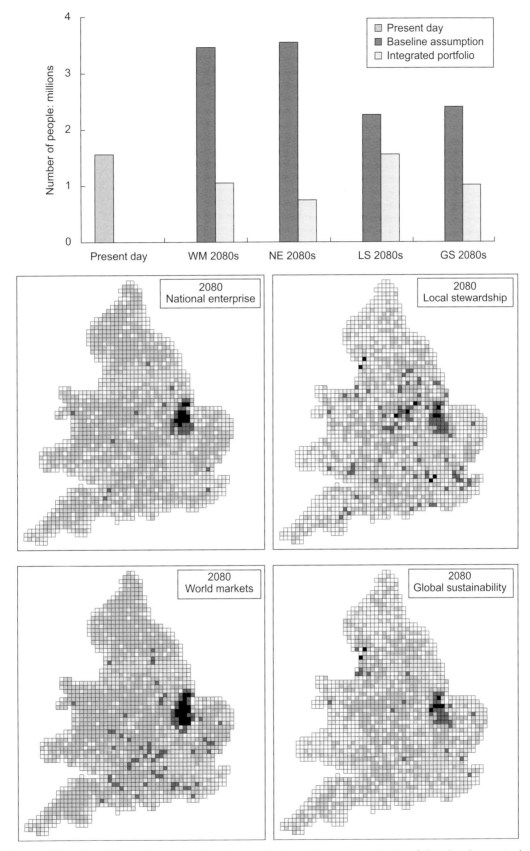

Fig. 25.3b. Number of people exposed to frequent flooding – response portfolios implemented

Table 25.4. Discussion of plots – expected annual probability of flooding (Fig. 25.2)

Scenario	Interpreting the effectiveness of an integrated portfolio of responses
Present-day	Generally the areas exposed to a higher probability of inundation are those in the north of England, along the east coast, mid Wales and the south-west of England (Fig. 25.2a). The high defence standards fronting the floodplains of the Wash, south Midlands, London and a number of specific coastal locations (for example north Wales) are reflected in a low probability of flooding in these locations
World markets 2080s	The significant investment in defence infrastructure proposed under this scenario, and the significant protection afforded to urban areas through the high target standards of protection (Table 25.1), yields a significant and widespread reduction in the probability of flooding. In particular, areas containing the major conurbations, for example the Thames and Humber corridors, are afforded significantly improved protection. In contrast, more rural areas, particularly those around the Wash (that are currently afforded a high degree of protection for agricultural reasons) experience increased flood frequencies. In general, the investment in coastal defences is successful in combating the potential for increased coastal flooding due to climate change
National enterprise 2080s	As under the world markets scenario, a significant emphasis is placed upon reducing flood probability rather than managing flood losses. This emphasis is again reflected in a significant decrease in flood frequencies showing a similar pattern to that observed in the world markets
Local stewardship 2080s	The management of flood risk under this scenario is mixed. All land-use types receive some level of protection and in many rural areas this translates to providing for greater protection from flooding than provided today. Exceptions to this include areas that are presently well protected but are more sparsely populated. Highly urbanised areas continue to receive protection from flooding to a similar or marginally improved standard when compared to present-day
Global sustainability 2080s	A balanced range of measures covering both structural responses (aimed at reducing flood frequency) and non-structural measures (targeted towards reducing the impacts of flooding) are considered. This yields a less dramatic reduction in flood probability than observed under the other scenarios when compared to the baseline assumption. Significant improvements can, however, be observed in the coastal strip and the major conurbations lining the Thames and the Humber estuaries. If the emphasis on structural measures were to be increased, and standards increased to those adopted in world markets, a further large reduction in flood probability would be possible

Table 25.5. Discussion of plots – number of people exposed to frequent flooding (Fig. 25.3)

Scenario	Interpreting the effectiveness of an integrated portfolio of responses
Present-day	Many of the areas with a high probability of inundation are rural and contain relatively few people. The most significant contributions therefore come from discrete, less well protected, urban areas that expose large numbers of people to frequent flooding. These include parts of the Thames Valley and the Lancashire to Humber corridor among others
World markets 2080s	Reflecting the high level of protection afforded to urban areas, the number of people at high risk significantly reduces relative to the baseline (by approximately 70% from 3.5 million to 1 million). The number of people at risk in the extensive rural floodplains of East Anglia, however, increases compared to the baseline scenario
National enterprise 2080s	As under the world markets scenario, the emphasis placed upon reducing flood probability leads to a substantial decrease (80%) in the number of people at high risk (from 3.5 million to 800 000). The moderate improvement over world markets reflects the protection of rural as well as urban areas
Local stewardship 2080s	The change in the number of people at high risk reflects the pattern of changing flood probabilities and reduces by approximately 20% compared to the baseline (from 2.3 million to 1.5 million – equivalent to present-day levels of exposure)
Global sustainability 2080s	The protection provided to the major conurbations reduces the number of people at high risk by approximately 60% compared to the baseline (from 2.4 million to 1 million). Both major conurbations and more sparsely populated rural areas receive an improved level of protection

Results of the investment analysis

The need for structural solutions to supplement the non-structural measures reflects the relative reliance placed upon structural and non-structural responses within each of futures. Within each future the structural responses are used to *top-up* the standard of protection against flooding to the defined target standards following implementation of the non-structural responses.

Table 25.8 summarises the investment costs associated with implementing the structural components of each of the integrated portfolios of responses. As expected, the results show a striking contrast in the level of investment in defences between the 'protection'-led approaches adopted in world markets and national enterprise (requiring nearly £80 billion capital investment in defence raising) compared to the more 'management'-led approach adopted in global sustainability (requiring a significantly more limited investment in defence infrastructure of £20 billion). Under local stewardship, the less ambitious targets for flood protection

451

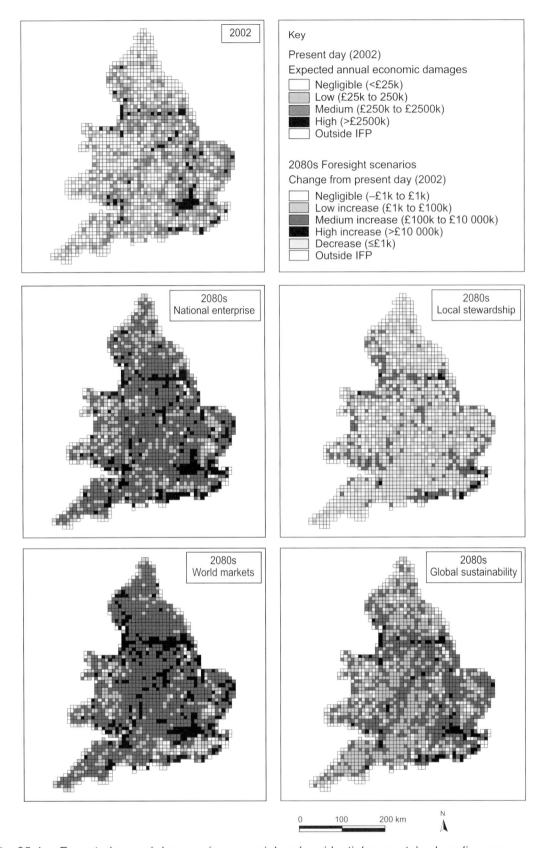

Fig. 25.4a. Expected annual damage (commercial and residential property) – baseline case

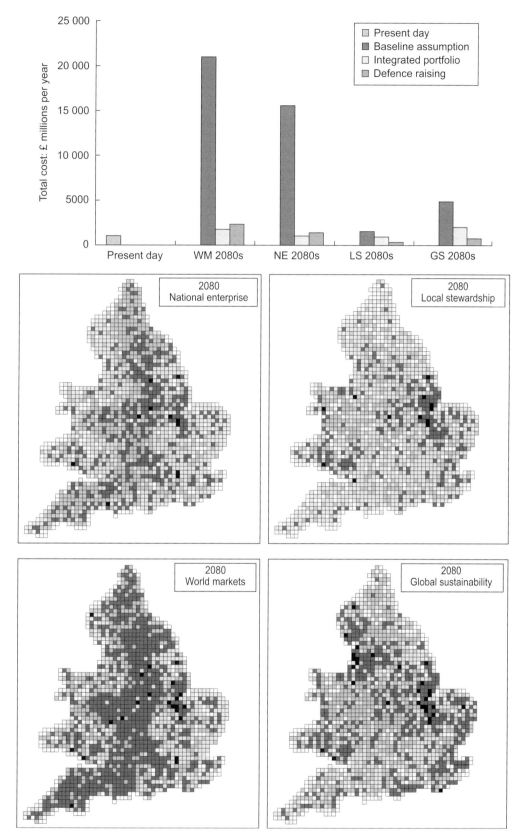

Fig. 25.4b. Expected annual damage (commercial and residential property) – response portfolios implemented

Table 25.6. Discussion of results – interpretation of expected annual damage: residential and commercial properties (Fig. 25.4)

Scenario	Interpreting the effectiveness of an integrated portfolio of responses
Present-day	The principal contributions to the national exposure to economic damage are associated with a limited number of areas of high economic importance. In particular, these include Greater London, the south-east coast, parts of East Anglia, along the Severn Estuary and the corridor from the Lancashire coast to the Humber
World markets 2080s	The pattern of economic damage provides a striking contrast to the baseline case (exhibiting a reduction of 90% in the expected annual damage from £21 billion to £1.8 billion). The major urban conurbations stand out as exhibiting a significant reduction in their exposure to flood damages, reflecting the raised defence standards. Elsewhere the exposure to economic damage is more evenly distributed than observed in the baseline case and leads to a clear divide in the level of exposure between those living within the cities and those in more rural communities. The natural tendency for coastal floodplains to be urbanised is reflected in the substantial investment in new defences (see Table 25.9) and the corresponding reduction in economic damages observed at the coast
National enterprise 2080s	Similar to the world markets scenario, adopting an integrated portfolio of management responses produces a large reduction in expected annual damage (from £15.5 billion to £1 billion – similar to present-day). The continued protection of both urban and rural areas is reflected through a dramatic decrease in risk when compared to the baseline case in the Thames, Humber and Severn estuaries as well as in a number of less-densely populated areas
Local stewardship 2080s	Under the baseline management scenario, economic damage is widely distributed. This remains the case following implementation of the integrated portfolio of responses. Key changes, however, include a reduction in coastal damage and the increase in damages expected in the areas of the East Anglian fens that are at present well protected – a level of protection that would be reduced under this scenario
Global sustainability 2080s	A reduction in expected damages is observed in the major conurbations. This reduction is most striking in the Thames, Humber and Severn estuaries. The implementation of measures to manage flood losses and the effectiveness of land-use management also delivers a significant reduction in damage in less urbanised areas when compared to the baseline case. As under the other scenarios, the fens experience an increase in risk reflecting the reduced protection afforded to rural areas

Table 25.7. Discussion of results – expected annual damage to agriculture

Scenario	Interpreting the effectiveness of an integrated portfolio of responses
Present-day	Expected agricultural damages are relatively evenly distributed across England and Wales. The most striking exception is in the vicinity of the Wash, where large areas of Grade 1 agricultural land lie within the floodplain and, although well protected, significant risk remains. A number of smaller areas also stand out as exhibiting high agricultural risk; including parts of the south coast and north-west. The areas of poorer agricultural land (Dartmoor, west Wales, Pennines, etc.) are categorised as low risk while the major built-up areas (London, Birmingham, etc.) exhibit negligible exposure to agricultural damages, reflecting the limited agriculture in these areas
World markets 2080s	Implementing an integrated portfolio of measures dramatically reduces the expected annual damage of £35 million (under the baseline case) to £12 million. The largest reductions occur in the south-west, Midlands and north-east. This reflects the improved defence standards for areas of high-grade agricultural land that sits within broader, well protected, urban areas (see, for example, the Humber and Thames estuaries). The key exception to this is in the heartland of the East Anglian fens, where the standards observed today are not maintained into the future
National enterprise 2080s	The implementation of a similar portfolio of responses as in world markets yields a similar reduction in agricultural damages
Local stewardship 2080s	Agricultural damage under the baseline assumption increases to £65 million per year by the 2080s. Although the implementation of a portfolio of measures is successful in reducing damage (by approximately 20%) the effectiveness has a distinct regional variation. Outside of East Anglia, agricultural damage is reduced by between 50 and 90%. Within the fens, however, the highly valuable grade 1 land sees a marked increase in the expected damage (up by 50% to £33 million p.a. – over half of the future national exposure)
Global sustainability 2080s	Implementing an integrated portfolio of measures has a mixed impact on agricultural damage. As in world markets, urban areas are well protected. This reflects in a decrease in agricultural damage compared to the baseline assumption in the majority of coastal floodplains and those on the outskirts of urban areas, such as those within the Thames and Humber estuaries. The use of non-structural measures to protect property and people within less-densely populated areas, however, provides for an increased flood probability and hence associated agricultural damage. This is demonstrated in the Midlands and the north-east where little change is observed over the baseline case

455

Table 25.8. The additional investment required in defences to 'top-up' the protection afforded by defences following implementation of non-structural responses

Region	Residual investment in defence raising: £m			
	World markets	National enterprise	Local stewardship	Global sustainability
East Anglia	20 846	19 967	6587	5314
Midlands	8106	8570	1263	1940
North-east	6354	6577	1637	1887
North-west	3922	4052	1215	1189
Southern	13 845	13 588	3586	4162
South-west	8943	9386	2305	2490
Thames	6835	7259	2612	3201
Wales	6790	7781	2908	2181
Total	75 641	77 180	22 113	22 364

and the mixed approach to flood risk management translate to an investment in defence infrastructure similar to that under global sustainability.

While these figures provide a broad feel for the scope of the financial investment needed in engineering solutions, it should be remembered that they all underestimate the full cost of implementing the various portfolios. For example, the costs of implementing non-structural responses are not included and these will be higher under the local stewardship and global sustainability scenarios when compared to world markets and national enterprise. This reflects the greater reliance on such measures. Additional costs associated with environmental mitigation measures are not included and could be substantial; particularly in the more environmentally sympathetic futures of global sustainability and local stewardship.

To provide further insight into the potential scale of investment required, a hybrid future scenario was also considered. Within this additional analysis the climate and demographic future associated with the global sustainability was linked to an engineering-led management style more associated with world markets and a target SoP similar to those currently adopted in England and Wales today. This engineering-based approach substantially reduces risk levels and succeeds in reducing the annual expected damages to around present-day values. Table 25.9 details the investment costs associated with this scenario broken down according to the type of works required. A crude comparison between the total investment in structural measures within this scenario (£52 billion) and the use of a portfolio approach adopted within the global sustainability future (£22 billion) demonstrates the large cost savings that an integrated approach can achieve – in addition to the wider benefits to the environment and its greater sustainability.

Table 25.9. Investment required to raise defences to achieve present-day standards in the 2080s under the global sustainability scenario

Floodplain type	New build	Sign. major works	Major works	Sign. minor works	Minor works	No works	Total investment: £m	Length of defence improved: km
Lowland valley	56%	27%	13%	4%	0%	0%	11 732	48 879
Steep valley	55%	30%	11%	4%	0%	0%	8141	36 383
Coastal	74%	20%	4%	1%	0%	0%	32 355	17 279
							52 228	102 541

Conclusions

The quantified national analysis provides a range of useful insights. The primary inferences are summarised below:

- Future flood risk can be managed if appropriately planned for. Depending upon the future climate and our adopted management preferences the investment cost will, however, vary significantly.
- Non-structural responses, used alongside more traditional structural approaches, can provide a significant contribution to reducing risk. This reinforces the notion that to manage flood risk effectively, the flood manager must utilise an integrated understanding of the drivers of flood risk and the wide range of possible responses (Sayers and Meadowcroft, 2002; Sayers et al., 2002; Hall et al., 2003b).
- The use of non-structural responses as part of an integrated portfolio can, in some cases, provide substantial cost savings – both economically and in broader environmental and social terms.
- The most striking potential for reducing flood risk through effective management is associated with the world markets future – from £20 billion p.a. in the baseline case to £1.8 billion p.a. Combined with an increase in wealth, this represents a considerable reduction in the impact of flooding on the economy. However, this comes with a high price to the environment, and the reliance on defence improvements raises considerable issues of sustainability.
- The costs of implementing the structural component of the response portfolios ranged from around £75 billion (world markets and national enterprise) down to £22 billion (global sustainability and local stewardship). This reflects the different levels of protection against flooding afforded in each scenario and also demonstrates a clear division between the investment in, and hence reliance upon, flood defences within world markets and national enterprise futures, and the mixed approaches adopted under the other two scenarios.
- Towns and cities are likely to become better protected under all futures; whereas protection for the less densely populated and rural areas is likely to decline in all futures.
- The agricultural heartland of the East Anglian fens, where the present-day defences afford a high degree of protection, experience a significant reduction in the SoP provided under all futures. This suggests that present practice and expectations in these areas will need to be reviewed.
- There is a marked inability to reduce the number of people living within the floodplain in all futures. This reflects the inertia within the housing sector and a reluctance to abandon existing housing under all futures.
- Achieving a low-emissions future could reduce flood risk by 25% assuming a high growth economy is maintained – a significant contribution to reducing flood risk but not a panacea.
- The RASP HLM modelling tool (and supporting datasets) have been shown to be a powerful tool in providing flood risk managers with useful quantified insights into future policy directions. Such quantified analysis is likely to be a key component of future evidence-based policy making and strategy planning.

References

Hall, J.W., Dawson, R.J., Sayers, P.B., Rosu, C., Chatterton, J.B. and Deakin, R., 2003a. 'A methodology for national-scale flood risk assessment', *Water and Maritime Engineering*, 156(3), 235–247.

Hall, J.W., Meadowcroft, I.C., Sayers, P.B. and Bramley, M.E., 2003b. 'Integrated flood risk management in England and Wales', *Proceedings of the American Society of Civil Engineers*, Natural Hazards Review.

HR Wallingford, 2000. National appraisal of assets at risk from flooding and coastal erosion, Technical Report volumes 1 and 2, HR Wallingford Report TR107.

HR Wallingford, 2004. Risk Assessment for flood and coastal defence for Strategic Planning – RASP. A Technical Summary. Environment Agency publication R&D Technical Report W5b-030/TR.

Sayers, P.B., Hall, J.W. and Meadowcroft, I.C., 2002. 'Towards risk-based flood hazard management in the UK', *Proceedings of ICE*, Civil Engineering 150, May, pp. 36–42.

Sayers, P.B. and Meadowcroft, I.C., 2002. 'Risk, performance and uncertainty in flood and coastal defence – a defining review', Proc. of the Defra Conf. of River and Coastal Management.

Tapsell, S.M., Penning-Rowsell, E.C., Tunstall, S.M. and Wilson, T.L., 2002. *Vulnerability to Flooding: Health and Social Dimensions*, Philosophical Transactions of the Royal Society London – Series A, Mathematical, Physical and Engineering Sciences, 360(1796), 1511–1525.

Part 7
Sustainability and governance

26 Sustainability of flood risk management responses

Andrew R. Watkinson, Sarah E. Cornell and Robert Tinch

This chapter explores the sustainability of the different flood risk response options (Chapters 18–23) in the four future scenarios – world markets, global sustainability, national enterprise and local stewardship. These scenarios have been used throughout the Foresight futures framework (OST, 2002). They are not predictions of the future, although all are plausible and none of the scenarios is regarded from the outset as being more likely than the others (Berkhout and Hertin, 2002; Berkhout et al., 2002). Today's world can be regarded as a mixture drawn from all the scenarios, so the four futures outlined provide a way to clarify present-day choices by exploring the consequences of alternative assumptions about how future society may develop.

A long-term view of sustainability

Sustainability guides the development of society in a way that 'meets the needs of the present without compromising the ability of future generations to meet their own needs', according to the widely used Bruntland definition (WCED, 1987). In this analysis, looking several decades into the future, it is important to emphasise that sustainability is about *present-day* decision making regarding local-scale and immediate development needs, yet incorporating a global and intergenerational perspective to tackle or avoid non-sustainability (Guimaraes, 2001). Much of the recent sustainability discourse relates to the definition of operational principles and indicators that set bounds on this non-sustainability. For instance, the UK government's 1999 *A Better Quality of Life* report (TSO, 1999) defines a set of guiding principles to be adopted consistently across departmental activities, followed up with over a hundred national and regional indicators to track progress (Defra, 1999; DETR, 2000).

As society changes, however, the ethos and principles underpinning sustainable development also evolve. This evolution can also be seen in the UK now. For instance, the government's strategy document, *Securing the Future* (TSO, 2005), addresses changes in nature and society in terms of a linked socio-ecological system, emphasising social learning and individual behaviour as the means for achieving sustainability, much more than in its 1999 strategy, which seemed to give precedence to economic growth. Projecting well into the future – as in this analysis – is necessary, because the timescales of climate change preclude 'short-term

461

sustainability', but it must be borne in mind that future sustainability will be about *future* decision making in its own contemporary context, which will differ from today's political, cultural and technological setting.

Sustainability is possible under the four scenarios, but the concept of sustainability is very different in each of them. The critical differences lie in the mechanisms for achieving sustainability and the (pre)conditions for them to work well. In world markets and global sustainability, the belief is that sustainability can be sought and achieved by 'top-down', large-scale strategic action (steered by the state in global sustainability, and driven by market or private mechanisms in world markets), whereas national enterprise and local stewardship emphasise local-scale decision-making, suggesting that sustainability would be constructed 'bottom-up' from many small-scale actions.

In this analysis, the measures of future sustainability have to be quintessential rather than operational and specific like today's indicators. Certain generic problems are known to arise from imbalances in the nature/society system (unfairness, economic inefficiencies, irreversible environmental damage and poor risk management), so we chose sustainability criteria that address these problems (see Chapter 24). In the following section, we provide an overview analysis of the responses, identifying which would best constitute the core of a robust and sustainable flood risk management portfolio. The remainder of this chapter explores in more detail what cost-effectiveness, environmental quality and social justice might mean under the four scenarios.

Sustainability implications of responses to flood risk

The assessments of individual responses described in earlier chapters (see Part 5) conclude that no single measure would effectively reduce flood risk on its own, and that many technically effective measures had serious negative impacts when assessed against sustainability criteria. Given the stark differences in world view in the four scenarios, it is not surprising that no individual response is expected to be effective in dealing with flood risk while meeting sustainability criteria across all four scenarios. However, several measures perform well across three of the four, and might thus be considered more robust to socio-economic and climatic change.

Fluvial and coastal zone

Table 26.1 indicates responses that produce a reduction in flood risk across at least three of the scenarios *and* carry no sustainability penalties in terms of cost-effectiveness, environmental quality or social justice. Social justice was often identified as a hurdle to sustainable flood management, so where responses fail on these grounds in just one or two scenarios, this is also indicated. The responses highlighted by the use of stars in the right-hand column are those policies that are effective in reducing flood risk across most scenarios, but some may require careful implementation because of issues over social justice or precaution. Note that these policies are not necessarily the most effective in reducing flood risk.

The ideal situation is where flood risk management options actually provide wider benefits – the win–win situation. Table 26.2 shows options that reduce flood risk under at least three scenarios *and* provide sustainability benefits across at least three scenarios. None of the responses produces win–win situations (++) across all three sustainability criteria, but catchment-wide storage, land-use planning and coastal defence re-alignment potentially produce environmental benefits and reduce flood risk, and any sustainability penalties could be accommodated with careful implementation.

Table 26.1. The flood response measures that result in a reduction in flood risk across at least three scenarios and which have no sustainability penalties (√) associated with a) cost, b) the environment or c) social justice. Responses marked with a single cross fail on social justice in one of the four scenarios, and responses marked with two crosses fail on social justice in two scenarios. Stars in column d indicate responses that pass all three sustainability criteria (★★★), all three sustainability criteria except for social justice in one scenario (★★), and all three sustainability criteria except for social justice in two scenarios (★)

Measure	Sustainability criteria			
	a) Cost-effectiveness	b) Environmental quality	c) Social justice	d) Overall
Rural infiltration				
Catchment-wide storage	√	√	√	★★★
Rural conveyance				
Urban storage				
Urban infiltration				
Urban conveyance				
Pre-event measures	√	√	√†	★★
Forecasting and warning	√	√	√†	★★
Flood fighting	√	√	√†	★★
Collective damage avoidance				
Individual damage avoidance	√	√	√†	★★
Land-use management				
Flood proofing	√	√	√††	★
Land-use planning	√	√	√	★★★
Building codes	√	√	√	★★★
River conveyance	√		√††	
Engineered flood storage	√		√††	
Flood-water transfer				
River defences	√		√†	
Coastal defences	√		√††	
Coastal defence re-alignment	√	√	√††	★
Reduce coastal energy		√	√††	
Morphological coastal protection		√	√	
Abandonment				

Table 26.2 also shows those options that raise concerns in their effectiveness in flood risk reduction and in meeting sustainability criteria: the lose–lose options (−−). Urban storage and flood-water transfer give particular cause for concern, followed by urban conveyance, urban infiltration, collective damage avoidance and rural land-use management.

Intra-urban zone

Only one response, urban area development, operation and form, failed significantly on the sustainability criteria in the judgement of the experts, and then only under the world markets scenario. In two scenarios, this response was effective and potentially beneficial in terms of the sustainability criteria. Table 26.3 highlights responses that performed particularly well across at least three scenarios in terms of flood risk reduction and incurred no sustainability penalties. These include main drainage form, maintenance and operation; storage above and below ground and, to a lesser extent, source control. However, the experts agreed that the success of these responses depends on how they are implemented.

Three responses (Table 26.4) reduce flood risk under at least three scenarios and provide benefits in cost-effectiveness or environmental quality, but again no

Sustainability and governance

Table 26.2. Win–win (++) and lose–lose (−−) responses for flood risk reduction and a) cost-effectiveness, b) environmental quality and c) social justice. Effective under at least three scenarios (++). Not effective under more than one scenario in reducing flood risk and incurring sustainability penalties (−−)

	a) Cost-effectiveness	b) Environmental quality	c) Social justice
Rural infiltration			
Catchment-wide storage		++	++
Rural conveyance			
Urban storage	−−		−−
Urban infiltration	−−		
Urban conveyance			−−
Pre-event measures	++		++
Forecasting and warning	++		++
Flood fighting	++		
Collective damage avoidance			−−
Individual damage avoidance			
Land-use management			−−
Flood proofing	++		
Land-use planning	++	++	
Building codes	++		
River conveyance	++		
Engineered flood storage	++		
Flood-water transfer		−−	−−
River defences	++		++
Coastal defences			
Coastal defence re-alignment	++	++	
Reduce coastal energy			
Morphological coastal protection		++	
Abandonment			

responses produce win–win situations across all three sustainability criteria. Two responses give cause for concern in their ability to reduce flood risk under more than one scenario, while also incurring sustainability penalties: building development, operation and form, and groundwater control.

Table 26.3. The flood response measures in the urban zone that produce a reduction in flood risk across at least three scenarios and which have no sustainability penalties (✓) associated with a) cost, b) the environment or c) social justice. Responses marked with a single cross fail on social justice in one of the four scenarios. Stars in column d indicate responses that pass all three sustainability criteria (★★★), and all three sustainability criteria except for social justice in one scenario (★★)

Measure	Sustainability criteria			
	a) Cost-effectiveness	b) Environmental quality	c) Social justice	d) Overall
Building development, operation and form				
Urban development, operation and form		✓	✓[†]	
Source control	✓	✓	✓[†]	★★
Groundwater control				
Storage above and below ground	✓	✓	✓	★★★
Main drainage form, maintenance and operation	✓	✓	✓	★★★

464

Table 26.4. Win–win (++) and lose–lose (−−) responses for flood risk reduction and a) cost-effectiveness, b) environmental quality and c) social justice. Effective under at least three scenarios (++). Not effective under more than one scenario in reducing flood risk and incurring sustainability penalties (−−)

	a) Cost-effectiveness	b) Environmental quality	c) Social justice
Building development, operation and form		−−	−−
Urban development, operation and form		++	
Source control		++	
Groundwater control		−−	
Storage above and below ground	++		
Main drainage form, maintenance and operation			

Cost-effectiveness

The appraisal of flood risk responses indicated only seven failures under the cost-effectiveness criterion across all four scenarios: urban storage, urban infiltration, morphological coastal protection, reduce coastal energy, urban development, operation and form and groundwater control. The main reason for the small number of failures is straightforward: because we evaluate each individual policy option on its merits, we are in effect looking at cost-effectiveness from the perspective of implementing only one policy; most of the policies would be better than nothing.

Costs will be a much more important consideration when several responses are used together, because the actual reduction in risk associated with any given addition to a mixture of responses will depend crucially on the other measures already included within it. The costs too might vary – at the extreme, some policy options may be mutually exclusive, but more generally one policy may influence both the costs and the effectiveness of another. Care will obviously be needed to avoid 'double-counting' of both costs and effectiveness when such interdependent policies are combined in a portfolio.

Cost-effectiveness of a portfolio of responses in the fluvial and coastal zone

The quantitative analysis for fluvial and coastal flooding (Chapter 25) determined the additional investment costs associated with achieving the new targets of standard of flood protection under each scenario in 2080 (Table 26.5). These costs do not include land purchase or the costs of the non-engineering responses, and can thus be regarded as a lower limit. Neither do they include ongoing maintenance or periodic replacement of defences, nor the increased cost of maintaining higher defences. In order to make some allowance for the latter we continue with today's baseline cost of approximately £500 million per year.

In summary, risks can be greatly reduced by implementing a portfolio of responses. The capital costs of implementation (all in 2004 prices) are higher in consumer-orientated scenarios (£76 billion for world markets, £77 billion in national enterprise) than in citizen-focused scenarios (£22 billion for global sustainability and local stewardship). This is due to differences in the target standards of flood protection, in the effectiveness of implementation of responses, and also in the pattern of socio-economic development in the different scenarios. In all scenarios except local stewardship, the benefits in terms of risk reduction clearly exceed the costs, even bearing in mind that the costs quoted are lower limits.

This summary does not consider the timing of expenditure, a potentially important factor. Sudden increases in expenditure may be needed for some responses

Table 26.5. Fluvial and coastal flood risks, expressed in terms of Expected Annual Damages (EAD), and management costs for England and Wales in the 2080s

	Present day	World markets	National enterprise	Local stewardship	Global sustainability
Flood risks					
Baseline case, EAD: £m/year	1040	20500	15100	1500	4860
Integrated portfolio – target standards of flood protection relative to present-day	1	2	2	0.75	1
Risks with integrated portfolio, EAD: £m/year		1760	1030	930	2040
Risk reduction, EAD: £m/year		18700	14000	570	2820
Flood management costs					
Total capital costs, England and Wales, fluvial and coastal: £m		75600	77200	22100	22400
Additional capital costs to achieve risk reduction: £m/year		1600	1600	500	500
Cost-effectiveness: benefit/costs		12	9	1	6
Baseline cost: £m/year	500	500	500	500	500
Total annual cost: £m/year	500	2100	2100	1000	1000

(Dlugolecki, 2004), but managing the response portfolio should allow for a gradual increase overall. Neither has any attempt been made to generate cost and benefit streams over time or to discount these in any way. Instead, the total capital costs have simply been divided by 50 to take some account of the asset life cycle.

To go further in the analysis of cost-effectiveness would require rather detailed analysis of decision-making processes over time under each scenario, alongside consideration of economic and environmental changes. In the absence of such a major research undertaking, the cost figures only provide an approximate indication of the different levels of physical defences required under each scenario, but in conjunction with the cost-effectiveness ratings of the response groups, they provide a starting point for consideration of portfolios of measures that might reduce the need to spend the identified costs on flood defence infrastructure.

Cost-effectiveness of a portfolio of responses in the intra-urban area

The analysis of the intra-urban area produced a less detailed picture of the risks and costs (Table 26.6) because of methodological constraints. Nevertheless, the analysis suggests that implementing a portfolio of responses substantially reduces risk in all scenarios, with the expected annual damages cut to approximately half the baseline. This is less than in the fluvial and catchment zones (Table 26.5) because of the non-linear relationship between flooding and the amount of water, demonstrating the difficulty of reducing damages within the urban zone even with substantially increased standards of protection. As for the fluvial and catchment zones, the benefits in terms of risk reduction clearly exceed the costs, except in the case of local stewardship, while the portfolios of responses in the national enterprise and global sustainability scenarios were more cost-effective than in the world markets scenario.

Wider costs and benefits

The cost-effectiveness considerations that we have been able to quantify are rather limited. Many potentially important costs and benefits were not included in the cost-effectiveness deliberations, particularly those relating to social and environmental impacts. Although these were partially considered in the sustainability analysis, the focus was on thresholds – is it sustainable or not? – rather than optimisation.

Table 26.6. Intra-urban flood risks, expressed in terms of Expected Annual Damages (EAD), and management costs for England and Wales in the 2080s

	Present day	World markets	National enterprise	Local stewardship	Global sustainability
Flood risks					
Baseline case, EAD: £m/year	270	7880	5055	740	1870
Residual risks with integrated portfolio, EAD: £m/year		4200	2400	490	720
Risk reduction, EAD: £m/year		3680	2655	250	1150
Flood management costs					
Additional costs to achieve risk reduction: £m/year		540	260	400	110
Cost effectiveness: benefit/costs		7	10	0.6	10

The wider costs and benefits associated with catchment-scale flooding and coastal defence take various forms (Table 26.7). Some are directly market related. For example, managed re-alignment will not simply result in the loss of the value of the inundated land – partially off-setting this, land values could rise along the new coast-line. Studies of property markets have shown that proximity to water features is highly valued while, on the other hand, visual intrusion can be an important source

Table 26.7. The wider costs and benefits associated with the five major response groups

Response group	Capital costs	Ongoing costs	Wider benefits	Wider costs
Managing the rural landscape	Yes – design, land take, construction	Yes – subsidies, administration, management costs, auditing (except for conveyance)	Potential substantial benefits – habitats, recreation, pollution control, interface with agricultural water resource use	Possible pressure on marginal land, inappropriate afforestation
Managing the urban fabric	Yes, probably significant	Usually moderate	Aesthetic use, recreation, habitat	Possible health impacts in some scenarios
Managing flood events	Minor/moderate	Yes	Communication, community cohesion, some non-flood benefits to agriculture (e.g. Irrigation efficiency)	
Managing flood losses	Yes for some measures	Yes, also opportunity costs (land-use change)	Reduced non-financial costs of flooding	Equity concerns, displaced development, moral hazard – reducing the incentive for people to make adequate provision or precautions
River and coastal engineering	Yes, high	Yes, small fraction of capital costs	Potential for habitat or biodiversity benefits, potential amenity benefits	Non-market values associated with land loss; environmental damage (possible habitat or biodiversity losses; altered natural processes); visual intrusion

of economic damage if flood defence barriers block sought-after waterside views (Bourassa *et al.*, 2004). Other costs or benefits could be measured using markets, though less directly. For example, the ecosystem's support function of certain coastal habitats has direct implications for the economic value of fisheries, although the links may be difficult to measure, and the potential values may not be realised due to over-exploited fisheries. Then there are environmental goods and services with even less quantifiable market links (biogeochemical functions, for example) or with substantial non-market values (aesthetic beauty, species conservation).

Attempting to determine values for all the effects shown in Table 26.7 would be a lengthy, expensive and difficult process even for today's policy options. Never-theless, some general suggestions can be made. One of the major impacts of most policies will be on land values (including land beneath structures, i.e. the land component of property value). For example, installing flood protection structures will increase the value of the land behind, and protected coastal and riverside properties will be among those experiencing some of the greatest value increases. Those actually using the land might not be the ones who benefit – in particular, the rental value for protected land will increase, so (after some period of adjustment) much of the benefit will pass to land owners.

Recreational use values can also be very significant (over and above values to residents, reflected in property prices). These values will vary with preferences, incomes and provision of substitutes. One observation is that the marginal value of high-quality environments for recreation might be especially high in the world markets scenario, where people are wealthy, possibly time-poor, not particularly concerned with environmental protection *per se*, but very concerned with their own consumption of environmental and other goods and services; and where economic growth may have taken a heavy toll on the number and quality of suitable environ-ments available. In local stewardship, there might be rather lower marginal values, because of greater provision and lower incomes. It is possible that these values could be significantly modified by preferences in the citizen-orientated worlds, perhaps with very high non-use values, as people care more about others' consumption, about future generations, and ultimately about the environment itself rather than as a mere adjunct to human desires.

The values and incidences of these wider costs and benefits in each scenario are extremely uncertain. Preferences, incomes, levels of economic activity and environ-mental provision are all uncertain; crucially, the physical, hydrological and ecological links between natural systems and the functions they provide to society are uncertain and often poorly understood. This underlines the importance of basic and more holistic research into the socio-ecological system (Carpenter *et al.*, 2001).

Environmental quality

Fluvial and coastal zone

Many of the more effective risk-reducing responses in the fluvial and coastal zones appear to have significant environmental (and other) penalties in more than one of the four scenarios (Table 26.1). Coastal defences fail on environmental grounds across all four scenarios, while river defences, river conveyance and engineered flood storage fail under the consumer-orientated scenarios. In contrast, other response strategies appear to both reduce flood risk and have environmental (and other) benefits across the range of futures (see Tables 26.1 and 26.2). These responses are creating catchment-wide storage along rivers, coastal defence re-alignment, land-use planning, and morphological coastal protection.

Coastal defence re-alignment and catchment-wide storage are two of the most notable examples of this type, because they also score consistently well under the other criteria. However, managed re-alignment fails on social justice under two scenarios (Table 26.1), indicating that its implementation (and, by implication, that of catchment-wide storage too) must be sensitive to these concerns. The environmental benefits of such schemes are not automatic; they also depend critically on the way that they are implemented.

Related to these two strategies for enhancing natural buffers against flooding, managing exposure to flooding by way of land-use planning also scores highly in terms of all the criteria. Proactive land-use planning of floodplain areas is essential to realising the full benefits of managed re-alignment and catchment-wide storage. Such planning would include:

- identifying floodplain areas where managed re-alignment and increased rural storage could have significant benefits in terms of reducing flood risk;
- preventing new development in these areas as an immediate aim; and
- in the longer term, encouraging abandonment of existing land-uses that limit the scope of appropriate areas being reverted to floodplain.

This demands an understanding of the benefits of these policies for reducing flood risk at the catchment, estuary and sub-cell/cell scale. While such research is beginning (Pethick, 2002), it needs considerable development before this approach can be operational within flood management.

Morphological protection along the coast is also consistent with managed re-alignment, as the concept is based on large-scale manipulation of the coastal configuration to more favourable shapes for reducing flood risk. Providing space for this adjustment often implies significant amounts of managed re-alignment. However, the science-base for this approach remains undeveloped, requiring considerable research before risk-reduction benefits can be estimated and the approach adopted on a wide scale. At a smaller scale, beach recharge and recycling are approaches that offer the potential to maintain natural beach habitats and flood defence functions in an environmentally sympathetic manner, as long as the source of the recharge material is also considered (HR Wallingford, 2004).

A key environmental threat identified across all four scenarios is the decline of freshwater coastal grazing marsh. Most grazing marshes are dependent on human management for their existence, and there are limited sites for replacement habitat within the coastal zone. Large net losses would be expected due to a combination of planned re-alignments and unplanned coastal defence abandonment in all futures. However, more sympathetic water management of inland grazing marshes (Smart *et al.*, 2006) and increased rural storage along rivers by incorporating wetland areas into washlands could provide significant areas of replacement freshwater habitats and grazing marshes in inland locations (c.f. Nicholls and Wilson, 2002).

The four response strategies identified at the beginning of this section should be seen as complementary, offering higher environmental benefits if implemented in a long-term coordinated and proactive manner. While they can be pursued in isolation, from an environmental perspective they would provide greater benefits if pursued together at the widest landscape scale. In order to achieve this, land-use planning would need to aim to preserve and enhance the space available for rural storage and managed re-alignment. At the same time, increasing storage should receive immediate priority, creating new inland grazing marshes and related freshwater habitats before significant losses occur around the coast through managed re-alignment. Sites for re-alignment should also take account of the potential for morphological protection. Through such policy integration, there could be significant reductions in flood risk with substantial environmental benefits.

All the proposals that offer flood risk reductions and environmental benefits imply allowing significant areas of land to revert to floodplain. Existing proposals for floodplain development, such as the Thames Gateway, indicate the substantial pressure on many floodplains (Lavery and Donovan, 2005). In areas where development pressures are greatest, the benefits of these landscape-scale policies are potentially greatest, but it is in these circumstances that the scale and timing of the implementation of these policies also presents the greatest challenge.

Technical uncertainties may also hinder application of some of the above policies in more developed areas where high defence standards will need to be maintained (Halcrow et al., 2002). This suggests that a wide variety of responses to managing flood risk will be applied and the approaches that yield significant environmental benefits will be more difficult to realise in developed and developing areas. Where land is at a premium, as in many coastal areas, environmental trade-offs may need to be considered between floodplain habitats and agricultural habitats in the greenbelt (c.f. Defra, 2005).

The detailed environmental implications of the above strategies are unclear, but if implemented widely they will result in significant changes to the environments of coastal and river systems. In some ways, it would be a reversion towards the environmental mixtures that existed before significant human flood management, not the current mixtures, but the changes should maintain and indeed enhance a wide range of habitats. An additional benefit of increasing storage on rivers could be increased base flows, which may confer benefits in terms of avoiding droughts and maintaining fluvial ecosystems in a warmer climate (see Hulme et al., 2002).

Finally we note that a more strategic and dynamic approach to flood management is already emerging. Catchment and shoreline management planning are developing a more strategic perspective of future flood management, integrated with environmental concerns in the UK through, for example, the CHaMP (Coastal Habitat Management Plans) and RBMP (River Basin Management Plans) processes. Managed re-alignment is widely discussed within these activities and is being implemented in some trial sites (Halcrow et al., 2002; Winn et al., 2003). Large-scale recreation of freshwater habitats is also being considered (e.g. English Nature's Fens Floodplain Project). There is increasing willingness to consider the measures presented here, including the dynamic changes they imply. The challenge is to do this more effectively, fully addressing the technical and social concerns mentioned above.

Intra-urban zone

Building development, operation and form, and groundwater control are relatively ineffective responses in terms of reducing flood risk and also produce environmental disbenefits (Table 26.4). In contrast, urban development, operation and form, and source control are seen to be potentially effective in reducing urban flood risk and providing environmental benefits. These benefits come from controlling new development and the promotion of coherent green spaces to increase flood storage and conveyance. They also come from the reopening of culverted watercourses, the creation of detention ponds and the aesthetic use of water in the urban area through sustainable urban drainage systems (HR Wallingford, 2003; Shutes et al., 2005). Again, the way in which these responses are implemented will be critical in determining the extent of the environmental benefits. Some of the source control responses, in particular, have the potential to cause both environmental and health and safety problems if implemented poorly.

Inevitably there will be problems in retrofitting these measures within established urban areas (Waters et al., 2003). However, a priority consideration in urban development should be the preservation of greenspace, including brownfield sites where these provide good options for flood storage and conveyance. Consideration of the environment should also be a priority in all new urban development schemes, not only in terms of the aesthetic and recreational environment but also in terms of flood risk management.

Social justice

Fluvial and coastal zone

The social criterion for sustainability in this study was social justice: the impacts of options on the comparatively disadvantaged and on future generations. The experts appraising the response options identified serious concerns about their differential impact on some sectors of society under some scenarios. Indeed, there were more failures in social justice than for any other criterion in the fluvial and coastal catchments, with the following responses likely to have problematic implementation:

- **Coastal defence re-alignment**
- **Coastal defences**
- **Reduce coastal energy**
- **Flood proofing**
- **Increased river conveyance**
- **Engineered flood storage**
- Abandonment
- River flood defences
- Urban storage

- Forecasting and warning
- Collective damage avoidance
- Flood fighting
- Flood-water transfer
- Individual damage avoidance
- Pre-event measures
- Land-use management
- Urban conveyance

The six responses in bold are expected to be most-effective in flood risk reduction under all scenarios, but fail on social justice criteria in two or more scenarios. In some cases, the reason for concern about the differential impacts on poorer or more vulnerable sectors of society relates to the mechanisms for funding and uptake of the options; in others, it is linked to the impacts of the actions themselves, in particular where changes in land-use are required.

Social justice is very tightly related to the narratives of the four scenarios (OST, 2002). Under world markets and national enterprise, about half of the response options (12 and 14 of the 25 responses, respectively) failed on social justice grounds. However, the only responses that failed solely on the grounds of social justice were land-use management, flood proofing, individual damage avoidance, coastal defence re-alignment and reduce coastal energy. In these scenarios, it is assumed that individual wellbeing is assured through the pursuit of national or supra-national socio-economic aims. Measures would be taken for the national (or global) good, and would logically be focused on assets of national significance, unless some wealthy individual or group was able and willing to pay for them. This implies that these assets would mainly be fixed entities or structures. Assets of low significance, or entities such as 'community' for which values are difficult to define, would tend to be low on the priority list for responses; and negative impacts on these assets or sectors would not be seen as socially important. We might say, taking today's perspective, that these measures are imposed unjustly upon communities or individuals, but under those scenarios, it would seem eminently fair to provide flood risk protection on that basis. The high value placed on fixed assets and the pressure to maximise economic gains in a market system would tend to encourage the use of fixed or structural defences, where the expenditure and effectiveness are most controllable.

In global sustainability and local stewardship, the underlying assumption is that national or global wellbeing follows from policies that address the needs of all members of society. The focus is much more on community inclusiveness, shifting the balance away from top-down decisions about what should be part of the national asset base. Measures relying on community engagement will be more feasible, tending to self-perpetuate because they are seen as a means of assuring fairness in these scenarios.

Where fluid entities like 'community' or 'fairness' are highly valued, there is less need to be solely reliant on fixed or structural solutions to the flood risk problem. In global sustainability, more regulated markets and socio-political systems have the scope to assure community-level wellbeing, rather than being led by external forces as much as in world markets. Given that social cohesion and community wellbeing are a priority in global sustainability, it is not surprising that no responses fail on social justice in this analysis. The two responses that fail on these grounds under local stewardship (abandonment and flood water transfer) indicate that an over-emphasis on local management can be socially divisive too, when there is inadequate scope for strategic planning and balancing of 'winners' and 'losers' associated with the measures.

From a sustainability perspective, social justice does not just address the problems of under-represented or comparatively deprived sectors of society; it considers future generations. World markets and national enterprise again are most prone to economic impatience, and thus risk merely postponing socially divisive or damaging impacts.

Where there is concern for social justice, the clear message from this analysis is that there will be a much greater need to take account of it in the implementation of flood policies than has perhaps been necessary to date. Where this relates to the mechanisms for funding and uptake, planning, implementation and education should be carried out as equitably as possible. Where the issue relates to impacts, particularly in terms of flood risk and land use, consideration must be given to incentives and mechanisms that will reduce inequalities in terms of social justice including relocation and compensation.

Intra-urban zone

The same issues arise in the intra-urban area in relation to social justice but not to the same extent. Only two of the measures that were effective in reducing flood risk (urban development, operation and form, and source control) failed on the grounds of social justice, but in this case only in the world markets scenario.

Decisions today for future sustainability

Tables 26.1 and 26.3 list options for flood risk reduction with the potential to bring about a range of useful benefits. There will, of course, be a need for engineering responses to meet the increased flood risk in all of the future worlds, but this analysis shows the implementation of a portfolio of responses has the potential to decrease the cost and reliance on engineering. Where individual responses raise concerns in relation to their impacts on the environment and social justice, the key message is that it is how the responses are implemented rather than the responses themselves that are at issue.

The response measures analysed here range from those that require strategic vision and control (landscape-scale planning and land-use change, in particular) to more locally tailored or organically evolving measures (flood proofing, damage avoidance, even abandonment). However, it is still vital to ensure that the different pieces of the puzzle do indeed add up to a coherent picture of sustainability, whatever the scenario.

There is tension in world markets and national enterprise with the timescale for sustainability – there is little intrinsic drive to consider future generations in worlds with such an emphasis on present consumerism and individual gain. In both global sustainability and local stewardship, continuity is recognised as an important aspect of community life, and there may thus be more of a propensity to take a longer-term view. Uncertainty about the longer-term future drives the need for a precautionary approach (CEC, 2000), with two-way communication between those in power and the public, and with ongoing monitoring.

References

Berkhout, F. and Hertin, J., 2002. 'Foresight futures scenarios – developing and applying a participative strategic planning tool', *Greener Management International*, 37, 37–52.

Berkhout, F., Hertin, J. and Jordan, A., 2002. 'Socio-economic futures in climate change impact assessment: using scenarios as "learning machines"', *Global Environmental Change*, 12, 83–95.

Bourassa, S.C., Hoesli, M. and Sun, J., 2004. 'What's in a view?', *Environment and Planning A*, 36, 1427–1450.

Carpenter, S., Walker, B., Anderies, J.M. and Abel, N., 2001. 'From metaphor to measurement: resilience of what to what?', *Ecosystems*, 4, 765–781.

Commission of the European Communities, 2000. 'Communication from the Commission on the Precautionary Principle', CEC, Brussels, COM(2000)1.

Defra, 1999. *Quality of Life Counts*, Department of the Environment, Food and Rural Affairs, London, updated 2004, available online www.sustainable-development.gov.uk/performance/qolc99.htm

Defra, 2005. *Making Space for Water: Developing a New Government Strategy for Flood and Coastal Erosion Risk Management in England*, Consultation and First Response Documents, Department of the Environment, Food and Rural Affairs, London, available online www.defra.gov.uk/corporate/consult/waterspace/

DETR, 2000. *Regional Quality of Life Counts – Regional versions of the national 'headline' indicators of sustainable development*, The Stationery Office, London, with updates.

Dlugolecki, A., 2004. *A Changing Climate for Insurance*, Association of British Insurers, London, available online www.abi.org.uk/climate change

Evans, E., Ashley, R., Hall, J., Penning-Rowsell, E., Sayers, P., Thorne, C. and Watkinson, A., 2004. *Foresight Future Flooding. Scientific Summary: Vol. II – Managing future risks*, Office of Science and Technology, London.

Guimaraes, R.P., 2001. 'The politics and ethics of "sustainability" as a new paradigm for public policy formation and development planning', *International Journal of Economic Development*, 3, 1–54.

Halcrow, CSERGE and Cambridge Coastal Research Unit, 2002. *Managed Realignment Review*, Defra/Environment Agency, London, Research Report FD 2008, available online www.defra.gov.uk/science/project_data/DocumentLibrary/FD2008/

HR Wallingford, 2003. *Maximising the Ecological Benefits of Sustainable Drainage Schemes*, HR Wallingford, Wallingford, SR 625.

HR Wallingford, 2004. *Sustainable Flood and Coastal Management*, Defra/Environment Agency, London, Project FD 2015, Scoping Report 2, 48–74, available online www.sfcm.org.uk

Hulme, M., Jenkins, G.J., Lu, X., Turnpenny, J.R., Mitchell, T.D., Jones, R.G., Lowe, J., Murphy, J.M., Hassell, D., Boorman, P., McDonald, R. and Hill, S., 2002. *Climate Change Scenarios for the United Kingdom: The UKCIP02 scientific report*: 120, Tyndall Centre for Climate Change Research, University of East Anglia, Norwich.

Lavery, S. and Donovan, B., 2005. 'Flood risk management in the Thames Estuary looking ahead 100 years', *Philosophical Transactions: Mathematical, Physical and Engineering Sciences (Series A)*, 363, 1455–1474.

Nicholls, R.J. and Wilson, T., 2002. 'Integrated impacts on coastal areas and river flooding', in *REGIS: Regional Climate Change Impact Response Studies in East Anglia and North West England*, eds Holman, I.P. and Loveland, P.J., Department for Environment, Food and Rural Affairs, London, 54–101.

OST, 2002. *Foresight Futures 2020: Revised scenarios and guidance*, Office of Science and Technology, London, available online http://admin.foresight.gov.uk/servlet/Controller/ver=850

Pethick, J., 2002. 'Estuarine and tidal wetland restoration in the United Kingdom: policy versus practice', *Restoration Ecology*, 10, 431–437.

Shutes, B., Ellis, J.B., Revitt, D.M. and Scholes, L.N.L., 2005. 'Constructed wetlands in UK urban surface drainage systems', *Water Science and Technology*, 51, 31–37.

Smart, J., Gill, J.A., Sutherland, W.S. and Watkinson, A.R., 2006. 'Predicting the habitat requirements of waders breeding on grassland', *Journal of Applied Ecology*, 43, 454–463.

TSO, 1999. *A Better Quality of Life – Strategy for sustainable development for the United Kingdom, 1999.* The Stationery Office, London, available online www.sustainable-development.gov.uk/publications/uk-strategy99/index.htm

TSO, 2005. *Securing the Future: Delivering UK sustainable development strategy.* The Stationery Office, London, available online www.sustainable-development.gov.uk/publications/uk-strategy/uk-strategy-2005.htm

Waters, D., Watt, W.E., Marsalek, J. and Anderson, B.C., 2003. 'Adaptation of a storm drainage system to accommodate increased rainfall resulting from climate change', *Journal of Environmental Planning and Management*, 46, 755–770.

Winn, P.J.S., Young, R.M. and Edwards, A.M.C., 2003. 'Planning for the rising tides: the Humber Estuary Shoreline Management Plan', *The Science of the Total Environment*, 314–316, 13–30.

World Commission on Environment and Development (WCED), 1987. *Our Common Future*, ed. Bruntland, G.H., Oxford University Press, Oxford.

27 The Governance of responses

Andrew R. Watkinson, Sarah E. Cornell and Andrew Jordan

Previous chapters have explored a number of responses that may reduce flood risk under the four Foresight futures. However, their success crucially depends not only on having a toolbox of potential measures to select from, but also a suitably supportive framework of governance in which to deploy them in practice. Governance is a 'notoriously slippery' term (Pierre and Peters, 2000: 7), but essentially it refers 'in its widest sense, to the various ways through which social life is coordinated' (Heywood, 2000: 19). The governance of flood management is therefore concerned with understanding the various mechanisms (whether hierarchical, market based or network related) through which different management responses can be selected and applied to reduce flood risks.

In this chapter we consider what these governance frameworks might look like under the four future scenarios, together with the implications that this may have for particularly important facets of flood management, such as its financing, the viability of different flood responses (e.g. private insurance), as well as the wider issues of risk perception and the balance that will need to be found between private and government-led intervention. The latter is especially important as it will affect the viability of certain management options as well as their overall effectiveness in reducing flood risk. Finally, we consider the role that governance may play in the development of a portfolio approach to flood risk management, together with some of the practical obstacles and opportunities to developing such an approach.

Introduction

There is, as yet, no commonly agreed definition of the term 'governance'. Hirst (2000), for example, offers five different interpretations, Rhodes (1996) six, and van Kersbergen and van Waarden (2004) no less than nine! Summarising a vast literature, governance is essentially concerned with understanding 'the various ways through which social life is coordinated' (Heywood, 2000: 19). Policy analysts and political scientists have traditionally examined how different actors, processes and policy tools interact to steer the development of society (see Box 27.1). However, by using the term 'governance' instead of 'government', many are signalling the fact that the successful implementation of a policy (like flood management) is increasingly dependent upon a much wider array of public, private and voluntary organisations than would traditionally be included within the 'governmental' framework (Flinders, 2002: 52). Moreover, these organisations are no longer assumed to be dominated by central government, hence the growing interest in forms of governance that rely upon the market or networks, rather than the hierarchical rule of law or of public sector ownership. Consequently, many scholars believe that governance is essentially concerned with the question of how best to control and coordinate complex *networks* of different actors (Flinders, 2002: 54; Rhodes, 2003: 6–7). Some scholars believe that networks are 'fit' for many purposes, because they are capable of self-organising and self-steering (thereby reducing the government's role substantially). Rhodes (1996: 660) goes as far as to claim that governance 'is self organising, inter-organisational networks'. However, many question this assumption; central government will inevitably be drawn into managing networks through various hierarchical and non-hierarchical mechanisms, irrespective of the degree of governance.

Governance is therefore important in our consideration of future flood management because:

- Governance determines how flood management is delivered, since most responses – and portfolios of responses – depend on governance mechanisms, such as regulation, the market, central government funding, or public awareness campaigns, being in place.
- Governance affects the way society as a whole is organised, determining society's adaptability to changes, such as increasing flood risk.

Box 27.1

What is governance?

Governance has traditionally been used as a synonym for *government* – the forms and functions of the state, especially central government (Stoker, 1998: 17), but social scientists now treat these as two analytically distinct terms. In a very broad sense, governance refers to the multifarious ways in which society is steered. Used in this way, governance draws attention to the ways in which central government interacts with civil society to reach mutually acceptable decisions about the direction in which society is travelling. Crucially, under a system of *government*, society is mainly steered by central government departments issuing regulations and charging taxes. In a system of *governance*, society itself undertakes more and more steering, through the work of businesses and local authorities (Schout and Jordan, 2005). Moreover, non-regulatory mechanisms, such as the market, are more important when governance is dominant (Jordan *et al.*, 2005). Corporate social responsibility schemes and voluntary agreements are also tools of governance. More particularly, governance refers to 'a change in the nature or meaning of government' (Bevir and Rhodes, 2003: 45). It is often used to emphasise the declining ability of central government to steer society. This shift in power has been: upwards to regional and international organisations such as the European Union; downwards to regions and devolved localities; and outwards to international corporations, non-governmental organisations and other private or quasi-private bodies (Pierre and Peters, 2000: 83–91). Therefore, governance refers to the emergence of new governing styles that blur the boundaries between and within public and private sectors as a result of the privatisation of government assets, the creation of independent regulators, as well as globalisation and Europeanisation.

- The way in which governance is configured determines how society meets the cost of flood risk management. As this shapes the distribution of the costs and benefits within society, governance strongly affects the politics that form around the issue of flood management.

The latter point is particularly important. Social justice is a major concern in relation to the implementation of flood management policies in some scenarios (see Chapter 26). By choosing different combinations of responses, it may be possible to share the overall burden of flood management in a way that fulfils social justice requirements.

Governance in the future

Scenarios

Governance is a central feature of the scenario approach of the Foresight Flood and Coastal Defence Project. It is implicit in our analysis that, in the different Foresight futures, different degrees of steering of flood management and coastal defence would be undertaken by government and other bodies, such as businesses and local authorities, using non-regulatory mechanisms such as the market (see Table 27.1).

Under the Foresight futures, one axis is concerned primarily with the scale of governance from global to local (Fig. 26.1). In two scenarios, world markets and global sustainability, society is steered at a national or international scale, whereas governance is more likely to take place at a more local scale in the national enterprise and local stewardship scenarios. However, the second axis also has implications for the nature of governance. In world markets and national enterprise, the state has a lesser role: society relies on market or private mechanisms for policy delivery. In effect, society is assumed to be 'self-steered' with less control by central government. In global sustainability and local stewardship, the state steers society more actively. Government, therefore, dominates over governance, be it local or more international.

Table 27.1 Governance under the four Foresight scenarios

World markets	National enterprise	Local stewardship	Global sustainability
• Customer-orientated governance in a rights-based culture • Limited public involvement at the local level • Preference for instruments based on self-regulation, transparency, public–private partnerships and economic incentives • Pressure to reduce taxes • Relative decline of public expenditure (but high GDP growth)	• Customer-orientated governance with a 'statist' approach • Very little involvement at local level • Preference for instruments based on economic incentives and self-regulation • Pressure to reduce taxes • Relative decline of public expenditure	• Heavy regulation of markets • Citizen-orientated governance with participatory approach • Very strong local participation • Decision making is devolved, with strong emphasis on local level • Preference for traditional regulation and planning instruments • Local implementation varies • High levels of taxation • Relative increase of public expenditure (but low GDP growth)	• Fairly heavy regulation of markets • Citizen-orientated governance with strong consultation • Strong public involvement at the local level • Policy mix of negotiated agreements, market instruments and traditional regulation • Relatively high levels of taxation • Relative increase of public expenditure

Crucially, in each of the four scenarios, the costs associated with flooding are paid for differently. The policy tools for flood risk management also differ. For example, flooding expenditures in world markets are more likely to be met from private funds such as insurance schemes, whereas under global sustainability there will be a much greater role for public expenditure met through general taxation. Consequently, in world markets, there is likely to be greater emphasis on ensuring a cost-effective protection of economically important assets, particularly though private schemes. Central government is unlikely to play a strong role in managing flood events, but it might be expected to orchestrate larger, engineering-type interventions to protect nationally important areas. In contrast, wider-scale preventative policy responses in urban and rural areas are likely to be more commonplace under global sustainability, linked to longer-term sustainability strategies such as the reform of the Common Agricultural Policy and sustainable urban drainage schemes (SUDS).

A scenario-based approach does not imply that the four Foresight futures are mutually exclusive or that society moves inexorably towards one to the exclusion of the rest. In fact, history shows major transitions in the nature of the institutions responsible for flood risk management and in the dominant beliefs about social and environmental responsibility (see Box 27.2), reflecting wider changes in society's values, ethics and modes of action.

It is not our intention to predict the future in relation to governance or to make recommendations about appropriate governance structures. Rather, scenario analysis provides one way of simplifying future change and laying bare the fundamental implications of adopting different policy responses. In particular, it helps to highlight some of the considerations that may need to be borne in mind when developing portfolios of responses. Crucially, some policy responses are more likely to work better in some scenarios than others, particularly when they work with the grain of the prevailing governance systems.

Box 27.2

An historical overview of the governance and ethics of flood management

- Prior to the nineteenth century, flood provision was based on individual or local enterprise. What has changed most since then is the overall scale of interventions and the interdependence of communities. This means that the costs and benefits, direct and indirect, are now much less likely to be internalised to the same group of people. In the 1930s and 1950s, the emergence of a strong national flood management policy meant that there was a marked divergence among those who paid the direct costs of interventions, those who, as a result of the actions, benefited directly from them, and those who were affected indirectly, benefiting or losing out.
- Over time, more emphasis has been placed on the indirect or incidental beneficiaries and losers. Historically, those suffering only indirect consequences could expect little support from central government. For example, throughout the long history of fen drainage, and in the 1917 tragedy at Hallsands in Devon, whole communities were displaced as a result of interventions designed to benefit other people. In both cases, it could be argued that the priority was to support nationally important industry, rather than to protect those immediately affected.

- At various stages, society has wanted to control nature – e.g. eighteenth-century fen drainage, post-war land reclamation, and arguably, some of today's restoration of natural habitats. Occasionally, the society/environment interface has been more adaptive, for example, in 'flood-friendly' building construction. The ideal of balancing socio-economic systems and the natural environment was formally stated at the 1992 United Nations Conference on Environment and Development although sustainability concerns were already emerging in the UK across many sectors.

- Shifts in social priorities have been accompanied by substantial changes in governance arrangements. Cycles of concentration and dispersal of control are evident in the past. For example, land drainage boards were established to manage multiple land owners, while, more recently, the UK has witnessed changes in the opposite direction (i.e. more decentralisation and self-steering), with the emergence of multi-agency partnerships, following the 1996 creation of the Environment Agency bringing together environmental protection, flood risk management and public engagement functions.

- An ethical shift is becoming apparent. There is a move away from utilitarian aims, where actions maximise overall final well-being, towards social responsibility throughout the process, framed in terms of duties, rights and social contracts. It is interesting that policy makers have not really sought to penalize the perpetrators of flooding, although examples abound where actions – even flood management interventions – have increased flood risk in neighbouring areas. The idea that 'polluters should pay' is becoming more embedded in UK and EU policy. It may be the natural (rights-based) corollary to the utilitarian 'beneficiary pays' principle in some scenarios that the 'causer' of floods should also pay.

Governance frameworks

In looking 30 to 100 years into the future, the one thing we can be sure about is that the current institutional and governance framework will change dramatically. The insurance market could be radically different; the environment ministry (Defra) and the Environment Agency probably will not exist in their present form. The EU may have disappeared too, its Habitats and Water Directives being little more than footnotes in history. There are, however, a number of more general governance-related issues that need to be factored into any analysis of the future. Here we briefly consider four: scale, integration, participation and adaptability.

Scale: the first axis of the Foresight futures (Fig. 27.1) relates to the scale of governance. This refers to the geographical scale at which any policy responses are implemented. If flood risk management is to be effective, the spatial reach of the governance tools and steering systems used in any portfolio of responses must match the spatial scale of the problems they seek to address (Berkes, 2002). A strategic overview at the scale of system functioning and national coordination also needs to be matched to local needs. The creation of the Broads Authority in 1989, as the local planning authority for the Norfolk Broads, is illustrative of an authority that matches the scale of the problems it seeks to address (Shaw, 1989).

Integration: flood management bears, to varying degrees, upon many sections of government, including development planning, agriculture and management of the rural environment, the water industry and transport. Consequently, there needs to be horizontal coordination among these sectors, and adequate vertical coordination between governance systems operating at differential spatial levels. The difficulty of

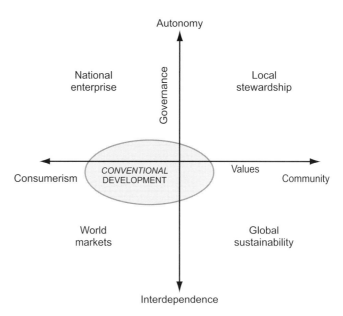

Fig. 27.1. The four Foresight futures and conventional development in relation to two drivers of change: social values (x axis) and systems of governance (y axis). (After OST, 2002)

achieving adequate coordination is particularly clear in relation to policy responses in upland catchments. Such responses typically need to involve multiple agencies at the local level working together within a much wider (and often spatially quite remote) policy framework, such as the Common Agricultural Policy, that is steered at a supra-national level, in this case by the EU.

Participation: the increasing desire for more inclusive community-wide involvement in fluvial and coastal management (Edwards *et al.*, 1997) is typical of the shift from government to governance. Advocates for such an approach argue that it is more legitimate, in that it obtains community consent and provides benefits from specialised local knowledge (O'Riordan, 2003). It may also lead to less-contested outcomes if management plans can be designed to receive broader support. Indeed, the very nature of integrated coastal and catchment management relies on extending stakeholder involvement. There are, however, governance dilemmas in including multiple stakeholders, especially when strategic objectives conflict, or when decisions made at a larger scale, in government or the EU for example, do not match neatly with local requirements.

Adaptability: the same degree of success in delivering some response measures under the four scenarios may result from their very different governance structures. Flood-insurance cover is an example (Fig. 27.2). Arrangements for post-event recompense for losses could be market based or controlled by state regulation. Risks could be pooled across society or cover could be targeted at particular risk groups. Consequently, many variants and combinations of governance could give the same overall level of cover to communities. The design of a portfolio of responses needs to consider how a particular response will be delivered and whether its implementation will become more or less effective if the nature of governance changes. The key here is how best to ensure adaptability.

Who pays?

The question of governance is intimately associated with the thorny question of who pays for the management of flooding. Direct costs associated with most of the response measures are significant, raising several issues for financial governance.

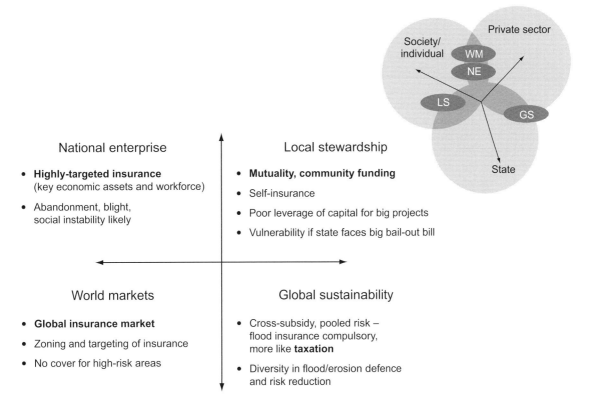

National enterprise

- **Highly-targeted insurance**
  (key economic assets and workforce)
- Abandonment, blight,
  social instability likely

Local stewardship

- **Mutuality, community funding**
- Self-insurance
- Poor leverage of capital for big projects
- Vulnerability if state faces big bail-out bill

World markets

- **Global insurance market**
- Zoning and targeting of insurance
- No cover for high-risk areas

Global sustainability

- Cross-subsidy, pooled risk –
  flood insurance compulsory,
  more like **taxation**
- Diversity in flood/erosion defence
  and risk reduction

Fig. 27.2. An example from managing flood losses of how post-event recompense for flood losses might vary under the four Foresight futures with different roles played by the state, individuals and the private sector

The role of the state in providing for flood risk reduction has varied in the past, but present-day society expects some degree of care from the state, and individuals generally accept a modest degree of contribution to communal action in exchange for that care.

Several conventional options are available for raising funds for state-led action on flood risk. Taxation raises funds for the state at regional or national level, predicated on the view that society as a whole benefits from strategic state decisions made in its interests. Local taxes could be raised directly in areas that most need flood management measures. In areas of higher flood risk, the funds for risk reduction are obviously concomitantly higher; the financial demands on the local communities could become onerous.

Alternatively, general (national) taxation could be used. The 'levelling' effect of pooled taxation spreads the financial burden, and can allow the implementation of strategically important actions that would otherwise be constrained by local resource availability. The flipside is that there are often tensions between local and national aims, especially since the available tax resource is finite and subject to multiple alternative demands. Pooled taxation decisions may be less strategic, because the immediacy of local needs either to implement an action or to deal with cost escalation is diffused and, unlike more responsive modes, applying pooled resources may also give signals for further development expansion in flood risk areas well after unviability is recognised locally.

Alternative funding mechanisms that the state can invoke are levies, typically on activities that may contribute to flood risk, development levies, carbon tax and so on, or subscriptions for the use of flood reduction measures, analogous to road tolls. In pursuit of national sustainability, some responses are expected to have negative side-effects on particular individuals or communities. The governance implications have already been discussed, but there are financial implications too.

Flood protection for individual households has not been a statutory right in the UK (see Box 27.2). Yet, as land and environmental resources become increasingly squeezed by economic developments such as housing and climate pressures, the need may arise for significant local changes in flood and coastal protection, often to meet a range of other national social aims, including international commitments on sustainability. An option is compensation for indirect or individual losses incurred in flood-prevention measures for social gain, for instance, where individuals or communities relinquish property as part of a strategic flood management plan. Compulsory purchase mechanisms are effective and reasonably acceptable options for property.

This analysis also has implications for the management and provision of large-scale emergency flood relief. Planning and financial governance instruments often focus on a steady progression in the increase in risk. If, as seems likely, climate change is characterised by stepwise changes and an increase in the variance of climate variables – that is, erratic periods of drought and storminess – severe flooding events could follow each other in quick succession. Extreme flood events are more likely in the high-emissions scenarios, which will also have a lower propensity for precautionary thinking and community contingency planning. Emergency state intervention might be necessary if a series of severe events were to deplete the public and private resources available for flood management.

The role of markets and incentives

Several flood-management responses can be delivered through the market or other mechanisms, with a varying degree of independence from the state. Corporate voluntarism can shape building codes, for instance. Several measures for managing flood losses can be effectively implemented through the markets. The voluntary sector could be important in the implementation of some measures, particularly in post-event reparation.

Individuals have always assumed the right to protect their own property. While this right may be curtailed in scenarios where strategic landscape planning is a priority and central government has more power, a significant amount of flood management expenditure could, in the more consumerist scenarios, come from individuals. The supply and nature of flood insurance will depend very much on the governance characteristics of the scenario in question. For example, in world markets, the vibrant international finance markets would make insurance cover available only as long as returns on investment are favourable. In the global sustainability scenario, the dynamism of international markets would still be important, but state intervention might result in a highly regulated insurance market, with government reinsurance schemes. In this case, risk would be pooled, possibly through compulsory insurance for all – in effect, an 'environment tariff'. Communitarian values extend over a large spatial area in this scenario, so national (or even EU level) compensation schemes may be viable. In local stewardship, concern is more locally focused. There is less recourse to the global market. So self-insurance or local-level mutual societies providing cooperative insurance cover would be likely. More responsive social behaviour is expected: coordinated community and local government support following floods, 'living with floods' policies, or relocations would be likely consequences of serious flood events. In many ways, national enterprise has a high potential for leaving individuals vulnerable. They may bear the brunt of paying for flood management measures, and there would be limited capacity for insurance or for government underwriting of the national insurance industry.

Ensuring that markets, individuals and other organisations contribute to the strategic investment in flood risk management may require new incentives. If the strategic overview is lost, the installation of measures in the dynamic and multi-use environments of rivers and coastline may result in adverse impacts elsewhere in space, in time, or in the structures of society. Market regulation can control those effects and allow the strategic vision to be achieved without a full reliance on direct state funding. Of course, markets will fund flood management measures only when it makes commercial sense for them. They will not provide funds for the broader social aims to which the state may subscribe, so a combination of regulation and incentives may need to be devised to direct private sector actions in appropriately strategic forms.

The provision of incentives can fine-tune actions so that they also contribute to the mitigation of environmental problems and enhance social justice. Where state mechanisms, the markets, and other institutions are all deployed in implementing a portfolio of responses, it could be hard to distinguish a specific flood management budget. Measures aimed solely at mitigating flood risk may imply a relatively narrow allocation of financial responsibility, whereas novel approaches would need to be sought for measures that are designed to bring flood risk reduction as part of a suite of valuable benefits.

Risk perception and awareness

Risk perception and awareness have implications for the design of flood management policies, the effective delivery of some of the responses (for example, managing flood events and managing flood losses), and also society's willingness to pay for those responses through individual, community or state actions. This book attempts to assess flood risk and the potential responses to meet that risk. We cannot know the actual risk because the future is unknown, both in terms of climate and socio-economic development, which is why we have used climate and socio-economic scenarios. There is obviously a need to update the assessed risk as new information becomes available as a result of monitoring and research. Responses to the assessed risk will, however, depend as much on the perception of risk, by individuals, communities and the state, as on the assessed risk (Eiser, 2004). Perception of risk is affected by the nature of the risk, knowledge, trust, communication about risk, trade-offs, and whether a risk is imposed or voluntary. As a consequence, it may be very different from the actual or assessed risk and may be either amplified or attenuated (Pidgeon *et al.*, 2003).

Risk perception in the future will also depend on the extent of extreme events. For example, if we experience a prolonged period, say a decade, where floods are few and minor, as awareness declines, the actual flood risk could increase as a result of building in flood-prone areas and less investment in defences. On the other hand, major flood events, such as the 1953 or 2000 floods, heighten awareness and lead to a tightening of policy and institutional responses. In theory the latter could lead to a perception of flood risk being more important than it actually is relative to other risks. This change in perception may take place over many years or decades. There is also the problem that with the projected increase in winter rainfall and decrease in summer rainfall, the public will have to handle the mixed message of increases in both drought and flooding.

In order to manage the problem of risk awareness in such a climate, there is a need for better communication of risk so that society's perception of risk will hopefully converge and be proportionate to the assessed risk. Government, institutions, the media and the education sector all have a role in informing and educating about risk – a prerequisite for successful risk management. Good governance will in this case depend upon openness and transparency, involvement, proportionality, evidence and consistency.

Governance options for a portfolio approach

Taking into account the various issues raised above, it is possible to identify a number of key points to take into account when developing portfolios of responses:

- Strategies and choices of both governance and response need to match the *scale* of the flood risk.
- Different elements of *governance* – both government and non-government – need to support the concept of a portfolio of responses to increased flood risk, to allow its integrated implementation.
- The portfolio of responses, and its governance arrangements, need to be *adaptable* over time, in response to changing societal and climatic drivers.
- Much future flood and coastal defence, and the appropriate portfolio of responses, are likely to require *funding* by government, to promote long-term solutions, appropriate standards and equitable outcomes. However, the public's acceptance of this approach is likely to vary across the scenarios.
- While recognising the central role of all levels of government in flood and coastal defence, *market mechanisms* and *incentives* have the potential to play an important role in promoting risk reduction under some but not all the scenarios.
- There is a need for better *risk perception* and *public awareness raising measures*, coupled with close community participation, to inform and enable citizens to be active and supportive partners in all risk management programmes. But these things will not just 'happen'; appropriately designed governance frameworks will be needed to support and facilitate them.
- There is a need to *monitor* the implementation and effectiveness of measures, to re-evaluate risk and respond to shortfalls in the standard of protection. Again, all these things require the right governance arrangements to be in place.

Obstacles and opportunities

With reference to the general considerations described above, we highlight here a number of specific obstacles and opportunities that relate to the governance of the response themes. Table 27.2 indicates what forms of governance are likely to be effective in supporting the implementation of the responses in the five response themes identified in Chapters 17–21.

Management of the rural landscape

Only the more community-orientated scenarios (local stewardship and global sustainability) will have the governance structures in place to allow effective management of rural landscapes. Financial incentives to land managers provide a potentially powerful and effective tool for influencing land management practices. However, these may conflict with other incentives, such as those provided for agricultural and environmental goods. They also rely on integrated assessments of the use of rural environments.

Managing the urban fabric

This group of responses is also likely to be relatively ineffective under the world markets and national enterprise scenarios, except where it is considered to be highly cost effective. Urban densification may preclude some response measures, but greater urban green space could reduce flooding by improving storage capacity

Table 27.2 Governance and policy response themes under the four foresight scenarios

Response theme	World markets	National enterprise	Local stewardship	Global sustainability
Managing the rural landscape	Limited other than in intensively managed agricultural areas	Limited other than in intensively managed agricultural areas; spatial coordination also problematic	Potentially strong but spatial coordination may be problematic	Potentially very strong as part of shift to less-intensive agricultural support systems
Managing the urban fabric	Generally only where it is cost-effective	Generally only where it is cost-effective locally	Commitments to local SUDS, but spatial coordination may be poor	Commitments to local SUDS
Managing flood events	Effective forecasting but strong reliance then placed on local/individual flood proofing and temporary defences in the most economically important areas	Less coordinated forecasting; local/individual flood proofing and temporary defences in the most economically important areas	Possibility of asset removal and effective evacuation programmes in certain localities	Central government planning and awareness schemes linked to evacuation programmes and flood fighting
Managing flood losses	Mainly property-level actions; self-insurance supplemented by charitable donations	Mainly property-level actions; self-insurance supplemented by charitable donations	Potentially strong local support networks; pooled insurance to share costs in flood-prone areas; local floodplain charging schemes	State compensation for losses; tax credits and strong land-use planning to steer development away from flood-prone areas; national flood-plain charging schemes
Engineering and large-scale interventions	Strong preference for large-scale schemes to protect nationally important economic areas	Strong preference for large-scale schemes to protect nationally important economic areas	Strong local opposition to large-scale schemes; limited government investment may curtail other large scale schemes, e.g. re-alignment	Integration of engineering with greater use of softer approaches such as re-alignment, energy generation and, where necessary, surrender of the most flood-prone areas

and infiltration. In terms of storage capacity, surface storage is likely to be cheapest but there are issues of ownership, operation responsibility and health risk to be resolved. While integrated planning and design for flood management could bring social, economic and environmental benefits, the potential for integrated response is currently inhibited by fragmented governance structures and the disinclination of the participating actors to 'self-organise'.

Managing flood events

Chapter 20 highlighted that while there is scope for improvements in science and technology to achieve large reductions in risk through measures concerned with managing flood events, issues of governance and stakeholder behaviour will often crucially determine the extent to which they can be implemented in practice. The key here is effective forecasting and warning, linked to education and public awareness.

Managing flood losses

These responses fall into two major categories (Chapter 21) – those designed to reduce levels of risk to existing assets, properties and their inhabitants, and those intended to limit the increase in risk that will accompany land-use change, including urban development and the building of new properties in flood-prone areas. These require individual stakeholders, communities and higher authorities to operate effectively, so there need to be clear and practical incentives to implement flood proofing and encourage prudent land-use decisions. Even within market dominated futures – where the insurance industry might be expected to play a key role – there is a strong need for government rules and regulations. In terms of land-use planning, both the state and markets have the potential to play key roles in preventing development in flood-prone areas. The withdrawal of cover by the insurance industry, however, could create a major problem for existing properties within the floodplain.

River and coastal engineering

River and coastal engineering will continue to play a role in flood risk management under all of the Foresight futures, although coastal engineering is not considered a high priority under local stewardship. There may even be strong opposition to large-scale schemes in the global sustainability scenario. Realigning infrastructure, such as roads and railways, offers the potential to reduce the extent of coastal defences, but the funding mechanisms to achieve this are unclear except, perhaps, under global sustainability. The incorporation of renewable energy opportunities within coastal defence schemes could perhaps influence cost-effectiveness. Clearly, all future infrastructure projects should take flood risk strongly into account.

Although Chapter 25 identifies concerns over the viability of the engineering responses under the world markets and national enterprise scenarios, it is clear from their implementation under local stewardship and global sustainability that they could form part of a sustainable solution to flood risk. Issues of governance will be critical in delivering flexible and adaptable engineering schemes that are well integrated with natural systems and that do not exacerbate social inequality.

Finally, we draw attention to the fact that this analysis has assumed correspondence between the UKCIP climate scenarios (Hulme *et al.*, 2002) and the socio-economic scenarios outlined in the Foresight futures (OST, 2002). The link derives primarily from the assumed pattern of emissions, but of course there are other combinations of scenario (IPCC, 2000). An assumption in our quantitative analysis was that a high-growth economy, the world markets scenario, inevitably leads to further development in the floodplain and a consequent increase in the required standards of protection. However, in this scenario there is a real opportunity to use incentives and the insurance market to discourage development within the floodplain. These factors may achieve similar results to tightly controlled land-use planning in the global sustainability scenario. This essentially allows the response of land-use planning to be decoupled from the scenario and to provide a more effective response to flood risk than identified in Chapter 23.

In summary:

- There are likely to be difficulties in delivering some of the more community-based responses, such as land management, where there is a reliance on market or private mechanisms for policy delivery.
- Within urban areas, the current fragmented governance structures are likely to inhibit the potential for integrated response.
- Education and increased public awareness will be central to the delivery of responses where stakeholder behaviour is important.

- There need to be clear and practical incentives in place to encourage a number of responses such as flood proofing and appropriate land-use decisions.
- Given the potential negative impacts of engineering responses on the environment and social justice, individual engineering decisions must be tested against the three pillars of sustainability.

This is not a comprehensive list. In the next chapter we explore the strategic choices that have to be made if we are to build successful portfolios of responses that reduce flood risk in a sustainable manner.

References

Berkes, F., 2002. 'Cross-scale institutional linkages: perspectives from the bottom up', in *The Drama of the Commons*, eds Ostrom, E., Dietz, T. and Dolsak, N., National Academy Press, Washington, DC, 293–322.

Bevir, M. and Rhodes, R., 2003. *Interpreting British Governance*, Routledge, London.

Edwards, S.D., Jones, P.J.S. and Nowell, D.E., 1997. 'Participation in coastal zone management initiatives: a review and analysis of examples from the UK', *Ocean and Coastal Management*, 36, 143–165.

Eiser, J.R., 2004. *Public Perception of Risk*, Office of Science and Technology, London, 2004, available online www.foresight.gov.uk

Flinders, M., 2002. 'Governance in Whitehall', *Public Administration*, 80, 51–76.

Heywood, A., 2000. *Key Concepts in Politics*, Palgrave, Basingstoke.

Hirst, P., 2000. 'Democracy and governance', in *Debating Governance*, ed. Pierre, J., Oxford University Press, Oxford.

Hulme, M., Jenkins, G.J., Lu, X., Turnpenny, J.R., Mitchell, T.D., Jones, R.G., Lowe, J., Murphy, J.M., Hassell, D., Boorman, P., McDonald, R. and Hill, S., 2002. *Climate Change Scenarios for the United Kingdom: The UKCIP02 scientific report: 120*, Tyndall Centre for Climate Change Research, University of East Anglia, Norwich.

Intergovernmental Panel on Climate Change (IPCC), 2000. *Special Report on Emissions Scenarios (SRES): A special report of working group III of the Intergovernmental Panel on Climate Change*, Cambridge University Press, Cambridge.

Jordan, A., Wurzel, R.K. and Zito, A., 2005. 'The rise of "new" policy instruments in comparative perspective: has governance eclipsed government?', *Political Studies*, 53, 477–496.

Office of Science and Technology (OST), 2002. *Foresight Futures 2020: Revised scenarios and guidance*, Office of Science and Technology, London.

O'Riordan, T., 2003, 'Connecting people to nature', *Ecos*, 24, 5–9.

Pidgeon, N., Kasperson, R.E. and Slovic, P., 2003. *The social amplification of risk*, Cambridge University Press, Cambridge.

Pierre, J. and Peters, B.G., 2000. *Governance, Politics and the State*, Macmillan, Basingstoke.

Rhodes, R.A.W., 1996. 'The new governance: governing without governance', *Political Studies*, 44, 652–67.

Rhodes, R.A.W., 2003. 'What is new about governance and why does it matter?', in *Governing Europe*, eds Hayward, J. and Menon, A., Oxford University Press, Oxford.

Schout, A. and Jordan, A.J., 2005. 'Coordinating European governance: self organising or centrally steered?', *Public Administration*, 83, 201–220.

Shaw, M., 1989. 'The Broads Act 1988: a framework for planning and management', *Journal of Planning and Environmental Law*, April, 241–246.

Stoker, G., 1998. 'Governance as Theory', *International Social Science J.*, 155, 17–28.

van Kersbergen, K. and van Waarden, F., 2004. '"Governance" as a bridge between disciplines', *European J. of Political Research*, 43, 143–171.

Part 8
Synthesis

28 Strategic choices

Andrew R. Watkinson, Edward P. Evans, Jim W. Hall,
Edmund C. Penning-Rowsell and Colin R. Thorne

Introduction

In the preceding chapters potential changes in flood risk by the 2080s have been identified and a portfolio of integrated responses to those risks has been analysed using scenario analysis. Care has been taken to account for the uncertainties that are inevitable in futures work, both when predicting levels of risk under the 'baseline assumption' and when judging the efficacy of responses intended to bring those risks down to acceptable levels. In this chapter, we draw these threads together while exploring the implications of our analysis for decision makers and reviewing the impact of the Foresight Flood and Coastal Defence Project on stakeholders and policy makers.

Options for managing flood risk

The costs of flood management

The analyses presented in Part 3: Assessment of Drivers and Risks indicate that if fluvial and coastal flood risk management technologies, policies and expenditure were to continue unchanged, then by the 2080s the expected annual damages (EAD) associated with flooding in the river and coastal floodplains of England and Wales could increase to somewhere between about £1.5 billion to £21 billion under the local stewardship and world markets scenarios, respectively. The corresponding EAD for pluvial flooding in intra-urban areas could be in the range of £0.75 billion to £8 billion. These increases in flood risk and consequential damages stem partly from climate change and partly from the degree, nature and geographical distribution of socio-economic development. In this context, it should be noted that some policy options that affect the extent to which socio-economic development impacts flood risk are integral to the scenarios. For example, it is envisaged under global sustainability that there would be very little new development in areas at risk of flooding on river and coastal floodplains.

Fortunately, a range of responses that could reduce future flood risk are available to us and their efficacy was considered in Part 6: Assessment of Flood Risk Responses. It is clear that no single response measure or group is capable of providing an effective solution to the expected increase in flood and coastal erosion

Table 28.1. The growth in GDP relative to the present-day under the four Futures scenarios (a) together with the flood risks expressed in terms of the EAD and the baseline costs of flood defence for the business as usual option (continuation of current flood-management policies and expenditure into the future) (b) and the costs expressed as a percentage of GDP (c). The data are for England and Wales with the coastal, catchment and intra-urban area combined

	Present day	World markets	National enterprise	Local stewardship	Global sustainability
a) Growth in GDP relative to present-day	1.0	14.1	4.6	2.6	8.1
GDP: £ billions	1070	15 100	4910	2780	8630
b) Baseline case, EAD: £million/year	1320	28 380	20 160	2240	6730
Baseline cost: £ million/year	820	820	820	820	820
c) EAD as a percentage of GDP: %	0.13	0.19	0.41	0.08	0.08
Total baseline cost of flood defence as a percentage of GDP: %	0.08	0.01	0.02	0.03	0.01

risks. Rather, it is envisaged that the UK will need portfolios of flood response measures and that the make up of the most effective portfolio varies between the different future scenarios. The four portfolios we have analysed, together with the future under the baseline flood management assumption dealt with in Part 3, provide decision makers with a range of options, applied under different future scenarios, to assist in policy formulation. It should be remembered, however, that we have not explored how the options would be implemented in detail and that other futures, with different combinations of greenhouse gas emissions and socio-economic development, could occur (IPCC, 2000). Moreover, we would again stress that the numbers given can only be indicative. In our analysis, we have been able to explore a limited range of flood risk management options – they are but exemplars of what could be done and achieved by integrated flood risk management.

There is also considerable uncertainty in our numerical analysis. This uncertainty derives from the outputs in Part 6: Assessment of Flood Risk Responses and is the result of scientific uncertainty in the data and the models, as well as true uncertainty in that the nature and outcomes of future events is yet to be determined and so cannot be known with certainty. Moreover, the estimated costs associated with flood risk management responses exclude those for land purchase and non-structural measures. The economic analysis is a preliminary one and can only be considered as indicative, in comparison with other more recent analyses of the costs of future flooding in the coastal zone (Nicholls and Tol, 2006) and analyses of climate policies that, for example, explore the impacts of technological change (Barker *et al.*, 2006) and discounting (Guo *et al.*, 2006).

Table 28.1(a) lists the risks that might accrue if we continue with the present technologies and policies for flood risk management at current levels of investment – that is under the baseline assumption. These risks are expressed in terms of EAD relative to GDP (see Table 28.1(b) and (c)). Risk as a proportion of GDP rises by a third in the high-growth, high-emissions, world markets scenario, but decreases by a similar amount under global sustainability, which is also a high-growth scenario, but with lower emissions. There is little change in the ratio under local stewardship, but the steep rise under national enterprise highlights the dangers of low growth and high emissions.

Tables 28.2 and 28.3 illustrate the impact on flood risk and management costs of exemplar integrated portfolios of flood management responses. These show that the increase in flood risk by the 2080s could be pulled back to somewhere between current and twice current levels. We first consider the river catchment and coastal

Table 28.2. The target standards of protection for the integrated portfolios of flood management for the catchment and coastal zones in England and Wales under the four futures scenarios (a) and their impact on flood risk (b) and the costs of flood management (c)

	Present day	World markets	National enterprise	Local stewardship	Global sustainability
a) Target standards of flood protection relative to present-day	1	2	2	0.75	1
b) Residual risks with integrated portfolio, EAD: £m/year		1760	1030	930	2040
Risk reduction, EAD: £m/year		18 700	14 000	570	2820
c) Flood management capital costs: £m/year		75 600	77 200	22 100	22 400
Additional annual capital costs to achieve risk reduction: £m/year		1600	1600	500	500
Total annual costs as a percentage of GDP: %	0.05	0.01	0.04	0.04	0.01

zone (Table 28.2). The figures for additional annual costs in Table 28.2 were calculated by dividing the total cost by the number of years elapsed, in this case 50. However, increases in flood risk management expenditure are likely to increase non-linearly over time to reflect affordability. It is not possible to predict the profile of these increases but, if we assume incremental growth over 80 years, the annual uplift would range between £12.5 million and £40 million. By the 2080s, this would be equivalent to a 3 to 7-fold increase in annual expenditure on flood risk management. On this basis, the rate of increase in costs would only exceed the rate of increase in GDP under the national enterprise scenario.

Under world markets, we supposed a doubling of the present standards of flood protection. The costs are high but considerably below the reduction in risk, which comes down from 20 times today's level to twice that level. Risk reduces to a similar level under global sustainability, with its medium-high growth and low emissions, but at one-third of the investment cost for flood risk management of that under the world markets scenario. A major element in this lower cost is that non-structural responses (which have not been costed) can be implemented better

Table 28.3. The target standards of protection for the integrated portfolios of flood management for the intra-urban area in England and Wales under the four futures scenarios (a) and their impact on flood risk (b) and the costs of flood management (c)

	Present day	World markets	National enterprise	Local stewardship	Global sustainability
a) Target standards of flood protection relative to present-day	1	2	2	0.75	1
b) Residual risks with integrated portfolio, EAD: £m/year		4200	2400	490	720
Risk reduction, EAD: £m/year		3680	2660	250	1150
c) Additional costs to achieve risk reduction: £m/year		540	260	400	110
Total annual costs as a percentage of GDP	0.03	0.01	0.01	0.03	0.005

and more fully, owing to more favourable governance under a global sustainability future. Present standards of flood protection are maintained under this scenario and it may well be possible to reduce risk even further and in a sustainable way. However, in a national enterprise future the penalties of low growth and high emissions can be seen in flood risk management costs, which are as high as those for world markets, but which are less affordable – a conclusion also reached by Nicholls and Tol (2006).

Turning to the intra-urban area, it can be again seen that the portfolios of responses are capable of reducing expected annual damages, although not to the same degree as for river and coastal flooding (Table 28.3). The reductions range from 34–61%, in comparison to 38–93% for the river and coastal flooding. More-over, there is considerable residual risk, with EADs ranging from 15 times (world markets) to twice current levels. These residual levels of EAD can also be expected to continue to rise with time.

The direction of future society – that is, the scenario(s) that actually materialise – is far from the control of flood risk managers, although high-profile projects, such as new tidal defences for the Thames Estuary could be used as beacon projects that might help to shift societal attitudes and expectations. On the whole, however, flood risk managers have to work within the economic, political and institutional constraints of the day. Yet within those constraints, government must decide on the risk of flooding it is prepared to accept. In essence, it can choose from three options:

- Maintain current flood policies and expenditure, accept reduced standards of flood protection and, hence, a substantial increase in flood risk, and live with the increase in expected annual economic damages.
- Maintain flood risk to levels similar to the present by the application of a suitable portfolio of flood response measures.
- Reduce flood risk further, which may be difficult in economic and sustain-ability terms under some scenarios but feasible under others.

The analysis presented here indicates that society has considerable choice in how it responds to changes in flood risk (see also, Nicholls and Tol, 2006). However, in considering the options, it should be noted that current funding already includes an element of investment for the future through the application of climate-change allowances and sensitivity analyses. This should cover some of the potential increases in the probability of flooding. Furthermore, if defences are upgraded when they are being renewed as part of the normal asset-replacement cycle, the marginal costs of increased standards are much reduced. These issues have not been taken into account and would tend to balance the underestimation of overall flood risk management costs caused by omission of costs of the non-structural responses.

The fact that, to be effective when needed, stepped increases in flood risk management investment would have to begin decades in advance of expected increases in flood risk, raises issues of inter-generational equity. Is it justified to divert investment from other public goods in the present generation, to provide levels of protection that are likely to be more appropriate to the higher levels of wealth of future generations? While the central London sewer system is a good example of the long-lasting benefits that may be derived from the farsightedness of past generations, there are bound to be issues concerning the wisdom of putting the needs of future generations ahead of those of the present.

Controlling climate change

Scenario analysis highlights the pressures that current flooding systems, natural and human, will face in the future. It has shown that these pressures arise from changes to both climate and society. We have not attempted a comprehensive analysis of how drivers of climate change and societal change contribute to the increase in flood risk individually, although in the expert judgement-based ranking exercise (Chapter 12) climate-related drivers ranked highly. However, we have considered the potential effect of decoupling climate change from socio-economic change under the world markets scenario.

In Chapter 13, we quantified future flood risks for a future scenario which embodied world markets socio-economics (high economic growth) and low emissions of greenhouse gases: a scenario equivalent to the IPCC A1T scenario (IPCC, 2000). This showed that reducing emissions in a high-growth economy could reduce expected annual damages from £21 billion to £15 billion, under the baseline assumption on flood risk management. Thus, decoupling the drivers of climate change and socio-economics in this one case indicates that control of global emissions can have a positive effect on future flood risk, reducing the EAD by just over 25%. Like the exemplar portfolios (Tables 28.2 and 28.3) this does not pull back risk to anywhere near current levels but, taken together with appropriate flood risk management measures, controlling emissions to reduce climate change constitutes an attractive combination of options.

However, achieving the low climate-change scenario would demand either substantial decreases in emissions of greenhouse gases and changes in societal behaviour, or enormous technological investment to 'macro-engineer' the world's climate. This latter approach may be feasible and acceptable well before 2080 (Govindasamy *et al.*, 2003). However, at present there is no cost comparison for these two distinct approaches. In any case, global control or mitigation of emissions does not actually solve the problem because there are inherent time lags within the global system, particularly in relation to sea-level rise (Nicholls and Lowe, 2006).

An important implication of this analysis is that societal behaviour has the dominant influence on flood risk. This agrees with the RegIS report, which also concluded that coastal habitats would be affected more by the decisions that society made on how to manage the coast in the face of sea-level rise than by sea-level rise itself (Nicholls and Wilson, 2002). We conclude that attempting to control the climate change driver, either by pursuing a strategy of emissions reduction or through major technological effort, would be best considered as part of the contribution to flood risk management, alongside the evolving portfolio of responses outlined in the previous discussion.

In summary, our analysis indicates that integrated flood risk management must lie at the core of our response to changes in the drivers of flooding and coastal erosion, but that we could make the task substantially easier by pursuing mitigation policies that will reduce climate change and flood probabilities through the control of greenhouse-gas emissions and macro-engineering the climate. Nicholls and Tol (2006) similarly stressed adaptation as a response to rising sea levels and coastal flooding in the short to medium term as a consequence of time lags within the system, while emphasising that mitigation reduces the risk of extreme sea-level rise due to the decline of the Greenland or Antarctica ice sheets. Mitigation must, however, start now if it is to deliver its benefits in time.

A route map for flood risk management

A range of responses measures and groups have the potential to reduce flood risk. These fall within a series of themes: managing the rural landscape, managing intra-urban flooding, managing flood events, managing flood losses and river and coastal engineering. These measures vary in their effectiveness in reducing flood risk under the different scenarios (Chapter 25), and in terms of their sustainability (Chapter 26). They also vary in the way that they can be implemented, in terms of governance (Chapter 27).

Having decided to reduce the increase in flood risk expected to occur under the baseline assumption, a decision then has to be made, given the uncertainty in future flood risks, about how to implement responses. Three important issues emerge from this consideration: the sustainability and robustness of implementation; the timescale of implementation; and its operational control in terms of reversibility and adaptability.

Targeting responses: sustainability and robustness

Flood risk management in the UK has a history of targeting responses to flood risk at various stages along the source-pathway-receptor continuum, in an attempt to reduce both the probability of flooding and the consequential damage when floods occur. For example, one reaction to the 1953 floods along the east coast of England was to reduce the risk of future coastal flooding by upgrading and extending the coastal defences. This was subsequently supplemented by beach nourishment, again targeted on blocking the flood pathway and, consequently, reducing the probability of flooding. In parallel, other responses targeted the receptors. For example, a storm-surge forecasting service was also set up to improve flood event management and thereby reduce losses by making receptors less vulnerable. In the same vein, in recent years, a national 'rainfall radar' system has been developed for forecasting and reducing the impacts of pluvial and river floods. The consideration of flood risk in land-use planning has also been strengthened – again to manage down losses by targeting receptors.

While the need for a portfolio approach targeting responses on all elements of the source-pathway-receptor continuum to reduce both the probability and consequences of flooding has long been recognised in the UK, our analysis indicates that we should favour some responses more than others (see Chapter 26). The selection of responses will vary depending upon the value of the assets at risk, the probability of flooding, cost-effectiveness, environmental impact and the importance placed on achieving social justice. Responses identified as being particularly effective in reducing flood risk across scenarios, and which also score well on other sustainability criteria, include catchment-wide storage, land-use planning and building codes. These responses should, therefore, be given high priority in any implementation strategy. The analysis reported here also demonstrates that engineering responses will remain crucial to managing flood risk under all future scenarios. Nicholls and Tol (2006), in a global analysis of the implications of sea-level rise for coastal flooding, similarly conclude that upgrading of coastal defences will be a key response.

Serious questions may be raised concerning whether responses that address only the pathways and receptors of flooding can provide robust and sustainable solutions in the long term, given on-going and progressive climate change. In this context, mitigating the climatic *sources* of flooding would undoubtedly contribute to an effective long-term solution to the problem. But, as the chapters in this volume have recounted, there are considerable social and technological challenges to be met if we are to reduce or mitigate the increases in precipitation, storm surges, wave heights and relative sea-level rise that are currently expected to occur during rest of this century.

Under some future scenarios we risk becoming overly dependent on engineering measures to block pathways close to receptors – which may not be sustainable in terms of cost-effectiveness, environmental impacts and social equity. In others we may have to learn to live with more frequent and severe flooding and coastal erosion, which is not an attractive prospect. However, neither outcome is inevitable. A shift in emphasis towards targeting responses on reducing the numbers and vulnerabilities of people together with the number properties and value of assets at risk, while at the same time managing near-source pathways to promote flooding in flood suitable areas and so take pressure off flood vulnerable areas, would clearly help to deliver flood risk management that is both sustainable and reliable however the future may unfold.

For example, in terms of reducing the consequences of flooding, thoughtful application of responses involving land-use planning and management reduces the consequences of flooding, flood-proofing buildings makes them more resilient to flood impacts, and relocating vulnerable people, infrastructure and assets out of the floodplain removes them from the risk of inundation due to river or coastal flooding. Similarly, managing flood pathways near source, through, for example, catchment-wide storage upstream in the river system or allowed morphological adjustments at key locations along the coast, reduces the probability that the structural flood defences protecting densely populated areas will be breached or overtopped. The global sustainability scenario illustrates the enormous potential of these types of responses through indicating their capability to manage down the increases in flood risk in the 2080s that are otherwise expected to occur under the baseline assumption.

There is then the potential to derive a long-term solution to future problems of flooding and coastal erosion in the UK. Achieving it in practice will, however, depend on delivering integrated flood risk management across a wide range of socio-economic activities and overcoming tensions between stakeholders and policy makers with contrasting priorities and responsibilities for stimulating and sustaining socio-economic development – both regionally and nationally. For example, in managing the urban fabric, the redevelopment of brownfield sites is attractive to government and developers alike. However, where such sites are located in river or coastal floodplains, the construction of homes, retail facilities or new industrial units commits society to long-term investment in providing appropriate flood defences, with costs of doing so likely to spiral upwards as the effects of climate change increase the probability of flood events equal to or greater than the design event for the flood defences.

Under these circumstances it is important to consider carefully not only the cost–benefit ratio of providing the necessary flood defences, but also *who* it is that enjoys the benefits and *who* it is that carries the burden of paying the costs. If and when there is a flood that breaches or overtops the defences, further issues arise concerning *who* bears responsibility for exposing people and their property to the risk and *who* eventually pays the bill for making good the damage. Depending on the systems in place, possibilities exist for substantial insurance claims, state aid for reconstruction and, in extreme cases, relocation costs for people or businesses unable to return to the area after the event. It could be envisaged that as the probability of floods approaching or exceeding the design event increases due to climate change and the frequency of serious floods and losses rises incrementally, there may come a point where even developments with what were initially considered to be adequate defences might become untenable. This would not only represent a market failure, with the possibility of substantial litigation, it might also force the state to intervene, perhaps as the insurer of last resort.

Historically, deployment of structural measures that reduce the probability of flooding by blocking pathways using engineered defences have allowed society to benefit through the development of floodplains. If future development in flood-plains is curtailed and growth is to be maintained then society will obviously need to look elsewhere, building in less commercially viable locations outside the flood-plain and probably incurring additional costs and lower returns on investment as a result. Thus, the future costs of sustainable flood risk management do not simply depend on how much developers can be persuaded to contribute towards the costs of protecting development in areas at risk from river and coastal flooding, but also how much of the return on investment they are willing to forego to avoid the *need* to protect floodplains from flooding in the first place. This immediately raises broader questions concerning, first, how much of the cost of locating redevelopment away from floodplains society is prepared to bear and, second, how on-going development on land that is currently protected for other valid reasons should be managed. Clearly, issues concerning whether and how to redevelop urban brownfield sites located in floodplains serve to illustrate a number of important questions for future flood risk management in the UK.

However best practice evolves with respect to brownfield sites, the wider point is that we need to develop decision-making processes that can effectively balance the true, whole-life costs of defending any area of floodplain against the real costs of developing elsewhere. This has done be done within the context of a future characterised by climate and socio-economic changes, clouded by uncertainty and conditioned by a preference for taking measures to reduce our overall exposure and vulnerability to flood damages. It follows that key, strategic questions relate to how we use land in generating sustained economic growth without creating a legacy of increased flood risk, and how we bring state and market forces to bear in breaking the cycle whereby increases in flood probability lead to increases in flood risk and demands for defences that are higher, stronger, more expensive and less sustainable.

The time horizon of responses

The time horizons associated with different responses vary considerably. Temporal dimensions vary not only in terms of the time necessary for implementation, but also the lead-in time before measures become fully effective in reducing flood risk and the duration of their effectiveness before they require renewal or replacement. For example, schemes to reduce coastal flood risk through re-aligning defences to allow morphological adjustment of the coastline (to better accommodate the forcing agents of erosion and deposition) will require considerable lead-in times if they are to be implemented at a sufficiently large scale to be effective and where they involve significant relocation of coastal communities, assets or infrastructure.

Certainly, a viable portfolio of responses cannot rely solely on measures with long lead times but will have to include some responses capable of rapid implementation to deal with imminent and short-term increases in flood risk. Conversely, attention should not be focused solely on quick fixes and resources must also be allocated to those measures that may take longer to take effect, but which have the potential to deliver flood risk reductions that are cumulative and long lasting. The attraction of these 'slow burn' measures is that, given time, they can permanently reduce the demand for new investment in flood risk management. In general, 'slow burn' options will involve near-source management of flood pathways and measures aimed at reducing the consequences of flooding. Conversely, engineered options can deliver quick reductions in flood risk but require on-going maintenance and periodic renovation or replacement. Moreover, the presence of engineered flood defences has, in the past, led to development within the protected area that increases the consequences (and so risks) of flooding inappropriately, while limiting subsequent flood-management options – or at least adding substantially to their cost. In the context of the climate change projections reported in this volume, while measures capable of delivering quick reductions in flood risk will be needed, it must not be forgotten that their comparative resource requirements are likely to increase relative to those of longer-term responses as the future unfolds.

A factor that prolongs the lead times associated with some otherwise attractive options is inertia. For example, even if land-use planning could be completely reformed to optimise its utility in flood risk management, turnover rates for the existing housing stock and other assets in the UK are so low that the resulting flood risk benefits would still take decades to become significant. In the case of other options with long lead times, such as improving flood-awareness education and the implementation of fiscal incentives, delayed efficacy stems from the need for major social and institutional changes to take hold, rather than any physical limitation on their implementation (see Defra, 2002; Treasury, 1998).

Given the substantial lead-in times that are unavoidable when implementing some important non-structural responses, the timing of the increases in flood risk expected during this century becomes doubly important. Under the higher emissions scenarios, climate change and its impacts on flood probabilities accelerate as the century approaches. Under these futures, it is imperative to act now with respect to responses which take time to implement (e.g. coastal re-alignment), or which have a long lead time before they deliver significant flood risk benefits (e.g. improved building regulations and land-use planning). There is little or no time to prevaricate if these responses are to be in place when needed to counter the acceleration in the rate of flood risk that is expected later this century if emissions rise at one of the higher rates. Delay will leave no alternative to increased reliance on – expensive – structural measures that can be implemented relatively quickly as the flood probabilities rise.

Within the intra-urban zone, there remains considerable uncertainty concerning when structures inherited from the Victorian era will eventually fail and how much longer it will be possible to extend their useful lives. The nature and longevity of urban infrastructure also poses challenges to managing future urban flood risk due to the considerable difficulties in retrofitting storage into existing urban areas and the lack of opportunity to reform the urban fabric associated with low rates of building renewal and replacement. Effective implementation of potentially powerful responses, such as above- and below-ground storage in the urban zone, will depend on allowing for the delays that inertia in urban renewal make inevitable. This requires that reviews be started now to identify those urban areas that are likely to experience the most serious increases in flood risk, in order that there is time for appropriate responses to be implemented.

In summary, the unavoidable conclusion to be drawn from a consideration of time horizons is that the time to invoke responses with long implementation and lead-in times is sooner rather than later. As the increases in flood risk that the responses are intended to counter will not actually materialise for decades, this represents a precautionary approach. However, the alternative is to rely increasingly on building higher and stronger structural flood defences later, with potentially adverse cost and sustainability consequences. In this context, time horizons beyond the current century should also be actively explored (Lenton et al., 2006) if we are to avoid burdening future generations with either substantial increases in flood risk or structural defences that eventually prove unsustainable.

Adaptable, reversible and irreversible responses

In reality, flood risk may change in ways different to those that we have described and modelled in this volume. What if climate change is less than is currently expected? Or what if there are societal changes that do not map on to any of the four envisaged scenarios? Or what if the west Antarctic ice sheet collapses, leading to a 5 m increase in sea level rather than the 60 cm increase expected by 2080? With some flood response options, the way is left open for reversing the measures if societal or climatic conditions do not change as expected. For example, stringent building codes may be further tightened or relaxed, or the extent of some rural conveyance management measures can be expanded or diminished. Conversely, some decisions on flood risk management are effectively irreversible. In particular, allowing development on floodplain land proves very difficult to reverse once householders and industry are in place.

Adaptable design is a further aspect of operational control, especially where there is uncertainty over the likely rate and extent of an expected increase in flood risk. Adaptive capacity can be incorporated into physical defences at the design stage, allowing incremental implementation and upgrade with time. For example, constructing flood embankments with a wider base than is initially necessary makes it easier to raise the crest and increase the standard of protection as risk is later re-evaluated. Some response measures identified in our analysis lend themselves better to this type of approach than others, but, as a rule, adaptability comes at the expense of higher initial costs. It follows that research that reduces uncertainty in predictions of future changes in flood risk and the effectiveness of specific responses is crucial to selecting the optimum capacity for adaptation to be built into schemes and structures. Research and post-project monitoring are also important in justifying the need for additional investment to allow for adaptability.

This is particularly true with respect to an extremely damaging event (or series of events) that has a very low probability of occurrence. While pressure on public funds precludes offering absolute safeguards, such risks cannot be ignored. The threat does not stem solely from single events of catastrophic magnitude or intensity. A series of 'normal' but severe floods in quick succession might push structural defences to their limit and, while community-based responses may have excellent coping strategies, they too may become stretched to breaking point. With respect to the possibility of flooding that is truly extreme in its magnitude, extent or duration it is vital to have the appropriate policy management options in place. In this context, having clear knowledge of options that have reserve capacity and that can be brought forward rapidly, is crucial.

Building a portfolio of responses

Our analysis indicates that no single response theme can effectively reduce the flood risk in even a single scenario, let alone all of the future scenarios. A portfolio of integrated responses is required. However, the portfolio needs to be assembled in the light of the following considerations:

Ensuring effectiveness and sustainability: the quantitative analysis of responses presented in Chapter 25 suggests that all the response groups described earlier could play a role in such a portfolio. However, there has been no attempt here to quantify exactly how each response group or measure would contribute to the overall reduction in flood risk that might be achieved. To move this forward, an analogous unit to the climate 'stabilization wedge' (Pacala and Socolow, 2004) might be useful in quantifying the efficacy of specific actions that reduce flood risk. However, in seeking to optimise the make up of a 'preferred' portfolio, it is worth remembering that responses vary in their effectiveness across scenarios. Moreover, only a small core of responses (Chapter 26) are found to be effective across all the scenarios and to carry no, or at least limited, sustainability penalties. Some, indeed, carry sustainability benefits.

Uncertainty: the uncertainties associated with future climate change, socio-economic development and flood risk mean that a range of decisions have to be made in determining the content of any portfolio of responses. Which responses should we implement immediately? What standard of protection do we provide? Do we prioritise measures that tackle the sources and receptors of flood risk rather than adopting a more direct, structural approach through flood defence? Over what timescale do we implement the responses? How do we maximise the flexibility of our portfolio by the use of reversible and adaptable responses that can be implemented incrementally? Furthermore, which forms of governance and incentives will be most effective in delivering these flood risk management responses?

Avoiding closing off options: it is important to consider whether decisions made in the near future may, to a greater or lesser extent, limit the options available to future generations and lock them into certain policy paths. We have already shown that the development of some urban brownfield sites in floodplains could lock us into increasingly expensive flood risk reduction measures. These issues are already receiving attention and some are being tackled but more needs to be done.

Managing portfolios in a changing environment: implementing a mix of responses is not, of course, the same as designing a portfolio that can manage changing and uncertain risk. Financial investors are used to dealing with uncertainty and advocate a portfolio of assets as the best means of hedging future uncertainty. Given the potentially rapidly changing environment, it makes sense to focus flood risk management on the evaluation of alternative portfolios and strategies of flood risk management (Awerbuch, 2000). To inform policy making, we will also need to monitor flood risk as it changes, together with the metrics of sustainability that guide policy development. Advanced forms of multi-criteria monitoring need to be developed to this effect.

Links with other policy areas: in managing the portfolio of flood risk responses, there must be coordination with other policy areas. In development planning for both rural and urban areas, flood management is a means to not just a single end, but to achieving a nested set of objectives that contribute to a better quality of life. Management of the rural environment for flood risk reduction cannot be considered separately from the management of the rural environment for agriculture, forestry, conservation and tourism. Experience shows the difficulty of manipulating any single sector or pursing any single aim. For example, the Foot and Mouth epidemic in the UK in 2001 vividly demonstrated how decisions to support the agricultural sector had a strongly negative impact on tourism (Thompson *et al.*, 2002). Implementation of flood management is made easier by bringing together a response portfolio within which the risks of the combined responses offset each other, and where the range of benefits from the responses can be aligned with a broader set of aims. This type of scrutiny may facilitate the implementation of a policy portfolio – ensuring all effects pull the same way – or reveal potential conflicts and pitfalls that would make implementation harder.

By analysing flood risk in terms of the three pillars of sustainability, we have highlighted how flood risk management relates to other aspects of the economy, environment and society. It remains a considerable challenge though, to develop decision-making processes across a range of sectors that will take this range of sustainability considerations into account.

Governance options

Overarching the technical issues of flood risk management are matters that relate to governance and who pays. In Chapter 27 we identified a number of issues that would need to be addressed in the development of a portfolio of responses to increased flood risk. These included:

- matching the scale of governance and response to the scale of the flood risk;
- integration of different elements of governance;
- development of an adaptable portfolio to address the changing uncertainties;
- monitoring the implementation and effectiveness of response measures;
- raising public awareness and risk perception.

Here we highlight a number of questions relating to governance and finance that might provide barriers to portfolio development. Do the governance measures that we have in place now allow for effective portfolio control? How do we balance the need for strategic control with local participation and empowerment? How do we deal with the question of institutional mismatch – matching the scale of the decision-making process with the scale at which management needs to be taken? How do we deal with trade-offs associated with flood risk management decisions? How do we decide who pays for a particular response when this varies between scenarios?

A key issue in portfolio management is control. To be able to exert strategic control in flood risk management implies investment and system reconfiguration to ensure effective portfolio delivery. One stumbling-block relates to institutional mismatch with the scale of the problem that is being addressed.

The governance and implementation of responses in the local stewardship scenario highlight the difficulty in taking a strategic view of flood management at the larger spatial scale. With power transferred upwards to regional and international organisations, such as the EU, and downwards to regions and devolved localities, there are considerable challenges in developing strategic control measures that will have support at a local level – where the decisions will be implemented. Dispersed power and a complex institutional landscape confers the advantages of inclusiveness, 'buy-in', the clarity of openly negotiated and agreed responsibilities, and scope to pool and jointly prioritise resources for best results. The advantages of partnership approaches that bring planners, operating authorities, community representatives and the best technical and scientific knowledge together are now recognised.

However, there are also dangers in pursuing and relying on an inclusionary approach (O'Riordan, 2004). These include the fact that long-term strategic policies may not be acceptable to shorter-term policy-design institutions and financing arrangements. A precautionary and robust approach to flood management requires a degree of vision and long-term commitment. Participatory approaches also have the potential to introduce significant delays into the system. This could be a problem as our analysis indicates that early implementation of policies with long lead-in times will be necessary if they are to reduce flood risk when needed.

Finally, we come to the question of who pays. The scenarios indicate a range of possibilities, ranging from the individual to the private sector and state, and by insurance, and local and general taxation. Some major flood defence projects can be funded only with government involvement – even if funding is raised commercially and repaid through levies or shadow tolls – while others, such as managing flood losses, could be paid for through either self-insurance, local floodplain-charging schemes or state compensation for losses. There are choices that have to be made, especially in relation to measures that can be funded by a range of mechanisms, if we are to successfully provide a robust funding stream for individual responses. Other costs are, of course, indirect. If we forgo building development on land as a result of flood risk management policies, there are opportunity costs to be considered, for example. Clearly, these issues need full consideration in areas where land is at a premium and at times may require explicit trade-offs to be made. For example, it may be necessary to release greenbelt land to relieve development pressure and restore natural floodplain functioning.

The nature of the institutional framework, in terms of the power balance between the public and private sectors, addresses elements of control and finance, but it cannot be kept separate from social trends and changing values and ethics. Exerting control in some measures, particularly through land-use planning and management, requires shifts in our thinking about property rights and the rights of individuals. Concerns about litigious reactions have hampered some broad-scale actions in the past. These will continue to arise and require careful management. In some cases, education and consensus-building may countervail, but this too would be resource-intensive.

In summary, we need to investigate which governance structures provide the most effective means of delivering and paying for appropriate portfolios of responses in a changing and uncertain future. In doing so we also need to address how to match the scale of governance and response to the scale of the flood risk, balance effective strategic control with local participation, raise public awareness and risk perception, and ensure that different elements of governance support the concept and delivery of a portfolio of responses, including monitoring the implementation and effectiveness of measures. These are and will remain major challenges.

Conclusion

The Foresight Project described in this book brought together over 60 experts from a wide range of disciplines to study the risks of flooding and coastal erosion for the UK during the remainder of this century. In addition, it brought together scientists with stakeholders from across government, business and society more widely, so that the *Future Flooding Report* (Evans *et al.*, 2004a, 2004b) evolved from a recursive process between scientists and those involved in the decision-making process. The whole process was steered by officers of the Office of Science and Technology (now the Office of Science and Innovations) with the support of the Chief Scientific Adviser to the Government, Professor Sir David King, and the *Future Flooding Report* was produced with the help of non-specialists, so that the language used was relatively jargon-free and accessible to all interested parties.

This approach is an example of the analytical deliberative process to decision making, whereby the risk analysis and decision-making process is developed with recursive interactions among a range of stakeholder groups including scientists, practitioners and policy makers (Norton, 2005). The benefits have exceeded those that would have been derived from a serial approach, where there is a one-way flow of information from scientists toward policy makers, and the impacts have been wide ranging.

The outcomes of the Foresight Project have been summarised one year on from the publication of the report (Foresight, 2005). These outcomes encompass better understanding of the future challenges, highlight research priorities and inform cross-government strategy. Here we highlight those related to policy.

In the one-year review, Eliot Morley MP, then Minister for Environment and Agri-Environment in the Department for Environment, Food and Rural Affairs, stated that, 'An important area [this project] will feed into is my department's 20-year strategy. Through this, and a number of other channels across government, the project will leave a lasting impression on the approach we take to flood risk management in the UK.' Of particular note is the extent to which thinking from the Foresight Flood and Coastal Defence Project has been incorporated in the policy-making discussion document *Making Space for Water* (Defra, 2004). HM Treasury also reported that it found the project a valuable contribution to preparations for the Spending Review 2004, ensuring continued support for a high level of funding for flood risk management. Other bodies, whose policies have been influenced by the project, include the Association of British Insurers, Cabinet Office, Council of Mortgage Lenders, Department of Transport, English Nature, Environment Agency, Local Government Authority, Northern Ireland Assembly, Office of the Deputy Prime Minister (now the Department of Communities and Local Government) and the Welsh Assembly Government.

It is hoped that the project will now act as a stimulus to subsequent studies that have the time and resources to explore specific issues in more depth than was possible here. Indeed, many complementary research initiatives are starting or are already underway, supported by Defra, the Environment Agency, the UK Research Councils and the European Commission, among others. These ongoing and future studies will serve to flesh out and progressively update the insights provided here.

References

Awerbuch, S., 2000. 'Getting it right: the real cost impacts of a renewables portfolio standard', *Public Utilities Fortnightly* (15 February), 138, 44–55.

Barker, T., Pan, H., Kohler, J., Warren, R. and Winne, S., 2006. 'Decarbonizing the global economy with induced technological change: scenarios to 2100 using E3MG', *Energy Journal*, 27.

Defra, 2002. *Flood and Coastal Defence Funding Review: Report on the outcome of consultation*, available online www.defra.gov.uk/environ/fcd/studies/fundrev.htm

Defra, 2004. *Making Space for Water*, Department for Environment, Food and Rural Affairs, London.

Evans, E., Ashley, R., Hall, J., Penning-Rowsell, E., Saul, A., Sayers, P., Thorne, C. and Watkinson, A., 2004a. *Foresight, Future Flooding. Scientific Summary: Vol. I – Future risks and their drivers*, Office of Science and Technology, London.

Evans, E., Ashley, R., Hall, J., Penning-Rowsell, E., Sayers, P., Thorne, C. and Watkinson, A., 2004b. *Foresight, Future Flooding. Scientific Summary: Vol. II – Managing future risks*, Office of Science and Technology, London.

Foresight, 2005. *Foresight Flood and Coastal Defence Project: One Year Review*, www.foresight.gov.uk/Previous_Projects/Flood_and_Coastal_Defence/One_Year_Review/Review.html

Govindasamy, B., Caldeira, K. and Duffy, P.B., 2003. 'Geoengineering Earth's radiation balance to mitigate climate change from a quadrupling of CO_2', *Global and Planetary Change*, 37, 157–168.

Guo, J., Hepburn, C.J., Tol, R.S.J. and Anthoff, D., 2006. 'Discounting and the social cost of carbon: a closer look at uncertainty', *Environmental Society and Policy*, 9, 205–216.

IPCC, 2000. *Special Report on Emissions Scenarios (SRES): A special report of Working Group III of the Intergovernmental Panel on Climate Change*, Cambridge University Press, Cambridge.

Lenton, T.M., Williamson, M.S., Edwards, N.R., Marsh, R., Price, A.R., Ridgwell, A.J., Shepherd, J.G. and Cox, S.J., 2006. 'Millennial timescale carbon cycle and climate change in an efficient Earth system model', *Climate Dynamics*, 26, 687–711.

Nicholls, R.J. and Lowe, J.A., 2006. 'Climate stabilisation and impacts of sea-level rise', in *Avoiding Dangerous Climate Change*, eds Schellnhuber, H.J., Cramer, W., Nakicenovic, N., Wigley, T. and Yohe, G., pp. 195–202, Cambridge University Press, Cambridge.

Nicholls, R.J. and Tol, R.S.J., 2006. 'Impacts and responses to sea-level rise: a global analysis of the SRES scenarios over the twenty-first century', *Philosophical Transactions of the Royal Society A: Mathematical Physical and Engineering Sciences*, 364, 1073–1095.

Nicholls, R.J. and Wilson, T., 2002. 'Integrated impacts on coastal areas and river flooding', in *Regional Climate Change Impact and Response Studies in East Anglia and North West England*, eds Holman, I.P. and Loveland, P.J., pp. 54–101, UKCIP, Oxford.

Norton, B.R., 2005. *Sustainability: A philosophy of adaptive ecosystem management*, University of Chicago Press, Chicago, IL.

O'Riordan, T., 2004. 'Inclusive and community participation in the coastal zone: opportunities and dangers', in *Managing European Coasts: Past present and future*, eds Vermaat, J.E. and Turner, R.K., Springer, Berlin.

Pacala, S. and Socolow, R., 2004. 'Stabilization wedges: solving the climate problem for the next 50 years with current technologies', *Science*, 305, 968–972.

Thompson, D., Muriel, P., Russell, D., Osborne, P., Bromley, A., Rowland, M., Creigh-Tyte, S. and Brown, C., 2002. 'Economic costs of the foot and mouth disease outbreak in the United Kingdom in 2001', *Revue Scientifique et Technique de L'Office International des Epizooties*, 21, 675–687.

Treasury, 1998. *Modern Public Services in Britain: Investing in reform*, The Stationary Office, available online www.archive.official-documents.co.uk/document/cm40/4011/4011.htm

Index

Page numbers in italics refer to diagrams and illustrations. The abbreviation WM/NE/LS/GS refers to the world markets, national enterprise, local stewardship and global sustainability scenarios of the Foresight Future Flooding Project.

505